The
Experimental
Psychology
of Sensory
Behavior

John F. Corso

Professor of Psychology and Chairman
Department of Psychology
State University of New York, Cortland

The Experimental Psychology of Sensory Behavior

HOLT, RINEHART AND WINSTON, INC.

New York   Chicago   San Francisco   Atlanta   Dallas
Montreal   Toronto   London

To Josephine Ann

PREFACE

The primary evidence of the rapid advance of psychology is the continuing need for textbooks. This volume was written after nearly two decades of teaching courses in experimental psychology to both graduate and undergraduate students at the university level. During this time, I have been impressed by the vastly increasing number of publications in the field and the relatively small impact these publications have had on the undergraduate courses that are typically offered in the psychology curriculum. In addition, I have carefully observed both the assiduous efforts of students within this curriculum and their serious attempts to master the subject matter, laboratory techniques, and quantitative methods of experimental psychology. For many students, however, the task has been a difficult one.

There are no doubt many well-founded reasons for this situation; but, in my opinion, two factors are primarily responsible: (1) the average student is academically unprepared for a course in experimental psychology, and (2) the content of the course (and oftentimes, the textbook) is too broad. In this textbook, therefore, I have presented selected material from the related disciplines which underlie the science of psychology, and I have restricted the scope of topics in experimental psychology primarily to research methodology and sensory processes. Although there are many references to the experimental literature in these areas, the tutorial line moves from specifics and classical problems to general theories of behavior in contemporary experimental psychology.

To accomplish this, I have organized this textbook into four major parts. Each of these parts has a unique and direct purpose with respect to the teaching of a course in experimental psychology. Also, the content of certain chapters in this book will provide a useful and concise introduction to selected topics in experi-

v

mental psychology which are usually treated in seminars at the graduate level. The order of chapters has been developed to lead the student gradually into the substantive core of experimental sensory psychology, and then into general behavioral theories. However, the order of chapters may be easily rearranged if some other objective or sequence is preferred.

Part I, *Foundations of Psychology,* consists of four chapters related to the areas of philosophy, physics, and physiology. These are the disciplines which form the bedrock of the science of psychology. Without a thorough and complete understanding of this material, the student is likely to find himself faltering in his intellectual pursuit of experimental psychology, particularly at the theoretical and methodological levels. The student is made aware that psychology is the scientific study of the behavior of organisms; these organisms are not empty shells. They have neurophysiological structures and they respond to physical forces in the environment. As psychologists, we attempt to discover empirical laws which relate the conditions of stimulation to resulting responses; more generally, we attempt to formulate scientific theories of behavior. For these objectives, the material in Part I is indispensable.

Although some students often complete certain courses in the areas covered in Part I, they need to be exposed to the relationship of these areas to psychology. The aim of Part I is to insure that the student will have at least some introduction to physics, philosophy, and physiology and that his attention is directed toward the integration of this knowledge in his study of experimental psychology.

Part II, *Quantitative Methods in Psychological Research,* contains three chapters. It begins with a systematic discussion of theories and levels of measurement and proceeds to the presentation of selected experimental designs and psychophysical methods. The material on statistics and psychophysical methods is not intended to be exhaustive; only those methods are considered which are most frequently used in contemporary research. Furthermore, the treatment of each method has been limited to the type of problem to which the method has been most frequently applied. The material contained in Part II is developed on the assumption that the student is at least familiar with measures of central tendency, variability, and product-moment correlation.

This part of the book presents the student with problems in the measurement of behavior and describes some of the techniques which are employed in a quantitative psychology. It attempts to remedy, in part, the most frequent complaint of the student in experimental psychology: specifically, his inability to understand the statistical or quantitative treatment of the data as reported in published articles. To resolve this problem, each statistical design and each psychophysical method included in Part II is described in detail and is then applied in a completely worked-out example. When the material in Part II has been completed, the student should be able to contribute significantly to the design of experiments to be performed in conjunction with the laboratory work which is usually an integral part of a course in experimental psychology.

There are three chapters in Part III, *Classical Problems in Experimental Psychology.* The aim of Part III is to provide the student with some of the material that has appeared in the psychological literature over the years and that may be considered to be in the realm of classical or traditional psychology. Problems of threshold, adaptation, and sensory malfunctions are considered as general phenomena, that is, they are described as being present universally in the various sensory modalities. Hence, the student is provided with unifying concepts and is shown how these concepts manifest themselves in sensory psychology. Also, the material on physiology presented in Part I now becomes more meaningful, since the explanation of these general phenomena is often made in neurological terms. Selected theories of sensory behavior are sytematically reviewed for various modalities and it is within the context of these theories that the normal sensory processes are explained, as well as the sensory abnormalities.

Part III forms the bridge from which the student proceeds from classically derived theories, specific to particular sensory modalities, to contemporary theories in experimental psychology. These theories are held to account for psychological phenomena which are not modality specific. The material in Part III represents more or less the traditional view of sensory psychology; it is the familiar ground of the psychophysicist and the sensory specialist. However, the student in experimental psychology should not be left marooned on this island; he must be brought into contact with the contemporary approaches to the sensory and perceptual processes. These approaches are presented in Part IV.

Part IV, *General Theories in Contemporary Experimental Psychology*, consists of four chapters. The material covers theories of sensory discrimination, information theory, adaptation-level theory, and theories related to sensory deprivation. These theories, unlike those presented in Part III, are considerd as general theories; they represent one of the current trends in experimental sensory psychology, that is, the trend to develop broader theories capable of accounting for psychological functions irrespective of modality. These theories view many of the classical problems from a different frame of reference; they often provide new insights from which experimental studies may be derived. They also introduce new concepts into psychology which permit the study of fundamental processes not previously considered under the traditional theories.

The material in Part IV represents the "new look" in contemporary sensory psychology; it provides the student with a broad perspective along the theoretical front of experimental psychology dealing with sensory and perceptual processes. The theories contained in Part IV may all eventually vanish from the scientific scene, but the student will have had the opportunity to consider the major current theories in this segment of psychology.

Acknowledgments of aid for this textbook must, in large measure, reflect the influence of the psychologists who have most significantly affected my own views regarding the science of human behavior. First of all, I am indebted to the late Professor Donald Snygg, who introduced me to this field nearly thirty years ago. Then, I am pleased to acknowledge the rigorous, quantitative approach to psychology offered at the State University of Iowa through Professor Don Lewis, the late Professor Kenneth W. Spence, Professor Gustav Bergmann, and Professor E. F. Lindquist, among others. Twenty years ago, these scholars convinced me that the most fruitful basis for the science of psychology rested upon a combination of behaviorism and mathematics.

I also wish to express my sincere appreciation to the many students who were not only exposed to much of this material, but who participated in the various research studies I conducted at the Pennsylvania State University during the course of a decade. Many of these studies are cited in the present volume.

Special credit should be given to the reviewers of the various chapters of this textbook for their constructive criticism. The reviewers include Professor Alphonse Chapanis, The Johns Hopkins University; Emeritus Professor Karl M. Dallenbach, University of Texas; Professor Allen L. Edwards, University of Washington; Professor Herbert Feigl, University of Minnesota; Professor Harry Helson, Kansas State University; Dr. Richard J. Herrnstein, Harvard University; Professor David T. Lykken, University of Minnesota; Professor Donald R. Meyer, The Ohio State University; Dr. Michael G. Saslow, University of Washington; Dr. Herbert S. Terrace, Columbia University; and Professor Jack A. Vernon, University of Oregon Medical School. The careful reading of chapters by these reviewers has greatly aided and improved this work; but, of course, I must assume the sole responsibility for any inaccuracies, errors, or shortcomings that remain in the published version.

Cortland, New York
August, 1967   J.F.C.

CONTENTS

I

Foundations
of Psychology

Chapter 1

THE PHILOSOPHY
OF SCIENCE

Orientation

The philosophy of science is not an integral part of science itself, such as chemistry and psychology are parts of science. It is a way of *talking about* science to determine the presuppositions and characteristics which form the frame of reference within which intellectual curiosity leads to scientific discovery. The philosophy of science attempts to make explicit the fundamental objectives of scientific activities, the basic assumptions about the nature of the real world, the primary principles of operation, and the adequacy of the methods involved. Every science is built upon specific basic concepts; the role of philosophy is to define and to systematize these propositions so that individual scientists may be guided in their activities.

Philosophy, however, is not science. It does not generate data nor formulate generalizations. One group of psychologists has asserted correctly that the "philosophy of science has little or nothing to do with how research gets done in psychology" (Taylor, 1959). While it is true that many divergent statements may be collected on the definition of science and on the meaning of scientific method, it does not follow that an understanding of the underlying philosophical implications has little or no value for the psychological researcher. For centuries, the investigators of scientific method have attempted to reduce the process of scientific discovery to a prescribed routine, so that it might be communicated and taught; but this task has been an illusory one, with little likelihood of future success. Nevertheless, there are principles relevant to the conduct of research which assist in the process of scientific discovery. Even Nobel prize winners must learn—and learning implies the learning *of* something, whether it be related to specific procedures or to general scientific methodology. In contrast with those principles that assist in discovery, there are also erroneous principles that constrict, hinder, and delay scientific progress. These are the pitfalls to be avoided. Minimally, a thorough understanding of the philosophy of science should remove some of the intellectual barriers which might prevent an earnest researcher from developing and extending current scientific thought.

If we, as psychologists, are to become proficient in research, we must have direct knowledge of the scientific method and firsthand experience in the application of the method to specific psychological problems. Reading about the philosophy of science is a desirable, but insufficient, condition for the development of excellence in research. As an eminent theoretical physicist is said to have remarked, "If you want to know the essence of scientific method don't listen to what a scientist may tell you. Watch what he does." The material in this chapter lays the foundation for scientific activity; it provides the ground rules that must be followed. However, skill and artistry in research can be attained only by serving a long and arduous apprenticeship in the conduct of research. This will result ultimately in the maximal achievement of each individual according to his own interests and abilities.

The Meaning of Science

Some Misconceptions about Science

The progress of science in the past few centuries has developed at a tremendous and, for some, a terrifying pace. "We are now in the midst of an explosion of scientific and technical knowledge estimated to be building at a rate which now dramatically doubles with each decade" (Day, 1966, p. 372). Atomic bombs, antibiotics, tranquilizers, man-made satellites, and four-dimensional worlds are now commonplace items in conversation and newspapers. There seem to be no bounds which limit scientific curiosity. Although most people are desirous of the tremendous humanitarian benefits that science can provide, there are many who are anxious about the possibilities of dreadful inventions and, perhaps, the ultimate disaster which might result if science is permitted to continue at its current rate. Some contend, more generally, that science and the machine age are responsible for the misery and maladjustment of vast segments of our civilization. Such views condemn science as a social evil which should be abandoned.

The response to these assertions lies in the recognition that there is a difference between scientific knowledge and its application. In the first instance, we are interested in knowing about the nature of things; in the second, we are concerned about how we live. Scientific knowledge, in itself, is socially and morally neutral. It is neither good nor bad. The manner in which this knowledge is applied, however, depends entirely upon ourselves. *Men,* not "science," must bear the responsibility of whether the discoveries of science will be used for the betterment or the detriment of humanity. In a broader sense, it is the social-political-economic structure of a society which must account for the conditions within that society.

In recent years more and more scientists have warned of the risks contained in certain scientific developments. Consider, for example, the dangers inherent in the atomic and hydrogen bomb, the marked rate of population increase in most countries of the world, the control of biological evolution through genetics, and the potential control of man himself through psychological and sociological knowledge. Glass (1965) and others have stressed the idea that "science is no longer . . . the ivory tower of the recluse, the refuge of the asocial man" (p. 1261). There is, however, a caution to be observed.

> In these matters the ethic of the matter requires the scientist to state his opinion on matters of social concern, but at the same time to distinguish clearly between what he states to be fact and what opinion he holds. Moreover, his opinion about matters within his technical sphere of competence is an "informed" opinion; his opinion about other matters, even other scientific matters, is that of a layman. He must in all honesty make clear to the public in what capacity he speaks (Glass, 1965, p. 1261).

Another misconception about science is that it includes only the "hard-core" subject matter areas, such as astronomy, physics, and geology. This view places the "hard-core" subjects in opposition to the humanities, such as literature and philosophy, and to the arts, including drama and music. Sometimes the attempt is made to provide an explicit distinction between scientific areas by dividing the various subject matter fields into the so-called natural sciences and social sciences. There is some justification for this, but it provides a misleading dichotomy. The phenomena of individual and group behavior are as much the object of natural science as any other phenomena. As a general method, science can encompass this entire range of events.

The issue seems to be whether or not science can deal with the *values* of a society, that is, with its aims, goals, and ideals. The implication is that the methods of science are appropriate up to some point; beyond that, there are areas which must be dealt with on faith or by personal judgment alone. It must be admitted that science cannot dictate value standards to any society (Feigl, 1949), but this does not mean that problems of value and attitude must be ignored. Scientific measurements can be made to determine inherent compatibilities and differences of individual and group value-systems. From these, appropriate actions may be planned by responsible social and civic leaders to reconcile any conflicting interests and thereby reduce the underlying tensions which might otherwise lead to open conflict. "There have been many revolutions in our time, but I think that in the long run [the] psychological revolution . . . in the theory and practice of shaping the behavior of the young will be the most important revolution of all for the success and happiness of man on this planet . . ." (Platt, 1966).

Although it is not very probable that *all* complex social phenomena will be reduced ultimately to a single set of mathematical equations, the history of science indicates that many problems which have appeared insoluble at one time have yielded eventually to scientific ingenuity. Perhaps the reason for declaring that values are not subject to scientific treatment is that many individuals have come to regard science as something quite different from what it is in reality. It has been viewed as absolute, irrevocable, neutral, objective, and exclusive of human events. Thus, it has not been viewed in its proper perspective as a method of *inquiry* and intelligent *control*, characterized by *tentative decisions*. In certain limited areas, such as in matters of health, man has decided to solve his problems by means of this method. A broader approach, however, suggests that eventually most, if not all, problems might be handled in this manner. There is no human situation which lies automatically beyond the bounds of intelligence and scientific inquiry. Some writers (Parsons, 1961) have even proposed that an experimental approach to religion be adopted in order that those conditions related to the growth of the human community can be investigated empirically, within the context of social transactions and creative events.

Science Defined as Methodology

The words "science" and "scientific method" have had such wide application that they have acquired a variety of meanings. The most important of these stem from two points of view: (1) that science consists of activities designed to generate verifiable knowledge about man and the world in which he lives, and (2) that science refers to a body of facts and principles systematically organized into certain subject matter areas, such as astronomy, physics, and psychology. Stated briefly, science is comprised of both *method* and *content*. This does not mean, however, that the scientific method consists of a singular, infallible formula for conducting research, nor that content consists of a conglomeration of immutable facts. We will now examine this interpretation of science in greater detail.

Suppose that we were to take a cross-sectional view of the numerous daily activities which occur within various organizations and laboratories conducting research. We would be thoroughly impressed by the extreme diversity of operations. There would be the mixing of chemicals, the manipulation of slide rules, the solution of differential and integral equations, the running of rats in a maze, the implanting of electrodes in the head of a chicken, the dissection of cats, the development of photographic plates of celestial bodies—yet, each of these activities would be taking place within the general framework of science. Science consists of a complex network of activities, all of which are intimately related. There are predictions, laboratory manipulations, controlled observations, calculations, and theoretical explanations; but none of these, nor all of them taken together, can be considered the essence of science.

It is easy to find branches of science where any one of these criteria has had little or no influence. In astronomy, there are no laboratory manipulations; in archaeology, there is no controlled observation and relatively little measurement; in zoology, there is only the beginning of mathematical formalization. Thus, while the types of activities which have been mentioned can be classified as scientific, they are not universally present in each and every science. The activities may be present in varying degrees; the extent of their combined presence will determine the degree to which a given subject matter area has attained a scientific status.

The critical and distinguishing feature of science is its *general method*. This aspect places a common foundation beneath apparently dissimilar activities. The emphasis is not on the subject matter nor on the accomplishments; it is on the method used to discover new facts and principles. We consider the "scientific method as . . . those procedures which, as a matter of historical fact, have proved most fruitful in the acquisition of systematic and comprehensive knowledge" (Black, 1954). This definition of science stresses that in the past certain procedures and modes of thinking have been successful in advancing our knowledge in certain areas of inquiry. Consequently, it can be anticipated that the extended use of this general method will continue to yield new information in the ever-expanding fields of present-day science.

Steps in the Scientific Method

The scientific method is based on scientific thinking. This method does not consist of a single, invariant set of steps which must be followed to solve a problem; instead, each problem must be faced as a new challenge requiring originality and orderly thought. The general scientific method, however, does provide the guidelines which lead to the essence of science: the *observations* of the scientist must be distinguished from his *inferences* about them. There is a difference between recording the magnitude of salivary output, detecting the presence of hydrochloric acid, or measuring the extent of peripheral vasodilation, and stating that a subject is angry. The scientist's prejudices and personal opinions must be excluded from his experimental investigations. We must deal with empirical observations, not with the subjective fancy or the idiosyncratic whims of the researcher. This is the attitude that characterizes science.

Although the steps of the scientific method are neither sharply delineated nor chronologically invariant, there are certain portions of the method which can be designated arbitrarily. In general, the scientific method consists of five phases. (1) The scientist selects a *problem* which he proposes to study. This will be a function of his personal interests, ability, and background. Having selected a problem, the scientist attempts to simplify it by asking a specific question which will delimit the area to be studied, and through a careful theoretical and factual analysis, he will identify the factors or variables involved. (2) A *hypothesis* is then formulated in empirical terms which expresses the factors, relations, or conditions to be explored in the study. If supported by the evidence collected in the course of the study, the hypothesis will represent a tentative solution to the problem or, by logical inference, might offer support to some other existing explanation or theory. (3) The scientist devises a controlled *testing situation* in which to collect unbiased observations relevant to his specific hypothesis. Procedures must be used that will adequately test the hypothesis under consideration and that will provide an accurate record of the experimental events. The precision of the measurements required in the testing situation will depend upon the particular problem being studied. (4) After the data have been collected, they must be *organized* and *analyzed* by appropriate statistical or mathematical techniques. This step in the scientific method makes it possible to extract the meanings inherent in the data.

The results of the analysis provide the basis from which logical *conclusions* about the problem may be reached. (5) The final step in the conduct of a scientific study permits the scientist to *evaluate* the findings of his study and to extend or *generalize* his findings to other problem areas. A significant piece of research will, through generalization, not only raise new questions, but will provide theoretical implications that are relevant for explaining other phenomena in somewhat similar situations.

Each of the foregoing steps in the scientific method has been presented purposely in a highly oversimplified manner. The intent has been to provide a general view of the scientific method and to show that each step presents a challenging situation for the individual scientist. In the later portions of this book, we will see how various investigators have solved specific problems in psychology and thereby we will gain a more detailed perspective of the intricacies of the scientific method.

While science has been depicted as encompassing a general method, the steps in the method can be varied in many ways to explore a particular problem. Each study will have its own specific experimental *design;* that is, its own procedures, materials, apparatus, statistical or mathematical analysis of the data, and sample of subjects. The basic scientific requirement is that the empirical testing situation must constitute an *appropriate setting* in which the phenomena or functional relationships encompassed by the hypothesis may be expected to occur, if they exist. The design of the study must fit the specific problem to be explored. This is the point at which the successful researcher molds and adapts the existing procedures and techniques to meet the requirements of his own particular problem. When necessary, however, he must be able to develop new methods or to design new techniques of instrumentation, either personally or in conjunction with experts in other disciplinary fields. The creative scientist, the one who makes important discoveries or who opens new paths, does not limit his choice of problems to those for which appropriate experimental methods and evaluative procedures have already been established. His major concern is to select a worthy problem, not to search for an existing method. This situation stimulates the progress of science by imposing new demands for advanced tools and techniques of investigation.

Facts and Scientific Knowledge

The second major aspect of science, which supplements that of methodology, is *content:* facts and accumulated knowledge. The facts of science refer to phenomena—objects, events, or changes—for which there is substantial evidence obtained by empirical procedures. The simplest (most elementary) kind of fact for the psychologist involves *immediate sensory experience,* with no further verbal or conceptual elaboration. This is the type of experience which underlies the behavior of an infant who exhibits a startle response when exposed to a sudden loud noise. Other examples include touches, odors, pains, and visual experiences which occur, but which are not elaborated symbolically by the individual in relation to their situational significance. These immediate elemental experiences are classically called sensations. They are related primarily to sense organ activity, such as that which occurs in the eye or in the ear and in the associated nervous system leading to a particular sensory area in the brain. Sensations are completely and directly related to the characteristics of the external and internal environment acting upon the individual at a given moment.

Earlier in this chapter, science was described as a general method based upon the *observations* of the scientist. If one accepts the view that psychology is or is to be developed as a science, then an important issue is raised. Specifically, immediate sensory experience is private and is not open to observation by the scientist. The only witness to these inner events is the one having the experience. Other individuals cannot share the experience itself; they can only witness or observe the *report* of the experience. The report may or may not have any relationship to the experience which is implied or intended. Consider, for example, the statement of the college sophomore who looks into the eyes of his "girl friend" and sighs, "I love you." Whether this is an accurate statement or a complete statement is a matter of conjecture, since there is no way of verifying the fidelity of the report of personal experiences. Consequently, experience lies outside the field of scientific psychology. There are no objective methods for obtaining factual knowledge about the experience of others.

Notice, however, that while the experience is private, the report is public and open to observation. Thus, the report may be taken as a legitimate datum of psychology. We can, for example, count the number of times our college sophomore says "I love you" in the course of the evening with "girl friend A" and compare this with the number of times he professes his love in the course of the evening with "girl friend B." From this comparison we could arrive at some tentative conclusions. The position that experience cannot be investigated scientifically does not imply that it is impossible for an individual to have personal knowledge of his own experience. Awareness may be considered as one kind of knowledge, but it is not scientific knowledge, since it cannot be verified. Those psychologists who emphasize the importance of experience in psychology and use subjective (private) terms to describe experience are called *phenomenologists*. They contend that experiential words are valuable in psychology and are indispensable in the formulation of psychological theories.

In the opposite camp, and in the majority in contemporary psychology, are those psychologists who are *behaviorists* in one form or another. They reject experience as the subject matter of psychology and emphasize the behavior of living organisms. These psychologists take the position that the raw data of a scientific psychology consists of particular acts of behavior, adjustment, or performance in a context which considers the organism in relation to its physical and social environment. This point of view differentiates between the observer and the observed: they are two different individuals, whereas in the phenomenal approach the observer and the observed are one and the same individual. The nature of the objects studied (the individuals observed) will be defined by what they can *do* in their particular contexts. Thus, scientific psychology attempts to determine the characteristics of individuals and the laws pertaining to their actions by operational (objective) techniques, rather than by introspective, intuitive, or rational (subjective) techniques of phenomenology.

It follows, then, that the language of psychologists may contain two kinds of words: behavioristic and experiential, and that the theories which psychologists formulate may be of two corresponding kinds. As presented in this textbook, psychology is experimental and scientific; it is based upon objective theories and formulations and attempts to avoid experiential terminology by stressing the observation of behavior. This approach minimizes the ambiguity of language and adopts the methodological pattern which has been found to be so markedly successful in the history of the natural sciences. According to this view, the behavioral scientist who is interested in the qualitative and quantitative aspects of immediate sensory experience (sensations) must redefine these terms so that he is working experimentally with *observable* responses in appropriately designed situations.

The study of behavior requires the use of the same rigorous methods as in other sciences. The weaknesses of a purely introspective analysis are generally well known: (1) Its terms are not precise and require quantification. What, for example, is a "*pleasant*" experience? (2) The verbal report may be misleading. Even an observer with a red-green color deficiency may report that he sees grass as "green" due to his acquired speech habits. (3) The report may be an intended deception. Consider the example of our college sophomore. How do we know he was telling the truth? (4) The observer may not be able to report on all the critical variables which are operating in a particular situation and what is reported may not correspond with the facts in a particular discipline. Direct observation indicates that the earth is flat, but scientists know that it is essentially round. Science is an enterprise which includes many disciplines. If psychology is to flourish, it must use a language and method which permit the sharing of data (Cole, 1953). (5) Speech and introspective descriptions do not provide a direct access to the "mind" or provide us with firsthand knowledge of behavioral processes. Inferences about these processes must be made from a verifiable set of observations. If introspection did provide a direct channel to the "mind," the problems of psychology would have been solved many years ago.

The same objective orientation described for immediate sensory experience applies to those events that are somewhat higher on the factual continuum and are designated as *perceptual* experiences. Again, these experiences are not directly observable but, as a process, perception is initiated by a stimulus and serves to mediate a behavioral response. For example, the visual stimulation provided by the colored patterns on the skin of a rattlesnake and the auditory stimulation provided by the shaking of its rattles both serve to initiate different neural activity in specific sense organs. Stimulation of the eyes and ears gives rise to visual and auditory sensations. These sensations in turn set off a sequence of perceptual activity in the central nervous system which leads to a recognition (a *percept*) of the rattlesnake: the perceptual process mediates the overt behavior of running away. From a behavioral viewpoint, perception provides the initial preparation for a response or leads to a terminal adjustment in a given stimulus situation.

Sometimes, however, the response which is mediated by the process of perception is not immediately observable, although the implicit response may be entirely appropriate and adequate for that given situation. For example, perception may inhibit overt activity, as when we turn angrily to see who has pushed us in a crowd only to see the face of a policeman staring blandly in our direction. Perception is not necessarily followed by observable motor responses; but the process of attaining a percept, nevertheless, determines what future reactions will occur, whether covert or overt. Perceptual facts, in a way, represent a combination of the effects of direct sensory stimulation and the meanings which we have learned to attach to such stimulation from previous experiences in somewhat similar situations.

At the highest end of the factual continuum are facts and meanings that are not related directly to sensory experience; these facts and meanings are obtained through *inductive* or *deductive reasoning*. Although such meanings are highly conceptual, they are accepted as facts when they are supported by sufficient empirical evidence. For example, it is a fact that there is a particular relationship between chronological age and mental age. From birth to about 20 years of age chronologically, the mental age of a normal individual increases; beyond that, it shows a gradual decline (Wechsler, 1939). Notice that age and intelligence are both concepts which are never actually experienced. They are inferred from specific empirical events and the relationship between them is based upon numerous observations that have been made under carefully controlled testing conditions.

Facts, scientifically defined, must be discovered; they are the products which are generated by the machinery of the scientific method. The task of the scientist is centered around the search for new facts and, having established a fact, the scientist must be able to provide an adequate explanation of the fact and to show its theoretical or practical significance. Even when facts are in opposition to the scientist's own beliefs, or those of people in authority, they must be accepted since they are based on unbiased observations of natural events. The use of the scientific method insures that the facts which have been discovered by one investigator can be verified by other investigators who might question the finding.

Science is a *continuous* and a *cumulative process*. New facts are added to old; old facts are modified. In science, no fact is given as an absolute certainty or as something that will never change; scientific truth is modified as new knowledge is gained. Thus, we speak of science as a *self-corrective* system. This differs from theology, for example, in which a truth once revealed must remain unchallenged for all time, since its renunciation would weaken, or might even destroy, the foundation of a given religion. Science encourages a doubting attitude. The student of science should develop a questioning, critical attitude toward the so-called facts of life. He should learn never to accept a conclusion until the facts from which it has been drawn have been examined carefully and the procedures by which it was derived have been scrutinized objectively. This critical attitude leads to the discovery of errors and false conclusions in our own work and in the work of other investigators; it suggests the possibility of new approaches to old problems. Science progresses on the wings of doubt; each new bit of evidence that results from scientific curiosity permits the correction or modification of a proposition previously held to be true. Through the scientist's effort, these new modified facts are arranged into diversified patterns to facilitate their interpretation and to provide areas of scientific knowledge about similar phenomena. This organization grows into more and more abstract levels of complexity until general principles and laws are evolved which can account for all the events in a particular field of inquiry. The content of science, then, is knowledge; it consists of the accumulation of systematically organized facts which have been derived from the scientific method and which are both tentative and verifiable.

Emphasis in Science

The assertion is often made that science can be divided into two categories: *pure* and *applied*. This is an erroneous way of thinking since scientific activity cannot be neatly compartmentalized. The usual rationale for this distinction is based on the notion that the "pure" researcher is searching for fundamental facts and principles to be added to the general body of knowledge in a given subject matter area. Supposedly his concern is with the establishment of scientific laws derived from the investigation of basic relationships between events in order to fit the explanation of these events into some existing conceptual framework. Thus, the results of "pure" research are said to be theoretically significant; there is no intent that they should be useful immediately or even eventually in the solution of existing problems.

"Applied" science, however, is said to be directed toward the investigation of particular problems, currently or potentially in existence. It is maintained that techniques of science are used to answer a question or to test the application of a law of nature in a specific instance. In the field of psychology, the evaluation of shock therapy, the development of propaganda techniques, and the design of radar consoles would be examples of applied research, according to this twofold distinction of science.

One of the major objections to this arbitrary division of science or research is that the history of science is filled with instances in which the results of investigations conducted for their own sake have subsequently found numerous applications in everyday activities. Although the "pure" scientist is motivated by an insatiable curiosity and desire to explore the uniformities of nature, he has little realization whether or not his discoveries will be used to advance human welfare or to further scientific technology. The pioneering work of Newton (1642–1727) involving the passage of sunlight through a glass prism is a classic example. About a century and a half later, this principle of fractionating a white beam of light into a rainbow of colors was utilized in the invention of the spectroscope. This device, which is basically a combination of a prism and a telescope, has become a standard tool in the laboratory analysis of chemical substances.

In such fields as biochemistry, physiology, and bacteriology, new ideas and new tools developed by the physicist and chemist are being used to study biological problems—the use of isotopes has been one of the most successful attempts of the last three decades (Conant, 1948). Is this "pure" or "applied" science? There is no way of knowing beforehand when the "pure" research of a scientist may be turned suddenly into a tremendously valuable application. A more appropriate way of thinking about research is in terms of the *number* and *kinds* of variables to be explored and controlled in a particular investigation. This eliminates the dichotomous classification of research and emphasizes that both experimental complexity and degree of environmental control are variables which lie on a continuum.

As the number of experimental variables to be explored increases or becomes more diversified, the individual experimenter is likely to need the assistance of specialists from other scientific disciplines in order to conduct his research. Consider the tremendous scope of talent required for the conduct of a successful program of research in the design, development, production, and operation of a man-operated space vehicle; or, more simply, in the discovery and evaluation of a new tranquilizer. This emphasis on specialization and the need for knowledge from related areas has tended to promote the grouping of talent into research teams. This is especially noticeable in the field of human engineering where psychologists, anthropologists, physicians, electrical engineers, mathematicians, aeronautical engineers, sociologists, and others are organized into teams to solve interdisciplinary problems of a practical nature. Although such operating teams are scoring tremendous successes in today's science and technology, it should be remembered that many outstanding scientific discoveries have been made, and will continue to be made, by the individual experimenter who has escaped the narrowing confines of the specialist.

The primary factor that should be considered in the "pure-applied" issue is the number of environmental variables which can be controlled in a particular investigation. Theoretically, in a laboratory situation the experimenter can control all the variables which are likely to affect his results. For example, in a hearing experiment, he can control the ambient noise, the temperature and relative humidity of the room, the barometric pressure, the manner in which the auditory signal is presented and so on. This is the end of the research continuum that might be designated as "pure" research. All relevant variables are under the control of the experimenter. At the other end of the continuum, there would be "applied" research in which only a few, if any, of the relevant variables would be under the control of the experimenter. This might be the case in the evaluation of two textbooks in psychology. The experimenter, for instance, might have no voice in the selection of the books, the subjects to be used in the study, the hours at which the classes are to meet, the kinds and number of examinations to be given, or the amount of time to be spent in homework assignments. Between these two ends of the research continuum, we would find various gradations in the degree of control exercised by the experimenter. This concept of research destroys the "pure-applied" dichotomy and ignores the question of the immanent utility of the experimental findings. Furthermore, it suggests that no single standard can or should be adopted as the criterion for scholarship or excellence in research.

The "pure and applied" issue which we have considered represents only one facet in understanding the spirit of science. The meaning and spirit of science have been discussed in the present section and may be summarized as "longing to know and to understand; questioning of all things; search for data and their meaning; demand for verification; respect for logic; consideration of premises; and consideration of consequences" (Wolfle, 1966, p. 1699). These are the basic objectives or methods of thought which characterize science and which to a large extent permeate the field of psychology.

Some Assumptions of Science

The Reality of Space, Time, and Matter

All scientists with a materialistic bias accept, at least implicitly, a set of funda-mental *axioms* related to the world in which we live. Certain characteristics of objects and events are taken for granted; that is, they provide a convenient start-ing point for scientific activity. The physical world is taken, at first glance, as a panorama of heterogeneous things which have determinate, though often chang-ing, positions in space and time. *Space, time,* and *matter* are affirmed as the realities of the physical universe. We tend to think of events in spatial and temporal terms, of things as having position and size, of substances as possessing properties, of phenomena and processes as having antecedent conditions. These categories fur-nish the framework around which the body of scientific knowledge has been built.

The classical view of space is that objective space exists and extends in all di-rections. This implies that the physical world, as spatially known, is measurable and ordered in a continuous manner. Usually, spatiality is treated in a tridimen-sional schema of verticality (up-down dimension), horizontality (right-left dimen-sion), and depth (near-far dimension) with reference to an arbitrarily specified locus of origin. Whether or not space is finite or infinite depends on the meanings which we attach to these adjectives and, at the present time, the issue must be settled on philosophical rather than empirical grounds.

The scientist also attests that *time* is a real, measurable quantity that involves the notion of succession (Bergmann, 1960). That is, the temporal dimension is a continuous and irreversible series of durations. Some process, preferably a move-ment, is taken as a standard and other processes are referred to this as a unit. If two processes begin and end together, they are said to occupy the same time. This leads to the concepts of temporal *simultaneity* and *succession*. For longer periods, time is characteristically organized into phases called the past, the present, and the future. The consideration of the limits of the time dimension, the beginning and the end, remain in the sphere of metaphysical discussions.

The philosophy of modern materialism asserts, among other tenets, that matter is anything which is real and has dimensions, that is, that it occupies space and exists in time. A material thing is any substance which is tangible, discernible, and possesses dimensionality. Naively, we maintain that objects exist externally to us; that they have an independent existence. We accept their existence to be as certain and as real as our own existence. Furthermore, everything that exists must possess properties that are present in some degree or amount. These properties and their interrelationships are considered to be amenable to objective observation and subject to measurement, either by instruments presently available or by instruments yet to be developed. Although all matter is held to be real in the materialistic view, not all real things are necessarily composed of matter. Political systems, for example, are real but they are not material. Nevertheless, such systems and their associated activities fall within the domain of science, as do all behavioral phenomena. Science involves the study of the relationships among phenomena or activities which occur in the materialistic or natural world; the observations of these occurrences are anchored in a spatiotemporal base.

Modern scientists, however, no longer adhere to the traditional concepts of absolute time, absolute space, and matter which is solid and eternal. The enlargement of scientific knowledge in the last half century has modified the mechanistic conception of the universe as proposed by Newton. While the Newtonian theory explained the movements of heavenly bodies, the mechanics of discrete and continuous masses, the conservation of energy, and the meaning of heat, it was inadequate in its treatment of electrodynamics and the nature of light. With the accumulation of new facts, the mechanical foundation of physics based on the theory of action-at-a-distance gave way to the concept of electromagnetic fields spreading with the speed of light (Einstein, 1940). Eventually, two theoretical systems essentially independent of each other were developed: the *theory of relativity* and the *quantum theory*. Both of these have had a tremendous impact on science and on the philosophy of science. As an alternative to the mechanical theory which described physical phenomena as actual space-time events, we now have a theory of light and matter that is based on the *statistical distributions* of events as a function of time. The issue remains as to whether physical theory will ultimately represent reality in space and time dimensions, or whether events in nature can only be known on a probabilistic basis. In the final analysis, the choice will probably be made in favor of the view that yields the simplest logical formulation as the foundation for the description of all physical phenomena.

The Orderly Universe

When we consider the vast number and diversity of objects and events which are present in our world at any given moment, there seems at first glance to be nothing but complexity and confusion. There are microbes, men, rainstorms, elections, volcanoes, frogs, multiple births, ballistic missiles, syllogisms, differential equations, and papaya trees, to mention only a few examples. There are similarities and differences of kinds, of degrees, of substances, of organization, of species—shades of variation that tax the limits of human understanding. Yet, despite this diversity and complexity, science has struggled to discover the regularity, order, and schemes of classification which are assumed to underlie nature. The scientist believes that the universe is, or can be, logically arranged into an orderly and consistent pattern. There is *regularity*, *uniformity*, *consistency*, and *stability* in the world of nature. Our cosmos is not chaotic. If under a given set of conditions some particular phenomenon is seen to occur, then a repetition of the *exact* conditions will yield an identical phenomenon. This belief has provided one of the cornerstones in the foundation of science. Without this consistency, all science would be impossible. Existence itself would be impossible.

Science is a search for the *rules of order* in the universe. Careful study and controlled observations lead to an understanding of the meaningful relations that exist between and among all natural events. These relationships, expressed in the form of statements or mathematical equations, form the general rules or laws which describe the world about us. This stability of relationships enables the scientist to predict accurately from the immediately given events or conditions to subsequent events or conditions.

The postulates of *permanence* and *order,* however, do not demand or require that natural phenomena never change. They imply that these phenomena change so slowly in time that the scientist has an opportunity to learn about them, or that these changes are so infinitesimal that they are inconsequential in the relationships which have been established. The first implication would be present, for instance, in learning how a person's visual acuity deteriorates with advancing age (presbyopia); the second would be exemplified in the constancy of the intelligence quotient which relates mental age to chronological age. In general, the changes that occur in the physical world are slow; there are finite changes and limited possibilities of change. This has made it possible to attain a high degree of predictability in natural events—there are forecasts of weather, eclipses, chemical reactions, and academic grade-point averages. Life on our planet has become easier and more effective through the ability of science to make predictions concerning the regularity and repetition of recurrent phenomena. The achievements of science are limited only by the extent to which nature exhibits orderly and uniform patterns of organization.

The Concept of Determinism

Science is built on the assumption that all the endless changes in the universe and all the events observed in the world about us are the result of some fundamentally stable and natural process, or processes. This is *determinism.* Events follow events in an orderly, inevitable sequence. Some precise conditions can account for every event, even if we never discover what they are. In the normal course of events, the caterpillar must become a butterfly; it cannot become a bird. The acorn must grow into an oak tree; it cannot become a rose bush. Determinism holds that each occurrence follows from specific, antecedent conditions to which it can be traced, at least in principle. Under ordinary circumstances, whenever a metal is heated it will expand. Thus, the antecedent conditions determine or are responsible for the subsequent events; "under specifiable conditions a specifiable outcome will occur in all cases" (Grünbaum, 1952). This is "100 percent" determinism. The grades a student receives at the end of a course are determined, theoretically, by the quality of his performance throughout the semester. Similarly, the grades received will be responsible for the student's plight or good fortune after graduation.

Science is based on the notion that finite occurrences are related temporally to finite determiners. Sometimes, however, the eliciting factors of an event are not known, and new observations must then be made in a scientific manner until an appropriate answer is obtained. This holds for psychological events as well as those natural events which occur in other areas of inquiry. Natural determinism views individual preferences, attitudes, drives, and emotions in the same way as hurricanes, atomic emissions, and magnetic fields. Each natural event lies temporally between the particular set of conditions or events which preceded it and those which will follow it. This implies that for a single phenomenon there may be both a large number of antecedent factors and consequences, as in the case of an automobile accident. This is the rule, not the exception. The aim of science is to determine which factors are related in an orderly and systematic manner to a given situation, and which factors are irrelevant.

The concept of determinism is essential to the scientist in two ways. First, in performing an experiment, the scientist exercises a high degree of *control* over the situational variables in order that, at a particular instant, he can establish the conditions which are necessary to elicit the phenomenon in which he is interested. The stability of the temporal sequences among variables makes it possible for the experimenter to exercise his control over them. In a classical conditioning experiment, for instance, the temporal duration of the conditioned stimulus, the unconditioned stimulus, and the interval between them are precisely controlled so as to elicit a conditioned response. The conditioned response is not a capricious event; it is a lawful event based upon a particular temporal sequence of activities.

Second, determinism underlies the concept of *prediction*. The scientist depends upon the stability of the sequences he has discovered. In the previous example, the scientist can predict that given a certain sequence of temporal intervals and events, a conditioned response will be established. If at a given moment the state of an organism in a particular region of space is precisely given, and if the law or laws which apply to this situation are completely known, then the state of affairs in that region at a later moment can be predicted, provided the situation is not altered by some unknown or unforeseen circumstance. Without natural determinism, science would have no basis for prediction, since there would be no reason for linking future events to those of the present or to those of the past.

In recent years, the developments in the field of physics have led some scientists to question the postulate of strict determinism and to adopt a determinism of the *statistical* type. They have accepted the *principle of uncertainty* or *indeterminacy* and the notion that the events in our universe do not follow *precisely* from specifiable antecedent conditions, that is, that under specifiable conditions a certain result will occur but only in an explicitly stated percentage of cases. This view suggests, and rightly so, that there are different types of empirical laws, one of which is *statistical lawfulness.* Sometimes such a law is called a probability law. A statistical or probability law is a statement about "the limiting values of frequences in an infinite series of similar events in the same configuration" (Bergmann, 1947). For example, statistical lawfulness is seen in the repeated throw of a die; the law makes no prediction whatsoever about the individual event (configuration) but describes the ensemble (distribution) formed by the series of throws. It specifies the expected relative frequencies of occurrence of the various values of the die *in the long run* and *in a random (chance) manner.* In other words, the law states that the relative frequency of a certain character in successive samples from a large population converges randomly toward a certain number in the same way that the proportion of heads converges toward 0.5 if we continue to throw a coin.

According to present physical theory it is theoretically impossible to achieve anything but statistical prediction about certain phenomena, for example, the "movement" of subatomic particles. The extension of this view of relative chance in the area of physics to the area of psychology establishes the possibility that behavioral laws can only be of the statistical type. Presumably the Newtonian ideal of a complete process theory of behavior has been eliminated. This thesis could of course be true, but at the present stage of development in psychology we already have a substantial body of statistical knowledge about behavior and the *theoretical* impossibility of obtaining more complete knowledge has not been established. A theory of behavior is one thing and a physical (physiological) theory is another. The prospects of an eventual comprehensive process theory (complete knowledge) in one area do not depend upon the brightness or dimness of prospects in the other. This is a function of the connections that exist between the two kinds of theories. We must certainly pay attention to developments in related disciplines, but it would be premature to abandon our search for process theories in psychology in favor of statistical lawfulness. Determinism is the axiomatic cornerstone of scientific progress and adherence to this principle provides the impetus whereby research psychologists seek to establish empirical laws which "govern" behavior.

The general assumption of determinism is shared by all natural scientists, including psychologists. Behavior is a natural phenomenon. Therefore, it springs from natural processes; it is lawful; it can be measured and described; with appropriate cautions it can be predicted and controlled. Unfortunately, when behavior is described in such scientific terms, some people immediately reject psychology as a science, either explicitly or implicitly. They point to the principle of indeterminacy in physics to support their argument, but this principle does not negate the concept of determinacy. It merely suggests that human behavior is enormously complex and may involve certain processes of such limited dimensions that they ultimately may be inaccessible to the psychologist. This may place some restriction on the degree of predictability and control of human behavior, but it does not imply that behavioral events are unlawful. The answer to the issue of determinism in psychology will, of course, lie in the psychologist's ability to demonstrate lawfulness in the behavioral phenomena which he investigates. Empiricism, not logic or rationalism, will play the deciding role (Russell, 1929).

The General Objectives of Science

Understanding the Events in the Universe

Science begins with a set of *presuppositions*. Some of these have already been considered in the preceding section, but one further assumption must be made: that man is capable of knowing about the objects and events in the world as he attempts to discover certain empirical truths. The discovery of empirical truths requires that the scientist study the phenomena in which he is interested in order to obtain the initial facts from which a more comprehensive pattern will subsequently be molded. Facts, however, can only emerge from careful and controlled observations. Thus, the scientist is forced to accept some further assumptions; these are related to the process of observation. Specifically, (1) there must be an acceptance of the reliability of human perceptual processes and of the instruments which extend man's sensory abilities; (2) reliance must be placed on the process of remembering, with or without the introduction of techniques and devices designed to aid recall; (3) inductive and deductive reasoning must be considered as trustworthy, although in times of doubt it may be checked by others to insure its accuracy; and (4) small, unbiased samples of nature must be accepted as a valid basis for making inferences about the world as a whole. Having accepted these premises, the scientist proceeds to set up situations that will permit him to observe the natural phenomena which he seeks to understand.

The *understanding* of natural events is based upon the discovery, accumulation, and interpretation of facts that are consistent with other verified knowledge. Isolated facts are of limited usefulness and must be arranged logically by the scientist into new patterns, or integrated into the general systems of knowledge already established. "Facts are only concretions in a larger conceptual system; they do not exist aside from a theory" (Kline, 1961, p. 1043). Such a rational analysis will often reveal new meanings or new relationships which were previously undetected by the scientist. In the final step, the scientist may be able to formulate some general principles or laws to account for all the phenomena, facts, and relationships that are present in some restricted area of study. Understanding is an aim of science and it involves the systematic organization of knowledge derived from observation and induction; as our knowledge increases, the limits of our understanding are continually broadened.

Understanding may be considered to include two subprocesses: description and explanation. The distinction between description and explanation is an arbitrary one, but it has been found to be logically useful. *Description* consists of the scientist's attempt to isolate, measure, and specify the variables and the interrelationships among variables which are present in the phenomenon under investigation. These facts or data are derived from carefully controlled observations; they involve only the simplest abstractions beyond the observations of the scientist. Strictly speaking, description is limited to observational statements. In a complete description, all factors relevant to a given situation have been determined and, at least in principle, have been expressed in quantitative terms. The aim of the descriptive process is to provide a series of factual statements from which subsequent rational analyses may be made to determine the more abstract meanings, or lawful relationships, among the variables specified.

The generality and utility of the descriptive process may be detected by considering some of the forms in which description is found in the various sciences. A primary form of description is that of *classification*. All sciences attempt to organize their multitude of facts, events, and processes into smaller, more manageable units or classes based upon observed similarities. The periodic table in chemistry is an example of the classification of all known elements according to certain relatively stable properties and associative tendencies which have been discovered in chemical reactions. In this way, the halogens may be treated logically as a group, rather than considering iodine, bromine, and the other elements separately.

A second form of description is that of *ordering* events on a continuum. This implies that the events not only have some property or characteristic in common, but that these common dimensions are measurable, quantitatively or qualitatively. This permits the events to be arranged in a systematic manner on some desired continuum. In physics, we have an ordered scale of hardness in which each substance in the scale is capable of scratching all other substances placed at some lower point on the scale. Diamonds, for example, will scratch glass. Description based upon the ordering of events is more precise than mere classification, since it provides a basis for determining measurable differences between and among objects or events.

The third form of description to be considered is that of *correlation*. In this case, the scientist has discovered from an extended series of observations that, in a given class of objects or events, whenever one characteristic is present, some other characteristic also is present. This association between two different characteristics of an object or event is called correlation. It extends beyond classification and ordering since it assumes, first of all, that the objects or events can be ordered on a continuum on the basis of some measurable property. The degree of correlation is expressed by a quantitative index (correlation coefficient) which by its positive or negative value indicates, respectively, whether the two associated variables are directly or inversely related. In psychology it has been shown that individuals with similar hereditary characteristics have similar intelligence quotients, other things being equal. This is an example of a positive relationship. A negative or inverse relationship might be expected, by some professors, between the number of days that students are absent from class and the grades they receive at the end of the semester. In each of these three forms of description, that is, classification, ordering, and correlation, the essential features of the process are fundamentally *observational*. There is little, if any, extrapolation from the empirical events to higher level, more abstract, concepts.

This step, the extrapolation to more abstract concepts, is provided in the process of *explanation*. At this point, the scientist who is attempting to understand a given phenomenon proceeds from the descriptive questions of "what" and "to what degree" to the explanatory questions of "how" and "under what conditions." Once the phenomena have been established through repeated verification and the magnitudes of the relevant factors have been determined, some rational explanation must be given to account for the observed events. Through *abstraction* and *symbolization*, the scientist is able to arrive at new meanings and new relationships which extend beyond the originally observed events. The facts of observation are manipulated symbolically to yield new concepts. Description evolves into explanation and the explanation attempts to show that natural events can be deduced from a general principle, or set of principles. Ideally, the natural sciences should deal ultimately with explanatory rather than descriptive concepts; but, in an extreme sense, explanation is never more than a complete description of the phenomena which have been observed. Consider, for example, the explanation of how the human circulatory system works.

Explanation differs from description in that it attempts to discover the antecedent conditions that are essential for the appearance of the given phenomenon. The discovery of the antecedent conditions makes it possible to predict and to control the phenomenon; when this can be done, we say that we understand it. Our understanding of natural events may be expressed economically in the form of verbal statements or mathematical equations or, at a higher level of abstraction, in the form of a theory. Successful explanations serve to increase our knowledge about natural events and to broaden our base of understanding. In time, new discoveries and new advances in science may require that some of the older explanations be modified or abandoned, but this is the way of scientific progress. It should not discourage the individual scientist, but should serve to lead him from trampled ground to new frontiers.

Prediction of Natural Events

Although the scientist may arrive at a comprehensive account of a given phenomenon, this is not the end of his activities. The discovery of facts, of uniformities among natural events, and of lawful regularities initiates another phase of scientific endeavor, that of *prediction*. Prediction is the process of forecasting; available knowledge is utilized to forecast the manner in which certain relevant variables manipulated in predetermined ways will affect the outcome of some future event. For instance, the industrial psychologist predicts that an applicant selected on the basis of a battery of tests will become a productive worker after he has been given a certain kind and amount of related training. In prediction the scientist uses his previous findings, or those of others, to derive a generalization or an implication which he believes will hold in a new, but somewhat similar, situation. Principles developed from specific instances are transformed into deductive generalizations.

The making of a prediction involves setting up some hypothesized relationships among variables, the truth of which cannot be determined on the basis of previous knowledge. For example, one study has shown that there is a difference in the number of trials required to learn lists of meaningful terms, like *kitchen,* than to learn lists of terms, like *absong,* which are meaningless (Noble, 1952). An experimenter might hypothesize from these findings that it should be easier for American school children to memorize a poem presented to them orally in English than to memorize a poem heard only in Chinese. There are certain immediately observed differences between the predicted situation and the one from which the prediction is made; nevertheless, there is some expectation that the principles of learning will be similar in both instances. From a general consideration, the predictor situation deals with single words, serial orders, and visual stimuli, while the predicted situation involves phrases, connected sentences, and auditory stimuli. Both situations, however, involve materials which differ in meaningfulness; hence, if the more meaningful material is easier to learn in one situation, it seems reasonable to hypothesize that it will be easier to learn in some other situation. We are trying to apply a principle which was evolved from previous research in order to anticipate what will happen in some future situation. The greater the differences between the conditions of the predictor and the predicted situation, the less certain we are that our prediction will be confirmed.

To test our hypothesis, we must devise a carefully planned situation, an experiment, in which certain precautions are taken to insure that the results of our test will not be influenced by factors other than those in which we are interested. Any differences in learning which we detect in our experiment must be attributable to the variables under study, that is, the meaningfulness of English and Chinese words in poetic form. If, after we have performed the experiment, we find that the English poem was actually learned with fewer repetitions, we have additional empirical evidence to support the learning principle involved. Our prediction has been confirmed. A failure of the prediction would have indicated the existence of some discrepancy: the experimental situation might not have been an appropriate one for evaluating the principle under consideration; certain relevant factors, like the intelligence of the subjects in each group, may not have been equated adequately; other factors like hearing ability may have been ignored; or perhaps the principle implied in the hypothesis may not, after all, have been as universal as we had anticipated. In the case of failure in our prediction, we might either try again in a more rigorously controlled and better-designed experiment, or abandon the hypothesis. Which of these particular courses of action will be followed in a given case will depend, among other factors, upon the intelligence, scientific acumen, and personality characteristics of the individual experimenter.

Control as an Aim of Science

The processes of understanding and prediction in science usually lead to the process of *control*, followed ultimately by technological applications. After a phenomenon has been thoroughly studied, certain relationships may be discovered between the antecedent conditions of the phenomenon and some of its later characteristics. Thus, a regularity in the sequence of events may be established. This regularity will provide the basis for prediction; likewise, it will permit the *control* of the given phenomenon. Control refers to the process in which the conditions determining a phenomenon are manipulated or altered to produce a desired outcome. The outcome may or may not coincide with our expectations, just as the results of our prediction were not certain; but, the greater our understanding of the phenomenon, the more likely it will be that the antecedent conditions will be manipulated appropriately to produce the anticipated end result. If we can predict accurately, we can control—since the two processes require both a knowledge of the relevant factors which determine a given event and the availability of techniques for varying their relative magnitudes.

Although the aim of science to control natural events is perfectly acceptable in areas like meteorology and bacteriology, it is rejected at least in part by most people whenever psychology is involved. The application of science to human behavior presents a view which is glaringly opposed to the notions of individual freedom, traditionally revered in our Western culture. Our daily activities indicate, however, that there is often considerable incompatibility between our verbalized philosophy of life and our routine behaviors. We separate our school children into fast- and slow-learning groups; we restrict marriages between individuals having certain blood characteristics; we limit voting behavior to individuals of certain ages; we reject college applicants who have low academic averages in high school; we fail military volunteers who show certain types of visual defects. Human affairs are, for better or for worse, already controlled to a high degree by legal, religious, ethnic, technological, ecological, biological, and other factors. If we are to accept the tremendous benefits which can accrue to our civilization from scientific progress, we must ultimately face the issue of control, to which a science of human behavior will inevitably lead us. We would hope, however, that the knowledge gained from the scientific study of behavior would be used to benefit mankind, as in vocational counseling, rather than to enslave or to destroy it. The significance of this issue has already been recognized (Oppenheimer, 1956):

> In the last ten years the physicists have been extraordinarily noisy about the immense powers which, largely through their efforts, but through other efforts as well, have come into the possession of man, powers notably and strikingly for very large-scale and dreadful destruction. We have spoken of our responsibilities and of our obligations to society in terms that sound to me very provincial, because the psychologist can hardly do anything without realizing that for him the acquisition of knowledge opens up the most terrifying prospects of controlling what people do and how they think and how they behave and how they feel. This is true for all of you who are engaged in practice, and as the corpus of psychology gains in certitude and subtlety and skill, I can see that the physicist's pleas that what he discovers be used with humanity and be used wisely will seem rather trivial compared to those pleas which you will have to make and for which you have to be responsible (p. 128).

In considering the relationships between disciplines, Kline (1961) has also foreseen the potential consequences and has written that:

> As the wealth of the world increases, as information accumulates, and as the importance of biological science is increasingly recognized there is every expectation that (if we do not scuttle ourselves in the interim) we shall be able to explain, predict, and control human

behavior. The moral and adjudicative values involved in who will do the describing, predicting and, particularly, the controlling are problems that must concern not only scientists but all of us in the immediate future. The prospect is unlimited but the responsibility is immense (p. 1013).

Psychology in the Hierarchy of Sciences

Science and Integrated Knowledge

In a preceding section of this chapter, science was defined as encompassing both a general method and a body of organized, verified knowledge. It was also emphasized repeatedly that science must be viewed as possessing a dynamic rather than a static set of characteristics. The concepts and logical structures which are developed through observations and experimentation are continually changing; these in turn suggest new possibilities and new courses of action. Scientific knowledge is thus never complete; but the state of knowledge at a given point in time cannot be ignored, since it provides the primary basis for further extensions and developments in a given field of study.

As a whole, our present educational system tends toward the analytic rather than the synthetic approach to knowledge. Thus, subject matter areas tend to be isolated and exhaustively studied, with little consideration being given to the relationships among the various areas. Until recent years, the common educational goal was one of specialization and the march to this goal started in early childhood. The advent of courses in general education and the growth of interdisciplinary areas, such as biophysics and psychopharmacology, have in part reversed this trend. Specialization is the anathema of integrated knowledge.

As science continues to make new discoveries and to generate broader theories, it becomes increasingly apparent that there is a fundamental unity in the knowledge of our world. The divisions of knowledge into subject matter areas are established merely as a matter of convenience. The facts must be collected and presented systematically if they are to be grasped and understood by the individual scientist, but the need for constant integration and synthesis must not be underestimated. Although the following section delineates scientific knowledge into more or less traditional fields of study, the student should realize that the various fields are related intimately. Knowledge is structured—not chaotic, disjointed, delimited, and incomprehensible.

Psychology among the Sciences

It is now generally agreed (Kantor, 1962) that psychology has succeeded in its quest for a place among the sciences. Since the time of Galileo and Newton, psychology has been attempting to improve its position among the sciences by various means, but particularly by developing quantitative methods and building theories to account for the phenomena within its sphere of interest. For the most part, spiritualistic philosophies and metaphysical presuppositions which belonged to the history of psychology have been abandoned; theoretical constructs and intervening variables are now examined quite carefully and, when they are found to be invalid, are ordinarily modified or perhaps eliminated. Psychology has so established itself among the sciences that it is not only accepted as such, but has served to influence other fields, especially the physiochemical, biological, and humanistic areas.

Consider physics, for example. Recall the crisis that occurred in the early part of this century when physicists realized that probabilities had to be substituted for the traditional certainties attached to the mechanical impacts of subatomic particles. With the assimilation of the *statistical* view the basic postulates of physics were radically altered. More recently, the concepts dealing with the relativity of motion have also altered physics, as has the need to deal with discontinuous as well as continuous events (Bergmann, 1943); but psychology was concerned with these matters long before the twentieth century. Classical psychophysics utilized *probabilities* of response, the *relativity* of judgments in the form of the Weber ratio, and raised the issue of *continuity* or *noncontinuity* of sensory experience such as pitch and loudness. Objective psychology has served to clarify the concepts of scientific behavior. A priori tendencies, such as those involving intuitive geometry and Newtonian mechanics, have been displaced by *operational* views through the writings of physicists (Bridgman, 1928) *and* psychologists (Pratt, 1945; Skinner, 1945; Stevens, 1935, 1939). Furthermore, by stressing the relationships between individuals and their environment, psychology has helped to clarify the distinction between things and events and operations upon them. With a shift away from traditional philosophy and psychology, physical scientists have been able to see that statistical mechanics, quantum mechanics, and relativity do not destroy their science, but indicate that new postulates are needed in view of expanded knowledge.

While we will not discuss the influence of psychology upon biology and the humanistic fields, the general direction of these lines should be indicated. In biology, the major impact has been upon the *ecological* behavior of organisms, especially with respect to discriminative functions. Thus, not only are the anatomical and physiological factors of sensory systems considered, but the objects and conditions of the environment are also included as component factors which interact to affect behavior in a specific setting. In humanistic fields, such as history, psychology is able to offer some clarifying concepts. For example, an objectivist would argue that history is independent of the historian and that the historian's role is merely to record what has happened. A subjectivist would hold that history is the product of the historian's labor: it is highly subjective and for the same period varies from writer to writer. The influence of psychology in this issue is to differentiate between history as events which serve as *stimuli* for acts of recording and history as *constructs* or *responses* made to these stimuli. Thus, psychology enters into the description of physiochemical, biological, and humanistic events as a participating discipline in the complex world of science.

This becomes even more apparent when we consider that "the ultimate goal of neurophysiology, psychophysiology, psychopharmacology, neurology, psychology, psychiatry, and related disciplines is the explanation, prediction, and control of human behavior" (Kline, 1961, p. 1013). If we consider these and other disciplines not directly concerned with behavior, the stereotyped tendency is to construct a hierarchy of levels among the various sciences. In such an arrangement the psychological level is ordinarily placed near the middle, with the sociological level (anthropology, economics, political science, sociology) above it and the biological level (biology, physiology, endocrinology, chemistry, and physics) below it, perhaps in descending order. Although such a systematization may at times be useful, it is too arbitrary and rigid to be completely acceptable. Notice, for instance, that the placement of such interdisciplinary fields as biochemistry and psychopharmacology could create a problem.

The concept of a hierarchy of disciplines is founded on a *unidirectional dependency*. Sociology depends upon people and their psychological behavior; psychology involves physiology as part of the internal environment; physiology relates to chemical reactions; and chemistry deals with the activities of atoms, molecules, electrons, and other subatomic particles. In theory, each discipline could exist without the discipline immediately above it in the hierarchy. However, the processes at one level are often incomprehensible unless the processes going on at the next higher level are known. Neurophysiological events, for example, would be incomprehensible without knowledge of emotional reactions. The point to be made with respect to the hierarchy is that despite its arbitrary structure, each level has its own parameters, laws, and theories, which means that psychological processes exist in their own right. Furthermore, the relationship of one level to another will depend upon the specific question that is asked. One of the difficulties with the hierarchical formulation is that since it is an arbitrary schema, it may limit both theory and practice, due to the confusions that may arise in shifting from one universe of discourse to another.

A modification of the concept of unidirectional dependency is shown in Figure 1-1. The upper section of the chart shows the relation of modern psychology and its most closely related fields; the arrangement, however, shows the various fields in a horizontal (lateral) arrangement rather than in the conventional vertical arrangement. Nevertheless, the fields are ordered in a unidirectional manner from left to right, with psychology placed between the physical-biological sciences and the social sciences. The dependency, however, is not shown to be among laterally arranged fields, but upon philosophy. The wide band denoting mathematics indicates that it underlies all fields of knowledge which attempt to be scientific. In the figure, the major "pure" fields of psychology are shown in small, solid-line rectangles; the "applied" fields are designated by the rectangles with the broken line. The solid connecting lines indicate the major lines of influence which were important in the development of a given field, while the broken connecting lines denote secondary influences.

A more recent alternative for the classification of sciences and the integration of knowledge has proposed a distinction between *nomological* and *typological* sciences (Tatarkiewicz, 1960). This proposal divides the sciences according to the table

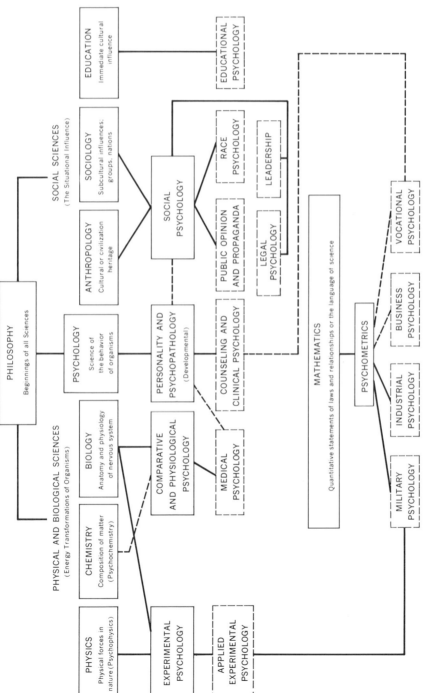

Figure 1-1. Schematic arrangement of the major areas of contemporary psychology and the various related fields of science. The "pure" areas of psychology are shown in the solid rectangles; the "applied" areas are shown in the broken rectangles. (From Royce. *American Scientist*, 1957.)

shown in Figure 1-2. This schema, however, uses the notion of science in a much broader sense than that proposed in this chapter. Our view has been that all sciences have certain basic characteristics in common, specifically methodology. Scientific knowledge, then, was taken as knowledge derived from observation and it aimed at the establishment of general laws.

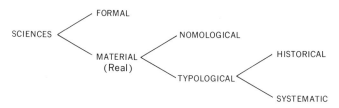

Figure 1–2. Classification of the sciences derived from a distinction between formal (axiomatic) sciences and material (natural) sciences.

The preceding table is derived from a much broader meaning of the term "science." In this view, not all sciences are empirical; some are *axiomatic* sciences, such as logic and mathematics. These are not *material* (real) but *formal* sciences. Such sciences are based on axioms rather than observation; they do not inquire into real objects but into the relationships between assertions or concepts. Accordingly, in the table of sciences, a major distinction is made between the formal and material sciences or, as Carnap (1935) phrased it, formal and factual science. Formal science consists of the *analytic* statements established by logic and mathematics; empirical science consists of the *synthetic* statements established in the different fields of factual knowledge.

The material or natural sciences are further subdivided into the *nomological* and *typological*. The nomological sciences are those sciences which seek to state empirical laws about natural phenomena, while the typological sciences are those which try to establish the various forms in which natural phenomena may occur and which seek to distinguish the natural groups within these phenomena. The first class of sciences establishes laws; the second, types. The nomological sciences investigate the characteristics common to all phenomena in a given field; the typological sciences study the different ways in which these phenomena may manifest themselves in this field. The major distinction between these two classes of sciences seems to be one which emphasizes the difference between scientific explanation and scientific description or classification, as previously discussed. Psychology, for example, would be included as a nomological science insofar as there are general laws of behavior, and as a typological science when individual differences in temperament, personality, and intelligence are stressed. Sociology, economics, linguistics, geography, botany, and all the historical sciences are typological according to this view.

The typological sciences are further subdivided into the historical and systematic. The *historical* sciences are those typological sciences that emphasize the *temporal* or *spatial* characteristics of certain phenomena, such as the history of art, which not only states when certain works were created but also what styles were formed in a particular period. The *systematic* sciences are those typological sciences that separate, contrast, and classify phenomena in an orderly manner as, for example, botany.

Although a critical analysis of this table of sciences would probably reveal that most contemporary natural sciences, like psychology, contain both nomological and typological characteristics, the schema has been presented to provide the reader with an alternative approach to the classical distinction of the sciences based on subject matter. The groups of sciences which this schema distinguishes have been distinguished earlier by other writers, but according to a different principle of classification.

Levels of Description and Reductionism

A careful consideration of the hierarchy of sciences in which psychology is placed reveals that the natural units involved in the various sciences become larger as we move, for example, from physics to anthropology, and that the levels of description proceed from the *microscopic* to the *macroscopic*. In physics, we consider matter as composed of subatomic particles and study matter in its relation to energy and other natural forces; in chemistry, we deal with atoms or molecules and investigate the changes which modify or alter the physical properties of matter as atoms or molecules are combined; in physiology, we treat animals and men as living structures composed of groups of functioning organs; in psychology, we study the behavior of living organisms as wholes in relation to their environments; in anthropology, we are concerned with the relationship among the human species and deal with the activities of groups of people. We proceed in this sequence from atomic particles to molecules, to organs, to organisms, to groups; each unit of study in this sequence subsumes all other units which are placed below it on the scale. This introduces the possibility that a given natural phenomenon might be described at a number of different levels.

To understand this point, we will examine the following illustration of a football game. A radio announcer might describe a football game always in terms of two opposing teams, A and B, that is, the team is the unit of description; or he might present the game in terms of the players in specific positions such as halfbacks, ends, and tackles, with the individual as the unit; or he might report the game in terms of the number of heartbeats that occur during each play or the amount of oxygen that is consumed by each player, with the organs as the unit; or the game might be analyzed in terms of the chemical changes in the bloodstream or in the muscle systems of each player, with molecules as the unit; finally, the entire game might be reported in terms of the electrical activity occurring in the nervous system of each player, with electrons and ions as the units. Although this is a bizarre example, it does illustrate that the choice of the unit of description and the level of description in a given study is a matter of convenience and expediency. In science, those units are chosen which are most likely to lead to observable regularities or laws.

The "best" description in a science is the one which most simply and most adequately accounts for the facts in that given field, and which is related to the largest body of organized knowledge in other fields. Since scientific areas are fundamentally interrelated, it might be argued by some people that the facts and principles of each discipline, like our football game, should be translatable into the language of any other discipline. This raises the issue of *reductionism,* in which it is asserted that the hierarchy of sciences might be collapsed ultimately into one or a few basic sciences. According to this view, each science should be reducible at least to the one immediately below it on the scale of complexity. Thus, the "explanations" of anthropology would be expressed in terms of the facts and principles of psychology; psychology, in terms of physiology; physiology, in terms of chemistry; and chemistry, in terms of physics. There are several arguments against reductionism, however. In the first place, as an example, to speak about reducing psychology to physiology implies that complete psychological theories have already been evolved which need only to be translated into physiology, according to certain rules of logic. Psychology is not in such a happy state at the present time. In the second place, there is the false conclusion that if reduction were to take place, for example, psychology to physiology, that the facts and principles in reduced form would be explained, somehow, more adequately. The explanation of an event rests upon the completeness of its description, not upon the unit of description. "There are no higher or lower, better or worse, disciplines except with respect to their relevance to particular problems" (Kety, 1960, p. 1869). The advocates of reductionism fail to see that certain phenomena must be dealt with on their own level of complexity; not all phenomena are reducible to some other level of scientific discourse. The *atomic dynamics* of the H_2O molecule does not explain the laws of hydrodynamics. As in modern physics, new levels of analysis and complexity necessitate the formulation of new concepts, and special or revised laws. The physicist, for instance, now recognizes three "worlds" or domains of experience—the electron world, the man-sized world, and the astronomical world of nebulae. There is not a one-to-one correspondence between the phenomena of any pair of worlds which might be selected. The phenomena on the minute scale of the electron world no more reproduce those on the scale of the man-sized world than the latter do on the scale of the world of nebulae. The psychologist must be prepared for the same eventuality. As we proceed from the infinitely small units of description to the infinitely large, different features of natural laws will become preponderantly important according to the particular world with which we are dealing.

It is certainly true that the existence of facts and theories in other areas, such as physiology and communication engineering, may provide useful guides for research in psychology, but there is no need to expect that theories in other areas will provide ready-made explanations in psychology. The unity of science which is sought in reductionism must be achieved through the use of a common methodology, not the anticipation of a common theory or set of laws. The similarity of concepts among the sciences and the reduction of psychological concepts to those of physiology, or physics, does not guarantee that the various disciplines share the same laws. Whether they do, and whether they can be deduced from similar theories, must ultimately be decided by empirical investigation. It should be remembered, however, that just as time may be saved, supposedly, by adopting an existing theory in some other discipline to account for psychological phenomena, considerable time and scientific effort could be expended fruitlessly in pursuing a false lead into the promised land.

Current Perspective on the Mind-Body Problem

Earlier in this chapter, it was stated that science involves both methodology and content (subject matter); it was also stressed that in this volume psychology is presented as a behavioral science which avoids a subjective vocabulary, or at least attempts to redefine such terms by specifying a set of physical operations which establishes their objective meaning. This view of psychology differs from that originally implied in the name "psychology," which was interpreted as the science of the mind, or soul. Thus, the classical frame of reference for the present discipline of psychology was mental, not behavioral.

Although we shall not present a summary of the history of psychology in terms of the development of these two approaches, it should be clear that the word *mind* has been used classically in two different ways. The first usage of the word may be given either a personal or a social interpretation. In the personal case, it designates those mental contents which are called memories, ideas, sensations, images, or other items in the "stream of consciousness"; in the social case, it refers to those characteristics which are culturally determined, such as a set of opinions, beliefs, judgments, values, sentiments, and items of information. The implication of this meaning of mind is that mind is neither a "conscious" activity, nor a function of the brain, but a content or a personal property of possession. Consider, for example, the common expressions "lose my mind," "give him a piece of my mind," "I have half a mind to. . . ."

The second usage of the word *mind* involves the concept of an active "consciousness" of objects, situations, motives, and so on, thus implying that there is an active determination and desire to achieve certain ends. In short, the body is inhabited by an entity—the mind or soul. Accordingly, a "minded person" acts as a prime mover. There is a difference between being awake and "conscious" and being asleep, or "unconscious," as from a blow on the head. In this view of the mind there is an element of power, or a faculty, or an active agency. This implies that there is an activity of the mind which controls and directs the activities of the body.

Much of the controversy in philosophical psychology consisted in speculations regarding the nature of this mind (soul) substance. Was mind a substantial thing, as separable from the body (dualism)? Or was there only one ultimate substance or principle in the universe (monism)? Was it mind (idealism) or was it matter (materialism)? Or was there some third thing which was the basis of both (pluralism)? If mind were a separate substance, where in the human body did it reside and just how did it exert its controlling function over the body? The answers to these questions, of course, varied according to the views of particular schools of philosophy or of particular philosophers.

Despite the long history of the mind-body problem, the issue is still raised in discussions of contemporary psychology and needs to be considered further. Feigl (1950) noted that the history of this issue yielded two conclusions: (1) the factual and logical components of the problem had to be untangled before the issue could be clarified, and (2) different philosophers had been concerned with different aspects of the problem. It is now recognized that the resolution of the factual questions in the first point will depend upon progress in such research areas as psychophysiology, and consideration of the second point indicates that many traditional questions in the total complex of the problem have been "pseudo-problems arising out of conceptual confusions." Nevertheless, the development of modern psychophysics and psychophysiology from the nineteenth century to the present has in general stressed *monistic* interpretations of the mind-body problem.

Modern psychology has no place for mind as a separate controlling entity, either existing apart from the body or dwelling in some deep recess of the brain. However, while it has been suggested that in the social sciences terms like "mind" and "matter" should be avoided (Neurath, 1938–1939), it is unlikely that these terms will be dropped from the psychologists' vocabulary, and the problem of studying activities commonly called mental will remain, regardless of the language or method of observation. These activities are now viewed as a special type of functioning of the organism in relation to its environment and not as the functioning of a special kind of "mind-substance."

Mental activities are therefore taken to be bodily activities and involve the functioning of the sense organs, nervous system and brain, glands, and muscles. If we consider a sampling of activities (behaviors) such as learning to write, speaking a foreign language, creating an abstract painting, remembering Lincoln's Gettysburg Address, or taking the first derivative of a given equation, we realize that these are all activities of living organisms. Some of them involve overt behaviors which can be readily observed and measured, while some of them involve more obscure activities beneath the body's surface which makes their observation more difficult by conventional methods. Regardless of the practical or experimental difficulties of observation, the behaviors are not radically different. As one psychologist phrased it (Skinner, 1953), "We need not suppose that events which take place within an organism's skin have special properties for that reason. A private event may be distinguished by its limited accessibility but not, so far as we know, by any special structure or nature. We have no reason to suppose that the stimulating effect of an inflamed tooth is essentially different from that of, say, a hot stove" (pp. 257–258).

This means that we cannot say that one group of behaviors is a function of a mind and the other a function of a body. Therefore this view precludes the question, "How does the mind control and direct the activities of the body?" The question becomes scientifically meaningless. There is no need to attempt to determine the manner in which a supposedly immaterial, nonphysical mind (or soul) substance or event could act upon the tissues and organs of the body. With this monistic conception, ideas and other experiential events are viewed as covert bodily responses; they are not products of the functioning of a unique kind of substance located in the head or heart, or elsewhere. It has even been suggested that "there is no reason why covert behavior could not be amplified so that the individual himself could make use of the additional information—for example, in creative thinking . . . The problem of privacy may, therefore, eventually be solved by technical advances" (Skinner, 1953, p. 282).

Gradually the classic doctrine that the individual is composed of two separate yet interacting systems—the mental and the physical—has been displaced by the view that the individual is a single functional unit which behaves as a unified and patterned whole. The component parts of the whole do not possess an independent existence and their function is determined by their relations to the whole. This means that there is no mind separate and distinct from the body. "The problem of explaining the mind on the basis of mechanistic physics . . . is actually only an apparent problem" (Frank, 1961, p. 126). Modern psychology assumes that "mind is a bodily process—an activity of the brain" (Hebb, 1958). For convenience we may speak of certain processes as thinking, remembering, and feeling as mental processes and certain other processes as breathing and digestion as bodily processes, but this division is strictly arbitrary and does not establish that there are two distinct entities, a mind and a body. "Such a distinction is artificial, obsolete, and mischievous" (Hall, 1960, p. 48).

This view of the mind-body problem may be better understood if an example is given.

> Mental arithmetic . . . is often thought of as being somehow different from ordinary arithmetic because in the one case the work is done "in your head" while in the other the figuring and calculation are done on paper. The first activity is considered to be mental because it is private and inside, the second as physical because it is observable and outside. But this is really an artificial and arbitrary distinction. Mental arithmetic often involves counting on fingers, talking to oneself, chewing the pencil, frowning, and the like. Hence it draws upon as many muscles—is as physical—as ordinary arithmetic, which is, of course, also mental. Learning to play a musical instrument, to kick a football, to saw along a straight line, or to control one's temper—all are mental as well as physical. We think with our fingers and hands as well as with our brains, and we learn with our muscles as well as with our nervous system. One activity, to be sure, may involve more muscles than the other, but all are dependent upon an active brain and nervous system, and there is no point where the physical leaves off and the mental takes over (Garrett, 1955, pp. 2–3).

Most behavior consists of a continuous series of integrated actions or responses. The task of the psychologist is to construct a theoretical explanation about the complex organismic processes that will account for these phenomena. Our knowledge of these processes is obtained primarily by inferences derived from public observation. The observations yield the data of the science of psychology; from these data, inferences are made regarding the structures and processes which occur and which may not be directly observable. The inferences may be regarded as *constructs* from which theories may subsequently be constructed. Sometimes the inference relates to a certain state such as anxiety. The inference "He is anxious" does not differ systematically from the inference "He is hungry." Both involve inferences from observed behavior in a particular setting—the inferences may be correct or erroneous, but they do not justify the conclusion that one relates to mind and the other to body. Both involve the activity of the whole organism over periods of minutes, hours, or days.

Sperry (1952) has expressed a neurological viewpoint on this problem quite directly by asserting that from an objective, analytical standpoint, the sole product of brain function is motor coordination. "The entire output of our thinking machine consists of nothing but patterns of motor coordination" (pp. 297–298). Thus, the solution of the mind-body problem is seen to lie "in further insight into the relationship between the sensori-associative functions of the brain on the one hand and its motor activity on the other."

> The layman naturally assumes the major work of the brain to be the manufacture of ideas, sensations, images, and feelings, the storage of memories, and the like, and often expects the physical correlates of these to be some kind of aural end product phosphorescing within the cortex or emanating from its convolutions. These subjective phenomena may, however, be regarded as phases of brain function itself, not products of it. Scientific analysis has failed to disclose any output at the cerebral level other than the miscellaneous by-products mentioned above (heat, electric potentials, carbon dioxide, and other metabolites released into the bloodstream, cerebrospinal fluid, and surrounding tissues). Excepting these, the entire activity of the brain, so far as science can determine, yields nothing but motor adjustment. The only significant energy outlet and the only means of expression are over the motor pathways (p. 298).

> . . . One need not feel distressed at the suggestion that all our noblest and most aesthetic psychic experiences may be found, on analysis, to consist merely of brain patterns designed, directly or indirectly, for the adjustment of muscular contraction and glandular secretion. This detracts nothing from their meaning and importance. In the same way our finest deeds consist only of patterns of muscle-fiber twitches, our greatest printed passages only of ink marks on paper, while our most ravishing music, as pointed out by William James, is but the rasping of hairs from a horse's tail on the intestines of a cat. Significance and meaning in brain function do not derive from the intrinsic protoplasmic or other analytic aspects of neural excitation, but rather from their higher-order functional and operational effects as these work upon successive brain states, upon the motor system, and thereby into the environment, and back into the brain (p. 310).

THE PHYSICAL
ENVIRONMENT

Orientation

Psychology is basically the scientific study of the behavior of living organisms in relation to their environment, both physical and social. Although several other sciences study organismic behavior in one form or another (Kline, 1961), it is the unique task of psychology to determine the manner in which environmental forces elicit and modify behavior, and to investigate how, in turn, the resulting behavior alters these forces. In this textbook, we are concerned with a restricted segment of psychology—experimental psychology—with special emphasis upon man's sensory and perceptual processes. From a theoretical viewpoint, these processes cannot justifiably be separated from the total response patterns of behaving organisms. Sensory and perceptual responses, like all other normal responses, involve integrated behavioral patterns consisting of sensory-neuro-muscular components. Nevertheless, the separation may be made on a logical basis since it permits the classification of specific theories, psychological subject matter, and research techniques into a convenient unit of study.

It is generally agreed in contemporary psychology that all behavior is initiated by stimulation or, stated more precisely, the occurrence of a stimulus elicits the occurrence of a response (Rozeboom, 1960). This stimulation may originate from conditions that are present either within or outside the organism. In either case, stimuli impinge upon the organism and activity of the organism is generated or maintained. An appropriate starting point, then, for the study of behavior is to investigate the various types of stimulation that may occur and to consider the various techniques of measurement and control that may be used in studying their effects. In adopting this approach, however, we are not going to consider the *total* environment, but only those forces normally included in the physical sciences that give rise to certain classes of behavior. To a large extent, this will arbitrarily exclude social forces from our study, as well as the unique products of mankind—language and literature. A consideration of these factors lies more appropriately in the field of social psychology.

The world about us is the reservoir from which man acquires knowledge. What we know and what we are depends, in part, upon our past history of sensory stimulation. This history, when coupled with the stimulation present at a given moment, determines to a considerable degree the particular behavior which we exhibit. The sensory processes are the links that connect all behaving organisms to their external environment and provide information about that environment, as well as about the organism's own internal environment. If we are to understand behavior, we must understand these processes. Differential, nonstereotyped behavior depends upon the organism's ability to discriminate and respond to minute differences in some aspect of the stimulus object. Observable changes in behavior are related intimately to stimulus conditions.

We will turn now to a detailed analysis of the physical environment in order to learn about some of the properties of matter which provide the cues for discriminatory behavior. In addition, we will consider certain problems in the measurement and control of stimuli which affect experimental procedures in psychology. As one psychologist has contended, what is needed to understand certain problems in psychology is "not more psychology but more physics" (Gibson, 1960).

The Physical Meaning of Stimulus

The Distinction between Objects and Stimuli

As we look about us in our man-sized world, we notice that the world consists of objects—trees, buildings, street lights, airplanes, tables, and numerous other things with which we are thoroughly familiar. In the course of living, we have learned to accept the existence of a material world filled with objects and events. These exist externally to us; they have an independent existence. Take a chair in your room as an example. The chair is a real thing. You can sit on it; you can push it; you can place things on it; you can leave it during your summer vacation and when you return, it will still be there. Others come into your room and see the chair. They touch it; they sit on it; and in general treat it in the same manner as you. They do not doubt for a single moment that the chair has a real existence.

Notice also that by having the chair in your room you have had the opportunity to observe it. The chair in your room feels harder to sit upon than your neighbor's; you see that the red fabric on the chair is not quite as faded as the matching draperies on the window; as you lower yourself comfortably into the chair, you can hear the springs and cushions being crushed into shape; you can smell the odor of cigarettes in the armrest long after you have removed the ash tray. All of these observations depend upon the presence of the chair and certain of its associated physical properties.

In our illustration, the chair is classified as a *stimulus object.* By definition, a stimulus object is any object or event which is capable of eliciting an observable change in the behavior of a normal organism. The segment of behavior that is observed, that is, the particular *response,* may be gross, such as an eyeblink, the running of a rat in a maze, or a finger withdrawal, or it may be restricted to some physiological or neurophysiological activity, such as a change in heart rate or in the electrical characteristics of a neural impulse. Ordinarily, the terms "behavioral response" and "physiological" or "sensory response" are used, respectively, to denote this difference in emphasis. The important aspect, however, is not whether the segment of behavior is large or small, but whether the change in the behavior is detectable and measurable. Although an object like our chair has the *potential* for eliciting a behavioral or sensory response, the occurrence of a specific response will depend, among other factors, upon the presence of a particular stimulus or group of stimuli. We can hear the squeak of the springs in our chair only if certain sound stimuli are present and our ears are functioning properly. The chair is the stimulus object; the physical sound waves constitute the *effective* stimulus; and our ears are the receptor organs. Whether or not a potential stimulus becomes an effective stimulus depends upon a large number of variables related to the individual and to the situation in which the stimulation occurs.

A *stimulus* is defined broadly as *any* antecedent circumstance that elicits or modifies the behavior of an organism. When dealing with sensory processes, however, the term is used with a much narrower meaning; it refers to any form of *physical energy* in the internal or external environment of the organism which excites a receptor mechanism, like the eye or the ear. According to this distinction, a change in some hormone level might be a stimulus in the general sense since it might affect, let us say, mating behavior; but it would not be a stimulus in the restricted sense of the term as it would not excite a particular receptor mechanism. Sensory stimuli are *attributes* or *properties* of stimulus objects (Rozeboom, 1960) and refer to various forms of physical energy, such as heat, sound, and light. One of the tasks of psychology is to isolate the invariant features of stimulus objects that are capable of eliciting invariant behavioral responses.

Adequate and Inadequate Stimuli

In man and in the higher animals, evolutionary changes have produced a number of receptor mechanisms; each of these is specialized for receiving a particular type of physical stimulation. The eye, for example, is the organ that receives light and excludes sound. Light is considered to be the normal stimulus for seeing. A stimulus which is the normal one, or the usual one, for a specified sense organ is called an *adequate* stimulus. Other stimuli, such as the mechanical pressures produced by pressing upon the eyeball, may elicit visual sensations, but these are not considered to be adequate or appropriate stimuli. An *inadequate* stimulus is one which elicits a sensory or behavioral response but which is not the normal one for that particular sense organ. An inadequate stimulus is merely an inappropriate or abnormal stimulus; it is not a stimulus which is incapable of producing a change in behavior.

The Distinction between Distal
and Proximal Stimulation

A distinction that is sometimes made in psychology is that between *distal* and *proximal* stimuli (Götlind, 1963). *Distal stimuli* represent the physical properties of a stimulus object measured *at some distance* from the individual, for example, the radiant energy from a neon sign measured at the source. The energy generated by, or reflected from, the stimulus object is subject to certain changes, both at the source and in the course of its transmission through the physical medium interposed between the source and the individual. Consequently, the pattern of energy that finally reaches the sensory organ must be differentiated from that which leaves the source. *Proximal stimuli* represent the pattern of energy measured *at the sensory organ* of the individual. Proximal events occur at the boundaries between the individual and the environment. When the proximal stimuli are of sufficient frequency, intensity, and duration, certain processes are initiated in the specialized structures of the sensory organs; these, in turn, trigger a chain of events in the complex neural network connecting the sensory organ to the brain.

The distinction between distal and proximal stimulation is an important one in experimental psychology. The particular empirical relationships established through research must be explicit as to which set of variables, distal or proximal, is specifically involved. The specification of the stimulus situation will differ depending upon which set is actually measured. For example, the characteristics of acoustic energy measured at a distance of one foot in front of a loudspeaker are not the same as those measured at the ear of a listener standing six feet away. Furthermore, a given distal pattern may produce different proximal patterns depending upon other situational factors. The distal pattern of light rays reflected from the book you are reading will produce a different proximal pattern in your eyes when your eyes are wide open than it will when they are half closed. As another example, certain visual cues to distance may or may not be present proximally; this will depend upon the distance between the individual and the stimulus object. Conversely, the presence of a certain proximal pattern does not provide a unique basis from which to infer the characteristics of distant objects or events. If, for example, we are listening to a symphonic concert in which the curtains are drawn across the stage, neither we nor the rest of the audience will know whether there is an orchestra behind the curtains or just an extremely fine stereophonic sound system.

The experimental psychologist dealing with sensory and perceptual processes must be aware of the differences between proximal and distal stimuli and, accordingly, he must be cautious in the measurement and specification of his experimental situation. He should be aware that the world of energy contains complex as well as simple facts; there are not only pure tones, but also complex patterns of speech sounds. If the regularities of sensory and perceptual behavior are to be understood, we must identify the invariant features of the stimulus situation, whatever these may be. It seems reasonable to assume that many invariant aspects of the world in which we live have yet to be discovered; perhaps the work of psychologists will suggest some profitable lines of inquiry to the physical scientists.

Some Quantitative Concepts in Physics and Their Applications in Psychology

Operational Definitions

All sciences are based upon a theory of measurement which at some point introduces fundamental concepts that are related to observable events (Newbury, 1953). This permits an experimental verification of the hypotheses that have been derived from theory and that contain the concept in question. In physics and psychology, scientific empiricism requires that the concepts that are introduced, such as mass, electrical conductivity, and habit strength, must be reducible to a set of certain physical operations. Concepts which adhere to this requirement are said to be *operationally defined* and possess *operational meaning*. An *operational definition* is a group of statements which reduces an unobservable concept into a publicly verifiable set of operations. This means that the fundamental concepts of any science are synonymous with the corresponding sets of operations. This insistence on operational definitions tends to minimize the ambiguities that would otherwise engulf the concepts of a given discipline. In the operational method of definition, the meaning of a term lies in the physical operations that are performed. For example, the concept of hunger drive in animal psychology is operationally defined in terms of the number of hours during which a rat is physically restrained from approaching and ingesting food. The operational definition provides an *objective* meaning to the concept by relating it to a set of operations that are publicly observable. Once a minimal number of such concepts have been established in a scientific area, it is possible by means of mathematical equations (publicly observable calculations) to derive *higher order* empirical constructs. The derived concept of *area*, for example, is mathematically related to the fundamental concept of length. (Area is equal to length times length.) *Speed* is a derived concept which is obtained by dividing the fundamental quantity of length by the fundamental quantity of time. In this way, a hierarchy of acceptable and meaningful terms may be constructed that rests upon a firm physicalistic basis. These terms may then be appropriately used in the formulation of scientific hypotheses or theories to explain the phenomena of a particular field of study.

The selection of the fundamental concepts in a science is an arbitrary matter, but once the selection has been made, all other concepts in that science must be derivable from those initially chosen. In physics, the usual selection of basic concepts has been limited to mass, length, and time, with force and electricity as derived concepts. Some writers (Little, 1953), however, have suggested five fundamental concepts: *length, time, force, electricity*, and *temperature*. The use of five concepts rather than three makes it possible to differentiate more clearly among the various kinds of physical phenomena: *geometrical, kinematic, dynamic, electrical,* and *thermal.* Each of these five fundamental concepts will be examined in turn.

Geometrical Concepts

Length, the first concept to be considered, is generally measured in the scientific world according to the metric system. The *standard international meter* (1 meter = 100 centimeters) is now accepted as the distance, measured at the temperature of melting ice (0° Centigrade), between two scratches on a platinum-iridium bar kept at the International Bureau of Weights and Measures near Paris, France. For greater accuracy, however, the standard meter has recently been calibrated in terms of the number of wavelengths of light in a certain sharp spectral line. Specifically, one standard meter is 1,553,164.1245 red-line wavelengths (643 mμ) of the cadmium spectrum. Two copies of the international standard are kept at the U.S. Bureau of Standards in Washington, D.C.; in terms of this standard, one inch equals exactly 2.54 centimeters and 39.37 inches equals 1 meter.

The principle advantage of the metric system is that the multiples and subdivisions of its units are related by the factor ten, or a multiple of ten. This makes the metric system compatible with our decimal number system. Some of the more common prefixes, together with their decimal equivalents, are given in Table 2–1. A unit a thousand times larger than the meter, for instance, is called a kilometer; one-thousandth of a meter is called a millimeter. The micron (μ) or micrometer is one-millionth of a meter. The millimicron (mμ) is a unit a thousand times smaller than the micron, that is, it is one-thousandth of a millionth of a meter. The names and definitions of the metric units of length are summarized in Table 2–1.

Sometimes the numbers used in the various sciences are extremely large or extremely small. To facilitate computations, such numbers may be written as the product of two factors. One of these factors lies between 1 and 10; the other is a whole-numbered power of 10. The first factor gives the *detail* of the number, while the second gives its *order of magnitude.* The number 8,560,000, for example, is equal to 8.56 × 1,000,000 or 8.56 × 10^6. Notice that 8.56 is the detail; 10^6 is the order of magnitude. The order of magnitude for each of the major multiples and subdivisions of the units of measurement in the metric system is included in Table 2–1.

The order of magnitude involves some power of 10 as indicated by an exponent, or superscript. In the previous example, the exponent of 10 is 6. The exponent of 10 indicates the number of digits by which the decimal point must be moved from unity, or 1. For a positive numerical exponent, the decimal point is moved that number of digits to the right of one. For example, $10^1 = 10$; $10^2 = 100$; $10^3 = 1000$, and so on. For a negative numerical exponent, the decimal point is moved that number of digits to the left of 1. For example, $10^{-1} = 0.1 = 1/10$; $10^{-2} = 0.01 = 1/10^2$; $10^{-3} = 0.001 = 1/10^3$.

Although the English system of linear measurement is arithmetically more

Table 2–1   Multiples and Subdivisions of the Units of Measurement
in the Metric System

Multiples (Greek prefix)		Decimal Equivalents	Order of Magnitude
million	—mega	1,000,000.	10^6
thousand	—kilo	1000.	10^3
hundred	—hecto	100.	10^2
ten	—deka	10.	10^1

Subdivisions (Latin prefix)		Decimal Equivalents	Order of Magnitude
tenth	—deci	0.1	10^{-1}
hundredth	—centi	0.01	10^{-2}
thousandth	—milli	0.001	10^{-3}
millionth	—micro	0.000001	10^{-6}

Names and Definitions of Metric Units of Length

$$
\begin{aligned}
1 \text{ kilometer} \quad (\text{km}) &= 10^3 \text{ meters (m)} \\
1 \text{ centimeter} \quad (\text{cm}) &= 10^{-2}\text{m} \\
1 \text{ millimeter} \quad (\text{mm}) &= 10^{-3}\text{m} = 10^{-1}\text{cm} \\
1 \text{ micron} \quad (\mu) &= 10^{-6}\text{m} = 10^{-3}\text{mm} \\
1 \text{ millimicron} \quad (\text{m}\mu) &= 10^{-9}\text{m} = 10^{-7}\text{cm} = 10^{-3}\mu \\
1 \text{ Angstrom} \quad (\text{A}) &= 10^{-10}\text{m} = 10^{-8}\text{cm} = 10^{-4}\mu = 10^{-1}\text{m}\mu
\end{aligned}
$$

cumbersome than the metric, it is as precise as the metric system and conversions between the two systems can readily be made by using the following equivalents:

$$
\begin{aligned}
1 \text{ meter} &= 1.09361 \text{ yards} = 3.2808 \text{ feet} = 39.37 \text{ inches} \\
1 \text{ yard} &= 0.9144 \text{ meter} \\
1 \text{ foot} &= 0.3048 \text{ meter} = 30.48 \text{ centimeters} \\
1 \text{ inch} &= 0.0254 \text{ meter} = 2.54 \text{ centimeters} \\
1 \text{ centimeter} &= 0.3937 \text{ inch}
\end{aligned}
$$

Once the fundamental unit of length has been defined, it is possible by means of mathematical relationships to derive other geometrical concepts. These include *area* (for a rectangle, length × width), *volume* (for a rectangular box, the area of the base × the height of the box measured perpendicular to that base), *angle* (the ratio of a circular arc to its radius, measured in similar units of length; when the arc equals the radius, the ratio is unity and the angle is called a *radian* which equals 57.3°), and *trigonometric functions* (for example, the sine of an angle in a right triangle is equal to the ratio of the length of the side opposite the angle to the length of the hypotenuse). Each of these derived concepts has its own unit of measurement. Thus, area may be expressed in terms of square inches (in²), square centimeters (cm²); volume, in cubic inches (in³), cubic centimeters (cm³); angles in degrees, minutes, and seconds or in radians (60 seconds = 1 minute; 60 minutes = 1°; 1° = 0.01745 radian); and trigonometric functions in degrees or radians and so on. Tables are available that indicate equivalent values and make it a relatively simple matter to convert any of the derived measures from one system of measurement to another.

The fundamental concept of length and the concepts derived from length are widely used in psychology, as well as in physics. In animal experiments, we find that mazes differ in length and physical size; the turning of activity wheels is translated into miles of running; stimuli in visual discrimination experiments involve different areas and shapes; electrodes are implanted at different spatial locations in the brain; approach and avoidance response tendencies depend upon the distances of the organism from the point of reinforcement; the running paths in mazes utilize various angular forms such as T, Y, and V; acquisition curves in learning studies are often expressed as mathematical functions.

In experiments with human subjects, there are tests of spatial relations; visual stimuli have different sizes and forms; movement time is measured as a function of the distance over which the hand must travel; auditory localization varies as a function of the angle between the listener's ear and the source of sound; the description of auditory stimuli can be given in terms of mathematical functions; the volume of a stomach balloon is related to subjective reports of hunger pangs; concept formation is studied using figures of different shape; electroencephalographic records vary as a function of the spatial location of the electrodes on the head; pursuit rotors utilize circular motion; transposition studies with children involve visual figures with different areas; photographic records of eyelid responses in classical conditioning studies provide linear equivalents of temporal intervals; visual illusions are based on specific geometrical arrangements of lines, curves, and circles; Rorschach tests are in part scored on the form which determines the response; optical range finders are designed according to principles of geometry; tactile communication systems depend upon the discrimination of spatial locations on the skin. We could extend this list indefinitely, but it should be apparent at this point that the fundamental concept of length and the concepts derived from it are widely used in modern psychology to designate certain aspects of the stimulus pattern.

Kinematic Concepts

The fundamental concept of length combined with that of time provides the basis for *kinematics,* that branch of physics which deals with the geometry of motion. The operational definition of time is given by the common process of reading an accurate watch or clock. For precise measurements, very accurate clocks have been made using the period of oscillation of a vibrating slab of crystal in a crystal oscillator or the vibrational frequency of atoms in a molecule. In both the English and metric systems, the unit of time is the *mean solar second.* The multiples of this unit do not follow the metric scheme of ten, but the minute and hour are certainly familiar to everyone. The maintenance of the standard time unit lies in astronomy and is based on the mean solar day which contains 24 hours, with each hour divided into 60 minutes of 60 seconds each. The mean solar day is taken as the yearly average of the period of time which elapses between two successive crossings by the sun of a given point in the sky. For calendar purposes, the length of a year is designated as slightly more than 365.24 mean solar days. Since the rotation of the earth defines the unit of time, no man-made standards are stored for purposes of reference.

Time measures are probably more often used in experimental psychology than any other single measure. Some examples include reaction time, time as a factor in maze retention, time relations between conditioned and unconditioned stimuli, time and motion studies, time error in psychophysical judgments, time scores on motor performance tests, time-constants in certain types of controls in man-machine systems, time delays in neural networks, time-scale distortions and their effects on speech intelligibility, pitch as a function of the temporal duration of tones, time (chronological age) as a factor in intelligence, and time (number of daylight hours) as a factor in the migratory behavior of birds. Numerous other examples can undoubtedly be added to this list by the reader without any difficulty.

There are several higher-order concepts that can be derived from the fundamental concepts of length and time. These include frequency, velocity, acceleration, angular velocity, and angular acceleration. *Frequency* (f) refers to the number of complete repetitions of a motion that occur in a unit interval of time. For example, if the motion repeats every 1/100 sec, the frequency is 100 times (cycles, revolutions) per second. In general, frequency is the reciprocal of period (T), $f = 1/T$. *Angular velocity* (ω) is defined as the rate at which an angle is described as a function of time. For example, a spot of mud on a white sidewall tire turning at a constant rate will sweep an increasing angle from a given reference point. The concept of angular velocity applies to a given body moving at a single rate of rotation; this differs from the simple concept of *velocity* which is defined as the rate at which a linear distance is traversed as a function of time. *Simple* or *linear* velocity is computed by dividing length by time and the magnitude of a velocity is called *speed*. All simple velocities are limited to motions in a straight line; thus, velocities may be constant in direction, but different in magnitude. The concepts of *acceleration* and *angular acceleration* will not be considered in this presentation as their use is primarily restricted to more advanced levels of psychology, particularly in advanced engineering psychology.

Dynamic Concepts

The third fundamental concept of physics we shall consider is *force* (F). Force may be considered as a push or pull on an object which tends to change its motion, to speed it up or to slow it down, or to alter its path of movement. At ordinary velocities much less than the speed of light, the inertial mass (M) of bodies can be treated as a constant, so that force may be defined as the product of mass

(*M*) and acceleration (*a*), $F = Ma$. By relativity theory, the inertial mass of a body increases detectably as its velocity approaches that of light (approximately 186,500 miles per second). The units of force are the kilogram per meter per second per second ($Kg/m/sec^2$) in the MKS (meter, kilogram, second) system and the gram per centimeter per second per second ($gm/cm/sec^2$) in the CGS (centimeter, gram, second) system. The two units are called *newton* and *dyne*, respectively. One dyne is the amount of force required to give a mass of 1 gram an acceleration of 1 cm/sec^2.

Mass and weight are often erroneously used as synonyms, but the mass of a body is not the same as its weight. The inertial mass of a body is the same under all conditions, except at speeds approaching that of light. The measurement of the mass of a body is a measurement of its inertia, whether it is near the earth or in orbit around the moon. Inertia is the tendency of a moving body to resist change in its speed. The mass of one body may be compared with that of another by a comparison of their inertias. Mass refers to a universal property of a particular body, independent of its location, and is operationally defined in terms of *force, length,* and *time.* Strictly, mass (*M*) at ordinary velocities is force per acceleration and is given by the equation:

$$M = F/a. \tag{2-1}$$

The operational definition for weight (gravitational mass) is completely different from that for inertial mass. The weight of a body of matter is a specific expression of force and arises because every object has mass and is being accelerated by gravity. Gravitational mass is a property of matter which is measured on a balance or scale; it indicates the force with which the earth attracts that body. Unlike inertial mass, the weight of a body due to the pull of gravity changes considerably when the body is moved from the earth to outer space, or to the moon. The closer a given body is to the center of the earth, the greater its weight. You would weigh more standing in Death Valley than at the top of Mount Everest. Weight is a changeable property of matter which varies with the pull of gravity while inertial mass is an unchanging property of matter in which gravity is irrelevant. Nevertheless, it is a striking fact that the inertial masses of all objects are proportional to their gravitational masses. This proportionality has been experimentally established for many different objects on many different occasions. Consequently, the same standard, the platinum-iridium kilogram, can be used in establishing the operational definitions for both gravitational and inertial mass.

The concept of weight, like the concepts of length and time, is used frequently in psychology. Some examples are found in dietary studies on the nutritive properties of certain foods; the stress effects of noise are evaluated in animals by weighing certain endocrine glands before and after given amounts of noise exposure; hunger drive in animals is established by restricting food intake to certain minimal levels; learning is known to vary as a function of the magnitude of the (food) reward; sensory functions are often studied by having subjects make judgments in weight discrimination experiments; some human engineering studies are concerned with optimal ways of carrying loads (weights) and determining the optimal size and weight of containers.

In psychoacoustics the concept of force is used to derive the concept of *pressure*, which is widely applied to specify the intensity of an auditory stimulus. Pressure (*P*) refers to the distribution of force over a given area. In the form of an equation,

$$P = F/A, \qquad (2\text{-}2)$$

where *F* is the force and *A* is the area over which *F* is applied. The MKS unit of pressure is the newton per square meter, but this unit is too large for experimental purposes in psychology. Therefore, the CGS system is used in which the unit of pressure is the *dyne/sq cm*. Although conversions are seldom necessary between the CGS and MKS systems, it may be helpful to know that 1 dyne $= 10^{-5}$ newton.

The concept of physical pressure is also found in psychological studies dealing with the human skin senses, in particular, pressure and pain. One of the problems in this area is to determine the nature and magnitude of stimuli which produce various sensations, such as "light touch," "dull pressure," and so on. In general, the stimulus object produces a mechanical deformation of the skin, such that sharp tension gradients are formed within the cutaneous tissues.

Electrical Concepts

It is now known that matter is composed of minute particles of positive and negative electricity, such that in ordinary matter the number of each of these is exactly the same. Common objects are not charged since they consist of molecules or groups of atoms which collectively are electrically neutral. However, if a sufficient number of similar particles or charges are combined, a quantity of electricity is produced which is measured in *coulomb* units. In the MKS system, one coulomb is defined as that charge which repels a like charge, placed 1 m away in a vacuum, with a force of 9×10^9 newtons. In the CGS system, the unit is the *statcoulomb*, which is that charge which repels a like charge, 1 cm away in a vacuum, with a force of 1 dyne. One coulomb equals 3×10^9 statcoulomb. It takes about 6 billion billion of the particle charges to make one coulomb of electricity.

In psychology and engineering, a more convenient measure of electricity than its quantity is its rate of flow. Just as we can have gallons of water in a container (quantity) and can measure the number of gallons of water per minute pouring from a hose (rate of flow), we can also measure coulombs and amperes of electricity. The ampere indicates the rate of flow of electric current and is measured in coulombs per second. Other definitions of the ampere are sometimes given in terms of newtons per meter, but such definitions are beyond our present need. The flow of electricity is usually designated as alternating current (AC) when the direction of flow is continuously reversing itself (for example, 60 times per second in ordinary house current), and as direct current (DC) when the flow is continuous in one direction, as in an automobile battery.

When electricity flows, the natural particles of electricity move through the conductive medium, usually a metal wire. Five factors control the flow of electricity through the wire: *time, cross-sectional area* of the wire, *length* of the wire, *material* of the wire, and the *difference* of *electrical potential* between the ends of the wire. The difference of electrical potential is the driving factor which transfers the charge from one point to another and is measured in *volts*. One volt is the potential difference between two points when 1 joule of work is required to transfer 1 coulomb of charge from one point to the other. The concept of potential difference is analogous to a difference in water level in which there is a flow of water from the higher to the lower level.

The concepts of electricity and the use of electrical and electronic instruments are so widespread in psychology that specific examples scarcely seem appropriate. Nevertheless, a few applications will be given. Electroencephalograms show variations of electrical potentials arising in different cortical regions; hand steadiness is inversely related to the number of electrical contacts made between a stylus and some circumscribed boundary; electrical shock is frequently used as the unconditioned stimulus in learning experiments; emotional responses are measured in terms of the electrical resistance of the skin; auditory and visual systems are studied by examining the electrical activity recorded from specific cranial nerves; electrical stimuli are used to excite the various senses of the skin; the relative strengths of animal drives are measured in terms of the number of crossings of a charged grid; heart rate is measured by an electrocardiogram; the detection of targets on a radar screen depends in part upon the electrical characteristics of the signal. Other examples may be added by the reader.

Thermal Concepts

The fundamental concept of temperature is the final concept that will be considered in this section. Temperature is basic to the theory of thermodynamics in physics and is an integral part of the science of *calorimetry*. The concept of temperature refers to the degree of hotness of a body. Like water "seeking its own level," temperature determines the direction of net transfer of heat from a body of higher temperature to one of lower temperature. The operational definition of temperature is given by the procedures by which a standard thermometer is constructed and by the method which is used in reading its scale. The conventional procedure for building a mercury-in-glass thermometer is to fix two reference points of temperature under a pressure of one standard atmosphere. One of these points corresponds to the position of the mercury when the thermometer is placed in a well-stirred mixture of pure ice melting in pure water; the other corresponds to the position of the mercury when the thermometer is placed in steam just above the surface of freely boiling water. By taking the ratio of the length of the mercury column above the point for melting ice to the total length between the ice and steam points, any other temperature may be defined. This procedure holds for any type of thermometer. Observe that the procedure described does not measure temperature directly; the temperature is measured indirectly in terms of some physical property which changes uniformly with temperature, as, for example, the volume of a given amount of mercury or the electrical resistance of platinum wire.

There are three temperature scales in common use, each of which assigns different degrees of temperature to the two fixed points. These values are summarized in Table 2–2.

Table 2–2   Degrees of Temperature at Two Fixed Reference Points

Type of Scale	Melting-Ice Temperature	Steam Temperature
Fahrenheit	32	212
Centigrade	0	100
Kelvin	273.16	376.16

The *Fahrenheit* scale is the one we usually refer to in everyday life; the *Centigrade* (or *Celsius*) scale is the usual laboratory scale, with temperatures below that of melting ice denoted by negative signs; the Kelvin scale is an absolute scale of temperature, with the size of its units equal to that of the centigrade scale and its zero point at the limit of coldness in the physical world where all molecular motion ceases. Conversions between these three scales may be made by the equation:

$$\frac{(F° - 32)}{180} = \frac{C°}{100} = \frac{(K° - 273.16)}{100}, \tag{2-3}$$

where $F°$, $C°$, and $K°$ refer, respectively, to the given temperature in degrees Fahrenheit, Centigrade, or Kelvin.

Heat and temperature, like mass and weight, are not identical concepts. Heat is identified with the internal movements of particles in matter; it is the kinetic energy of the random motions of atomic and molecular particles of which matter is composed. Temperature is a measure of the average kinetic energy of these particles. It is not necessary to have high temperatures to obtain large quantities of heat; the amount of heat depends not only on the temperature to which a given body is raised, but also on the kind and amount of matter of which that body is composed. The quantity of heat is measured in terms of the thermal properties of water. The *calorie* is defined as the amount of heat required to raise one gram of water one degree Centigrade. In the English system, the *British Thermal Unit* (BTU) is defined as the amount of heat required to raise one pound of water one degree Fahrenheit. When a substance is heated, there is an increase in the internal kinetic energy of the substance which becomes apparent as a rise in temperature, an increase in (gaseous) pressure, or a change of state (for example, ice to water). Heat is energy and, as such, it can be made to perform useful work, as through the steam engine; also, there is a mechanical equivalence between heat and other forms of energy.

The concepts of heat and temperature are found most frequently in psychology in the study of the senses of *taste, smell, cold, warmth,* and *pain.* In these cases, the temperature of the stimulus, for example, the temperature of a salt solution, is an important variable in determining the particular sensory response that will be made. The detailed exposition of this material, however, will be presented in subsequent chapters of this book. In applied psychology, temperature has been shown to be related to work efficiency. When, under certain conditions of humidity, the temperature rises above 96°F, motor functions such as those involved in receiving Morse code may be severely impaired (Mackworth, 1946).

The World of Energy

Thresholds—An Introductory Comment

In a preceding section of this chapter, it was pointed out that not every occurrence of energy is sufficient to produce a change in behavior. In order to act as a stimulus, the energy must be appropriate for a given sensory modality, and it must be of sufficient magnitude to initiate certain excitatory processes in the sensory organ and its associated neural network. The point of transition from no behavioral response to response introduces an important concept in psychology— the *absolute threshold* or, in classical terms, the *stimulus limen*. There are several different kinds of thresholds, all of which are statistically defined; these will be considered in detail in Chapters 7 and 8. The important point for consideration here is that the various thresholds are specified in terms of some measurable aspect of the physical stimulus. We turn now to the first step in determining a particular threshold for a given sensory system; we will consider different types of stimuli and the ways in which these stimuli can be measured and described in physical terms.

The Concept of Energy

The concept of energy is one of the most useful and most widely applied concepts in psychology and modern physics. We have already seen that the term stimulus (in its restricted sense) refers to some form of energy, either in the internal or external environment of the organism, which can evoke a neural response in a particular receptor mechanism. Stimuli are forms of energy which initiate the chain of events mediating a sensory response or a sequence of behavioral activities. Some preliminary consideration has already been given to certain quantitative concepts in physics, among which were included thermal and electrical energy. Our concern now is to develop the meaning of energy in more detail and to examine some of the more important classes of energy that comprise the organism's physical environment. In the later chapters, certain relationships that exist between the characteristics of a stimulus and specific behavioral responses will be fully described.

Although energy takes many forms, all of these forms have one thing in common: *the capacity for doing work.* In the science of *statics*, which deals with forces acting upon rigid bodies that retain their size and shape, *work* is defined as the result of force being exerted along a distance. When the force remains constant both in direction and magnitude and the point of application of the force is displaced along a single straight line, the equation for work (W) is given by:

$$W = FS \cos\Theta, \tag{2-4}$$

where F is the magnitude of the force applied, S is the length of the displacement of a given mass, and Θ is the angle between the direction of the force and that of the displacement. In the MKS system of measurement, the unit of work is called a joule: one joule equals 10 million ergs where one erg is equal to a force of one dyne applied for a distance of 1 cm. In the English system (foot, pound, second), the term *foot-pounds* is used. The concept of work in physics is usually associated with the material on torque and simple machines, such as the screw and the wedge.

In psychology, mechanical devices that perform work are involved in the generation of stimuli which elicit the cutaneous sensations of *touch, pressure,* and *vibration.* Figure 2-1 shows a mechanical apparatus for providing the necessary stimu-

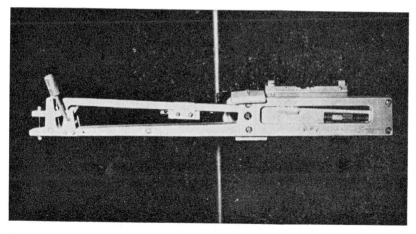

Figure 2-1. An aesthesiometer for providing mechanical stimulation in studies dealing with touch or pressure. (From Wenger et al., *Physiological psychology,* New York: Holt, Rinehart and Winston, 1956.)

lation in studies dealing with sensitivity to touch or pressure. This instrument is called an *aesthesiometer.* The weight on the point of the needle is controlled by the position of the metal rider on the lever. The needle is raised or lowered by adjusting the handle on the left-hand end of the apparatus. Stimulation of this type which occurs at a point on the skin is designated as *punctiform* stimulation and the intensity of stimulation is usually specified in *grams* or *ergs.*

Areal stimulation involves the application of a weight over a circumscribed region of the skin. In this case the intensity of the stimulus is usually specified in grams per square millimeter (gm/sq mm). A device for controlling the weight and area of pressure stimulation is shown in Figure 2-2. A given weight is raised and lowered at a constant speed by means of a screwgear driven by an electric

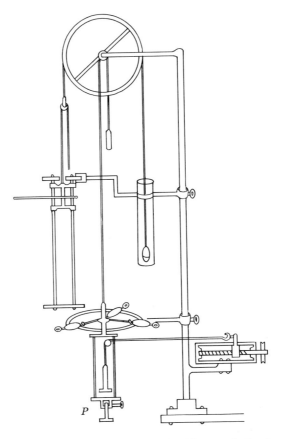

Figure 2-2. An apparatus for providing areal stimulation, with precise control of the weight and area of pressure. The applicator is labeled as *P*. (Adapted from Nafe, and Wagoner, *J. gen. Psychol.,* 1941.)

motor. The weights are circular aluminum discs of different areal size which are covered with blotting paper to control for extraneous temperature effects. A typical series of weights may range from 8.75 to 70 gm, with areas from 6.25 to 200 sq mm.

In the operation of machines, the output in energy is always less than the input. The wasted energy of work appears in the form of heat due to friction. This indicates that the concept of energy has a much broader significance than that within the field of mechanics. Since heat is a form of energy, it can be shown that a certain amount of heat is the mechanical equivalent of a definite amount of work.

One British Thermal Unit (BTU) equals 25,030 foot-pounds of work—the quantity of heat required to change the temperature of one pound of water by 1° Fahrenheit.

The concept of thermal energy is important in psychology in experiments dealing with the cutaneous senses of cold and warmth. Figure 2-3 is a schematic drawing of a punctiform temperature stimulator. The pressure of the blunt copper

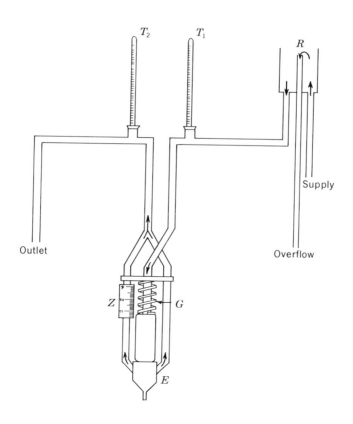

Figure 2–3. A punctiform temperature-stimulator. See text for details. (Adapted from Hall and Dallenbach, *Amer. J. Psychol.*, 1947.)

point (E) upon the skin is controlled by the tension of an adjustable spring (G), and the temperature of the point is determined by the flow of temperature-regulated water which enters a chamber containing an extension of the copper point. The water enters the chamber via the center tube and leaves by way of the two lateral tubes. Notice that the pressure of the point against the skin can be read on a scale (F) and that the temperature of the water entering and leaving the chamber may be read on thermometers T_1 and T_2.

phenomena (Little, 1953). These are *energetics*, such as mass and thermodynamics; *flow phenomena*, such as magnetic flux and electric currents; *field phenomena*, such as radiation and electrostatics; *periodic phenomena*, such as wave propagation and auditory oscillations; and *quantum phenomena*, such as nuclear reactions and light.

We will turn, therefore, to a detailed discussion of certain aspects of those types of phenomena that are of greatest importance in experimental psychology: quantum phenomena, periodic phenomena, and field phenomena. Within these three types, the selected examples of light, sound, and the electrochemical properties of matter wil be considered. An understanding of this material is fundamental to the study of the sensory processes of *vision, audition, olfaction* and *gustation.*

Electromagnetic Radiation

The entire gamut of electromagnetic radiation is known as the electromagnetic spectrum. The various classes of radiation in the spectrum are all essentially the same in that they travel with the same velocity, that is, at the speed of light (3×10^8 meters per second in a vacuum). They are all considered to be carriers of energy and, in a vacuum, they exhibit similar properties and differ only in wavelength (Little, 1953).

Although all electromagnetic radiations have similar properties, there are major differences in their manner of excitation and in their reactions with matter. The radiations of a given wavelength may, for example, be generated by the oscillation of an electric current as well as by molecular vibration. The only requirement for radiation is that electricity be accelerated. It makes no difference whether this occurs in the gases of the sun, in the slow oscillations of the current in the filament of an electric light bulb, or in the nucleus of an atom. The faster the oscillations of electricity, the shorter and more energetic will be the radiation; or, stated differently, the greater the acceleration, the shorter the wavelength of the radiation.

Figure 2-5 presents an arbitrary classification of the electromagnetic spectrum divided into eight groups according to wavelength. The descriptive names assigned to the various portions of the spectrum are historical and they provide a convenient classification according to the source of the radiation. There is, of course, some overlap among the groups, starting with the longest at the top and ending with the shortest at the bottom. The eight groups are long electric waves, radio waves, short electric waves, heat or infrared waves, visible light waves, ultraviolet light waves, X rays, and gamma rays. Some of the practical applications in which the various types of waves may be found are indicated in the right-hand column of Figure 2-5. Notice that the wavelengths in the electromagnetic spectrum range from extremely short gamma rays (one million-millionth of a centimeter) at one end, to very long electric waves (several miles) at the other end. However, only a small segment of this spectrum is capable of exciting the human eye. The wavelengths in this segment extend from about 380 mμ (millimicrons or thousandths of millionths of a meter) to about 760 mμ, that is, approximately 0.000038 to 0.000076 cm in length. When the entire electromagnetic spectrum is plotted on a logarithmic scale, the visible spectrum occupies only about 1/70 of the total range.

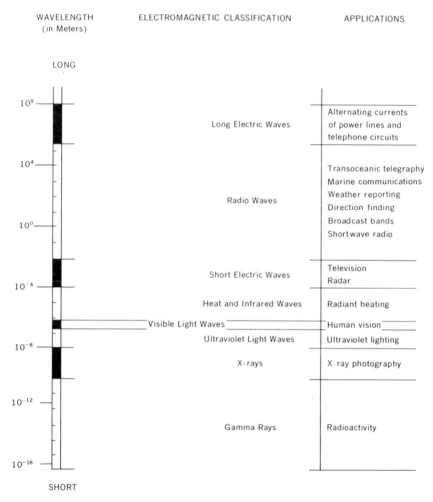

WAVELENGTH (in Meters)   ELECTROMAGNETIC CLASSIFICATION   APPLICATIONS

Figure 2–5. The electromagnetic spectrum arbitrarily divided into eight major types of waves.

Radiation, in addition to being classified according to wavelength, may be described by the manner in which its energy is distributed throughout the electromagnetic spectrum. There are two kinds of radiation: *characteristic* and *general.* *Characteristic radiation* is the kind in which the distribution of energy appears in the visible part of the spectrum as more or less discrete lines or bands of wavelengths which uniquely identify the source of radiation. A mercury atom, for example, will show lines as presented in Figure 2-6.

The second type of radiation, *general radiation,* is that in which the electromagnetic radiation is continuously distributed throughout the spectrum. General radiation results from the random motions of the atomic and molecular electrical charges which constitute all matter; consequently, there is no basis in this type of radiation from which to identify a particular chemical substance.

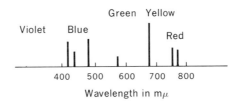

Figure 2-6. The visible electromagnetic spectrum for mercury.

One example of general radiation is that associated with a *blackbody*. A blackbody is an ideal body which would, if it existed, absorb all of the radiant energy falling upon it. The absorptivity of such a body would be 100 percent, and the reflectivity would be zero. Since no radiant energy would be reflected, such an ideal body, when illuminated, would appear perfectly black and would be invisible. The interest in such an ideal body, therefore, is not in its reflected properties, but in the character of the radiation emitted by it when it is heated. There are empirical laws which specify the density of the emitted radiant energy and describe the spectral distribution of the energy as a function of the temperature to which the blackbody is heated.

Experimentally, the nearest approach to the ideal blackbody is a hollow metal cylinder, blackened inside and containing a narrow slit or opening at one end. When such a cylinder is heated to a constant temperature, the radiation escaping from the opening closely resembles the ideal blackbody radiation. The opening is then referred to as a blackbody of known temperature and area.

Several physical laws have been formulated which describe the characteristics of this type of radiation; but, most importantly, the peculiarities observed in a series of carefully controlled experiments have provided the basis for the quantum theory of radiation. It was found that the energy contained in blackbody radiation is not distributed uniformly throughout the electromagnetic spectrum and that the wavelength at which maximal energy is localized is dependent upon the temperature of the blackbody. Figure 2-7 shows some typical curves for blackbody radiation. For a given temperature, there is a maximum of energy at one particular wavelength, with lesser amounts at all other wavelengths. As the temperature of the blackbody increases, the wavelength of maximal energy is decreased. Wien's *law of displacement* states that the wavelength for which the spectral emittance is maximum is inversely proportional to the absolute temperature (degrees Kelvin) of the blackbody radiator.

Historically, numerous attempts were made to derive equations that would explain the facts shown in Figure 2-7, but all such attempts based upon the classical wave theory of radiation failed. The classical theory assumed that the

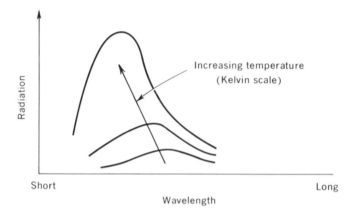

Figure 2-7. Typical curves for blackbody radiation, illustrating Wien's law of displacement.

emitted radiation was a continuous train of waves of electromagnetic energy. The *quantum theory* of radiant energy, however, dropped this assumption and proceeded on the basis that radiation is emitted and absorbed, not continuously but in discrete units, one at a time. Each unit, a *quantum*, contains an amount of energy (E) proportional to the frequency of radiation. This relationship is given by:

$$E = hf, \tag{2-5}$$

where f is a particular frequency and h is Planck's constant, with a value of 6.62377×10^{-27} erg-sec. The significance of Equation 2-5 for vision is that the absorption of quanta is the first step in photoreception which determines the sensory response of the eye.

Another important relationship is that frequency (f), in cycles per second, is related to wavelength (λ) by the simple reciprocal equation:

$$f = c/\lambda, \tag{2-6}$$

where c is the speed of radiant energy in empty space, that is, 186,500 mi/sec or approximately 30 billion cm/sec. Red light, for example, has a wavelength of 7×10^2 millimicrons; its frequency is 43×10^{13} cycles per second. Conversely, given the frequency of a wave, its wavelength may be computed by the relation: $\lambda = c/f$. When the value of f is known, Equation 2-5 may be easily solved.

The quantum principle has been so successful in solving problems in physics that Planck's theory is now universally accepted. This acceptance is made, however, with the realization that the quantum hypothesis cannot explain all the known phenomena of light. To explain some of these phenomena, the wave theory of light must be used. Accordingly, light may be considered to have both *quantal* and *undulatory* characteristics, but never both at the same time. For example, when light falls on the polished surface of certain metals and releases electrons (*photoelectric emission*), it behaves as though it were quantal; when it shows certain effects as in producing the shadow of an object (diffraction), it behaves as though it were undulatory. There is no need to argue the relative merits of the wave theory and the quantum theory; light and all electromagnetic radiations as currently understood have a dual property. The view we adopt depends upon the particular phenomenon in which we are interested. For the interaction of light and electromagnetic radiation with matter, the quantum theory suffices; for the interaction of light with other radiations, the wave theory provides the most adequate explanation. The psychologist in vision is free to use whichever concept is best suited for his particular problem.

We will now return to the concept of a blackbody and examine it in more detail. There are several ideas associated with blackbody radiators which are directly related to the experimental psychology of vision. One of these is the *color temperature scale*. This scale is unidimensional and is probably the most widely used scale for classifying light sources. The *color temperature* of a light source is the absolute temperature at which the walls of a blackbody radiator must be maintained so that the light at the aperture yields the *chromaticity* ("color quality") of the source to be specified. The *color temperature scale* thus depends upon the series of lights that are producible by blackbody radiation; the scale is specified physically by the absolute temperature (degrees Kelvin) at which the radiator must be uniformly maintained to produce a match in chromaticity. Thus, when the chromaticity of an unknown light source is matched by that of a blackbody radiator, its color temperature is specified by the absolute temperature of the radiator, given in degrees Kelvin.

The concept of color temperature, however, should be restricted to light sources whose colors can be matched almost exactly by a blackbody radiator at some temperature; it should not be applied to *selective* sources of light such as fluorescent lamps. Furthermore, even when a color match is made perfectly, it should not be assumed that the source and the blackbody radiator have the same spectral distribution of energy. For example, sunlight corresponds to a color temperature of approximately $5400°K$, but its spectral distribution is quite unlike that of the matching energy at the opening of the radiator. Color temperature is a specification of chromaticity and not a specification of spectral distribution.

The concept of color temperature has also been used for the purposes of general color measurement. In 1951 three standard light sources (*illuminants*) were adopted by the International Commission on Illumination. These are designated as Source A, which is typical of light from a gas-filled incandescent lamp of color temperature $2854°K$; Source B, which is an approximation of noon sunlight (same as Source A at $4870°K$); and Source C, which is an approximation of average daylight (same as Source A at $6740°K$). In visual research, one of these three illuminants is typically used to provide a standard source of noncolored light in the testing situation.

A second major relationship between blackbody radiation and psychology is found in the present reference standard for the system of *photometry* in which electromagnetic radiation is evaluated according to the visual effect it is capable of producing. Photometric units are conventionally expressed in terms of energy derived from the standard luminance of a blackbody aperture at 2042°K. This is the temperature of platinum at its melting point and the luminance of this source has been arbitrarily specified as 60 *candela*/sq cm. The candela is the fundamental unit of *photometric intensity;* one candela is equal to 1/60 of the output of the radiator under the specified conditions and is defined as 1 lumen per steradian (unit solid angle). The *lumen* is the unit of *luminous flux,* that is, light waves in the visible portion of the electromagnetic spectrum. Since the area of a sphere is $4\pi r^2$ and one steradian is the solid angle subtended by a surface area of r^2 at the center of the sphere, there are 4π steradians of solid angle around a point. If the point is a uniform light source of one candela, the *total* flux emitted by the source is 4π lumens. The luminous flux *at a given wavelength* is proportional to the amount of light energy (ergs per second) that is transferred under the standard conditions.

When luminous flux is irradiated from a surface, rather than from a point source, the energy cannot be specified in terms of a single solid angle. A new concept must be introduced, therefore, which depends upon the area of the surface; this concept is *luminance.* Luminance is proportional to the intensity per unit *projected* area of the surface, that is, the projection of the surface onto a plane perpendicular to the line of sight. The unit of luminance is the candela per sq cm of projected area. Observe carefully that the value of the area used in defining the unit of luminance is not the *actual* area of the luminous surface, but its *projected* area. This means that the luminance of a nonperfectly diffusing surface will depend upon the angle of view. More actual area will be seen when a surface is viewed obliquely than when it is viewed perpendicularly; hence, the luminance will be less. Fortunately, many primary sources of light, for example, fluorescent tubes, are almost perfectly diffusing so that luminance varies but little with the angle of view. Also, since luminance is a property of a surface, just as intensity is a property of a point source, the distance from which the surface is viewed does not affect this property; intensity and luminance are independent of the distance between the observer and the source.

So far we have considered ways of specifying the intensity and luminance of a source of light. The next question concerns *illumination*—the process by which luminous flux is supplied to the surface of an object, such as the top of a table. The areal density of luminous flux incident to a surface is designated by the term *illuminance.* Given a point source of luminous intensity I, the illuminance E, which is provided on a surface located at a distance D from the source, may be computed by the inverse-square law:

$$E(\text{foot-candles}) = \frac{I \text{ (candela)}}{D^2 \text{ (sq ft)}}. \tag{2-7}$$

According to Equation 2-7 as the luminous intensity (candela) increases, the illuminance increases in direct proportion, but as the distance between the source and the surface increases, the illuminance will decrease inversely with the square of the distance. Although there are several units in which illuminance may be specified, the foot-candle is perhaps the most widely used. The *foot-candle* is defined as an illuminance equal to one lumen falling upon one square foot of surface.

There are many different instruments with which measurements of light intensity may be made. The Macbeth Illuminometer (Figure 2-8) is one of those

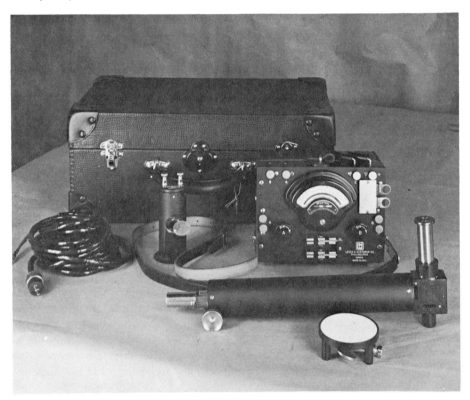

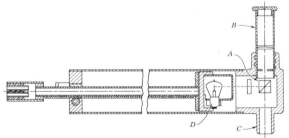

Figure 2–8   A schematic diagram of the Macbeth Illuminometer. See text for details. (Reproduced by courtesy of Leeds and Northrup, Philadelphia.)

commonly used in the psychological laboratory. It consists of a photometric screen (A), which is viewed through a telescopic eyepiece (B), and an aperture (C), which is pointed toward the surface being measured. The observer watches the photometric screen which is composed of two concentric rings. The inner ring is illuminated by light from the test surface, while the outer ring is illuminated by light from a calibrated source (D) mounted in a movable housing. The observer moves the calibrated source back and forth by means of a rack and pinion gear until the two rings viewed on the photometric screen appear equally bright. When a match is made, the measured value is read from the scale markings on the rod attached to the lamp housing. The illuminometer may be used to make measurements of light intensity, luminance, or illuminance by following a prescribed set of instructions (Barrows, 1938).

Acoustic Energy

In the preceding section, we considered electromagnetic radiation and classified the different types of radiation in terms of their wavelengths. While the undulatory theory presents electromagnetic radiation as a periodic wave phenomenon, there are other periodic phenomena of a much simpler variety. One of these is *circular motion*, which provides the basis for understanding the physical properties of sound waves.

Circular motion is the type of motion that may be presented by a point moving in a circle with a given radius; thus, the distance of the point from the center, its velocity, and its acceleration are all constant in magnitude, but vary in direction at a constant angular velocity (W). If this point is now projected upon the diameter of the circle, *simple harmonic motion* is produced. In Figure 2-9, the point moving in a circular path passes successively through the locations 0, 1, 2, and so

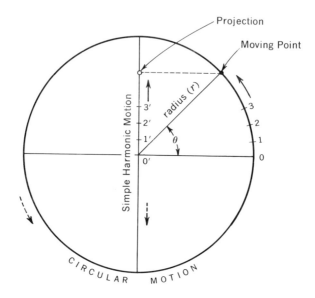

Figure 2–9. A schematic representation of circular motion and its projection into simple harmonic motion.

on, while the respective projections of this point on the vertical diameter appear at 0', 1', 2', and so on. Notice that the point in circular motion moves around and around in a circle, but that the projected point in simple harmonic motion moves up and down the vertical diameter. In simple harmonic motion, the distance of the projected point from the origin, that is, the center of the circle, is called its *displacement* (*y*). This may be stated mathematically as:

$$y = r \sin\Theta, \tag{2-8}$$

where *r* is the length of the radius of the circle, and Θ is the particular angle formed by the radius vector to the moving point and the horizontal diameter (x axis). The *amplitude* of the simple harmonic motion is fixed by *r*, which determines the maximal distance from the origin which the projected point can reach. For any given simple harmonic motion, the amplitude is constant, but the displacement varies as the *sine function* of time, that is, $\Theta = Wt$ where *W* is constant angular velocity and *t* is time. When both *r* and Θ are specified, the position of the point in simple harmonic motion is uniquely determined. The angle Θ is called the *phase* of the point in simple harmonic motion and varies from 0° to 360°. As the phase varies from 0° to 360°, the point in simple harmonic motion goes through one complete *cycle*. The number of cycles per unit of time (usually one second) is called the *frequency* (*f*). The time required for the point in simple harmonic motion to complete one cycle is called the *period* of the motion (*T*). For all forms of simple harmonic motion, the acceleration of the projected point divided by its displacement is always contant with a value of $4\pi^2/T^2$. This is the condition which precisely defines simple harmonic motion.

The significance of simple harmonic motion in hearing is that a *pure tone* is generated by a physical sound wave in which the air particles are moving in the back-and-forth manner just described for the projected point on the vertical diameter of the circle. In other words, when a pure tone is transmitted, the movement of air particles may be represented in terms of simple harmonic motion and its related concepts. This implies that the displacement of air particles may be plotted as a sine function of time. However, particle displacement is only one of several variables that may be specified and measured in relation to a sound wave. For psychologists, a more important variable is *instantaneous sound pressure*. This concept will now be developed in more detail.

The source of all sound (acoustic energy) lies in the *mechanical vibration* of material bodies, such as a tuning fork, a drumhead, a loudspeaker, or the vocal cords. Wave motion is required to transfer the energy from the source to the ear of the listener. Unlike electromagnetic radiation, which can pass through a vacuum, sound waves must be transmitted through an *elastic medium* in the form of a liquid, a solid, or a gas. The transmission of acoustic energy depends upon the combination of simple harmonic motion and a linear motion of constant velocity in the direction of propagation of the sound wave.

If, during the passage of a simple sound wave through a specific point in space, an appropriate measurement were to be made of the instantaneous acoustic pressure as a function of time, the obtained data could be represented by a sine function. This is shown in Figure 2-10. Notice that the back-and-forth motions of the air particles in simple harmonic motion have generated a sinusoidal pattern

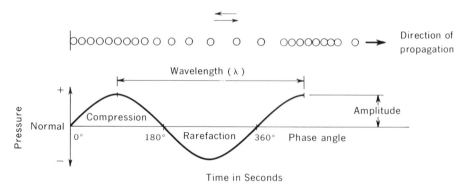

Figure 2–10. A graphical representation of the instantaneous pressure changes in a simple acoustic wave as a function of time.

of changing acoustic pressure. There is no physical movement of particular air particles directly from the source of sound to the ear of the listener. The graphical representation shows that, at a given point in space, the instantaneous sound pressure changes sinusoidally from greater than normal pressure (compression) to less than normal pressure (rarefaction). The horizontal line represents the atmospheric pressure of the normal, undisturbed air, that is, 15 lb/sq in. or about 10^6 dynes/sq cm at sea level.

Since the instantaneous sound pressure as a function of time is a sine function, the concepts of amplitude, period, frequency, and phase as applied to pressure are exactly analogous to those already specified for particle displacement. The concept of wavelength (λ) is also shown in Figure 2-10. Wavelength is the distance travelled by the acoustic wave in one period. For audible sound waves, that is, those from about 20 to 20,000 cycles per second (cps) the wavelength varies from approximately fifty feet for the low-frequency sounds to less than an inch for high-frequency sounds.

The wavelength (λ) of a given sound may be computed from the following equation:

$$\lambda = \frac{V}{f}, \tag{2-9}$$

where V is the speed of wave motion and f is the frequency in cps. The speed of propagation of sound waves varies according to the particular medium through which the waves are passing; but, for dry air at 0° Centigrade, the velocity is approximately 1088 feet per second and increases about 2 ft/sec for every degree (Centigrade) rise in temperature. A change in atmospheric pressure does not affect the velocity of sound. It is seen, therefore, that minute sinusoidal displacements of air particles are capable of creating instantaneous changes in sound pressure which are propagated from the source to the listener's ear. Without the occurrence of these changes in the air within the ear canal, nothing would be heard.

The simple harmonic motion which we have been considering for particle displacement and instantaneous pressure occurs in many sources of sound; each motion of this type is characterized by a particular frequency. It follows from this that whenever an object vibrates in such a way that more than one simple harmonic motion is present, more than a single frequency will be generated. This is what occurs in the production of musical tones. Violin strings, for instance, generate many frequencies simultaneously. This is due to the fact that the sound source (the string) not only vibrates as a whole, but also vibrates in smaller segments at the same time, and each segment has it own frequency. If the component frequencies that are produced are in the ratio 1:2:3:4, and so on, this is called a *harmonic series,* and the result is a *complex tone* with a unique wave form. In any complex tone, the amplitudes of the various components may vary, but the frequencies must maintain an integral relation even if there are fifteen or twenty components in the tone. The wave form of a complex tone (amplitude as a function of time) is characteristically periodic, but the form of a complex wave is no longer a sine function. Nevertheless, it has long been established that *any periodic* motion, no matter how complicated, can be *analyzed* into a series of simple harmonic motions of varying amplitudes, all of which are integrally related in frequency. Conversely, any complex motion can be created by *synthesizing* (adding together) an appropriate number of simple harmonic motions, each with the proper frequency, amplitude, and phase.

Figure 2-11 shows in Part A three simple harmonic motions, each with its own frequency and amplitude. All three motions have the same phase since they start at the same point in time. Assume the frequencies to be 100, 300, and 500 cps. Part B shows the complex *sawtooth* wave form that results when these three simple waves are combined and weighted according to the percentages given in Part A. The series of points shown in Part B may be obtained graphically by summating the ordinate values of the three waves in Part A at successive distances along the abscissa, corresponding to those designated by the points in Part B. The motion with the longest period (0.01 sec) is called the *fundamental* (100 cps), the *first partial,* or the *first harmonic.* The two remaining frequencies, 300 and 500 cps, are called the 3d and 5th partials or harmonics, respectively, since they bear a simple ratio to the fundamental frequency, that is, 3:1 and 5:1.

Part C of Figure 2-11 shows the situation in which, instead of starting with the three simple waves, we might have been given the complex tone, for example, that represented in Part B, and might have been asked to determine its component frequencies. Through appropriate laboratory methods involving a mechanical or an electronic wave analyzer, or through the application of specific mathematical techniques, the complex wave form can be analyzed into its three components; the results may then be plotted in the form of a *line spectrum* (Part

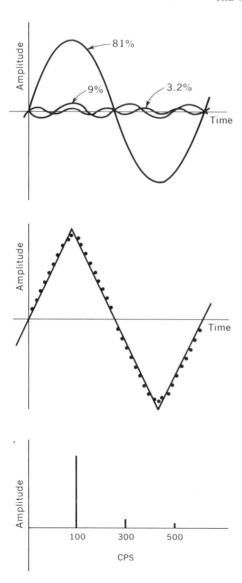

Figure 2–11. The synthesis and analysis of a complex sawtooth wave form. (Adapted from R. G. Fowler and D. I. Meyer, *Physics for engineers and scientists*, 1st ed., Figure 18-10, p. 321. Copyright 1958 by Allyn and Bacon, Inc., Boston. Reprinted by permission of the publisher.)

C). As in the case of electromagnetic radiation, the spectrum shows a line on the abscissa at the frequency of each partial, and the length of each line indicates the amplitude of vibration for that particular partial. Ordinarily a line spectrum would also show the phase of each partial, but in this case this is not necessary since the three components all have the same phase. It should be noted that with only three components, a good approximation of the sawtooth wave is obtained. If a larger number of harmonics were to be included, nearly perfect reproduction would result.

The specific wave form of a tone, as well as its associated line spectrum, is a function of the particular sound-emitting source. Although various musical instruments are capable of generating the same fundamental frequencies over certain portions of the musical scale, there are marked differences in their *tone quality* or *timbre*. It is on the basis of tone quality that different instruments and voices may be identified auditorily. Classically, it was believed that differences in timbre were due to differences in harmonic structure. Recent evidence indicates that the identification of musical instruments may not depend entirely upon the harmonic structure of a tone but may be affected by the peculiarities (transient sounds) which are generated by the onset of the tone (Saldahna and Corso, 1964).

The essential physical difference between music and *noise* is that music consists of *periodic* and *continuous* vibrations in an elastic medium, while noise results from vibrations which have *no periodicity* and are often *discontinuous*. The frequencies present in noise are not integrally related; they do not form a harmonic series.

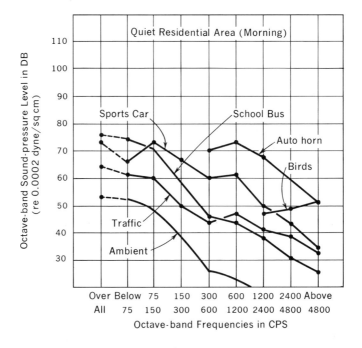

Figure 2–12. An octave-band analysis of different kinds of noise observed in a quiet residential neighborhood of Los Angeles, California. (From Veneklasen, *Noise Control*, 1956.)

When a sound contains a wide range of audible frequencies, uniform in amplitude and random in phase, the mixture is called *white noise* or random noise. White noise gives somewhat the same auditory impression as the sound of escaping air when the brakes on a large motor transport are released. Since noises contain numerous components extending over a wide range of frequencies and the wave form is continually changing, it is impossible to obtain an acoustic analysis equivalent to that for complex tones.

The usual procedure in analyzing noise is to measure the energy present within certain *bands of frequencies* and to report the results, as shown in Figure 2-12. The acoustic analysis in Figure 2-12 is for several different kinds of noise measured in a quiet residential neighborhood in Los Angeles, California. The curve marked "ambient" refers to the general background noise. The bands in this example are an *octave* wide, that is, the highest frequency in the band is twice the lowest frequency. For a more detailed description of the noise, the width of the bands in the analysis could have been reduced, for example, to one-third or one-half an octave. A photograph of an octave-band noise analyzer is shown in Figure 2-13.

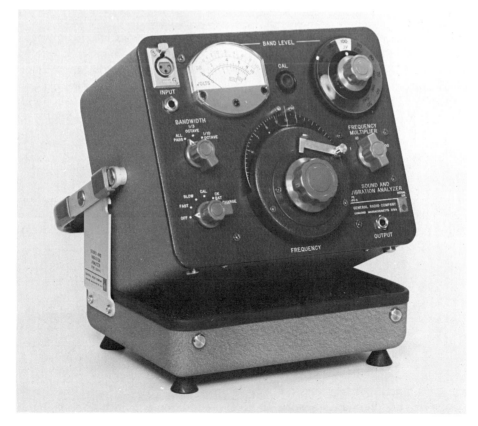

Figure 2–13. A noise analyzer for measuring the sound pressure per octave band. (From Peterson and Gross, *Handbook of noise measurement,* West Concord, Mass.: General Radio Company, 1963.)

Although we have mentioned the concept of instantaneous sound pressure in the discussion of pure tones, musical tones, and noise, we have not yet considered how acoustic pressure can be measured and specified. Notice that the ordinate of Figure 2-12 refers to a special scale designated as sound-pressure level. What is the unit of this scale and what type of apparatus can be used to measure the level of acoustic pressure in a given sound wave?

We can approach the answer to these questions by noting that in terms of *absolute* sound pressure, the human ear can respond from about one ten-thousandth of a dyne/sq cm to about 10 million or more dynes/sq cm. This represents a range of sensitivity of about 100 billion to 1 from the strongest to the weakest sound which man can hear. The use of direct units of physical pressure in psychoacoustics would therefore involve large numbers that would be cumbersome to manipulate and report. This problem is eliminated by the use of a *logarithmic* scale of pressure called the *decibel* (db) scale. This scale compresses the range of numbers so that the entire auditory intensity scale is contained from 0 to 140 db, approximately. The use of the decibel scale, however, eliminates any true zero point as the beginning of the scale; instead, an arbitrary reference is taken as the starting point.

The reference intensity most commonly used for the decibel scale of *sound-pressure level* (SPL) is 0.0002 dyne/sq cm (2×10^{-4} microbar). In order to specify the absolute intensity (pressure) of a sound in decibel notation, the intensity of the given sound is designated as N decibels above (or below) the reference intensity (P_0). The equation for computing the sound-pressure level of a given sound is written as:

$$N_{(db)} = 20 \log_{10} \frac{P_1}{P_0},$$ (2-10)

where $N_{(db)}$ is the sound-pressure level of the given sound in decibels above (or below) the reference intensity P_0, and the intensity of the given sound is denoted by P_1. For example, a given sound with an acoustic pressure of 0.002 dyne/sq cm is at $+20$ db SPL, since

$$N_{db} = 20 \log_{10} \frac{P_1}{P_0} = 20 \log_{10} \frac{0.002 \text{ dyne/sq cm}}{0.0002 \text{ dyne/sq cm}}$$
$$= 20 \log_{10} 10 = 20 \times 1 = 20 \text{ db.}$$

As its name implies, a decibel is one-tenth of a bel or, stated in reverse form, 1 bel equals 10 db. It is permissible, therefore, to specify SPL values in bels, if this is desired. An SPL value of 20 db, for example, is equivalent to an SPL of 2 bels. This practice, however, is not very common in psychology.

In specifying the sound-pressure level of a sound, the reference pressure must always be explicitly stated. The db scale is a *ratio* scale of intensities and unless the denominator of the ratio is given, the quotient cannot be meaningfully interpreted. The reference intensity for the SPL scale has been set at 0.0002 dyne/sq

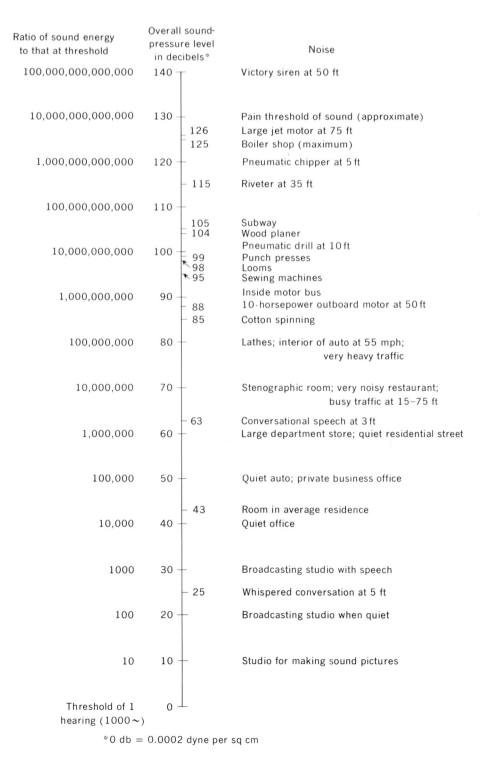

Ratio of sound energy to that at threshold	Overall sound-pressure level in decibels*	Noise
100,000,000,000,000	140	Victory siren at 50 ft
10,000,000,000,000	130	Pain threshold of sound (approximate)
	126	Large jet motor at 75 ft
	125	Boiler shop (maximum)
1,000,000,000,000	120	Pneumatic chipper at 5 ft
	115	Riveter at 35 ft
100,000,000,000	110	
	105	Subway
	104	Wood planer
10,000,000,000	100	Pneumatic drill at 10 ft
	99	Punch presses
	98	Looms
	95	Sewing machines
		Inside motor bus
1,000,000,000	90	
	88	10-horsepower outboard motor at 50 ft
	85	Cotton spinning
100,000,000	80	Lathes; interior of auto at 55 mph; very heavy traffic
10,000,000	70	Stenographic room; very noisy restaurant; busy traffic at 15–75 ft
	63	Conversational speech at 3 ft
1,000,000	60	Large department store; quiet residential street
100,000	50	Quiet auto; private business office
	43	Room in average residence
10,000	40	Quiet office
1000	30	Broadcasting studio with speech
	25	Whispered conversation at 5 ft
100	20	Broadcasting studio when quiet
10	10	Studio for making sound pictures
Threshold of 1 hearing (1000 ~)	0	

*0 db = 0.0002 dyne per sq cm

Table 2–4. The Sound-Pressure Levels of Some Familiar Sounds Expressed in Decibels above 0.0002 Dyne/Sq Cm.* (Adapted from *Human Engineering* by E. J. McCormick. Copyright © 1957, McGraw-Hill Book Company. Used by permission.)

cm since this value approximates the minimal acoustic pressure to which the human ear will respond at 1000 cps. Other values, however, may be used for the reference pressure. These alternate references provide the basis for the establishment of additional scales which have been found to be useful in the field of hearing.

While at first glance the decibel scale appears somewhat complicated, the computation of a few SPL values will help the student understand the meaning of the scale. However, the actual computation of SPL values can be avoided by using published tables that provide db values for given pressure ratios, and vice versa (Peterson and Gross, 1963). Furthermore, special meters have been developed, such as that shown in Figure 2-13, which measure sound-pressure level directly. The ordinate of Figure 2-12, then, expresses the sound-pressure level of noise per octave-band expressed in db above 0.0002 dyne/sq cm. Table 2–4 shows some common sounds located at their proper points on the decibel scale of sound-pressure level.

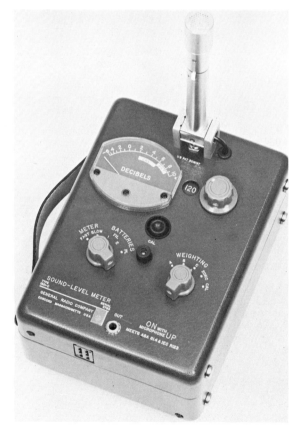

Figure 2–14. A sound-level meter for measuring the total acoustic pressure of tones or noise in terms of a standard reference (0.0002 microbar). (From Peterson and Gross, *Handbook of noise measurement,* West Concord, Mass.: General Radio Company, 1963.)

An example of another type of sound-level meter is shown in the photograph of Figure 2-14.

The instrument consists of a microphone, a calibrated attenuator, an amplifier, an indicating meter, and certain frequency weighting networks for measuring noise and sound levels in a particular manner. The operation of the sound-level meter is relatively simple. After the microphone is raised and the appropriate weighting network is selected, the sound-pressure level reading is taken from the indicating meter and an associated dial. The value read is the effective sound pressure, that is, the root-mean-square (rms) value of the instantaneous sound pressures over an appropriate time interval at the point in the sound field under consideration. (The rms value is the square root of the arithmetic mean of the squares of the instantaneous sound pressures. This value is used rather than simply mean pressure since the mean pressure of a sine wave over an integral number of cycles would be zero. Also, the rms value is more convenient in computations involving complex waves.)

Finally, it should be indicated that sounds, like electromagnetic radiation, exhibit complex phenomena associated with travelling waves; these include reflection, interference, and resonance. A consideration of these topics, however, lies beyond our needs at this level of study. These effects, however, cannot be ignored in research and must be controlled in the environment in which an experiment in psychoacoustics is to be performed. In recent years considerable advances have been made in the field of acoustical engineering, with the result that adequate techniques are now available for controlling these extraneous effects and for specifying the acoustical properties of the testing environment.

The Electrochemical Properties of Matter

The current theory of atomic structure asserts that the world of matter is composed of minute particles, called *atoms*. There are at least one hundred and three different kinds of atoms; each different kind of atom is called a *chemical element*. Silver, chlorine, oxygen, mercury, and sulfur are examples of chemical elements. Although it might seem that atoms would be indivisible, the atoms of all chemical elements have been broken into simpler particles. At least fifteen fundamental particles have already been discovered (Priestley, 1958). Some atoms disintegrate spontaneously and are said to be *radioactive;* others break down when placed in special instruments such as the cyclotron or the nuclear reactor.

On the basis of many experiments, it is now generally held that atoms consist of a positive nucleus composed of protons (positive particles of electricity) and neutrons (electrically neutral particles), and that this nucleus is surrounded by one or more negative *electrons* (negative particles of electricity). Electrons from the atoms of all chemical elements are identical and carry an individual charge of -1.60×10^{-19} coulomb. In an electrically neutral atom, the total negative charge of the electrons is equal to the total positive charge of the nucleus. The nucleus of an atom has a diameter of approximately 10^{-13} cm and most of the mass (99.9 percent) of an atom is concentrated in the nucleus. The electrons are situated at relatively tremendous distances from the nucleus. Proportionately, about the same empty space exists in an atom as in the solar system. The electrons are not like "solid balls," but are considered as diffuse clouds or shells of negative electricity surrounding the nucleus.

All of the atoms of a particular chemical element have the same amount of positive charge in the nucleus. The nuclear charge is fixed by the number of protons and is called its *atomic number*. For example, iron (designated symbolically as Fe) is atomic number 26; gold (Au), atomic number 79. The significance of atomic number is that it determines the ordering of the elements in terms of their chemical behavior, that is, their union with and separation from other atoms. This is due to the fact that combinations between atoms are formed by the electrical forces between electrons; these electrons in a neutral atom are the same in number as the atomic number of the atom.

The second most important property of an atom is its *atomic mass*. While there are several methods by which the absolute mass of atoms may be determined, only the relative mass needs to be known and specified for most practical purposes. The relative masses are expressed in *atomic mass units* (amu), in which 1 amu is defined as exactly 1/12 the mass of a particular atom of carbon, carbon-12 or C^{12}. In other words, the mass of the C^{12} atom is exactly 12 atomic mass units. Magnesium has an atomic mass approximately twice that of C^{12} and is given as 24.312 amu.

The atomic mass of chemical elements is conventionally given to the nearest whole number, which is then designated as the *mass number*. The mass number is the atomic mass of a particular element given to the nearest whole number; it is equal to the sum of the number of protons and neutrons which constitute the nucleus of the atom.

A convenient system of notation has been evolved to specify simultaneously both atomic number and atomic mass. Given a particular element, such as oxygen (O), a superscript added to the chemical symbol indicates the mass number and is usually placed to the upper right, while the atomic number is designated by a subscript placed to the lower left of the symbol. Thus, a particular atom of oxygen would be designated as $_8O^{18}$. This indicates that there are 8 protons in the nucleus of this atom and, accordingly, 8 electrons surround the nucleus in the neutral atom. Also, since the mass number is 18 and there are 8 protons, the nucleus must contain 10 neutrons.

At one time it was believed that all the atoms of a given element had exactly the same atomic mass, but experiments have shown that this is not true. Different atoms of the same element may differ in mass. Atoms that have the same atomic number but differ in mass are called *isotopes*. Some elements are found only in the form of a single stable (nonradioactive) isotope, such as iodine. Other elements, like radium, undergo spontaneous disintegration and produce isotopes. Uranium I and uranium II both have the same atomic number 92, but uranium I has mass number 238, while uranium II has mass number 234. The end product of each family of natural radioactive disintegrations is lead. Although the natural radioactive process can be observed and traced, it cannot be controlled since it is independent of temperature, pressure, and chemical forces. However, radioiso-topes may be produced commercially by irradiating particular substances in a nuclear reactor.

Numerous applications for radioisotopes have been discovered in medicine, agriculture, and industry. Radioisotopes have also been widely applied as *trace elements* in biological research. These are extremely useful in that the course of movement of the isotope can be followed as it is assimilated within a given organ-ism or as it passes from one organism to another. As specific examples of the use of radioisotopes, we need mention only the destruction of the malignant tissue of cancer by treatments of cobalt-60 and the therapeutic effect of iodine-131 in the treatment of hyperthyroidism.

Besides nuclear charge and nuclear mass, atoms differ in terms of energy level. This concept can be treated systematically by arranging the chemical elements in order of increasing atomic number. From this it will be found that several of the elements show a sort of family resemblance to each other with respect to their physical and chemical properties. Sodium and potassium are very much alike, as are fluorine, chlorine, bromine, and iodine. The *periodic law* states that the properties of elements recur periodically if the elements are arranged in order of increasing atomic number. The *periodic table* based on this law is a schematic ar-rangement of the elements according to their physical and chemical properties. The main classes of elements are the noble (inert) gases, the light metals, the heavy metals (brittle, ductile, and low melting) and the nonmetals, the lathanide (rare earth elements) and the actinide series.

Although the periodic table lists all the known elements, most of the material on earth occurs in the form of *compounds* of elements. The matter in living things consists mainly of compounds involving about two dozen elements, such as car-bon, hydrogen, oxygen, nitrogen, sulfur, phosphorus, and magnesium. From numerous analyses which have been made of many compounds, certain general principles have been derived. One of these is the *law of definite proportions*. This principle states that every sample of a particular substance always contains the same proportions by mass of all the elements into which it can be analyzed, pro-vided the sample is sufficiently pure. Common table salt (sodium chloride), for example, always yields one gram of sodium to each 1.5 grams of chlorine. For a given compound, the law of definite proportions holds regardless of the quantity of the compound with which we are dealing. It does not hold, however, for solu-tions (such as saltwater), alloys (brass, bronze, steel), or for many plastics.

When elements combine strongly enough to form an electrically neutral aggre-gate of atoms, the new unit of the compound is called a *molecule*. This is the small-est natural unit of the compound. Each molecule of a compound is like every other molecule of that compound, but the structure of the molecule is unique from compound to compound. The attraction between two atoms within a mole-cule is called a *chemical bond*.

There are two primary types of mechanisms involved in the formation of a chemical bond: (1) *ionic bonding* and (2) *covalent bonding*. The strength of the bond-ing forces is determined by the number and particular configuration of the electron charges in the atoms that are bonded. In *ionic bonding* (sometimes called electrovalent bonding), electrons are completely transferred from one atom to another. When two different atoms are brought together, the electrons of one atom come under the influence of the electrons and nucleus of the other. This interaction may produce an interaction to the extent that an electronic rearrangement occurs and a molecule is formed. An example of ionic bonding is found when sodium (Na) combines with chlorine (Cl) to form sodium chloride (NaCl), table salt. In *covalent bonding,* electrons are shared more or less equally between atoms. One atom is not able to pull an electron away from the other, so that the electrons must be shared in holding the atoms together. An example of covalent bonding is found in carbon tetrachloride. Most *inorganic* compounds are formed by ionic bonding, while *organic* compounds often exhibit covalent bonding.

In organic chemistry, an important branch of study is that of *optical isomerism.* Earlier in this chapter we discussed electromagnetic radiation in the form of light waves. These waves normally vibrate in every possible plane of the transmitting medium. It is comparatively easy, however, to restrict these waves to one plane only. This can be accomplished by placing in the path of light a piece of Iceland spar, which is a transparent form of the mineral calcite. A similar effect may be obtained by passing light through a sheet of synthetic material known as Polaroid. When light is transmitted in one plane only it is said to be *polarized.* Specially prepared crystals of Iceland spar for obtaining polarized light are called *Nicol prisms.* By passing a beam of light through two successive Nicol prisms, the intensity of the polarized light can be controlled and continuously varied. When both prisms are identically oriented, the light will go through both, but, as one prism is turned to a given angle, less light will be transmitted. When the two prisms are at right angles, no light will emerge. This technique for controlling the intensity of light is also applicable to sheets of Polaroid.

An effect related to polarization is that of *optical rotation.* Certain organic compounds possess the power of rotating the plane of polarized light. The effect occurs with dissolved or melted substances, as well as with crystalline substances. Those substances which show this effect are said to be optically active. If, when looking at the source of light, the rotation of the plane of light is to the right (clockwise) the substance is said to be *dextrorotary.* If the rotation is to the left (counterclockwise), the substance is said to be *levorotary.* Many naturally occurring organic compounds are capable of producing this effect.

In psychology, much experimental work involves *solutions;* we are often dealing with *mixtures* rather than pure chemical elements or compounds. Solutions are defined as homogeneous mixtures of two or more components and they can be gaseous, liquid, or solid in form. A common type of solution is the *liquid* solution, which is made by dissolving a gas, a liquid, or a solid in a liquid. If the liquid is water, the solution is called an *aqueous* solution. Two terms are conventionally used in the discussion of solutions: *solute* and *solvent.* The substance which is present in the larger amount is the solvent, and the substance present in the smaller amount is the solute.

The *concentration* of a solution may be specified in several ways. One of these is molarity (M) or *molar concentration*. The molarity of a solution is the number of moles of solute per liter of solution. (A gram atom of an element is the atomic mass of that element expressed as grams; for example, a gram atom of oxygen is 16.0 grams. In exactly the same way, the formula mass of a compound, expressed as grams, is called a *mole* of that substance; for example, a mole of water is 18.0 grams.) A 1-molar solution contains 1 mole of solute per liter of water. There is an important principle regarding moles which should be stated. Specifically, for any substance whose molecular formula is known, one mole always contains 6.03×10^{23} molecules (Avogadro's number). Therefore, regardless of the chemical constitution of the solute and solvent involved, an equal number of molecules is contained in equal volumes of solutions with identical molar concentrations. For this reason, there is a growing tendency in psychology to specify solutions in these terms.

A second specification of concentration is *normality* (N). The normality of a solute is the number of gram equivalents of solute per liter of solution. (One gram equivalent is defined as the mass of a substance which gains or releases the Avogadro number of electrons in a particular reaction.) A third specification of concentration is the *percent of solute*. The percent of solute may refer to percent by *volume* or percent by *weight*. A 12 percent alcohol solution by volume, for example, would represent a solution made up of 12 milliliters (ml) of alcohol and enough solvent to bring the total volume up to 100 ml. A 10 percent sugar solution by weight would represent a solution made up of 10 grams of sugar and enough solvent to bring the total weight up to 100 grams. Other techniques for specifying the concentrations of a solution are available, but these are the most common in psychology.

When certain elements and compounds are dissolved in water, the solution has the property of conducting an electric current. Such solutions are called *electrolytes*, of which there are three classes: *acids, bases,* and *salts.* There are several chemical definitions of acids and bases. According to one theory, an acid is a compound that in a water solution transfers a proton to a water molecule; a base is a compound that in a water solution accepts a proton from a water molecule. An example of an acid is sulfuric acid; of a base, ammonia. When portions of a strong base are added to a diluted aqueous solution of a strong acid, the base will neutralize the acid. Salts are compounds that, according to one definition, are formed by a typical metal with a typical nonmetal, for example, mercuric chloride, and that do not react appreciably in water. Such compounds are regarded as covalent compounds.

Pure water is said to be neutral and provides the dividing line between acids and bases. The purest water that may be prepared, however, has a small, measurable, electrical conductivity. This conductivity is not due to any dissolved electrolytes, but is an inherent property of water itself. The property is probably due to the ability of water molecules to react with each other to form *ions*. (An ion is an atom or group of atoms carrying a net electrical charge, either positive or negative. Positive ions are called *cations* and negative ions are called *anions*.) One of the ions formed by the dissociation of water is the positive hydrogen ion (H^+).

In pure water, the concentration of H^+ is 1.0×10^{-7} M. If an acid is added to the water, the hydrogen ion concentration increases above this value; if a base is added, it decreases below this value. As a convenience for working with small concentrations, the pH scale has been devised to express the concentration of H^+. By definition,

$$pH = \log \frac{1}{(H^+)} = -\log (H^+), \text{ or } (H^+) = 10^{-pH}, \qquad (2\text{-}11)$$

where (H^+) stands for the hydrogen ion concentration expressed in moles per liter. Given pure water at $25°C$, therefore, where the concentration of H^+ is 1.0×10^{-7} M, the pH is 7. All neutral solutions have a pH of 7. Acid solutions have pH less than 7; basic solutions have pH greater than 7. The pH of blood is normally about 7.4 and that of the gastric fluid of the stomach about 3 to 4.

In this section, we have presented some of the fundamental concepts of chemistry that are used in psychology. There is a considerable body of advanced material which lies beyond the scope of this presentation but which bears upon general organismic functions, as well as specific problems of behavior. In terms of physiologically active substances there are local and general anesthetics, viruses, antisyphilitics, tranquilizers, sulfa drugs and penicillin, proteins, vitamins, and hormones. All of these can affect the behavior of an organism, and an understanding of these and other substances is necessary for the understanding of certain specific behavioral processes. Wald (1958), for example, has shown that the photochemical processes related to night vision depend upon a special geometrical arrangement of the molecules in Vitamin A. Chemical theories have been proposed which postulate that changes in ribonucleic acid (RNA) molecules in the cell are the ultimate basis of memory, since RNA controls the formation of proteins and enzymes, as well as different substances (for example, acetylcholine) which are involved in the transmission of neural impulses. Flexner, Flexner, and Stellar (1963) have obtained evidence which tends to support the general idea that protein and enzyme synthesis is involved in the permanent changes that take place in the retention of learned material. These are but a few examples which illustrate that a knowledge of organic and inorganic chemistry is invaluable for the experimental psychologist working in certain areas of the discipline.

Some Facilities for Controlling
the Physical Environment
in Psychological Experiments

In the preceding section we considered some of the physical variables which characterize certain types of phenomena that occur in our natural environment. These phenomena as stimulus events are important determiners of behavior. If the specific relationships between these events and behavior, especially sensory behavior, are to be understood, it is necessary that we be able to measure accurately both the characteristics of the events and the responses. We have already considered some of the measurable aspects of isolated physical phenomena; in the later chapters we will concentrate on the techniques of measuring the behavioral variables. In this section we will describe some of the specialized types of facilities that have been employed to control the physical environment in which certain kinds of psychological experiments are performed.

The measurement of physical and psychological variables must always be performed under highly controlled conditions to avoid the effects of extraneous factors which might otherwise introduce errors into the obtained measurements. Such conditions are usually achieved in appropriately designed laboratories. In psychology several different types of laboratories or special chambers are used in research to restrict the physical environment to which the organism is exposed. By controlling certain characteristics of the physical environment and by manipulating other variables in the stimulus situation, an experimenter can determine the relationships that exist between physical events and behavior. For example, if we are interested in determining the amount of acoustic energy that will produce an auditory response at a given frequency, we must first of all place the subject in an environmental setting in which extraneous sounds are eliminated and then introduce a test signal of known magnitude. If certain procedures are followed, the results will provide the required information. If the acoustic environment were not controlled, the obtained measurements would be in error since not only the test signal but other sounds would impinge on the ear.

The Dark Room

The study of vision and its associated perceptual phenomena requires an environmental setting in which extraneous light is eliminated. The determination of the minimal amount of electromagnetic energy which will produce a visual response, for example, imposes the same requirements as the preceding example in audition. The usual designation for the testing room in vision is the *dark room.* This consists of an enclosed space in which there is no light except that introduced by the experimenter. Sometimes these rooms are fairly small, for example, 8 × 10 feet or smaller; at other times, the room may extend for 30 feet or more. The size of the room will often depend upon the particular kinds of experiments to be performed. Rooms in which threshold measurements or dark adaptation measurements are made need not be as large (long) as the rooms in which certain binocular depth perception studies are to be performed. The control of other aspects of the physical environment may be present in a dark room, such as in air-conditioning, but the primary requirement is that the quality and amount of light and the location of all light sources must be determined by the experimenter.

The Anechoic Chamber

The analogue of the dark room in vision is the *anechoic chamber* in hearing. An anechoic chamber is a room in which very little sound is reflected so that echoes and standing waves are negligible. This provides an appropriate setting for auditory studies or free-field studies of electroacoustic equipment. Both of these purposes require as low an *ambient noise level* as possible. Noises of external origin must not be able to penetrate into the room, while sounds generated within the room must decay as under free-field conditions.

These requirements are met by constructing the anechoic chamber according to certain principles of acoustical design which, among other factors, includes the use of wedges (made of some material like Fiberglas) on the walls, ceiling, and floor. Figure 2-15 shows a portion of the anechoic chamber at The Pennsylvania

Figure 2–15. The anechoic chamber at The Pennsylvania State University. (From Berger and Ackerman, *Noise Control,* 1956.)

State University (Berger and Ackerman, 1956). This chamber in its inside dimensions is 7.5 ft wide, 12.5 ft long and 6 ft 5 in. high. The calibration measurements of the room indicate that, from 100 to 100,000 cps, the chamber has an ambient noise level which per cycle is at least 10 db below the threshold of hearing obtained by free-field techniques.

To provide contact between the subject in the anechoic chamber and the experimenter in a separate control room, this particular facility has been provided with a two-way voice communication system and a closed-loop television system.

Thus, the experimenter can watch the subject on a monitor screen and the two can communicate or not, as required by the particular testing situation. Figure 2-16 shows an experimenter standing in the control room and discussing some data with an electronics technician regarding the calibration of certain audiometric instruments.

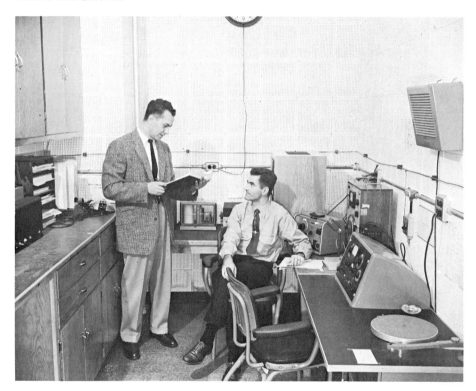

Figure 2–16. Control room for the anechoic chamber shown in Figure 2–15.

The Olfactorium

The problem of isolating and controlling environmental variables presents a particularly difficult problem in olfactory research. This is due to the tendency of the olfactory stimulus to linger in the air after it has been applied, thereby producing several undesirable effects. One of these is that the lingering stimulus tends to interact with subsequent stimuli to alter their odor. Another is that the continual exposure to the same stimulus reduces the organism's sensitivity to that stimulus through sensory adaptation. The invention of the *olfactorium* was an attempt to eliminate, or at least to minimize, the effects of uncontrolled environmental variables in olfactory research.

Figure 2-17 shows the olfactorium at Cornell University (Foster, Scofield, and Dallenbach, 1950). Basically it is an odor-proof, odorless room, provided with devices which permit the controlled presentation of olfactory stimuli. The two

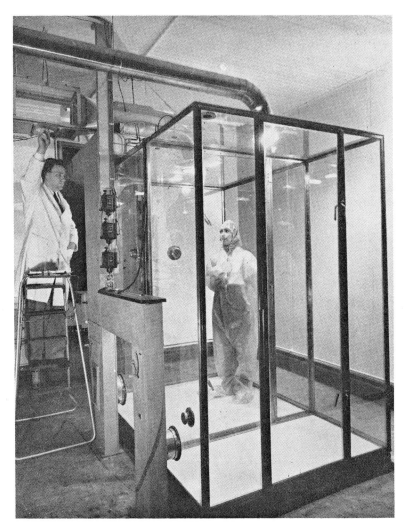

Figure 2–17. An olfactorium at Cornell University. (From Foster, Scofield, and Dallenbach, *Amer. J. Psychol.*, 1950.)

main parts of the olfactorium are: (1) the glass chambers and (2) the air treatment unit. The glass chambers consist of a small airlock (2.5 ft long, 5 ft wide, and 7 ft high) which permits the subject to enter the second or main testing chamber (5 ft long, 5 ft wide, and 7 ft high). The air supply system introduces filtered and controlled amounts of odor-free air into the main chamber, with the temperature of the air regulated from 0° to 35°C and the relative humidity from 10 percent to 100 percent. At full capacity, the 175 cubic feet of air in the main chamber of the olfactorium can be changed, if necessary, six times per minute.

The odorants are injected through a hole 12 inches above the floor in the test-

ing chamber. A small hole in the ceiling makes it possible to pump in other substances for mixing, or to attach a manometer for measuring the static pressure in
the chamber. Provisions are also made for introducing odors directly into the
incoming airstream by inserting an aluminum stimulus compartment, fitted with
a double vaporizer, into the main air duct. These various techniques make it
possible to present either pure air or odor-bearing air, with a predetermined composition, under known conditions of temperature, humidity, and pressure. Before
being tested, the experimental subject must first bathe to eliminate residual body
odors; then he must don a sterilized plastic envelope which covers all parts of his
body and head, except his face. Post-experimental deodorization is accomplished
in 45 minutes by automatically steaming the glass and polished, stainless steel
frame for 15 minutes and then drying the olfactorium by circulating fast-moving
hot air.

The Space Environment Simulator

With the increased interest in aviation and space flight in recent years, a new
facility has been developed to aid in the design of systems for maintaining an adequate environment for the pilot or astronaut. In some instances, the facility
simulates the sealed cabin of a space vehicle; the cabin is 6 ft in diameter and
8 ft long. One of these units has been built at the Aerospace Medical Research
Laboratories, Wright-Patterson Air Force Base, Ohio.

The simulator is designed to be used in an altitude chamber where atmospheric
pressure may be experimentally controlled, or it may be used in a normal laboratory. It is possible to control the temperature, humidity, oxygen partial pressure, and total air pressure over a wide range of habitable levels by automatic
or manually adjusted systems. If it is desired, an inert gas may be introduced for
experimental purposes and it can be automatically controlled at a selected level
of concentration. For all practical purposes, the cabin is leak proof, so that re-
circulating systems can be studied while a human subject is in the sealed cabin.
The activity of the subject is monitored during the operation of the simulator by
means of closed-circuit television, physiological data recorders, and voice communication systems. Under certain circumstances, the subject may be required
to wear a pressure garment. The system is capable of altering the pressure in the
garment so that decompressions may be accomplished which simulate the failure
of the space cabin. This is done by operating the cabin pumps or, if the simulator
is in an altitude chamber, by deflating the door seal. This type of facility is invaluable in the study of environmental conditions under which pilots or astro-
nauts may be expected to perform routine or emergency operations while in flight.

Chapter 3

THE HUMAN
NERVOUS SYSTEM

Orientation

The rise of modern science has produced numerous areas of specialization. Some, like psychology and physiology, are concerned with the study of the activities of living organisms. These areas of specialization, however, are not necessarily natural or logical divisions of science but reflect divisions of convenience according to which knowledge and techniques can be systematically arranged into disciplines. There are no rigid boundaries between or among these disciplines; each branch attempts in as expeditious a manner as possible to understand, to predict, and to control the phenomena with which it is concerned. To accomplish this, each branch of science develops its own specific and general theories in terms of its own particular technical vocabulary. It would be possible, therefore, at least at a logical level, to have two complete theories, one psychological and the other physiological, each of which would account for the various aspects of human behavior. If this were in fact true, then, as discussed in Chapter 1, psychological theory could conceivably be reduced or translated into an equivalent physiological theory.

The possibility of reductionism, while remote at the present time, does nevertheless impose a need for caution on the part of psychologists. Since both the psychologist and the physiologist are studying the same organism, the final outcome must comprise a set of facts, principles, and theories which are consistent between the two disciplines. This is similar to the ultimate description of matter; whether the problem is approached from physics or from chemistry, the end result must be compatible with the body of knowledge developed within each area. *Physiological psychology,* which is the study of relationships between bodily processes and behavior, assures that there is a possibility of showing that precise physiological activities within an organism are correlated with a given psychological process. This direct interdisciplinary attack on problems of behavior tends to minimize any inconsistencies which might otherwise arise through the study of psychology and physiology as isolated areas, with the expectation that they might ultimately be unified through reduction.

An understanding of the anatomy and physiology of the human organism provides the psychologist with several other advantages. First, the functional relationships which are discovered in behavior are more likely to be accepted if the structural relationships in the nervous system which underlie the behavior are known. For example, the patellar reflex (knee jerk), elicited by tapping the tendons of the quadriceps femoris muscle just below the patella (knee cap), is stronger when a loud sound is presented immediately before the tap. This enhancing effect of an extraneous stimulus on a reflex response is called *dynamogenesis* and can be explained on the basis that it is possible for auditory and kinesthetic stimuli to summate within the central nervous system.

Second, knowledge of the neural and physiological structures can lead to fruitful predictions of functions. A careful study of the non-auditory structures of the inner ear, for example, may lead to the conclusion that the three semicircular canals, due to their particular configuration, function to produce proper posture and balance in three-dimensional space. Similarly, observed functional relationships may suggest certain structural relationships in the neurophysiological system. The electroencephalographic detection of electrical activity in the lateral region of the head when the ear is stimulated with a tone may suggest, for instance, that there is some neural connection between the ear and that region of the brain.

Third, the psychologist must realize that structural changes in the organism may produce functional changes, and vice versa. For example, damage to certain portions of the ear will produce deafness, that is, the functions of hearing for a given individual will differ from those present before the damage was incurred. As an opposite example, certain disorders involving personal conflicts may alter functional relationships to produce structural changes in the stomach (ulcers).

An understanding of the anatomy and physiology of the human nervous system should provide the psychologist with a broader base from which to explore the domains of behavior, whether dealing with molar or molecular levels of description or searching for relevant variables within or outside the boundary of the organism being studied. All behavior is associated with concomitant physiological activity which, while it may be by-passed in a comprehensive *psychological* theory, may nevertheless provide useful guidelines to research in psychology, as well as a more adequate understanding of behavioral abnormalities.

The Concept of an Integrated Organism

A Simplification and a Precaution

In Chapter 2, we defined psychology as the scientific study of the behavior of living organisms in relation to their social and physical environment. Special consideration was given to the various forms of energy which comprise man's physical environment and which function under certain conditions as stimuli that initiate or modify psychological activities. It was also stressed that according to the principle of conservation of energy, energy can be neither created nor destroyed. It can only be transformed from one kind to another. The question immediately arises, therefore, regarding the ultimate disposition of the stimulus energy which impinges upon an organism. Specifically, what is the chain of events that occurs from the moment an adequate stimulus comes into contact with an organism biologically endowed to receive such a stimulus until the time the organism makes a particular response?

Although this question is a legitimate one, we should not be misled into thinking of behavior simply in terms of stimulus and response. Such a view is entirely too restricted. Graham (1950) has proposed a general formulation in which a response is said to be a function of several classes of variables. These include the properties of the stimulus, the various internal conditions of the organism, and the previous stimulations of the organism. The equation which denotes this relationship is:

$$R = f(a, b, c, d, \cdots, n, \cdots, t, \cdots, x, y, z), \qquad (3\text{-}1)$$

where R is a response or some measured aspect of it; a, b, c and d refer to certain aspects of the stimulus; n indicates the number of times the stimulus has been applied to the organism; t is time; and x, y, z denote the internal conditions of the organism, such as set, motivation, and so forth. The characteristics of the stimulus represent only *one* class of variables which affect behavior. While the other factors cannot be ignored, we can assume that they can be held constant and, for expository purposes, we can proceed to trace the temporal course of neurophysiological events as they occur within the organism.

Man as an Integrated Organism

When we observe a behaving organism, we are impressed by the integrated and orderly manner in which it responds to a wide variety of normal circumstances. Consider, for example, the numerous activities which each of us routinely performs during each day of the week. When we observe such behavior, we are very likely to forget that an organism, like man, is composed of groups of bodily organs which function together to carry out the processes of living. Some of these organs, such as the lungs, the heart, and the kidneys, are involved primarily in maintaining our internal bodily conditions, within certain narrow physiological limits conducive to normal cell functioning. These organs are sometimes called the *organs of maintenance* and the process of keeping the organism in a state of physiological equilibrium is known as *homeostasis*. The remaining organs of the body, according to this twofold classification, are the *organs of adjustment*. The organs of adjustment function as the individual attempts to satisfy his biological needs or his higher-order needs in the particular environment in which he finds himself. There are usually certain physical and social obstacles which must be removed or altered if the individual is to attain his goal; this provides the basis for learned behavior.

The organs of adjustment may be divided into three groups: (1) the sense organs or *receptors;* (2) the inherent mechanisms of the nervous system, sometimes called the *connectors;* and (3) the responding mechanisms or *effectors.* The receptors are specialized types of cells and associated structures which are actuated by different kinds of physical stimulation, external or internal, and which initiate the processes of neural excitation within the living individual. The various forms of energy which serve as adequate stimuli for man have already been considered in detail in Chapter 2. For review, these include *chemical* energy in the form of solids, liquids, or gases, *mechanical* energy (kinetic and potential) as in sound waves and physical contact, and *electromagnetic* energy in the form of heat and light. Paralleling these classes of energy we have four classes of receptors: *chemical, mechanical, thermal,* and *photic* receptors. Although the receptors are specialized to respond maximally to a given form of energy, they are able to respond in a limited fashion to other types of energy, including electricity, (compare with inadequate stimuli). The anatomical structures and the principal neural pathways for each class of receptors will be presented in Chapter 4.

The second group of structures, the connectors, consists of the nerve cell bodies and nerve fibers which comprise the organism's nervous system. The fundamental structural and functional unit of this system is the *neuron.* Neurons possess highly developed properties of *irritability* and *conductivity.* This means that they are sensitive to certain kinds of physical energy and that they are capable of propagating an electrical impulse (electrochemical change) along their cell walls. Such properties make it possible for the neurons to be combined functionally in a nervous system which can transmit, conduct, and integrate neural excitations in an extremely effective manner. The anatomical parts of the neuron and its functional characteristics will be considered in the next section of this chapter.

The third group of structures in the physiological receptor-connector-effector chain includes the responding mechanisms of *muscles* and *glands.* These are the structures which, in vertebrate animals, make possible the actual adjustive responses. The muscles of the body are characterized by the property of *contractility* and, when innervated by neural impulses arriving through the nervous system, are able to move the bodily parts in certain patterns with appropriate speed and accuracy. The muscles mediate behavioral adjustments of the organism in relation to the external environment. The glands, both duct and ductless, secrete chemical substances that tend to maintain the life processes of the organism at an adequate level. Thus, the glands may be considered as effectors which make adjustments primarily to the conditions present in the internal environment. Although the effectors are important structures in the general study of behavior, an extended treatment of their neuroanatomical characteristics lies beyond our particular needs. A limited consideration of the muscles as effector mechanisms will be provided, nevertheless, at the end of this chapter.

These three groups of complex physiological entities—the receptors, the nervous system, and the effectors—combine to form the behavioral part of the living organism. They function, under normal conditions, in a harmonious way and provide the organism with an effective means of responding and adjusting to the physical energies of the external and internal environment.

Homeostasis as an integrative principle is usually applied only to certain automatic regulatory processes, such as those concerned with the maintenance of body temperature, water balance, blood-sugar level, and calcium metabolism, but some writers (Morgan and Stellar, 1950) have expanded the concept so that it includes unified behavior in the presence of changing stimulus conditions that are threatening to the organism. In this view, gross behavioral adjustments are considered to be total neuromuscular reactions brought about by either external or internal conditions so extreme that they cannot be corrected by the limited functioning of certain organ systems. The displacement from equilibrium is so great that the homeostatic effects of a single system are inadequate for re-equilibration. For example, in the presence of extreme cold, the heightened activity of the thyroid gland, with its associated effects of quickened heart rate and increased muscular activity, will be insufficient to maintain a constant internal temperature; the organism must behave at a more molar level if it is to succeed in restoring its thermal equilibrium. Hence, the individual organism may move to a warmer environment, build a house, buy a fur coat, or change its diet to increase the caloric intake.

The concept of physiological homeostasis has also been given a behavioral parallel in the theory of *adaptation level* (Helson, 1959). This theory postulates that all behavior centers about the adaptation level or psychological equilibrium of the organism, the particular level depending upon the interaction of all stimuli which confront the organism at a particular time. The adaptation or adjustment of the organism is, thus, a function of three broad classes of stimuli: (1) the focal stimuli which are the primary, immediate determiners of the response; (2) the contextual stimuli which are also immediately present but which form a background for the primary stimuli; and (3) the residual stimuli which are present in the organism and which are attributable either to past experience or constitutional factors. Adaptation-level theory does not assume that all behavior represents an attempt to maintain a constant psychological equilibrium but, instead, tries to account for changing levels of adjustment, that is, varying degrees of acceptance, indifference, or rejection of particular stimulus situations, in terms of so-called outer (physically external) and inner (organismic) determinants of behavior. This theory will be presented in detail in Chapter 13.

Integrative Mechanisms of the Body

Whether or not we accept these theoretical views, or some other, as the basis for human behavior, one point remains unchallenged. Under the usual conditions of stimulation, man normally functions as an integrated organism consisting of a smoothly operating combination of tissues and bodily organs. This integration is achieved in part through the activity of the central nervous system. Through its action, the billions of individual cells of the body are unified into a tremendously complex structure which reacts in a meaningful way to various conditions of external and internal stimulation. Without this integration, man would otherwise be merely a conglomeration of cells, tissues, and organs forming a multicellular organism with no coordinated system of response. At best, such a system could adjust poorly to external changes in the environment. The integrated functioning of the nervous system is required for every behavioral *sequence of adjustment*. This functioning encompasses the arousal of neural excitations by external or internal stimuli, the transmission and correlation of these excitations within the nervous system, and the channeling of outgoing motor impulses into appropriate pathways to produce the proper sequence of responses. The various extensions of the nervous system reach nearly every part of the organism, and their coordinated activity produces rapid and precise action. When a large segment of this system is separated from the rest of the system, for example, if the spinal cord is completely cut, integration fails and control of the bodily parts below the injury is lost. Organismic unity requires and depends upon the integrated activity of separate and specific bodily parts.

The nervous system, however, is not the only integrating mechanism of the body. Its function is complemented by chemical and physical correlating mechanisms which usually involve the transport of substances through the *circulatory system*. Hormones, carbon dioxide, hydrochloric acid, and other substances are significant internal factors at some point or other which aid in maintaining the functional integrity of the organism. The digestive-circulatory tract, for example, alters food energy into glycogen and makes the fuel available to the neuromuscular system, where it is utilized as the organism struggles with the environmental forces which envelop it. Even the purely physical factor of heat tends to contribute to bodily integration. The heat generated in muscle contraction serves to accelerate the heart rate, thereby increasing the flow of blood to the active muscles; it also affects the temperature-regulating center of the thalamus, which in turn controls the vasodilation and sweating adjustment of the skin. These vascular and secretory adjustments facilitate the dissipation of the generated heat. Although the chemical and physical integrative mechanisms serve as part-systems within the total organismic system, their effects are most adequately described as being complementary to, and mutually interactive with, those of the neuromuscular system.

Methods of Studying Neurophysiological Structures and Functions

Although the student of psychology may never need to utilize the laboratory techniques of anatomy and physiology, he should have an appreciation of the methods that have been used to provide us with certain evidence on the structures and functions of the central nervous system. This topic is much too broad to be considered in detail in this textbook, but the principal methods can at least be touched upon to indicate the general approaches that have been used. Advanced courses in physiological psychology will undoubtedly be able to provide the student with specific laboratory skills which he may need in order to pursue a particular research problem.

Neuroanatomical Techniques

Many of the major characteristics of the human nervous system may be noted by an ordinary, general inspection. This will reveal the size, shape, position, and surface markings of the various structures in which we may be interested. Usually, however, certain details of the structure are required which can only be revealed by a careful *dissection* of the nervous system. This is the most direct way of studying the brain. By using a blunt instrument, the various portions of the nervous system can be separated from the surrounding tissues or organs so as to provide accessibility to those structures below the surface. If the nerve fibers are separated gently, numerous pathways may be traced for long distances and the neural interrelations may be ascertained. When a bulky structure is to be examined, in addition to the dissection, a series of gross *sections* must be made in various planes through the particular tissue or organ. This is done with a sharp knife or a highly refined slicing machine (*microtome*) in order to obtain a specimen for further study. The detailed analysis of minute anatomy must be performed by examining the excised portions of the nervous system under a microscope. This requires that the tissues must be thin and transparent so as to permit light to pass through them into the microscope, and finally into the eye.

The value of microscopic preparations in the study of the nervous system depends primarily upon their fixation and staining. Although it would be preferable to study tissues in their living state, it is difficult to obtain thin sections of living tissue. The thicker the section, the more difficult it is to distinguish the various structures within the tissue. Special techniques must be adopted, therefore, to kill the tissue from which the thin slices are later obtained. In studying the nervous system, small pieces of fresh tissue are fixed by placing them in solutions of formalin or alcohol. This kills the tissue and simultaneously preserves it from alteration during the successive stages of treatment. Water in the tissue is slowly removed, after fixation, by passing the pieces through increasing concentrations of alcohol. Melted paraffin or a solution of nitrocellulose is then used to impregnate the water-free tissues. After the paraffin or nitrocellulose has hardened, slices of tissue about 1 or 2 microns or less in thickness are cut from the block without any appreciable damage or distortion to the tissue. The slices are then stained with any one of a number of dyes, the particular dye depending upon the structure being studied. Different structures have different chemical compositions so that certain stains are used to color specific structures. In general, the stains used for the structures of the body are of little value in the study of the nervous system.

The special methods of staining that have been developed tend to supplement each other and they provide a composite picture of the entire structure of the nervous system and of the brain, in particular. Each method has its own specific purpose and shows certain details of neuroanatomy. The essential dyeing techniques are those which bring out the form and structure of neurons, those which differentiate myelinated and nonmyelinated fibers, and those which differentiate degenerating myelinated fibers from normal ones. After the sections are appropriately stained, they are immersed in a substance such as xylol to make them transparent. The sections are then placed on glass slides, covered with a solution of transparent resin, and sealed with a very thin piece of glass. This treatment prevents the tissues from drying out and being destroyed by their exposure to air. Sections prepared and mounted in this manner can be used for many years of microscopic analysis.

If a more expedient technique is required in the preparation, such as might be needed in hospital situations, fresh pieces of tissue may be brought into contact with solid carbon dioxide ("dry ice") and quickly frozen into hard blocks. The desired sections may then be sliced immediately, appropriately stained, and mounted on glass slides for microscopic examination.

The anatomical study of the nervous system often involves techniques and methods that are considerably more advanced than the relatively easy staining techniques to which some reference has already been made. One class of advanced methods utilizes technical procedures which evolve from the interruption of neurons either by disease or accident, or by specific experimental design. For example, in the *Marchi method,* degenerating fibers are made to stand out as black dots in a clear background by the application of osmium tetroxide (Os O$_4$). Thus, for example, if the pyramidal (motor) area of the cerebrum, which controls the muscular activity in the trunk and limbs, is injured experimentally, it is possible to follow the course of the pyramidal tract by observing the chain of black dots running through the brain and spinal cord.

Another class of advanced methods for studying the anatomy of the nervous system is based upon embryologic and comparative finds. In the *embryologic approach*, sections of the brain are studied when the brain is small. This presents a less confusing picture of the brain than that which is found in the adult with its myriad of fibers. Also, since the different neural tracts acquire their myelin sheaths at different times, the staining of young brains reveals additional neuroanatomical information. The *comparative methods* rely on the study of more lowly forms of life than man and proceed from simpler to more complex neural networks. This has several advantages. The lack of development of the higher cortical centers facilitates the study of the lower centers that control behavior, such as the reflexes. Furthermore, the comparative method permits the study of sensorimotor connections which may lead to certain conclusions regarding the relevance of particular neural structures. In the lowest animals, the behaviors exhibited tend to reflect the stimulus characteristics in a very direct manner, since the nervous system provides little elaboration between the receptors and the effectors. In the higher animals, the receptors become more numerous and more specialized, thereby increasing the range of environmental factors which can serve as sources of stimulation. The increased complexity of the nervous system at these levels makes possible a greater diversity of stimulus-response relationships. The comparative approach traces the development of the basic mechanisms of behavior and observes how they expand to provide supplemental abilities and forms of adjustment to complex environmental situations.

Experimental Methods

Our current views on the functions of the various parts of the nervous system are based to a large degree upon the evidence obtained from several experimental methods. One of these is the *method of ablation*. In this method, as indicated in the preceding section, the experimenter removes or severs some portion of the nervous system and then observes the resulting behavioral loss or alteration of function. The amount of destruction may be relatively small, such as that involved in destroying a part of the thalamus with a needle, or rather large as when the cerebral cortex is removed from one side of the brain. The purpose of ablation is to release the lower neural centers from the dominance of the higher neural centers. For instance, the spinal reflexes may be studied by severing the spinal cord at its point of juncture with the brain. A frog and a dog decorticated in this manner will exhibit different behaviors. The frog, after a few minutes, will continue to sit and hop like a normal animal, but the dog will show a high degree of impairment in its activities. The difference lies in the fact that animals, like the frog, with poorly developed brains have a greater proportion of neural circuits that are complete and self-sufficient in the lower segments of their nervous systems.

The method of ablation is usually combined with observations of the organism's behavior such as motor responses, reactions to stimuli, and so on, both *before* and *after* surgery. The level of observation may be primarily qualitative and uncontrolled, as when the part of the brain responsible for gross motor coordination is removed and the experimenter observes that the organism is unsteady in its movements; or the observations may be quantitative such that, in the given example, certain tests might be administered to provide a numerical statement of the amount of unsteadiness present after the operation.

The final step in this method involves the appraisal of the extent to which the tissue has been destroyed, or removed, together with a statement regarding the specific characteristics of the ablated area. This is accomplished by using the slicing and staining technique described in the preceding section. Caution must be exercised in using the method of ablation since the method really does not tell us what functions were performed by the ablated parts. It tells us only *what the remaining parts can do*. If the removal of a bit of tissue has little or no effect on a given function, this does not prove that the tissue was not involved in that function. The loss of the right forefinger does not prevent a right-handed person from holding a pencil and writing, but we cannot assume that the finger was not used before it was lost.

Another problem associated with the method of ablation has been the extraneous disruption or disturbance of the intervening cortical tissue which must

be damaged in order to reach a particular locus in the brain. This problem, however, has been overcome with the introduction of ultrasonic neurosurgery (Fry,
Mosberg, Barnard, and Fry, 1954). Basically, the technique consists of the irradiation of a selected brain structure by means of high intensity ultrasound (1
megacycle/sec) generated by a multibeam transducer. The irradiation apparatus
is shown in Figure 3-1 and the system for positioning the multibeam transducer is

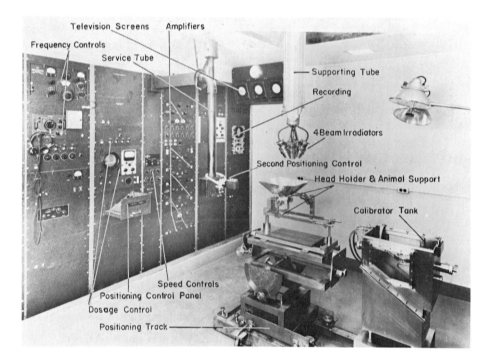

Figure 3–1.   The irradiation room in which ultrasonic neurosurgery is performed on animal and
human subjects. (From Fry, in Tobias and Lawrence (Eds.), *Advances in biological and medical
physics*, Vol. VI, New York: Academic Press, 1958. By permission of the publisher.)

shown in Figure 3-2. The intensity of the ultrasound from a single focusing lens is
not great enough to damage the cortical tissue through which it passes, but when
the beams from the four units are brought into coincidence, it is possible to produce large lesions of complex shape. The wavelength of the sound and the angle
of convergence of the ultrasonic beams are the primary factors which determine
the smallest size of the lesion to be produced; volumes of tissue smaller than 0.1
cu mm can be affected by accurately controlling the dosage of ultrasonic stimulation. Also, either temporary or permanent changes can be produced in almost
any brain structure desired. Ultrasonic neurosurgery is now being used in animal
research involving extensive neuroanatomical, behavioral, and physiological
studies (Fry and Fry, 1960).

A significant medical advance is being made with the use of ultrasonic neuro-

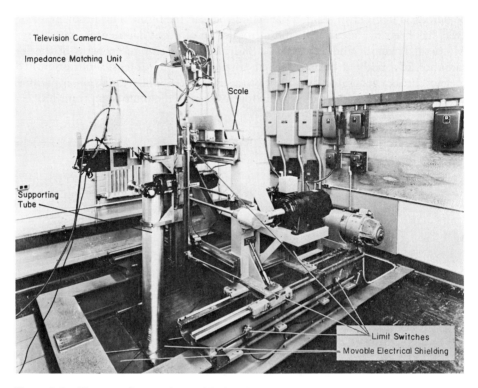

Figure 3–2. The control room for positioning the ultrasonic, multi-beam transducer. (From Fry, in Tobias and Lawrence (Eds.), *Advances in biological and medical physics,* Vol. VI, New York: Academic Press, 1958. By permission of the publisher.)

surgery in the modification of symptoms associated with various human disorders, such as those found in Parkinson's disease, cerebral palsy, and stump pains in amputees (Meyers, Fry, Fry, Eggleton, and Schultz, 1960). The procedure with human subjects is essentially the same as that for animals, but a special head-holder is required so that reduplication of the head's position in space can be achieved on successive days of treatment. A close-up of a patient in position in the head-holder in shown in Figure 3-3. The geometric accuracy attainable in the positioning of the ultrasonic focal point at a desired spot within the skull is well within the limits required for this type of research, but the anatomical accuracy, that is, the placement of the beam in a specific site of a given cerebral structure, is limited in precision due to the inaccuracies in the atlases of the human brain which are currently available.

A second experimental method is that of electrical stimulation. In this method, exposed parts of the nervous system, usually the brain, are stimulated by receiving an electrical current (AC or DC) delivered by means of wires attached to two electrodes. The active electrode, which is applied directly to the region to be stimulated, is usually a small metal rod insulated except at its tip. The tip of the rod may be covered with a bit of cotton saturated with a saline solution to provide better electrical contact and to prevent injury to the tissue being stimulated. The

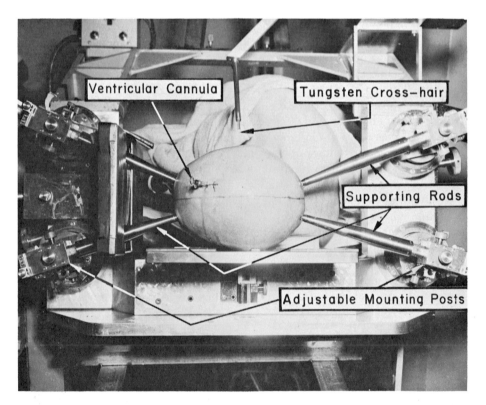

Figure 3–3. A close-up view of a human patient positioned in a head holder. The images of the tungsten cross-hair appear in X-ray photographs and are used to determine the coordinates of the brain site(s) to be irradiated. (From Meyers et al., *Neurology*, 1960, **10**, 271–277.)

other (neutral) electrode is attached either to the skin or to an exposed muscle to complete the circuit through the organism. The method of electrical stimulation has a distinct advantage over the method of ablation in that the structures being studied are part of an intact system. Thus, the exposed brains of animals and the brains of individuals undergoing certain forms of surgery may be conveniently stimulated, and the resulting responses may be appropriately noted. When a particular part of the left motor region of the cortex of a dog, for instance, is stimulated, there will be movement in some part of the right foreleg. In man, there is no area of the cortex proper which produces pain sensations when it is stimulated electrically. Under local anesthesia, the various areas of the brain may be stimulated and the subject may easily inform the experimenter of his sensations at each step in the procedure. When one area is probed, the subject may report, "I see some flashes of light"; at another area, "I feel something cold touching my hand." This method permits a high degree of cooperation between the subject and the experimenter. It provides positive evidence of neural functioning in contrast to the negative evidence of ablation. The effectiveness of an electrical stimulus in this method will depend upon its intensity, duration, and form.

One disadvantage of the method of electrical stimulation is that it fails to provide information on the *patterns* of neural activity which occur in the stimulated area. In the normal excitatory situation, the neural elements fire in some sequential order; but, under electrical stimulation, all of the neurons in the given area are discharged simultaneously. This probably seldom, if ever, happens in the normal action of the brain.

Current work in the electrical stimulation of the brain involves the chronic implantation of intracerebral electrodes both in animals and man. The electrodes are of two general types: (1) *needle* electrodes, with single or multiple leads—the latter offering the advantage of being able to stimulate more cerebral points with the same effort and operative trauma as with the single needle, and (2) *plate* electrodes, which are used for studying the surface of the brain. Several plate electrodes and needle electrodes may be implanted simultaneously in the brain of an animal, such as the monkey, so that up to fifty leads may be available for applying electrical stimulation to different parts of the brain, or to different parts of the same cerebral structure.

As part of the operative procedure for implanting a needle electrode (Delgado, 1961), the experimental animal is injected with a 5 percent solution of an anesthetic and, after its head is shaved, is placed in a stereotaxic instrument, as shown in Figure 3-4.

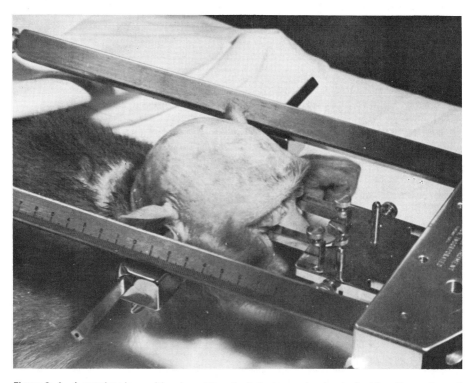

Figure 3–4. A monkey in position in a stereotaxic instrument prior to incising the scalp and drilling burr holes for the insertion of a needle electrode. (From Delgado, in Sheer, 1961.)

With appropriate aseptic precautions, a midline incision is made in the scalp; the scalp and associated tissues are separated or dissected away from the skull and, after the periosteum is scraped from the skull, burr holes (1.5 mm) are made with a dental drill at the points where the electrodes are to be inserted. The needle electrodes are then inserted by means of a micromanipulator. This is shown in Figure 3-5. The burr holes are then closed and the electrode is fixed to

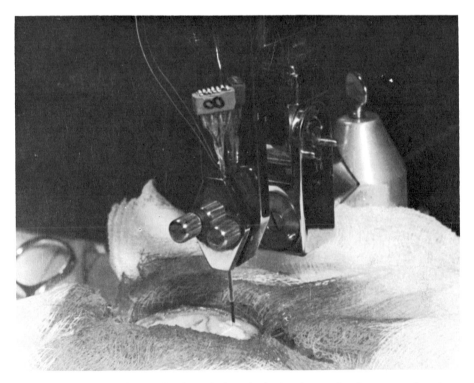

Figure 3–5. Insertion of a needle electrode into the brain of a monkey by means of a micro-manipulator. (From Delgado, in Sheer, 1961.)

the skull with dental cement. The top of the electrode is contoured to the shape of the skull and the electrical socket, after passing through an opening in the scalp, is tied securely to the skull by means of stainless steel wires looped through two additional burr holes. Figure 3-6 shows an X-ray photograph of two needle electrodes implanted in a monkey.

Recovery and healing of the animal after surgery requires about a week, following which testing of the animal may begin. Figure 3-7 shows a monkey in a learning situation in which a lever-pressing response must be performed to produce a food reward. In the first few days after surgery, the experimental animal may attempt to loosen and remove the electrical sockets, but in a short time the presence of the sockets is ignored. Numerous behavioral studies have been reported in which electrical stimulation was employed to determine the influence of different cerebral structures. For example, Hess (1948) stimulated part of the hypothalamus in the cat and observed that *defensive reactions* were evoked; Delgado, Roberts, and Miller (1954) stimulated certain cerebral areas and noted that this served to *motivate learning;* Olds and Milner (1954) induced *positive reinforcement* in the rat by stimulating the septal area of the brain; and Alonso de Florida and Delgado (1955) were able to obtain an increase in the *playful and contactual* activity of a cat in a group situation by stimulating the amygdaloid region.

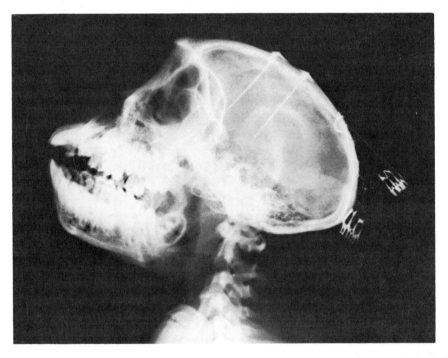

Figure 3–6. An X-ray photograph of a monkey's head showing the two needle electrodes implanted in the head. (From Delgado, in Sheer, 1961.)

In certain instances, such as in studying group behavior, the wires leading to the implanted electrodes place an undesirable restriction on the animal's movement and techniques other than *direct control* have been tried. One of these is *remote control,* in which a receiver is activated by induction or by means of a radio receiver implanted underneath the scalp (Mauro, Davey, and Scher, 1950). Although this technique eliminates the problem of leads protruding through the skin, it does not permit monitoring of the stimulus input to the cerebral structures or recording of the brain's electrical activity; more importantly, the intensity of stimulation varies with the orientation of the receiving antenna. To circumvent the latter problem, Delgado (1959) has developed an alternate technique of stim-

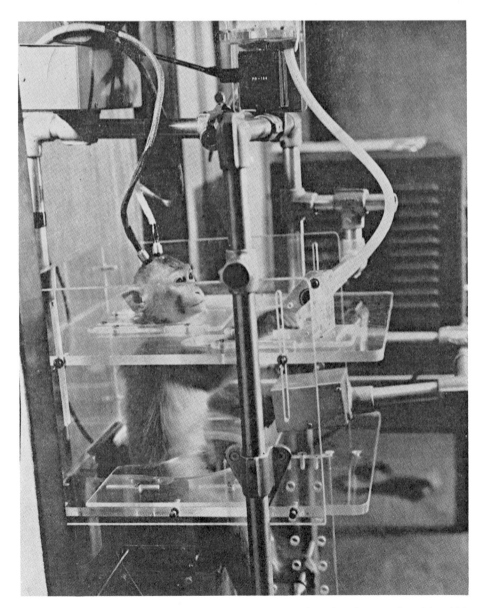

Figure 3–7. A monkey with implanted electrodes is shown in a learning experiment in which lever-pressing produces a food reward. When the animal is not being tested, it can be removed from the apparatus by disconnecting the electrical leads at the two sockets. (From Sheer, 1961.)

ulation in which an electrically-timed pulse is generated by a miniature transistor unit attached to the animal's collar.

Chronic implantation of intracerebral electrodes in man follows the same general approach as in animals, but utilizes a more highly refined stereotaxic technique and advanced roentgenographic procedures. Figure 3-8 shows the basic instrument used in positioning and inserting the stimulating electrodes. The *stereo-*

Figure 3-8. A stereoencephalotome in position on a human skull as part of the operative procedure used in implanting a needle electrode. The instrument is attached to the skull by four screws in such a manner that it can be easily removed when not in use; however, the four screws in the skull may remain for weeks or months to permit repositioning of the device whenever necessary. (From Spiegel and Wycis, in Sheer, 1961.)

encephalotome is fixed to the skull by four hollow stainless steel screws; these may remain in the skull for several weeks or months and can permit the repositioning of the stereoencephalotome whenever necessary. The stereotaxic device uses a three-dimensional coordinate system for the accurate location of cerebral structures, in which the system is defined in terms of arbitrary planes or lines relative to some well-known landmark, such as the pineal body. Bony landmarks are not used since they are quite unreliable.

The exact placement of the electrode is determined by a set of roentgenograms. A preoperative roentgenogram showing a lateral view of the brain is presented in Figure 3-9. The electrode is shown in its zero position (E) and, during the

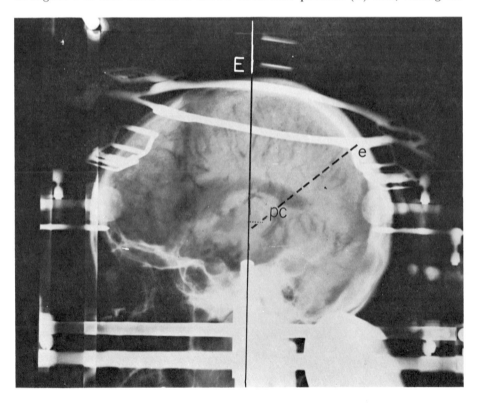

Figure 3–9. An X-ray photograph (roentgenogram) showing a lateral view of the brain prior to the implanting operation. The needle electrode is shown in its zero position (non-implanted) and, after the implantation, it will be in the position indicated by the line E. The depth of the electrode will depend upon the location of the particular cerebral structure to be stimulated. (From Spiegel and Wycis, in Sheer, 1961.)

operation, it will be implanted in the position designated as e. The techniques of implantation, including the use of polaroid roentgenograms, are so refined that the error of inserting the electrode is usually within 1 or 2 mm (Spiegel and Wycis, 1961).

Observations on the experiential correlates of electrical stimulation have been obtained from subjects with implanted electrodes (King, 1961). In this approach, interviews are held before, during, and after the administration of specific stimulation. Although the observations obtained by this method are likely to be distorted or biased, they do provide useful information about what the subject is experiencing under the given conditions. The following sample excerpt is an abridgment of an interview with a female subject who was stimulated in the amygdaloid nucleus (located in the anterior portion of the temporal lobe). A sequence of frames (Figure 3-10, a-e) from a filmstrip is coordinated with the subject's comments.

> Interviewer questions subject about how she feels.
> SUBJECT: "I just feel everything is all wrong. Like I can't be a part of anything. Like I didn't belong and everything is a dream or something."
> INTERVIEWER: "Did you feel this way before the operation?" (*He is referring to the implanting of electrodes.*)
> SUBJECT: "Yeah, I felt the same way. I didn't want anything and I didn't belong any more."
> Figure 3-10a shows a sample of the subject's responsiveness during this exchange. The subject's voice tone was extremely flat and lacking in emphasis. Her facial expression was blank and unchanging.

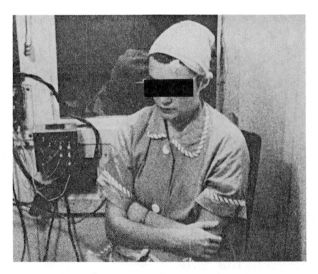

Figure 3-10. A series of still pictures from a film in which the amygdaloid nucleus of a female subject was stimulated by an electrical current. (From King, in Sheer, 1961.)

Figure 3-10a. The subject before stimulation.

> The region of the amygdala was then stimulated with a 5 ma. current.
> INTERVIEWER: "How do you feel now?"
> SUBJECT (*voice much higher in tone*): "I feel like I want to get up from this chair! Please don't

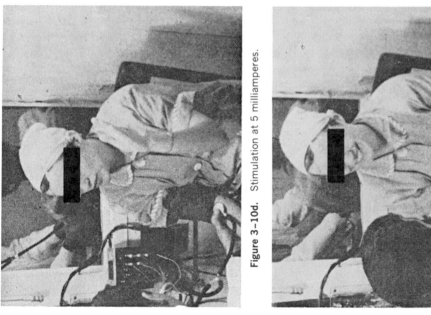

Figure 3–10d. Stimulation at 5 milliamperes.

Figure 3–10e. Stimulation at 4 milliamperes.

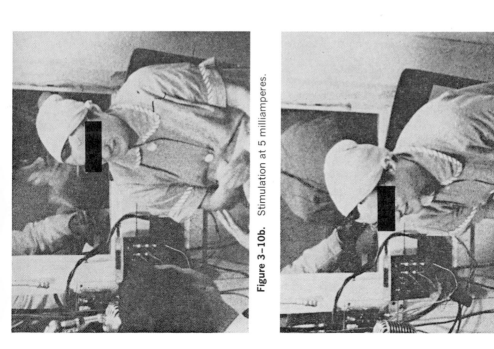

Figure 3–10b. Stimulation at 5 milliamperes.

Figure 3–10c. Stimulation at 4 milliamperes.

let me do it! (*There is a change to strong voice inflection and a marked alteration in facial expression to express pleading.*) Don't do this to me. I don't want to be mean!"

INTERVIEWER: "Feel like you want to hit me?"

SUBJECT: "Yeah, I just want to hit something. (*Appears and sounds aroused and angry.*) I want to get something and just tear it up. Take it so I won't! (*Hands her scarf to interviewer; he hands her a stack of paper, and without further verbal exchange she tears it to shreds.*) I don't like to feel like this!"

Figure 3-10b gives a sample of the subject's facial expression during this exchange.

The level of stimulating current was then reduced to 4 ma.

SUBJECT (*immediately changing to wide smile*): "I know it's silly, what I'm doing."

INTERVIEWER: "Now, feel better?"

SUBJECT: "A little bit."

INTERVIEWER: "Can you tell me any more about how you were feeling a moment ago?"

SUBJECT: "I wanted to get up from this chair and run. I wanted to hit something; tear up something—anything. Not you, just anything. I just wanted to get up and tear. I had no control of myself."

Figure 3-10c shows a sample of the subject's facial expression during this exchange.

The level of stimulating current was then increased to 5 ma. again.

SUBJECT (*voice loud and pleading*): "Don't let me hit you!"

INTERVIEWER: "How do you feel now?"

SUBJECT: "I think I feel a little better like this. I get it out of my system. I don't have those other thoughts (*her pre-existing mental symptoms*) when I'm like this. . . . Take my blood pressure. Make them cut this thing off, it's killing me! Take my blood pressure, I say! (*Strong voice inflection and facial appearance of anger.*) Quit holding me! I'm getting up! You'd better get somebody else if you want to hold me! I'm going to hit you!" (*Raises arm as if to strike.*)

Figure 3-10d gives a sample of the subject's facial expression during this exchange.

The stimulating current was then reduced to 4 ma.

SUBJECT (*wide smile and laugh*): "Why does it make me do this? I couldn't help it. I didn't have any control. I wanted to slap your face. I don't like to be done like that." (*Voice relaxed; tone apologetic.*)

Figure 3-10e gives a sample of the subject's facial expression during this exchange.

The stimulating current was then shut off and the interview directed toward a detailed review of what had gone on. Some new questions were put:

INTERVIEWER: "Did you see anyone? Your husband?"

SUBJECT: "No, I didn't. I didn't even think about my husband."

INTERVIEWER: "Did you feel any pain?"

SUBJECT: "No, it's just a feeling in my body. No pain."

INTERVIEWER: "Would you like to go through that again?"

SUBJECT: "No. It didn't pain, but I don't like the feelings."

INTERVIEWER: "Can you describe them?"

SUBJECT: "I can't describe it, just can act it. I felt better in a way; I wasn't worried any more." (*Her mental complaints.*)*

Evidence of this kind is of course not quantitative. Nevertheless, it does provide clues to behavior modification, particularly if the interview is supported by records obtained by tape recorders and motion picture photography.

A third experimental method is that of producing local stimulation by applying a *chemical* substance to a given portion of the nervous system. The application

*From H. E. King. Psychological effects of excitation in the limbic system. In D. E. Sheer (Ed.), *Electrical Stimulation of the Brain,* University of Texas Press, 1961. By permission of the publisher.

of strychnine, for example, to a neural structure such as the cerebral cortex will result in the repetitive discharge of the neurons having cell bodies in that particular region. When, for example, a few square millimeters of filter paper soaked in a weak solution of strychnine sulfate are placed on a given sensory region of the cortex, it will produce marked symptoms of stimulation for about 30 minutes in a particular part of the body. This often results in scratching behavior. Although it is difficult to localize the effects of the chemical and to control the strength of the stimulus in this method, the method nevertheless has an advantage over electrical stimulation; namely, that the cell bodies are activated. Electrical stimulation affects both nerve fibers and cell bodies. This makes it difficult to determine whether or not the neurons located in the particular region being studied are actually involved in the behavioral functions which are observed.

A fourth experimental method is that of observing the *electrical potentials* of neurons, as in the cortex. Electrical recording methods can be combined with other techniques, for example, strychninization or implanted electrodes, or may be used independently. A routine procedure, both in the laboratory and in the clinic, is to make an electrical recording of brain activity by placing two electrodes upon the scalp. These are spaced about 2 or 3 inches apart as shown in Figure 3-11, and are fastened by means of collodion over the region of the brain to be

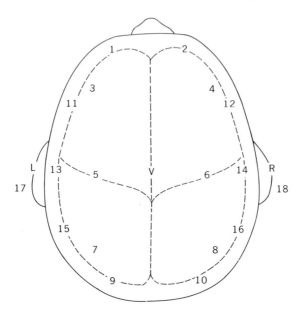

Figure 3–11.   Standard positions used in the placement of electrodes for obtaining routine scalp recordings of EEG waves. (From Walker and Marshall, in Sheer, 1961.)

studied. The potentials coming through the skull and scalp are amplified about a million times and are usually recorded by means of an ink-writing oscillograph. Frequently, two to six units are used to provide information simultaneously from many different regions of the brain. The resulting record is called an *electroenceph-alogram* (EEG) and represents "the algebraic sum of the potentials of billions of cortical neurons" (Gardner, 1963, p. 271). The potentials normally obtained range from a few microvolts to about 100 microvolts. Under abnormal conditions such as during a seizure or convulsion, these potentials may be greatly increased. By measuring the frequency and amplitude of each kind of wave and determining the percentage of time that certain rhythms are present in a given record, the trained clinician or experimenter can make certain inferences about the nature of the behavioral disorder. Figure 3-12 shows the contrast between the EEG of a normal subject and a patient suffering from chronic anxiety. Notice that the alpha waves (10 to 12 cps) are almost completely suppressed in the chronically anxious patient. The EEG is extensively used as an aid in the diagnosis of neurological disorders, for example, epilepsy, and in the location of brain tumors, injuries, and so on. It also reveals changes in cortical activity which can be induced by drugs and other forms of therapy.

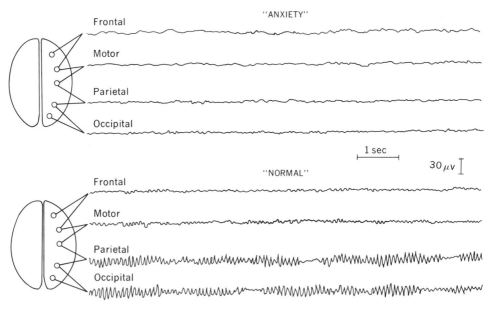

Figure 3–12. A comparison of EEG recordings obtained from a normal subject and from a patient suffering from chronic anxiety. (From Lindsley, in Sheer, 1961a.)

When the skull is opened through operative surgery or by accident, electrical waves may be recorded by placing the electrodes directly into contact with specifically localized areas of the brain. The *electrocorticogram* is obtained from the surface of the cortex; the *electrothalamogram* is obtained from the thalamus. Precautions similar to those in the method of electrical stimulation must be used in electrical recording to insure adequate contact and to prevent damage to the neural tissues. In some instances, mechanical holders are used to insert the electrodes or to manipulate them in three dimensions with considerable precision. With this technique, it is easy to obtain an accurate record of the locations of the points in the brain from which potentials were actually recorded. The potentials from the exposed cortex of human patients are usually 10 times as great as those recorded from the surface of the scalp, but the pattern of activity is the same.

Clinical Methods

The clinical methods of studying the functions of the nervous system tend to supplement the experimental methods. These methods generally involve the observation of the effects of lesions or of disturbances produced by accident or disease on the behavior of man and lower animals. Although the work in the clinic is essentially nonexperimental, all of the methods reviewed in the preceding section may be used to obtain clinical evidence. Those methods are not the sole property of the researcher. In effect, the clinical methods are distinguished by their *setting* and not by their procedures. For example, it is claimed that as long ago as the Franco-Prussian War (1870), two physicians availed themselves of the opportunity to stimulate directly the motor area of the brain of a soldier whose skull had been partially removed by a shell injury.

Clinical evidence, as all empirical evidence, must be interpreted with considerable caution. However, in the clinical case, an additional problem is introduced. The effects of brain injuries, diseases, tumors, or circulatory disorders are seldom highly localized and accidental lesions seldom occur at precisely the location which may be of primary interest to the researcher. Furthermore, detailed information on the physiological and psychological functions of a particular patient is usually not available before his disorder and cannot be obtained by any amount of examination, or testing, after the disorder is detected. Nevertheless, the methods which involve the operative removal of brain tissue, as in *frontal lobectomy,* or the severing of intracortical pathways, as in *frontal lobotomy,* provide useful information in establishing the correlation between severely abnormal behavioral states and underlying neurophysiological states. The careful integration of clinical and experimental methods can lead to new evidence and to theoretically significant results. The two general methods should yield not contradictory, but complementary, information on the structures and functions that are of importance in the study of behavior.

Major Divisions
of the Human Nervous System

The Neuron and Its Action

The human nervous system is an extremely complex structure consisting of approximately 10 billion *nerve cells* or *neurons,* each composed of a cell body and one or more elongated fiber projections. These neurons are linked in a finitely large number of combinations which form conduction pathways for certain electrochemical changes in the peripheral nerves, spinal cord, and brain. Although neurons have specialized properties of *irritability* and *conductivity* due to their delicate fiber projections or processes, their fundamental structure (cytoplasm, nucleus, and so on) is similar to that of a typical body cell. The neuronal structure is supported by a network of nonconducting (*glial*) cells called, collectively, *neuroglia*. These cells are revealed by special staining techniques and are found to have processes which are intertwined with nerve cells and fibers, or are attached to the walls of blood vessels.

Figure 3-13 shows the basic structure of a neuron and the several different forms in which it is frequently found. The cell body (*soma* or *perikaryon*) and the

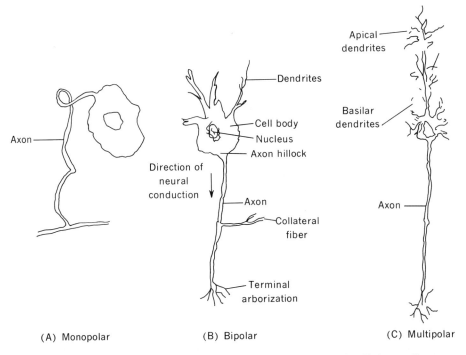

Figure 3–13.   Three types of neurons in the human nervous system classified according to the number of fiber processes.

fiber processes (dendrite and axon) differ in their physical size and in their neurological functions. While the bodies of nerve cells vary in diameter from about 4 to 130 microns, the processes may extend from a few microns to several feet in length. In a tall man, for example, a single neuron could be over six feet long, extending from the big toe to the base of the skull. In a full grown giraffe, some neurons reach the amazing length of over fifteen feet. The diameters of the processes, however, are microscopic and range from about 1 to 20 microns, depending upon the particular type of nerve fiber involved.

As viewed by light microscopy, the internal structure of the cell body consists of a large nucleus embedded in cytoplasm. The nucleus shows a well-marked chromatin network and nucleoli; the cytoplasm is fibrillated, with the neurofibrils extending from the dendrites, through the cell proper, and into the axon process. *Nissl granules,* consisting of nucleoprotein and organically combined iron, are distributed in the cytoplasm. The size and number of the granules vary with a number of factors, including the physiological condition of the cell. If the cell body is destroyed, the fiber processes also die.

The fiber processes (*dendrites* and *axons*) are characterized by their particular properties and can be differentiated in three major ways. (1) The processes differ in the direction in which they conduct nerve impulses relative to the cell body. Dendrites are located in the body in positions where they can be excited by environmental stimuli, by other neurons, or by sensory epithelial cells. The dendrites, then, are on the receiving ends of the neurons and conduct impulses toward the cell bodies. Such impulses are called *afferent* impulses. The axon is functionally connected to the dendritic endings of other neurons or to the effectors of the body (muscles and glands). This fiber process thus delivers the impulses carried by it. The impulses are conducted away from the cell body and are called *efferent* impulses. Since the membranes of the dendrites and axons are both capable of carrying impulses, the direction of conduction is determined by the electrical polarity that is established at the points of functional connection (*synapses*) between neurons. Excitations which are sufficiently strong always travel across the synapse from the axon of one neuron to the dendrite of another; within the neuron, however, the excitation normally passes from the dendrite to the axon. It should be noted, however, that when an axon is experimentally stimulated at any accessible point, the nerve impulse set up at the point of stimulation can travel either centrally or distally, that is, it travels as readily toward the cell body as away from it. (2) The dendrites are usually short, extending only a small distance from the cell body, while the axons often extend for much longer distances. In terms of their diametric sizes, the dendrites become progressively smaller the farther away they extend from the cell body, but the axon is fairly uniform in size throughout its entire length. Although the area of the cell body from which the axon originates is marked by a small cone-shaped elevation (*axon hillock*), the dendrites seem to be irregular extensions of the cell body. (3) Each neuron usually has several dendrites, but only one axon which may or may not give rise to *collateral branches* at right angles to itself. Also, the dendritic endings consist of treelike branchings which increase the surface area of the neuron: this permits each neuron to be linked or associated functionally with a large number of other neurons. The axon has one of two types of endings: the *terminal bouton,* which forms a functional connection with muscle fibers or glands, or *terminal arborization,* which connects functionally to the dendrites of other nerve cells.

Neurons may be further described in relation to their specialized functions in the nervous system. The differentiation is made on the basis of the total number of processes (dendritic and axonic) which are present in a given neuron (Figure 3-13). For example, *monopolar* or *unipolar neurons* are found in the cerebrospinal ganglia of man. These neurons, or primary sensory cells, have a single axon-like dendrite which is continuous with the axon and which serves to conduct impulses from some peripheral sense organ to the central nervous system. *Bipolar cells,* having one axon process and one dendritic process, are limited mainly to the special sense organs, such as the eye and the ear. *Multipolar cells* have one axon and two or more dendritic processes. These cells, which constitute the majority of nerve cells in the central nervous system, provide a complex network of endings on many other cells within the nervous system. There are numerous types of neurons, but this should suffice to show that the *morphological* characteristics of neurons, for example, the size and forms of their cell bodies, the number and lengths of their dendrites, and the lengths and diameters of their axons, are related to their location in the nervous system and to their functional interconnections.

As we have seen, the neuron is both the basic structural unit and the basic functional unit of the nervous system. While specialized receptor cells receive external energy in the form of stimuli, the nerve fibers (the axon processes of single neurons) are bundled into groups of nerves to provide conductive pathways for neural impulses traveling from one part of the nervous system to another. The neural impulses are electrochemical reactions which are initiated in the receptor cells and are ultimately conducted along the membranous covering of the neuron. The electrical changes probably represent the critical processes that are involved in the development and propagation of an impulse along the fiber, while the chemical changes in the nerve fiber are most likely related to the recovery processes that occur following neural activity. Let us examine the transmission process more closely.

In its normal resting condition, a nerve fiber is in a state of *polarization.* By placing an ultramicroelectrode within a nerve fiber and another on the external surface of the fiber, neurophysiologists have found that a small electrical potential difference exists between the inside and outside of the fiber that can be measured on a sensitive voltmeter. This transmembrane difference, the *resting potential,* is only a few thousandths of a volt; but, it is large enough to show that the outside of the neuronal membrane is positively charged, while the inside is negatively charged. If both electrodes are placed on the surface of the fiber, no current will flow and no potential difference will be detected; this indicates a state of equipotentiality along the surface of the neuron. Polarization is attributed principally to the difference in the potassium (K^+) ions, sodium ions (Na^+), chlorine ions (Cl^-), and unknown organic anions (A^-), and the permeability of the axon membrane to their concentrations, inside and outside the fiber. In the resting (nonconducting) nerve cell, the interior of the cell is electrically negative to the exterior.

In order to study the processes of neural excitation and conduction in the neuron, a common procedure has been to apply electrical currents to the resting, or inactive, nerve cell and to measure the resulting electrical changes. This is accomplished by placing two stimulating electrodes ($+$ and $-$) and two recording electrodes in contact with the outside of the nerve fiber, leaving a short separation between them. Different amounts of current are then applied through the stimulating electrodes and observations are made on the magnitudes of the potential differences which are detected by the recording device (*galvanometer*). When a very weak electrical current is applied for a short period of time, no deflection is noted on the galvanometer. This amount of current is said to provide *subliminal* stimulation since no neural impulse is generated—nothing happened to deflect the needle of the galvanometer. As the current is successively increased, a point is reached which will be sufficient to produce a visible change in the position of the needle on the galvanometer. This amount of current is said to be a *threshold* stimulus; it is sufficient to generate a neural impulse. As we proceed beyond this value, the galvanometer will be deflected each time the stimulus is applied, but the amount of deflection will remain constant. This tells us that the magnitude of the nerve impulse does not depend upon the magnitude of the initiating stimulus. The stimulus energy does not contribute to the energy present in the nerve fiber; it merely releases it. When the stimulus reaches the threshold value, neural activity is initiated and the nerve fiber responds with its maximal capability. For a given fiber, small stimuli do not give rise to small neural impulses and large stimuli, to large impulses. The axon of a neuron, and its cell body as well, either responds to the limit of its capability under the conditions of the moment, or it does not respond at all. This is called the *all-or-none law*. The absolute amount of energy which is required to excite a nerve fiber will depend upon the particular kind and size of fiber that is involved; although the kind of energy characterizing the stimulus may vary, the all-or-none law will hold, nevertheless, for the single nerve fiber.

The chemical action that occurs in connection with the application of the electrical stimulus is not entirely known, but the available evidence suggests a certain sequence of events. When subthreshold stimuli are applied, a *local excitatory process* is set up. The membrane potential confined to the region of the stimulating electrodes is altered slightly (*local electrotonus response*), but it is insufficient to trigger a neural impulse. The magnitude of the local excitatory process is a function of the strength and duration of the stimulating current. When the local process becomes large enough due to an increase in the stimulating current, a nerve impulse, or propagated disturbance, is initiated. There is a change in the *permeability* of the membrane of the nerve cell and the resting potential is reversed. The axon membrane temporarily becomes selectively permeable to sodium ions (Na^+) and relatively impermeable to potassium (K^+) ions. Consequently, Na^+ from the fluid surrounding the nerve fiber (interstitial fluid) flows rapidly into the nerve fiber, producing a greater concentration inside the fiber than outside. Since the resting ratio of external to internal Na^+ concentrations is in this way reversed, the polarization of the (resting) membrane is reversed. During excitation (*depolarization*), the exterior surface of the membrane becomes negative relative to the interior. This process occurs very quickly, about 1 msec after a sufficiently strong stimulus is applied, and is accompanied by a marked potential difference called a *spike potential*. It is the spike potential which, when triggered, follows the all-or-none law. Once the spike potential has been generated by the depolarization of the membrane, it moves along the membrane at a measurable speed, until it reaches the end of the fiber. The spike potential is followed in some fibers by a *negative after-potential* and then by a *positive after-potential*, both of which are probably related to certain metabolic processes required to reestablish the normal resting ionic distribution in the nerve fiber. Acting collectively, these three types of potentials constitute the complete *action potential* of a nerve fiber and determine its state of *excitability*. We will now consider the various phases of excitability which occur in a nerve fiber.

We have seen that before a nerve fiber is stimulated, the neuron is in a normal, resting state. Also, we have noted that two aspects of the stimulus must be considered in order to determine whether an electric current will or will not produce a spike potential. These are: (1) the strength of the current, and (2) the temporal duration of the current. Figure 3–14 shows that the effectiveness of an electric

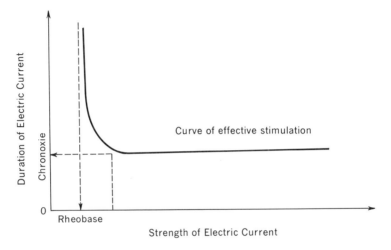

Figure 3–14. A graph showing that the effective stimulation of a neuron is a joint function of both current strength and duration.

current is a joint function of current strength and current duration. The stronger the current, the shorter the time required for it to excite the fiber. *Rheobase* is the strength of the weakest current which, if applied for an adequate time, is just sufficient to stimulate the nerve fiber. (A weaker current will not stimulate the nerve, no matter how long it is applied.) *Chronaxie* is the shortest time required for a current of twice the rheobasic strength to stimulate the nerve fiber. Strength-duration curves are useful in differentiating among various types of nerve and muscle tissues on the basis of their excitability. For example, the chronaxie of nerve fibers is considerably shorter than that of skeletal muscle fibers.

Although a stimulus below rheobase is incapable, by itself, of generating a neural impulse, the application of such a stimulus tends to facilitate the fiber. Thus, if a second subthreshold stimulus is applied to a given region in which the local excitatory process produced by a first subthreshold stimulus is present, the second local change will summate with the first. This combined effect (*summation*) may result in an excitation which is sufficiently strong to initiate a neural impulse.

The period of time during which summation can occur is usually not more than 0.5 msec and is called the *period of latent addition* or the *period of temporal summation.*

Following the period of temporal summation, there are four distinct phases in the *excitability cycle* of the neuron. Immediately after a neural impulse has been initiated, there is a short *absolute refractory period* (about 0.5 msec) during which time, that is, the duration of the spike potential, no stimulus applied to the same region, no matter how strong, can set off another impulse. Furthermore, an impulse generated elsewhere along the nerve fiber cannot pass through this area at that time. Both excitability and conductivity are momentarily lost. The absolute refractory period merges into the *relative refractory period,* during which the nerve is returning to normal sensitivity (partial refractoriness). Nerve impulses can be generated during the relative refractory period, but the stimulus must be more intense than usual. When excited, the fiber will respond with a subnormal spike. The third phase of excitability, the *supernormal period,* follows the relative refractory period and corresponds to the time during which a stimulus below the usual threshold value can excite the neuron. Finally, there is the *subnormal period* during which there is a reduction in the excitability of the fiber such that it takes a larger-than-normal stimulus to excite the neuron. Figure 3–15 presents a graphical summary of the various phases of the excitability cycle.

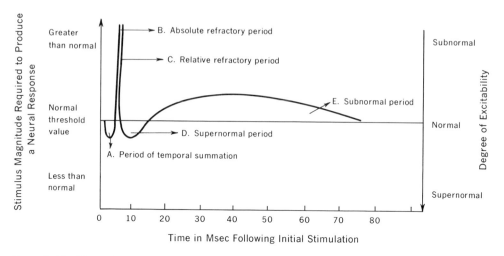

Figure 3–15. The excitability cycle of a nerve fiber expressed directly in terms of the magnitude of the stimulus required to produce an impulse following the initial stimulation of a neuron.

The entire excitability cycle varies from about 80 msec in large fibers to about 1 sec in small fibers, during which time the neuron completely recharges itself. Fibers with the largest diameter recover to about 90 percent of normal in 1 msec. The significance of the excitability cycle lies in the fact that the refractoriness of the neuron limits the number of neural impulses that may be generated per unit of time in a given fiber. More specifically, the absolute refractory time limits the fastest frequency of firing in a single fiber (with nearly full-sized spikes) to about

1000 impulses per sec. This creates certain difficulties for various psychological theories, such as theories of hearing, but we will consider these later on. It should also be pointed out that the all-or-none law is connected logically to the re- fractory periods. Although a strong stimulus does not produce greater neural impulses, it can fire a cell more frequently by acting earlier in the relative re- fractory period. The amount of stimulus energy is correlated with the frequency of neural impulses in a given fiber. Also, not all neurons have the same threshold. A stronger stimulus, for instance, will excite more cells in a given nerve (bundle of fibers). Thus, the repetitive excitation of a given fiber, and the total number of fibers excited in a given nerve, are determined by the magnitude of the stimulus and not by the all-or-none law, which applies to a single impulse in a single nerve fiber.

Changes that take place in the activity patterns of a neuron, however, in- volve more than spike potentials. Neurophysiological activity can be said to arise from two sources: (1) responses to stimuli and (2) spontaneous activity. Spon- taneous activity in nerve fibers may arise from the spontaneous release of chemical secretions (transmitters) at the synaptic junctions or may result from miniature excitatory postsynaptic potentials (small local changes in the neuron). These potentials not only change the excitability of large neurons but are capable of occasionally exciting small neurons with low thresholds. Thus, a single neuron which apparently has no synaptic input may be observed to give typical burst discharges (Strumwasser, 1963).

Any spike pattern which results from a stimulus condition is, therefore, a mix- ture of both types of activity. If the rate of stimulus presentation is sufficiently high, the contribution of spontaneous activity in the spike trains is relatively small; but if the rate is low, with the stimuli spaced temporally far apart, the neural responses contribute less than spontaneous activity. In view of this, it appears that a complete understanding of the behavior of the nervous system must involve the analysis of both the discrete spikes and the graded electrical activity (Gerstein and Kiang, 1960).

The rate at which a neural impulse travels along a fiber, regardless of how it is initiated, is determined by the diameter of the particular fiber. Fibers are generally grouped into three classes depending upon their rates of conduction. The fastest fibers (largest diameters, 1 to 20 microns) conduct at a rate of about 3 to 14 meters per sec; the slowest fibers (unmyelinated) conduct at a rate of less than 2 meters per sec. These values are considerably less than the speed of light, or of electricity, which travels at 300,000,000 meters per sec; they are even slower than the speed of sound, which travels at 331 meters per sec in air. This relative slowness of conduction indicates that it is erroneous to consider the transmission of a neural impulse as analagous to the passage of an electrical current in a copper wire. Neural impulses are propagated by the progressive spreading of *electrochemical*, not merely electrical, changes in specialized tissues.

In the usual situation, neurons are connected functionally in various complex combinations in such a manner that the nerve impulse may be transmitted from one neuron to the next. The critical point of contact where the functional juncture is made is called the *synapse*. Synapses are commonly formed by the terminal arborization of the axon of one neuron interlacing (but not fusing) with the dendritic branches of another neuron. Sometimes the terminal arborization forms a fine network around the cell body of the second neuron. Since each neuron has many dendritic endings and axon collaterals, it is normally connected to a large number of other neurons within the nervous system. This make possible the extremely complex network of neural patterns which underlie all behavior.

While synapses vary widely in their particular structure and arrangement, it is generally agreed that there is no *protoplasmic* continuity between successive neurons. The process by which the nerve impulse is transmitted across a synapse is not as yet completely understood, but it is believed to involve electrical activity similar to that which occurs in the nerve fiber. When the nerve impulse reaches the endings of the axon, the potential difference across the synapse may be sufficient to depolarize the membrane of the next neuron, thus generating a wave of negativity which is propagated sucessively through other neurons. Despite the lack of a clear explanation of synaptic transmission, there are certain synaptic phenomena which have been substantiated by experimental evidence. One of these, and probably the most important in terms of integrated neural activity, is the *functional polarity* existing at the synaptic junction. This condition is such that the nerve impulse passes in only one direction—from the axon of one neuron to the dendrite or to the cell body of the next neuron. The synapse acts like a "one-way street" which determines the direction of transmission of the nerve impulse and permits only unidirectional conduction.

Another important phenomenon is that of *synaptic blocking*. Although a nerve fiber may be capable of conducting impulses, there are several conditions in which blockage may occur at the synapse. After cardiac arrest, for example, synaptic transmission fails much more quickly than neural excitability. The effectiveness of general anesthetic agents are due primarily to their ability to block the transmission of the neural impulse at the synapse. Although the excitability of nerve trunks is not impaired under anesthesia, reflex movements and sensations are abolished.

Finally, the amount of synaptic resistance can be altered by nerve impulses to produce *inhibition* or *facilitation* (Ruch, Patton, Woodbury, and Towe, 1961). *Inhibition* is the elimination of a response through *chemical hyperpolarization* which tends to reduce the excitability of the postsynaptic neuron or to prevent it from firing after the afferent nerve impulse has reached the synapse. *Facilitation* refers to the phenomenon in which the nerve impulses from two or more afferent sources tend to produce firing in the postsynaptic neuron due to the summation of the excitatory processes at two synapses when the sources are activated simultaneously. Facilitation involves the convergence of afferent sources; without this consequence, the afferent impulses from a single source would be inadequate for exciting the postsynaptic neuron under the conditions existing at the moment. The processes of inhibition and facilitation are important in effecting the integration of bodily activities, such as arm movements which involve the *reciprocal innervation* of bicep and tricep muscles. When the bicep muscles contract, the antagonistic tricep muscles must relax. This is achieved by facilitating the flow of nerve impulses to the biceps and simultaneously inhibiting the flow to the triceps. The afferent nerve volleys effect this control by simultaneously initiating contraction in one group of muscles while inhibiting the contraction of the opposing muscles.

The Peripheral Nervous System

In an earlier section of this chapter, we were introduced to the general schema. whereby the behavioral adjustment of an organism was viewed as being dependent upon the integrated activity of the nervous system. The receptors, connectors, and effectors were presented as subclassifications of the nervous system, each having its own particular functional properties. We then studied in more detail the manner in which the basic structural and functional unit of the nervous system, that is, the neuron, was excited and propagated a nerve impulse. Some attention was also given to the processes involved in transmitting the nerve impulse from one neuron to another across the synaptic junction. Now we need to consider the gross anatomy of the human nervous system in order to understand how nerve impulses are transmitted, directly or indirectly, from receptors to effectors. Since a detailed study of the anatomy and physiology of man's receptor mechanisms at this point would tend to obscure the gross structural features of neural transmission, we will cover that topic in the next chapter. Let us for the moment accept the fact that man possesses specialized receptors or mechanisms which respond to different types of physical energy in the environment and which initiate nerve impulses that are subsequently transmitted through certain channels within the nervous system. Our problem then is to discover the neural pathways which exist between the receptors and effectors.

One way to begin is to classify the conductive pathways into three major groups: *afferent, internuncial,* and *efferent.* The *afferent* neurons are those which conduct impulses toward the central nervous system (CNS), that is, the brain and the spinal cord. These are often called sensory nerve fibers since they are excited by the activities of the receptor cells. Within the CNS, these fibers transmit nerve impulses from lower to higher centers of neural integration. The *internuncial* cells are interneurons which connect one part of the CNS to another; these are links which are not specifically characterized by upward or downward transmission, although this is only relatively true. The *efferent* neurons are those which conduct impulses within the CNS from higher to lower centers of integration. Outside the CNS, these neurons conduct impulses to the effectors, that is, to the muscles and glands, and accordingly are often referred to as motor neurons.

For purposes of discussion, the cells of the human nervous system may be grouped into two major subsystems: the *central nervous system* (CNS), which we have already specified as the brain and spinal cord, and the *peripheral nervous system,* which consists of all the ganglia (groups of cell bodies) and nerves (bundles of nerve fibers) outside the CNS. The CNS and the peripheral nervous system are not functionally distinct systems, but are conventionally designated as separate systems to facilitate the exposition of the gross anatomy of nerves. The division of the human nervous system into central and peripheral components is based upon the location of the particular nerves, and not upon their direction of conduction.

The peripheral nervous system may be divided into three major parts: the *spinal* nerves and their peripheral branches, the twelve *cranial* nerves, and the *peripheral* portion of the *autonomic nervous system* (ANS) which innervates the internal organs of the body. The *spinal nerves* are arranged in a regular order along the spinal cord and are classified according to the body regions in which they emerge. There are approximately 31 pairs of spinal nerves in man; these are distributed among the five portions of the spinal cord as shown in Table 3–1.

Table 3–1   Classification of the Spinal Nerves in Man

Name	Pairs Included	Number	Location along Spinal Cord
Cervical	1 through 8	8	Neck
Thoracic	9 through 20	12	Chest
Lumbar	21 through 25	5	Loin
Sacral	26 through 30	5	Sacrum
Coccygeal	31	1	Coccyx
	Total Number:	31 pairs	

The spinal nerves enter and leave the cord through lateral openings (*intervertebral foramina*) between the *spinal vertebrae* (the irregularly shaped bones which are joined to form a long, bony column). Each spinal nerve has two roots which are formed by the division of the common nerve trunk (mixed spinal nerve) as it enters the vertebral column. The common nerve trunk contains both afferent and efferent fibers. This is shown diagrammatically in Figure 3-16 which presents a transverse section of the spinal cord. The H shaped segment in the interior of the

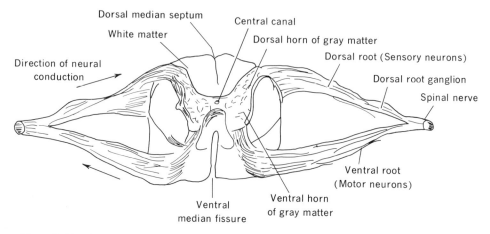

Figure 3–16. A diagrammatic representation of a transverse section of the spinal cord, showing the roots of spinal nerves and the arrangement of white and gray matter.

cord consists of gray matter (cell bodies of neurons) and is surrounded by white matter (nerve fibers covered with a myelin sheath). In general, the dorsal root (toward the back of the cord) contains sensory (afferent) fibers, while the ventral root (toward the abdomen) contains motor (efferent) fibers. Neural impulses in the spinal nerves, therefore, are propagated in a *dorsal-ventral* direction. This is known as the *principle of roots*.

After the dorsal and ventral roots of the peripheral nerves unite and emerge from the intervertebral foramen as spinal nerves, each spinal nerve divides into four primary branches: the dorsal ramus, the ventral ramus, the meningeal ramus, and the ramus communicans. These rami supply the muscles and skin of the body, the body wall, the extremities, and other body parts according to certain patterns of neural distribution. The dorsal and ventral rami divide into cutaneous (superficial) and muscular (deep peripheral) nerve trunks. These branch repeatedly and become progressively smaller as they extend peripherally. Ultimately, they divide into individual nerve fibers which terminate in their respective receptors or effectors.

The sensory afferent roots of the human spinal nerves serve most parts of the body, except the face. Impulses are received by the spinal nerves from various types of receptors which are distributed throughout relatively small areas of the body called *dermatomes*. Each dermatome contains tactual, thermal, and pain receptors in the skin, certain receptors in the blood vessels, pressure and pain receptors in the muscles, tendons, and joints, and some internal receptors in the digestive tract and body cavities. The boundaries of the dermatomes are not precisely defined, with each zone being served by segments of as many as three spinal nerves. Thus, the loss of a spinal nerve does not destroy sensitivity in a given zone; it merely reduces the sensory potentiality in that segment of the body.

The sensory afferent roots of the human spinal nerves serve most parts of the and all other striated muscles of the body, except some of those in the head and neck. The posterior primary branches (dorsal ramus) supply the muscles in the neck which, for example, bend the neck and turn the head from side to side. Most muscles are supplied by two or more spinal nerves. Like the skin areas, in which severing the posterior root of a single spinal nerve does not produce complete *anesthesia*, the overlapping innervation of muscles prevents complete paralysis (*areflexia*) of the musculature when the ventral root of a spinal nerve is severed.

The second major portion of the peripheral nervous system consists of the *cranial nerves*. These are nerves which have their origin in the brain itself. They are arranged in twelve pairs; but, unlike the spinal nerves, they are not distributed segmentally. Also, they do not have distinct posterior and anterior roots. Some of the cranial nerves primarily include afferent (sensory) fibers (I, II, VIII), while others (III, IV, VI, VII, XI, XII) primarily include efferent (motor) fibers. Some, like the spinal nerves, consist of both afferent and efferent components (V, IX, X). Table 3–2 presents a summary of the cranial nerves, including their names, their conventional number, their place of origin, and their primary afferent and efferent functions. The origin of the cranial nerves and the locus of the sensory

Table 3-2   The Cranial Nerves of Man

No.	Name	Origin in Brain	Afferent (Sensory) Innervation	Efferent (Motor) Innervation
I	Olfactory	Olfactory bulb	Mucosa of nose	(None)
II	Optic	Diencephalon	Retina of eye	(None)
III	Oculomotor	Midbrain	Eye muscles (except two)	Eye muscles (except two)
IV	Trochlear	Midbrain	Superior oblique eye muscle	Superior oblique eye muscle
V	Trigeminal	Pons	Skin and deep tissues of head and face	Chewing muscles
VI	Abducens	Pons	Lateral rectus eye muscle	Lateral rectus eye muscle
VII	Facial	Medulla	Taste buds of anterior 2/3 of tongue	Facial muscles and salivary glands
VIII	Acoustic	Medulla	Inner ear and semicircular canals	(None)
IX	Glossopharyngeal	Medulla	Throat, rear of tongue, and taste buds on posterior 1/3 of tongue	Swallowing muscles and one salivary gland
X	Vagus	Medulla	Thoracic and abdominal viscera, taste buds on epiglottis, skin of external ear	Muscles of heart and other viscera, speech, and swallowing
XI	Spinal Accessory	Medulla	(None)	Viscera (via vagus), throat and larynx, neck and shoulder muscles
XII	Hypoglossal	Medulla	Tongue muscles	Tongue muscles

endings will become more meaningful after the details of the receptor organs have been studied in the next chapter.

The final division of the peripheral nervous system is the *peripheral* portion of the *autonomic nervous system* (ANS). This consists of special nerves which supply the visceral structures of the body, such as the heart, lungs, stomach, adrenal glands, and urinary bladder. Actually, the peripheral portion of the ANS is comprised of some branches of the cranial nerves and certain branches of the spinal nerves which are distributed to the internal organs of the body. They also innervate most of the glands and blood vessels. The designation of the ANS is, therefore, merely another way of classifying the structures of the human nervous system.

In this presentation, we have divided the entire nervous system into its central and peripheral components, but another scheme of classification that is often used is to deal with the bodily parts which are innervated by particular nerves. This results in the distinction between the *somatic* and *autonomic* nervous systems, each with its central and peripheral components. The somatic nervous system, according to this division, includes all those parts of the nervous system (central and peripheral) which transmit impulses from the receptor organs, integrate them in the brain, and deliver motor impulses to the striated musculature of the limbs and body. The autonomic nervous system includes all those parts of the nervous system (central and peripheral) which innervate the cardiac muscles, the smooth muscles of the intestines, urogenital tract, and blood vessels, and certain endocrine glands. In general, the somatic nervous system mediates organismic adjustments to the *external* environment; the autonomic nervous system mediates adjustments to the *internal environment*. Such a division of function, however, is only relatively true since the two mechanisms are thoroughly interrelated with the responses of one affecting the responses of the other. This is evidenced in the field of psychosomatic medicine, which recognizes that bodily processes, such as digestion and heart action, may be influenced by the activities of the central nervous system in the form of worries and anxieties.

The somatic nervous system and the autonomic nervous system differ both functionally and anatomically. (1) The somatic nervous system includes both sensory and motor components, while the ANS is considered to be primarily a motor system, even though there are some sensory fibers in the viscera. (2) The somatic nervous system has all its synapses, except for the retina and the olfactory bulb, within the CNS, while the synapses and ganglia of the ANS lie outside the CNS. (3) The somatic nervous system innervates the striated muscles on the peripheral parts of the body, whereas the ANS innervates the glands and smooth muscle cells of the viscera and blood vessels.

The ANS is divided conventionally into two parts: the *sympathetic nervous system* (SNS) and the *parasympathetic nervous system* (PNS). The SNS leaves the central portion of the spinal cord, that is, in the thoracic and upper lumbar regions, with the axons of the autonomic cells passing out the ventral roots, together with the axons of the somatic motor nerves. A short distance outside the spinal cord, the sympathetic axons separate from the somatic axons and form the autonomic branch which enters a sympathetic ganglion. In man, there are 22 sympathetic ganglia which are arranged in a fairly regular order along the spinal cord. This arrangement of ganglia is called the *ganglionic chord* or the *sympathetic chain*. In each ganglion, the axon of the first neuron (*preganglionic fiber*) synapses with the dendrite of the second neuron (*post-ganglionic fiber*). The second neuron has its cell body within the ganglion and its axon entends to the organ innervated. There are also fibers passing from one ganglion to the next. The sympathetic chain innervates all visceral organs below the heart, including the liver, bladder, the adrenal glands, the stomach, the intenstines, and the urogenital mechanisms.

The PNS consists of fibers originating in the brain and emerging via the third, seventh, ninth, and especially the tenth, cranial nerves (cranial autonomic system; cranial division of the parasympathetic nervous system), and of fibers originating in the lower (sacral) region of the spinal cord (sacral autonomic system; sacral division of the parasympathetic nervous system). Unlike the SNS, the PNS has no parasympathetic chain, but does have numerous scattered ganglia which are located in or near the organs which are innervated. The cranial portion of the PNS serves the heart, the brain, and the head, including the iris of the eye and the salivary glands. The sacral portion of the PNS serves the rectum, the bladder, the colon, and the arteries of the genital organs.

Together, the SNS and PNS mediate most of the functions of the visceral organs in vertebrate animals. Each organ receives a double set of fibers, one from each division of the ANS. Impulses from the sympathetic and parasympathetic nerves always have antagonistic effects on the organ innervated. In general, the SNS mobilizes the activities of the body for work or to meet special emergencies; the PNS conserves the resources of the body. For example, the action of the PNS weakens and slows the heartbeat, while that of the SNS strengthens and accelerates the heartbeat. The SNS and PNS ordinarily function in a coordinated manner and thereby maintain a fairly stable equilibrium in the internal environment of the organism under a wide variety of working and resting conditions. The ANS is especially important in the mediation of emotional behavior and its functioning must be understood in order to explain the changes in response which occur in situations involving noxious or exciting stimuli.

The Central Nervous System:
The Brain and Spinal Cord

The central nervous system contains those nerves and associated structures which function primarily in the integration of organismic activity. This integration is achieved through the complex neural activity of the brain and spinal cord which, in general, can be described in terms similar to those used in the discussion of the neuron and its functions. However, the brain contains about half of the total number of neurons in the human body and these are connected in such a complicated manner that the functioning of the CNS cannot at the present time be described on the basis of individual, neuronal activity. There are, nevertheless, certain groups of neurons which form central structures that function in such a consistent manner that their contributions to neural organization are quite well known. Hence, we shall proceed to describe the central nervous system in terms of these larger structures, recognizing the fact that the neuron is still the basic structural and functional unit, without which the larger segment would not be able to participate in behavioral activities.

As we have already learned from the preceding section, the neurons of the human body may be classified as possessing afferent, internuncial, or efferent nerve fibers. By way of a crude analogy, we might conceptualize the CNS as an electronic communication center into which information about the external and internal environment may be sent via the afferent portion of the peripheral nervous system. This information is coded in neural terms and is the result of energy changes in the environment which act upon the organism's receptor mechanisms or bodily tissues. When this information is received, it is processed automatically. The neural inputs are integrated and coordinated through internal links (internuncial neurons) within the CNS, such that appropriate outgoing messages (efferent impulses) are transmitted via the efferent portion of the peripheral nervous system to the proper muscles and glands of the body. This is certainly a highly oversimplified, and an inadequate, sketch of the events which occur in the integration of neural activity; but, the analogy is intended only to point out that there are three major elements in the functioning of the human nervous system: afferent inputs, associative or integrative processes, and efferent outputs.

The CNS in man is located in the bony framework provided by the skull and spinal column. Lying within the bony framework, the CNS is covered by three membranes (*meninges*): (1) the tough *dura mater* which lies nearest the bone and attaches to the skull, (2) the *arachnoid* which is the middle layer and forms a delicate interconnecting network between the dura mater and (3) the *pia mater*. The pia mater contains numerous blood vessels and adheres closely to the brain and spinal cord.

The space between the arachnoid and pia mater (subarachnoid space) is filled with the clear, watery cerebrospinal fluid which engulfs the entire CNS, including both the brain and the spinal cord. The normal volume of fluid in the adult male varies from 100 to 500 cc; the fluid has a specific gravity of 1.004 to 1.006 and a normal pressure of 10 to 20 mm of mercury when the body is in the horizontal position. In the study of pathological conditions affecting the CNS, the pressure exerted by the cerebrospinal fluid may be measured on a *manometer* attached to a hypodermic needle. The needle is inserted into the subarachnoid space in the lumbar region of the spinal cord. Changes in pressure are noted and are used for diagnostic purposes, such as detecting tumors which may raise the intracranial pressure to 40 mm of mercury or higher. The cerebrospinal fluid may also be withdrawn through the needle and examined for bacteria, cells, or unusual chemical compounds.

When the meninges are removed, the brain is seen to be extensively folded (*convoluted*) and partially divided into two halves (*cerebral hemispheres*). The cerebral hemispheres consist of two major parts: (1) the *cerebral cortex* which is the outer gray matter composed of cell bodies and (2) the *inner white matter* which is composed of conducting nerve fibers. The most prominent portion of white matter is the *corpus callosum;* this is made up of bands of nerve tissue (*commissural fibers*) connecting the cortices of the two cerebral hemispheres. The remaining white matter consists of *association* fibers which pass from one part of the cortex to another within the same hemisphere and assist in the integration of cortical activities. Functionally, probably the most important neurons in the cortex are the afferent and efferent *projection* fibers. These are the fibers by which impulses enter the cortex (*afferent* projection fibers) from the thalamus, and other subcortical centers, and leave the cortex (*efferent* projection fibers) by downward projections to various subcortical centers such as the thalamus, midbrain, or ventral cells of the spinal cord.

The partial separation of the right and left hemispheres is formed by a deep depression (*fissure*) somewhat similar to those which separate the functionally different areas (*lobes*) within each hemisphere. In Figure 3-17, the four major lobes of the cerebral cortex (*frontal, parietal, temporal* and *occipital*) are readily visible, together with the names of the landmarks defining each lobe. In the next section, the functional significance of each of these lobes will be considered.

The *corpus callosum* and the portion of the brain known as the *cerebellum* can be seen in Figure 3-18. This photograph shows other structures which are revealed when a cross-sectioning of the brain is made in the *median sagittal plane* (between the right and left hemispheres). The cerebellum, normally separated from the hemispheres by a fissure containing a fold of dura mater, has important functions in the coordination of bodily movements.

Many of the structures of significance in the study of the human sensory processes can be seen only after the brain is removed from the cranial cavity. The average volume of the brain is about 1200 to 1500 cc. Figure 3-19 presents a photograph of the base of the human brain showing the *cerebellum,* the *medulla oblongata,* the *temperal* and *frontal* lobes, some of the cranial nerves, and certain other major structures which form part of the brain stem.

A median section through the cerebellum and brain stem may be seen by referring to Figure 3-19. At the lower end of the brain stem, which is a continuation of the spinal cord, is located the *medulla oblongata.* This structure is similar to the cord and serves in neural conduction and reflex coordinations, including breathing and heartbeat. On the ventral side of the brain stem is the *pons,* or bridge, comprised in part of a mass of fibers crossing from one side of the cerebellum to the other. The next higher structure is the *midbrain,* with two pairs of small swellings on its dorsal surface called the *superior colliculi* and the *inferior colliculi.* The former function as primitive visual centers, while the latter function as lower centers for hearing. At the upper end of the brain stem is the *diencephalon.* This consists of the *hypothalamus* on the ventral side and the *thalamus,* on the dorsal side. The hypothalamus and its associated structures are connected functionally to the peripheral autonomic system. The thalamus, in addition to its other functions, provides a sensory relay station (region of synaptic connections) for all the human senses (except olfaction). Each of the other senses has special nuclei in the thalamus from which the afferent and efferent projection fibers pass, respectively, to and from the cerebral cortex.

The *spinal cord,* the final portion of the CNS to be discussed, lies within the vertebral canal and is surrounded by the meninges. The cord extends for a distance of about 45 cm in adult males, about 42 cm in adult females, and passes from the medulla oblongata through a large opening in the base of the skull (*foramen magnum*) to the lower border of the first lumbar vertebra. Although the spinal cord does not occupy the entire length of the spinal canal, the meninges and subarachnoid space continue downward into the sacral canal. The cord is approximately oval in cross-section, but varies in diameter in certain places due to the connec-

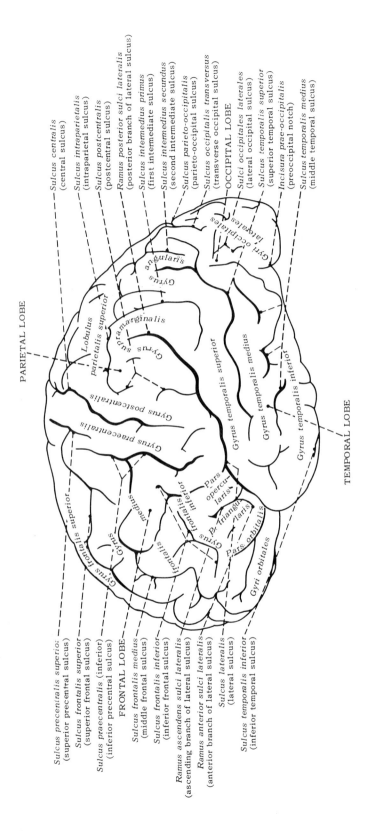

Figure 3-17. The lateral surface of the left cerebral hemisphere of the brain showing the four lobes and the principal fissures which divide them, together with other prominent landmarks. (After Wolf-Heidegger, Atlas of systematic anatomy, Vol. III, New York: Hafner Publishing Company, Inc., 1962. Reprinted with permission of the publisher.)

Labels around the figure:

PARIETAL LOBE

FRONTAL LOBE

TEMPORAL LOBE

OCCIPITAL LOBE

Sulcus centralis (central sulcus)

Sulcus intraparietalis (intraparietal sulcus)

Sulcus postcentralis (postcentral sulcus)

Ramus posterior sulci lateralis (posterior branch of lateral sulcus)

Sulcus intermedius primus (first intermediate sulcus)

Sulcus intermedius secundus (second intermediate sulcus)

Sulcus parieto-occipitalis (parieto-occipital sulcus)

Sulcus occipitalis transversus (transverse occipital sulcus)

Sulci occipitales laterales (lateral occipital sulcus)

Sulcus temporalis superior (superior temporal sulcus)

Incisura prae-occipitalis (preoccipital notch)

Sulcus temporalis medius (middle temporal sulcus)

Sulcus precentralis superior (superior precentral sulcus)

Sulcus frontalis superior (superior frontal sulcus)

Sulcus praecentralis (inferior) (inferior precentral sulcus)

Sulcus frontalis medius (middle frontal sulcus)

Sulcus frontalis inferior (inferior frontal sulcus)

Ramus ascendens sulci lateralis (ascending branch of lateral sulcus)

Ramus anterior sulci lateralis (anterior branch of lateral sulcus)

Sulcus lateralis (lateral sulcus)

Sulcus temporalis inferior (inferior temporal sulcus)

angularis

Gyrus

Lobulus parietalis superior

Gyrus supramarginalis

Gyrus postcentralis

Gyrus praecentralis

Gyrus frontalis superior

Gyrus frontalis medius

Gyrus frontalis inferior

Pars opercularis

P. Triangularis

Pars orbitalis

Gyri orbitales

Gyrus temporalis superior

Gyrus temporalis medius

Gyrus temporalis inferior

Gyri occipitales laterales

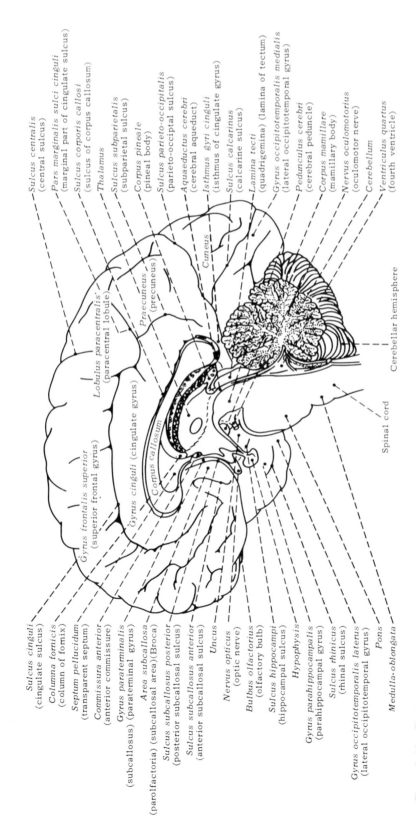

Sulcus centralis
(central sulcus)

Pars marginalis sulci cinguli
(marginal part of cingulate sulcus)

Sulcus corporis callosi
(sulcus of corpus callosum)

Thalamus

Sulcus subparietalis
(subparietal sulcus)

Corpus pineale
(pineal body)

Sulcus parieto-occipitalis
(parieto-occipital sulcus)

Aquaeductus cerebri
(cerebral aqueduct)

Isthmus gyri cinguli
(isthmus of cingulate gyrus)

Sulcus calcarinus
(calcarine sulcus)

Lamina tecti
(quadrigemina) (lamina of tectum)

Gyrus occipitotemporalis medialis
(lateral occipitotemporal gyrus)

Pedunculus cerebri
(cerebral peduncle)

Corpus mamillare
(mamillary body)

Nervus oculomotorius
(oculomotor nerve)

Cerebellum

Ventriculus quartus
(fourth ventricle)

Cuneus

Praecuneus
(precuneus)

Lobulus paracentralis
(paracentral lobule)

Gyrus frontalis superior
(superior frontal gyrus)

Gyrus cinguli (cingulate gyrus)

Corpus callosum

Cerebellar hemisphere

Spinal cord

Sulcus cinguli
(cingulate sulcus)

Columna fornicis
(column of fornix)

Septum pellucidum
(transparent septum)

Commissura anterior
(anterior commissure)

Gyrus paraterminalis
(paraterminal gyrus)

Area subcallosa
(parolfactoria) (subcallosal area) (Broca)

Sulcus subcallosus posterior
(posterior subcallosal sulcus)

Sulcus subcallosus anterior
(anterior subcallosal sulcus)

Uncus

Nervus opticus
(optic nerve)

Bulbus olfactorius
(olfactory bulb)

Sulcus hippocampi
(hippocampal sulcus)

Hypophysis

Gyrus parahippocampalis
(parahippocampal gyrus)

Sulcus rhinicus
(rhinal sulcus)

Gyrus occipitotemporalis lateralis
(lateral occipitotemporal gyrus)

Pons

Medulla-oblongata

Figure 3–18. The human brain showing some of the structures that are visible when the brain is sectioned in the median sagittal plane. (After Wolf-Heidegger, Atlas of systematic human anatomy, Vol. III, New York: Hafner Publishing Company, Inc., 1962. Reprinted with permission of the publisher.)

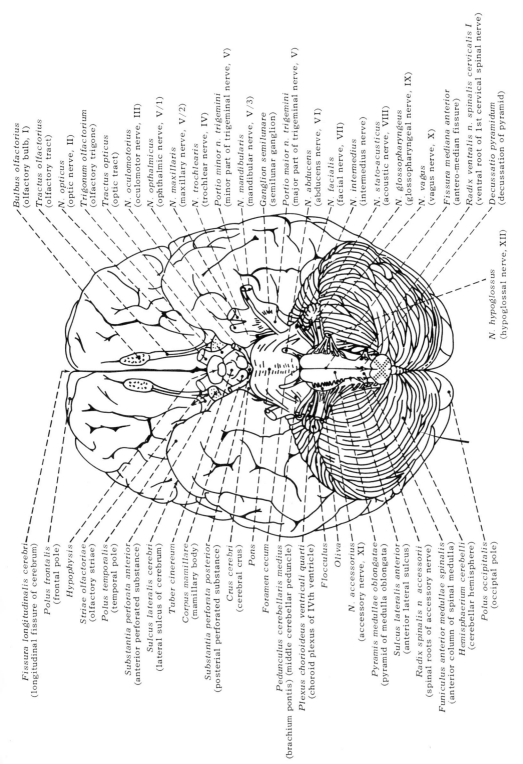

Fissura longitudinalis cerebri (longitudinal fissure of cerebrum)
Polus frontalis (frontal pole)
Hypophysis
Striae olfactoriae (olfactory striae)
Polus temporalis (temporal pole)
Substantia perforata anterior (anterior perforated substance)
Sulcus lateralis cerebri (lateral sulcus of cerebrum)
Tuber cinereum
Corpus mamillare (mamillary body)
Substantia perforata posterior (posterior perforated substance)
Crus cerebri (cerebral crus)
Pons
Foramen cecum
Pedunculus cerebellaris medius (brachium pontis) (middle cerebellar peduncle)
Plexus chorioideus ventriculi quarti (choroid plexus of IVth ventricle)
Flocculus
Oliva
N. accessorius (accessory nerve, XI)
Radix spinalis n. accessorii (spinal roots of accessory nerve)
Pyramis medullae oblongatae (pyramid of medulla oblongata)
Sulcus lateralis anterior (anterior lateral sulcus)
Funiculus anterior medullae spinalis (anterior column of spinal medulla)
Hemisphaerium cerebelli (cerebellar hemisphere)
Polus occipitalis (occipital pole)

Bulbus olfactorius (olfactory bulb, I)
Tractus olfactorius (olfactory tract)
N. opticus (optic nerve, II)
Trigonum olfactorium (olfactory trigone)
Tractus opticus (optic tract)
N. oculomotorius (oculomotor nerve, III)
N. ophthalmicus (ophthalmic nerve, V/1)
N. maxillaris (maxillary nerve, V/2)
N. trochlearis (trochlear nerve, IV)
Portio minor n. trigemini (minor part of trigeminal nerve, V)
N. mandibularis (mandibular nerve, V/3)
Ganglion semilunare (semilunar ganglion)
Portio maior n. trigemini (major part of trigeminal nerve, V)
N. abducens (abducens nerve, VI)
N. facialis (facial nerve, VII)
N. intermedius (intermedius nerve)
N. stato-acusticus (acoustic nerve, VIII)
N. glossopharyngeus (glossopharyngeal nerve, IX)
N. vagus (vagus nerve, X)
Fissura mediana anterior (antero-median fissure)
Radix ventralis n. spinalis cervicalis I (ventral root of 1st cervical spinal nerve)
Decussatio pyramidum (decussation of pyramid)

N. hypoglossus (hypoglossal nerve, XII)

Figure 3-19. A ventral view of the brain showing some of the cranial nerves and other major structures. (After Wolf-Heidegger, *Atlas of systematic human anatomy*, Vol. III, New York: Hafner Publishing Company, Inc., 1962. Reprinted with permission of the publisher.)

124

tions formed by the spinal nerves. On the dorsal side of the exposed spinal cord can be seen a slight longitudinal groove (*dorsal median septum*) beside which run several small arteries and veins. The ventral midline of the cord is formed by a longitudinal fissure (*ventral median fissure*) which contains a small artery and a few veins.

The nerve tissues extend laterally on both sides of the cord from the dorsal and ventral roots of the spinal nerves. These nerves and a transverse section of the spinal cord were presented diagrammatically in Figure 3-16. In addition to the spinal nerves, the spinal cord contains many *spinospinal,* or *propriospinal,* fibers which originate and terminate within the cord. These connect various levels of the cord and provide for coordinated activity, as in reflex behavior. In some types of movement patterns like stepping or walking, the normal functioning of the spinal cord depends upon the presence of certain activities in higher neural centers. While these patterns involve spinal mechanisms, they cannot be generated autonomously by the spinal cord.

The Muscles as Effector Mechanisms

Types of Muscle Cells

As we indicated in the discussion of man as an integrated organism, the means by which an organism responds to the events of the physical environment are through its effector mechanisms, primarily the muscles. Muscles may be divided into three main types: (1) *skeletal* or *striated,* (2) *cardiac* or *cross-striated,* and (3) *smooth* or *nonstriated.* The skeletal muscles are attached to bones by tendons and, when stimulated, act to move the bones with respect to each other. Skeletal muscles vary considerably in size and shape, but all are similar in that a *muscle fiber* forms the basic structural unit. Each fiber or muscle cell has many nuclei along its sides and may extend for many millimeters, although its diameter is only a few microns. The differences in muscle size are due to the number and size of the individual muscle fibers which, collectively, comprise the muscle. The cytoplasm within a muscle cell is called sacroplasm; myofibrils made up of alternating light and dark segments run lengthwise in the cell and give the cell its characteristic striated appearance. Numerous capillaries of the circulatory system are located between the skeletal muscle fibers.

Skeletal muscles are innervated by the axons of motor neurons which leave the spinal cord and brain stem through the ventral roots of the cord or through certain cranial nerves. The hundreds of axons which enter a muscle subdivide into numerous tiny branches, each terminating in a single muscle fiber at the *motor end plate* or *myoneural junction.* The nerve cell, its axon, and the associated muscle fibers (whether only a few or several hundred) form a *motor unit.* Whenever a nerve impulse travels along a given axon, all of the muscle fibers in the corresponding motor unit are excited. The number of motor units per muscle varies for different body members. In the thumb muscles, there are many units with only a few fibers per unit; in the leg muscles, there are fewer motor units with a large number of fibers per unit. The precision of the movement of different body parts depends upon the underlying number of motor units and their composition. A muscle consisting of many motor units with few fibers per unit is capable of generating extremely fine and accurate movements.

As in the case of nerve fibers, the stimulation of skeletal muscle fibers produces energy changes which are accompanied by electrical activity and corresponding refractory periods. All muscle fibers contract when stimulated, but not at the same rate. Those which contract rapidly fatigue more easily than those which contract more slowly. One or both types of fibers may be found in the same muscle. The contraction of skeletal muscles is entirely and directly mediated by the reflex and "voluntary" activity of the central nervous system. When skeletal muscles are denervated, they lose their tone and gradually atrophy.

The *cardiac* or *cross-striated* muscle fibers constitute the greater portion of the heart. Again, the fibers are multinucleated with cross-striations as in skeletal muscle. One of the unique features of the heart is that with stimulation large parts of it contract almost simultaneously. This serves to exert pressure and is necessary for the efficient expulsion of the blood contained within the heart. Cardiac muscle thus differs from skeletal muscle since it is both *automatic*—the tissue has an intrinsic ability to generate spontaneous and rhythmical impulses—and a *functional syncytium,* that is, the whole tissue responds electrically like a single large cell. However, the cells of the heart are surrounded by a distinct membrane so that there is no anatomical continuity between cells. The basis of the functional syncytium is probably related to the close approximation of the cells and to their large areas of contact.

Regardless of the mechanism or process underlying the functional syncytium, the spread of neural activity in the heart differs from that of nerve or skeletal muscle fibers. In nerve fibers, the activity travels in one direction; in syncytial tissues the spread of activity is two- or three-dimensional. Innervation of the heart is supplied by both divisions of the autonomic nervous system, with the parasympathetic fibers being carried via the vagus nerve. Increased activity of the sympathetic division accelerates the rate of heartbeat. Although heart rate is regulated by the nervous activity of the ANS, cardiac contractions are, as indicated, intrinsically rhythmic and can occur synchronously and spontaneously even when the heart is denervated; cardiac fibers contract at regular intervals even in the embryo before they receive their nerve supply.

The *smooth* or *nonstriated* muscle cells are of two kinds: (1) *visceral* smooth muscle which is found in the walls of the gastrointestinal and genitourinary tracts, and (2) *motor-unit* smooth muscle which is found in certain structures requiring direct neural control, such as in the intrinsic muscles of the eye. Smooth muscle cells differ from striated muscle cells due to their lack of cross-striations and their relatively slow period of contraction. In most organs, the smooth muscle cells are innervated by both divisions of the ANS, but continue to function even though their nerve supply is completely severed. In such cases, as in the glands, other means of excitation, for example, hormones, may serve to initiate activity.

Chapter, 4

HUMAN
RECEPTOR SYSTEMS

Orientation

In the preceding chapter we considered the major divisions of the human nervous system, both central and peripheral. We learned about the nature of the neural impulse and the various paths by which these impulses could enter and leave the brain. One very important aspect of neural activity remains to be discussed. We must review the structures characterizing the human receptor organs in order to discover how physical energy (stimuli) acting upon these structures can set off the chain of events that may ultimately lead to a behavioral response. The source of stimulation may be present in either the external or internal environment but, as we have seen in Chapter 2, there are only four primary forms of energy which can serve as adequate stimuli: (1) electromagnetic radiation, including photic effects, (2) mechanical energy, including vibratory, pressure, and acoustic effects, (3) chemical energy, in solid, liquid, or gaseous form, and (4) thermal energy, which might properly be considered as a special part of the electromagnetic energy spectrum. In man, there are specialized structures biologically adapted to respond to each of these various forms of energy. In this chapter we shall consider what these organs of reception are, how they transform the stimulus energy into the electrochemical form of neural impulses, and how these impulses travel along certain neural pathways, pass through various centers of neural integration, and ultimately arrive at specific projection or localization areas in the brain.

The Receptor System for Photic Energy

Photic energy, as defined in Chapter 2, consists of the visible portion of the electromagnetic spectrum, with radiation wavelengths varying from about 400 to 700 mμ. The receptor organ for this type of energy is the eye. The eye, together with its peripheral conductive mechanism and its central projective mechanism, forms the basis for the sense of vision.

There are three main physiological features of the eye upon which normal vision, in part, depends: (1) the set of *extrinsic muscles* that move the eyeball in three directions; (2) the internal structure of the eyeball that serves as an *optical system* for focusing light rays; and (3) the *receptor cells* in the innermost part of the eye that generate nerve impulses when acted upon by light. Each of these will be considered in turn, beginning with the conductive and central mechanisms of vision.

As shown in Figure 4-1, each eye is provided with a set of six extrinsic muscles

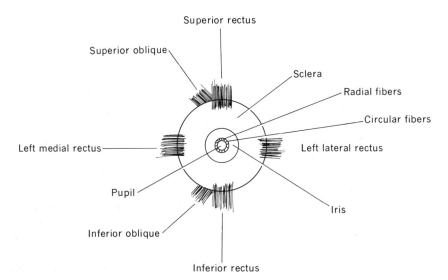

Figure 4–1. A front view of the left human eye, showing the six extrinsic muscles and certain optical structures.

attached at one end to the bony eye socket and at the other end to the tissues of the eyeball. These muscles are able to move the eyeball to the left or right (by means of the lateral rectus and medial rectus muscles), up or down (by means of the superior and inferior rectus muscles), and slightly rotating around a horizontal axis (by means of the superior and inferior oblique muscles acting, respectively, with the inferior and superior recti). The *reciprocal innervation* of the muscles occurs in such a manner that the two eyes are normally moved simultaneously and by the same amount. Thus, the two eyes maintain *conjugate* positions at all times; that is, they always point together to the same portion of an object, not to some part nearer or farther away. This provides a single perception of the object viewed; when the object is near, the eyes rotate inward (*converge*) to provide this single perception. The extent to which the two eyes must converge to provide a single view will depend, in part, upon the distance between the object and the viewer. The closer the object, the greater the degree of convergence that will be required. When direct muscular effort is inadequate to bring the visual axes to the same point of convergence due to improper coordination of the eye muscles, *strabismus* (squint) is said to exist. If the target is quite distant, that is, beyond 30 feet, the visual axes of the eyes should be essentially parallel. If they are not, it indicates the presence of muscular imbalance and is designated as *heterophoria*. Under normal conditions, even when the eyes are resting passively, a certain amount of tonic convergence is present. Actually the two eyes do not see the same object in exactly the same way since each eye views the object from a slightly different angle; this is due to the interpupillary separation between the two eyes, about 65 mm. Consequently, two views of the same object are generated that serve as sensory cues for *binocular depth perception*. Although it was classically believed that the afferent nerve impulses passing from the extrinsic muscles to the brain contributed to this process, there is some evidence that tends to refute this position.

The primary structure for vision is the eyeball, which is schematically presented in Figure 4-2. The outer portion of the eyeball consists of an approximately spherical shell of connective tissue known as the "white" of the eye (*sclera*). It is about 22 mm in diameter, about 1 mm in thickness, and merges at the front of the eye into the transparent *cornea*. The cornea has a radius of curvature of approximately 8 mm. At the rear of the eyeball, the optic nerve fibers pass through the sclera and exit on the *nasal* side of the principal optical axis. A network of pigmented connective tissue and blood vessels (*choroid*) lies within the sclera; at the front of the eyeball, the choroid merges into the *ciliary body* and then into the pigmented *iris*. The circular aperture of the iris forms the *pupillary opening*, or the pupil of the eye. There are two sets of smooth muscle fibers (*circular* and *radial*) in the iris which, acting in antagonism, serve respectively to constrict and dilate the pupil. This action, which is controlled by the ANS, is largely reflexive and is determined by the amount of light striking the eye. In bright light, the pupillary opening may be less than 2 mm in diameter; in very dim light, it may be over 8 mm in diameter. Since this amount of change increases the area of the opening by a factor of about seventeen, it follows that the size of the pupil is an important factor in determining the effectiveness of a visual stimulus. Also, the reflexive behavior of the circular and radial muscles provides a relatively rapid means of establishing an appropriate adjustment of the organism to wide changes in the light intensity of the environment.

The *crystalline lens* is suspended from ligaments (*zonula*) attached to the *ciliary body* and has the remarkable property that its shape may be changed by the action of the *radial* and *circular* fibers of the *ciliary muscle*. These fibers are attached to the

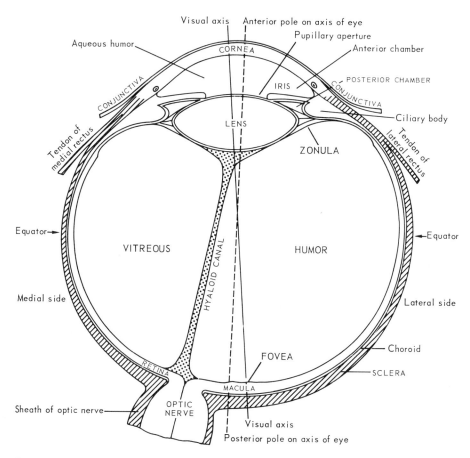

Figure 4–2. A schematic view of the horizontal section of the right eyeball. (From *Human anatomy* by Morris, B. J. Anson (Ed.), 12th ed., copyright © 1966, McGraw-Hill Book Company. Used by permission.)

ciliary body at one end and to the suspensory ligaments (*zonula*) at the other end. The ciliary muscles are so arranged that their contraction pulls the ciliary body toward the lens and loosens the fibers (*zonula*) supporting the lens. The lens then assumes a somewhat bulging form due to its own contractibility. Relaxation of the ciliary muscles places tension on the fibers (*zonula*) so that the lens is flattened. This modification in the shape of the lens produces a change in the optical focus that varies with the distance of the object from the viewer. The process is called *accommodation* and serves to generate a sharp image on the receptive surface at the rear of the eyeball. Normally, there are certain neural connections in the brain between the fibers controlling the ciliary muscles and those controlling the extrinsic muscles of the eyes; the balanced action of these muscles is such that, as the curvature of the lens is changed, the eyes appropriately converge. The degree of accommodation that is possible is a function of both the contractile power of the ciliary muscles and the elasticity of the crystalline lens. For objects at a distance of six feet or more, the ciliary muscle is relaxed; as the object approaches nearer and nearer within six feet, the muscles contract more and more. The nearest distance at which an object is clearly seen is called the *near point of distinct vision.* For a normal 10-year-old child, this distance is only about 7 cm from the eye. With advancing age, however, the elasticity of the lens decreases, and the near point of vision moves further and further away until, at 70 years of age, it is about 400 cm. This condition (*presbyopia*) can be corrected by wearing convex eyeglasses (thicker in the center than at the edge) to compensate for the loss of elasticity in the crystalline lens when viewing near objects, as in reading.

The optical system of the eye consists of the internal structures of the eyeball, which are also diagrammatically shown in Figure 4-2. These structures are transparent and permit light rays entering the eye to pass from the anterior to the posterior portions of the eyeball, in much the same way as light rays pass from air through water. The initial element in the system is the *cornea,* with its outer surface acting like a lens and providing a considerable degree of *refraction,* that is, bending of light waves. Behind the cornea is a small chamber containing a clear, salty liquid called the *aqueous humor.* This is similar in composition to the cerebrospinal fluid and continually undergoes absorption and formation. At the posterior of the small chamber is the crystalline lens. In the preceding paragraph, we considered how the deformation of this structure changes the focus of the eye during accommodation. For distant objects, the *radius of curvature* of the anterior surface of the lens is about 10 mm and that of the posterior surface, about 6 mm. For near objects, the curvature increases (the radii become smaller), but the anterior surface always remains slightly less rounded than the posterior surface. The light rays passing through the lens enter the large posterior chamber of the eyeball, which is filled with a gelatinous substance called the *vitreous humor.* This humor helps to preserve the nearly spherical shape of the eyeball.

In addition to the cornea and the crystalline lens, which provide two interfaces at which refraction occurs, that is, at the boundary between the air and the cornea, and between the aqueous humor and the crystalline lens, the vitreous humor provides a third interface. Here refraction occurs when light passes from the posterior surface of the lens into the dense vitreous humor. The combined effects of the refractive surfaces are similar to those present in a convex lens with a refractive index approximately the same as water, 1.333. (The *index of refraction* is the ratio of the velocity of light in air to the velocity of light in the substance under consideration.)

The *retina* is a layer of the eye containing light-sensitive cells organized into a complex neuronal network. The action of the optical system and its associated structures brings rays of light from external objects to a focus upon the retina of the eye. The retina forms the innermost of the three layers surrounding the eyeball (protective sclera, nutritive choroid, and light-sensitive retina) and lies about 15 mm posterior to the *nodal point* (optical center) of the lens. It has an average thickness of about 300 mm and extends over approximately two-thirds of the interior surface of the eyeball. In the retina, at the back of the eyeball, there is an area about 1 mm in diameter which apears yellow when examined through an *ophthalmoscope*. Within this "yellow spot" (*macula lutea*) is a small depression called the *fovea centralis*, or, simply, the *fovea*. It has a diameter of less than one quarter of a millimeter. Due to its special anatomical structure, the fovea provides us with our most sensitive vision under daylight conditions. About 5 mm to the nasal side of the eyeball, there is an opening in the retina, approximately 1 mm in diameter, through which the nerve fibers from all parts of the retina leave the eye to form the *second cranial* (optic) nerve. The point of exit is called the *optic disc* or "blind spot," since this part of the retina contains no light-sensitive cells like those found in the retina proper. Expressed in functional terms, the blind spot occurs on the temporal side of the *visual field*, about 15 degrees from the point of fixation, and subtends about 3 degrees. Under normal conditions of binocular vision we do not ordinarily notice the blind spot in each eye, as the part of the visual field that is missing in one eye is present in the other. The visual fields of the two eyes overlap, in part. Even when viewing an object with *monocular* vision, the blind spot will not be noticed unless the optical image happens to fall entirely on that portion of the retina and careful observations are made. The missing portions of monocular images that are larger than the blind area are "filled in" on the basis of our previous perceptual experiences.

A schematic section of the layers of the human retina is presented in Figure 4-3. Although ten different neural layers of the retina have been identified and described in detail (Polyak, 1957), only the three most important layers of cells are shown here. The outermost set of cells, that is, those nearest the choroid, are the visual receptor cells known as *rod* and *cone* cells; near the middle of the retina is a layer of bipolar cells; the innermost layer contains ganglion cells. Thus, the first and second synaptic junctions of the visual system occur within the retina. It should also be noted that the arrangement of retinal cells is such that light must pass through the many layers of the retina before reaching the receptor cells.

In the human eye there are approximately 6.5 million cones and approximately 130 million rods. These are so distributed that in the fovea centralis there are only cones, approximately 34,000. Toward the nasal and temporal periphery of the retina, the number of cones per unit area is considerably reduced, while the rods (absent in the fovea) increase in density up to approximately 20 degrees on each side of the fovea and then decrease rapidly. Since there are only about one million optic nerve fibers to serve more than 130 million rod and cone cells, it is clear that there must be a general convergence of fibers within the retina. The anatomy of the retina reveals that there are two major systems of neurons. One is identified exclusively with the cones, such that there is a *single path from a cone* to a bipolar cell to a ganglion cell, as in the fovea. The other system consists of *mixed rods and cones* which converge on bipolar cells and, in turn, there are several bipolar cells which converge on ganglion cells. In the periphery there may be more than 250 rods and cones per ganglion cell. This complicated arrangement affords a basis for neural interaction between different retinal areas. A third type of connective system in the retina which provides further interaction is that formed by *intraretinal association neurons*. These include horizontal cells, centrifugal bipolar cells, and perhaps some amacrine cells. Despite the *areal interaction* afforded by these neuronal systems, it is possible to study cone and rod functions in isolation by restricting the stimulus, respectively, to the fovea or to the extreme periphery of the retina.

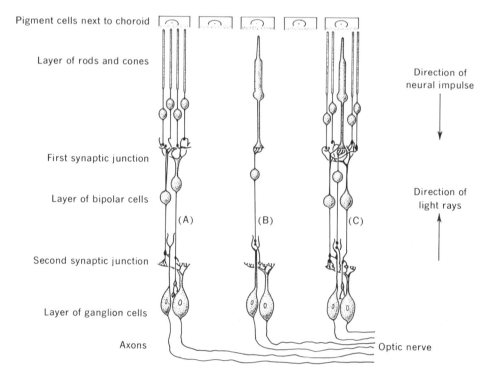

Figure 4-3. A schematic section through the layers of the human retina, showing three types of connections among the receptor cells: (A) multiple rod system; (B) single cone system found only in the fovea; (C) mixed rod and cone system. (Adapted from Polyak, 1941.)

The rod and cone cells show further differences in both their anatomical structure and visual functions. Over most of the retina, the cones range in length from approximately 0.029 to 0.085 mm and in width, from approximately 0.0025 to 0.0075 mm. The rods are more cylindrical and thinner than the cones, their length varying from 0.040 to 0.060 mm and their width averaging about 0.002 mm. The outer segment of the rods and cones, that is, the part of the receptor cell nearest the choroid, contains a photosensitive substance that differs in the two types of cells. In the rods, it is called *rhodopsin* ("visual purple"); in the cones, a red-catching pigment (erythrolabe) and a green-catching pigment (chlorolabe) have been identified (Rushton, 1959). The absorption of light energy in the rod and cone layers of the retina produces photochemical changes in the pigmented substance of the receptor cells, thereby releasing certain active compounds. These compounds act to produce nerve impulses in the receptor cells, which then pass through the bipolar and ganglion cells on their way to the brain. While the process involving the photochemical changes in the rods is fairly well understood, that involving the cones is still obscure. When the rod cells are exposed to light, there is first a rapid reaction in which the rhodopsin bleaches into *protein and retinene.* In the dark the reaction reverses itself and rhodopsin is synthesized. However, even with continued exposure, rhodopsin can be synthesized by a slow thermolabile reaction in which vitamin A is formed and combines with the available protein. Vitamin A from the bloodstream tends to maintain an approximate constant level of vitamin A and rhodopsin in the retina. The velocity with which the photochemical processes occur depends directly upon the intensity of the light and the degrees of concentration of the light-sensitive material in the rods or cones at that time.

According to the *duplicity theory* of vision, the rods and cones react differently to photic energy and these different retinal functions are made to account for most of our visual experiences. In general, the cones are involved in our ability to discriminate fine detail under high levels of illuminance and to recognize differences in hues, while the rods are involved in our ability to see objects under conditions of low illuminance when hues cannot be distinguished.

The conductive mechanism of the human eye primarily involves the optic nerve, which carries the neural impulses from the rods and cones of the retina to the brain. We have already considered how the rods and cones (receptor cells) form synaptic connections with the ganglionic cells of the retina, the axons of which pass along the inner retinal surface and leave the eyeball through the optic disc. These axons, together with blood vessels, form the *optic nerve.* The nerve from each eye continues back from the eyeball toward the midline of the head where, upon entering the cranium, the fibers from the two eyes converge and then separate at a place called the *optic chiasma.* The unique feature of the separation is that the fibers from the nasal *(medial)* half of each retina cross to the opposite side in the optic chiasma. Thus, the fibers from the right-hand side of each retina are collected and proceed to the right cerebral hemisphere; fibers from the left-hand side of each retina proceed to the left cerebral hemisphere. Since objects in the right side of the visual field, for example, form their images on the left side of each retina due to the reversing action of the lens, this separation produces a projection of the two images (corresponding parts) in the same side of the brain (left, in this case). Notice, also, that this half-crossing of fibers *(semidecussation)* results in each retina having some connection with both sides of the brain.

Beyond the chiasma the optic nerve fibers do not go directly to their final cortical destination. Those fibers derived from the temporal (lateral) half of each retina remain uncrossed and become associated with the crossed fibers from the opposite eye to form the right and left *optic tract.* These tracts extend backward along the surface of the brain stem to the right and left *lateral geniculate bodies* of the thalamus. Some of the optic tract fibers, however, either directly or by collaterals, do not go to the lateral geniculate bodies but pass to the *pretectal region* near the *superior colliculus.* These are the afferent fibers which make connections with the motor nuclei of the third, fourth and sixth cranial nerves controlling pupillary light reflexes and eye movements. The fibers arriving at the lateral geniculate bodies make synaptic junctions with fourth-order neurons to form optic radiations which continue, uninterrupted, and terminate in the striated area of the right and left occipital lobes. In the lobes, a larger portion of the cortical area is functionally related to the fovea of the eye than to the periphery.

Figure 4-4 shows the apparatus used for recording electrical signals from vari-

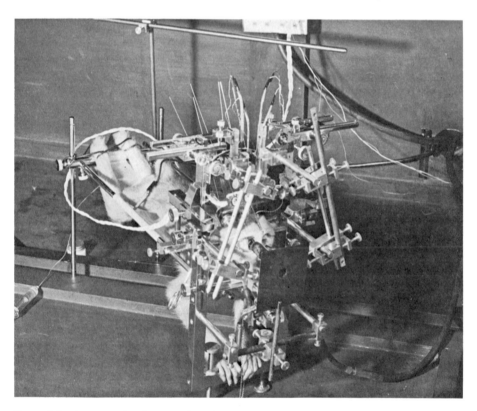

Figure 4–4. An apparatus for recording electrical responses at various points along the visual pathway of a monkey during stimulation by light. The points from which recordings are made include the optic nerve, optic tract, lateral geniculate body, optic radiations, and visual cortex. (From Lindsley, in Sheer, 1961.)

ous points along the visual pathway of a monkey while a light is being presented. If, for example, a repetitively flashing light is presented as a stimulus, the sub-cortical stations along the pathway will follow the flashes up to approximately 100/sec. However, the visual cortex will follow only up to approximately 50/sec. Thus, the limitation of the visual system to respond discretely to flashes of light seems to be imposed by the cortex, with the result that visual fusion is obtained at flash rates lower than those that can be handled adequately by the rest of the visual system (Lindsley, 1961a).

In addition to the visual tracts associated with the geniculate bodies and the pretectal region, the central physiological mechanism underlying the visual processes includes both the *reticular formation,* a structure located in the lower mid-brain, and the *occipital lobes* of the cerebral cortex of the brain. The specific functions of the reticular formation are not yet fully understood, but sufficient evidence has been gathered which indicates that if visual perception is to occur, neural impulses from the ascending part of the formation must be discharged into the cortex at the same time that impulses arrive from the retina. Apparently, the ascending reticular impulses serve to arouse the cortex and prepare it to receive the afferent impulses generated by a visual stimulus. When the descending portion of the reticular formation receives efferent impulses from the cortex, it discharges signals which meet the afferent impulses coming in from the eyes, ears, and other receptor organs. This serves to block the afferent sensory impulses, preventing them from reaching the cortex. Thus, the reticular formation seems to act both as a *facilitator* and an *inhibitor* of neural activity (Lindsley, 1961*a*).

In the cortex, as we have indicated, the visual tracts terminate in the projection areas of the occipital lobes. However, our present knowledge of neuronal integration in the cortex indicates that the simplified conception of projection areas must be modified. In contrast with the classical view, it no longer appears that the primary receiving area for a given sensory modality contains a direct (one-to-one) mosaic representation of the receptors' activity. Studies in vision have established that "neurons of the visual cortex integrate afferent impulses from the eye, from vestibular receptors, and from the nonspecific reticulothalamic system. These various afferents converge mostly on the same optical neuron" (Jung, 1961, p. 667).

Five special types of neurons for binocular stimuli and five special types for thalamic stimuli have been identified; the stimulation of these neurons results in various patterns of response excitation and inhibition. For example, the evidence suggests that some retinal and cortical neurons discharge reciprocally. When certain on-neurons are activated by the onset of a light, other neurons in the same retinal or cortical area are inhibited (maintain depressed or suppressed activity followed by a burst of impulses when the light is turned off) (*reciprocal inhibition*). *Lateral inhibiton* between central and peripheral portions of the receptive field may also occur due to the interaction among the retinal or cortical on-off neurons (those which fire at the start and after the end of a stimulus). When the on-responses occur at the center of the field, the off-responses are obtained at the periphery, and vice versa.

These two principles (reciprocal inhibition and lateral inhibition) are basic to neuronal responses involving diffuse and patterned light, and may be used to explain the coordination that occurs in the organization of the visual system. Furthermore, lateral inhibition has been found to occur in cats in the somatosensory neuronal system (Mountcastle, 1957) and in the auditory neuronal system (Katsuki *et al.,* 1958). Thus it appears that lateral inhibition may be a general principle of afferent systems and serves to improve the functional efficiency of a given system beyond that imposed by the concept of point-to-point correspondence between receptors and cortical projection areas.

The Receptor Systems
for Mechanical Energy

The Auditory System

In man, the auditory system consists of the receptor organs (the ears), the neural conductive mechanism, and the central projection areas in the cerebral cortex of the brain. The adequate stimulus for hearing is conventionally defined as mechanical energy in the form of acoustic waves with a fundamental frequency below 20,000 cps. In Chapter 2, we learned about the physical characteristics of sound; now we will examine the structure of the ear and trace the physiological events that occur in the auditory system when the ear responds to an adequate stimulus.

Figure 4-5 presents a cross-section of the human ear with its three major anatomical divisions: the *outer, middle* and *inner* ears. Functionally, the outer and middle ears normally serve to collect and transmit acoustic vibrations by air conduction, and then by bone conduction, to the inner ear where the neural impulses of the auditory portion of the *eighth cranial* (acoustic) nerve are generated.

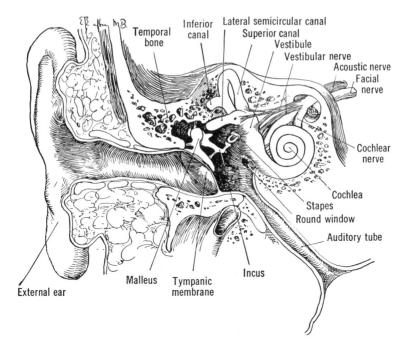

Figure 4–5. A semischematic drawing of the human ear. (After Brödel, from Gardner, *Fundamentals of neurology,* 4th ed., Philadelphia: W. B. Saunders Company, 1963.)

In the outer ear, sound waves first strike the pinna (*auricle*) and are channeled into the *external canal*, at the end of which is located the eardrum (*tympanic membrane*). The external canal is about 2.5 cm in length, with a diameter of about 7 mm; it has a natural resonant frequency of about 3500 cps. The tympanic membrane is slightly oval with the larger diameter being about 9.2 mm and the smaller, about 8.5 mm. The area of the membrane is approximately 69 sq mm. Behind the membrane is the middle ear, an air-filled cavity spanned by three small bones (the *ossicular chain*) called the hammer (*malleus*), anvil (*incus*), and stirrup (*stapes*). When the acoustic wave strikes the tympanic membrane, it produces vibrations of the same frequency in the membrane which, in turn, are transmitted through the ossicular chain, since the malleus is attached to the inner side of the membrane. The ossicles, however, are so formed that they act as a lever system to reduce the amplitudes of vibration present at the eardrum, while increasing the pressure exerted at the footplate of the stapes. This pressure per unit of area at the footplate is more than 30 times that at the eardrum. The increase in pressure is due to the combination of the peculiar pivoting action of the ossicles and the small area of the footplate (about 3.2 sq mm).

Two other structures in the middle ear should be mentioned. The first is the *Eustachian tube* connecting the middle ear cavity to the upper part of the throat behind the nasal cavity. This tube is *normally closed* but opens momentarily whenever an atmospheric pressure differential exists between the outer ear and the middle ear. When the tube is opened, air rushes into or out from the middle ear cavity depending, respectively, upon whether the pressure in the cavity is too low or too high. For example, when riding up a high mountain, our ears will "pop," that is, the excessive pressure in the middle ear forces the Eustachian tube to open, thereby reducing the pressure to a value equivalent to that of the external atmosphere. Equalized pressure in the outer and middle ear cavities is usually maintained by the habitual action of swallowing.

The second auxiliary structure of the middle ear is a set of *intra-aural muscles:* the *tensor tympani* and the *stapedius,* which are attached to the malleus and the stapes, respectively. The tensor tympani muscle is innervated by a branch of the trigeminal (fifth cranial) nerve, whereas the stapedius muscle is supplied by a branch of the facial (seventh cranial) nerve. Experimental evidence (Dallos, 1964) supports the hypothesis that the contraction of the two muscles is a reflex response to intense sounds and serves as a protective mechanism for the inner ear. With the contraction of the muscles, there is usually a reduction in the efficiency of sound conduction across the outer and middle ears, particularly for tones of low frequency. This is fortunate since low-frequency sounds are more damaging to the inner ear than high-frequency sounds, if pressure is held contant. While the intra-aural muscles provide some protection for continuous sounds, they have little protective effect against sudden noises; the latencies of the inter-aural reflexes (about 100 msec) are sufficiently long so that a sharp wave front will pass before the contractions can occur.

The extension of the acoustic reflex, probably through the reticular formation, produces a change in respiration which results in momentary inhibition. Any further spreading of the reflex influences the general body musculature so as to immobilize the body for an instant or to bring the individual to a sudden standstill.

The inner ear is located in a complex cavity (*the bony labyrinth*) deep within the *temporal bone*. Fitted inside the bony labyrinth is a series of interconnected ducts and sacs (the *membranous labyrinth*) filled with a viscous fluid (*endolymph*). A watery fluid (*perilymph*) separates the membranous labyrinth from the bony labyrinth. A diagram of the membranous labyrinth of the internal human ear is shown in Figure 4-6. Of the three major divisions of the labyrinth (the *cochlea*, the *otolith organs*, or utricle and saccule, and the *semicircular canals*), only the cochlea is involved in hearing. The remaining parts function in the maintenance of bodily orientation; these will be considered in a separate section of this chapter.

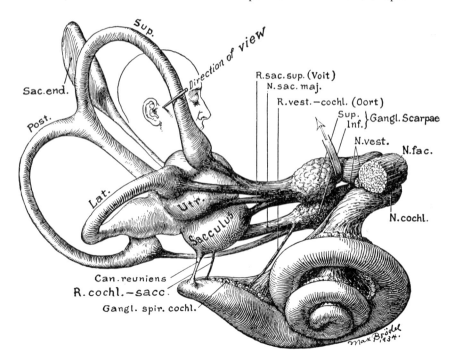

Figure 4–6. The human membranous labyrinth, showing the structural relations of the cochlea, the semicircular canals, and the otolith organs (utricle and saccule). (From Hardy, *Anat. Rec.,* 1935, **59**, Figure 7, p. 412.)

The connection between the middle ear and the inner ear is made at the footplate of the stapes, which fits exactly into the membranous oval window at the base of the cochlea. The cochlea is a coiled structure with approximately two and five-eighths turns; it is divided longitudinally into three tubes (*scala*) by two membranes running the entire length of the cochlea. As shown in Figure 4-7, *Reissner's membrane* separates the *scala vestibuli* and the *scala media* (cochlear duct), while the *basilar membrane* separates the *scala media* from the *scala tympani*.

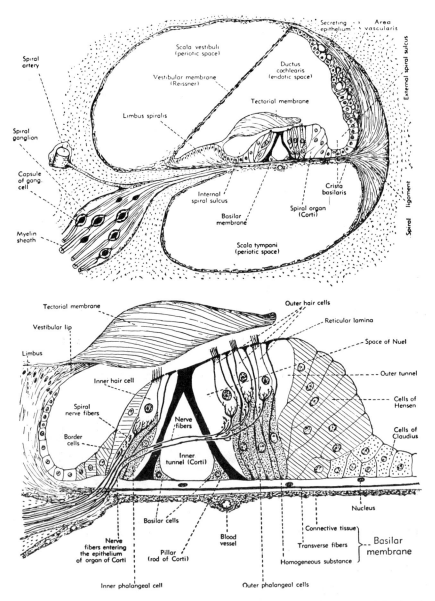

Figure 4-7. *Upper,* the vertical section of human cochlea showing organ of Corti and adjacent structures. *Lower,* the organ of Corti and basilar membrane in greater magnification. (From Rasmussen, *Outlines of neuroanatomy,* 3d ed., Dubuque, Iowa: William C. Brown, 1943.)

The scala vestibuli and the scala tympani contain perilymph and are continuous at the *apex* of the cochlea through a pinhole opening (*helicotrema*); the cochlear duct contains endolymph. At the base of the vestibular canal is the *oval window* into which the footplate of the stapes is attached, as we have already indicated. The round window is a similar opening at the base of the scala tympani and is closed by a thin membrane facing into the middle ear near the opening of the Eustachian tube.

Situated in the cochlear duct is the *organ of Corti*, the complex mechanism that attaches to the basilar membrane and contains the specialized receptor cells for hearing. These cells are called *hair cells* since they have hairlike processes at their free ends, with twelve to fifteen cilia per cell. Above the hair cells is the *tectorial membrane*, a fine gelatinous membrane into which the cilia are imbedded. Although the bony cochlea becomes progressively smaller in the cross-sectional area from the base to its apex, the basilar membrane becomes wider and wider. At the apex of the cochlea, it is approximately six and one-quarter times as wide as at the basal end (0.08 mm at basal end; 0.50 mm at apical end). The receptor cells are spaced quite evenly along the basilar membrane and are divided into two groups called *inner* hair cells and *outer* hair cells, depending upon their location within the organ of Corti. There are about 3500 inner hair cells arranged in a single row and about 20,000 outer hair cells divided among three outer rows. The hair cells are stimulated when the vibrations of the tympanic membrane are transmitted across the middle ear by the ossicular chain, such that the pivoting movements of the stapes in the oval window impart pressure changes in the cochlear fluids. Since these fluids are incompressible at the pressures involved, inward movements of the stapes are immediately transformed into outward movements of the round window. The problem, however, of explaining exactly how the pressure waves in the cochlear fluids affect the basilar membrane is still a theoretical issue; we will consider this in Chapter 10. Nevertheless, it is generally agreed that the pressure waves produce movements in the cochlear fluids that disturb the basilar membrane. This disturbance is accompanied by upward and downward movements of the hair cells, toward and away from the tectorial membrane, with the result that the cells are alternately compressed and stretched. The deformation of the hair cells apparently produces a change in the membrane potentials, which subsequently stimulate the endings of the afferent nerve fibers surrounding the cells.

The primary conductive mechanism for the sense of hearing is the auditory portion of the *eighth cranial* (acoustic) nerve. The afferent neurons of the eighth nerve make contact with the hair cells of the organ of Corti; each nerve fiber connects with one or two inner hair cells. The external hair cells, however, are innervated by multiple fibers. Located within the central core of the cochlea (*modiolus*) in the spiral ganglion of Corti are the cell bodies of approximately 30,000 ganglion cells whose axons form the beginning of the auditory branch of the eighth cranial nerve. It should be noted, for theoretical reasons, that there are more nerve fibers than there are inner and outer hair cells combined; this means that a single auditory nerve fiber may gather impulses from receptor cells widely separated along the basilar membrane. The fibers of the auditory nerve leave the cochlea at its base and extend about 5 mm to the *cochlear nuclei* (dorsal and ventral) of the medulla. There synaptic connections are made with second-order neurons which proceed to other centers. Some of the axons of the second-order neurons from the right and left ears remain in their respective cerebral hemispheres, but many others cross to the contralateral side and make connections in certain structures (*trapezoid body* and *superior olivary nucleus*) at the level of the *pons*. Third-order neurons then run upward in the *lateral lemniscus,* terminating at the *inferior colliculus* of the midbrain (acoustic reflex center) or continuing to the *medial geniculate body* of the thalamus. From the medial geniculate body, the axons of fourth-order neurons form *radiation fibers* in each hemisphere which spread to the appropriate *temporal lobe* (right or left) of the cerebral cortex.

The neural connections from the cochlear structures to the temporal lobes are extremely complicated, but three major points should be stressed. (1) Both ears have connections to both the right and left temporal lobes, thus providing neural pathways through which binaural interaction can occur. (2) In the central mechanism of hearing, that is, in each auditory cortex, different frequencies of excitation at the cochlea are projected and localized at different cortical regions. Tones of high, middle, and low frequency are separated spatially in the cortex as they are in the auditory nerve. (3) The decussation of fibers of the auditory nerve produces a condition in which cortical responses from the *contralateral* ear are stronger than those from the *homolateral* ear.

The Tactile System

The tactile system, one of several systems in which the receptor cells are located in the skin, is adequately aroused by mechanical pressures of sufficient magnitude to deform the skin tissue. It is not direct contact alone, however, that elicits touch sensations, but the presence of a deformation gradient involving receptive elements over a given cutaneous area that constitutes the immediate physical stimulus. The slope of the gradient is related to the amount of mechanical energy that is present in the deforming stimulus; its effectiveness is the same whether the skin is disturbed by pressing or pulling. This indicates that the essential condition for stimulating the tactile system is the production of tension within the cutaneous tissues containing receptor cells. In physical units, the significant variable for eliciting touch sensations is tension, operationally defined as force per linear distance of contacted skin surface, for example, gm/mm. The rate at which the skin is deformed is also an important variable.

Histologically, the skin may be considered as consisting of three primary layers as shown in Figure 4-8: (1) the *epidermis,* (2) the *dermis,* and (3) the *subcutaneous tissue.* The epidermis, or outer layer, may be further divided into four sublayers, two of which are the stratum corneum of superficial dead cells, and the stratum germinativum (Malpighian layer) containing many free nerve endings. The dermis lies adjacent to the epidermis and the two layers merge along a highly irregular boundary. Within the dermal layer there are specialized nerve endings, blood vessels, sweat-gland ducts, hair follicles (roots) and small nerve trunks.

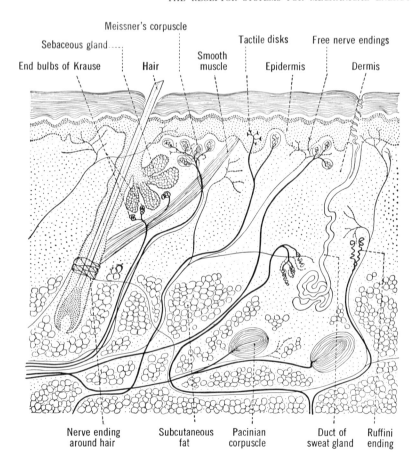

Figure 4–8. A schematic section of the nerve supply of the human skin. (After Woolard, from E. Gardner, *Fundamentals of neurology*, 4th ed., Philadelphia: W. B. Saunders Company, 1963.)

Below the dermis lies the subcutaneous layer, which consists chiefly of bundles of elastic tissue that extend inward to the bones and muscles of the body. Most of the larger blood vessels, sweat glands, hair follicles, and nerve trunks are located within this layer. In addition, the subcutaneous layer contains the secreting tissues of the oily (sebaceous) glands and several types of specialized nerve endings. Since the skin varies markedly in structure from place to place on the body, it should not be expected that each section of the skin will contain all of the neuro-anatomical elements mentioned in this paragraph.

Our interest in the general structure of the skin is directed toward the various types of receptor cells embedded within the several cutaneous layers that are believed to mediate tactile sensations. Two principal types of endings of nerve fibers can be found in the skin: *nonencapsulated* and *encapsulated* nerve endings. The simplest type of nonencepsulated endings are the nonmyelinated terminal arborizations (*free nerve endings*) in the epidermal and dermal layers of the skin. In the hairy regions of the body, the nerve endings form *basket-like skeins* around the hair follicles, as shown in Figure 4-8. The encapsulated nerve fibers are those in which the unmyelinated endings of the fibers are surrounded by a special capsule of connective tissue which varies in thickness and arrangement. In the hairless regions of the body, *Meissner corpuscles* in the dermal layer of the skin form the encapsulated endings which apparently mediate tactile sensitivity. These corpuscles are about 40 to 100 mm in length and about 30 to 60 mm in diameter. They usually occur in groups of two or three, with as many as ten groups per square millimeter of skin surface. While it is possible that other types of pressure receptors may exist in the skin, the case for free nerve endings and Meissner corpuscles is based in part upon the correlation between regions of maximal tactile sensitivity and regions of greatest density of end organs. Numerous types of encapsulated endings other than Meissner corpuscles have been discovered in the skin, some of which will be considered later in this section.

The conductive mechanism for the tactile system involves an anatomically complex arrangement of nerve fibers. At the peripheral level, the nerve fibers forming the specialized receptors of cutaneous sensitivity (touch, pain, cold, warmth) approach the epithelium in bundles. Although a given bundle carries fibers that serve a given area of skin, there is no special grouping of fibers within these bundles. The neural impulses initiated by adequate cutaneous stimuli are conducted centrally by 30 of the 31 pairs of spinal nerves and 4 of the 12 cranial nerves (V, VII, IX, X). The thirty-first pair of spinal nerves (the first cervical pair) has no sensory roots. A particular spinal nerve serves a given region of the skin called a *dermatome* of that nerve. Usually there are branches of two or more spinal nerves present in a local region so that overlapping innervation is found throughout the skin surface of the body.

As the peripheral branches of the nerve fibers enter the spinal cord, they are sorted into groups, each of which functions for a particular cutaneous modality. The neural impulses for each modality ascend the spinal cord in their own tracts. In the tactile system, the impulses from the first-order afferent neurons enter the spinal cord via the dorsal roots and ascend in the posterior tract a varying number of spinal segments before terminating in the gray matter of the cord. At this point, synaptic connections are made with second-order neurons, a few of which cross to the opposite side of the cord. These ascend as a small bundle in the ventral spinothalamic tract until they reach the medulla, where their course becomes uncertain. Most fibers of light touch are conducted upward on the homolateral side of the spinal cord and cross in the lower regions of the medulla oblongata. From here, they continue to ascend in the dorsal portion of the medial lemniscus of the opposite side.

The Proprioceptive Systems

Most of us are normally not aware of the importance and functional significance of the *proprioceptive* systems in our daily lives. Without these systems, activities such as those involved in walking, muscular coordination, balance, body posture, and other motor skills would be performed with considerable difficulty, if at all. The smooth functioning of our bodily parts and the maintenance of our postural orientation depend upon a class of receptor mechanisms that are stimulated by mechanical energy associated with the movement of certain organs and tissues of the body.

The proprioceptive systems may be divided into two subclasses: the *kinesthetic* and the *vestibular*. *Kinesthesis* refers to the sensitivity of movements of bodily structures, for example, arms, legs, tongue, and eyeballs, due to the excitation of receptor cells located in the muscles, tendons, and joints of the body. The *vestibular* sense involves the perception of spatial movement and spatial orientation of the body as a whole, due to the excitation of receptor cells located in the nonauditory labyrinth of the ear. The static and dynamic balance of the human body is dependent, in large measure, upon the proper functioning of the vestibular mechanism in conjunction with the sense of vision.

THE KINESTHETIC SYSTEM.   To understand the physiological basis of kinesthesis, some attention must be given to the specific types of receptor cells found in the muscles, tendons, and joints and to their modes of stimulation. The impulses that are set up by muscular movement, motion and flexion of joints, tension on the tendons and ligaments, and positioning of the body members are involved primarily in reflexive behavior, but sometimes we may become directly aware of the associated sensations, such as when we are carrying a heavy package.

The muscles and tendons of the body are supplied with several different types of receptor cells, some of which are related to cutaneous sensitivity; those involved in postural reflexes are the *muscle spindle* and *Golgi tendon organ*. The muscle spindle consists of a number of thin muscle fibers (*intrafusal fibers*) that are surrounded by a connective tissue and embedded in the muscle itself. The connective tissue attaches at its ends to a muscle fiber, to a tendon, or to other connective tissues. As shown in Figure 4-9, there are three major types of fibers that may be found in the muscle spindle: (1) *annulospiral endings*—the helically-shaped, nonmyelinated endings of large myelinated (primary) afferent fibers (8 to 12 μ in diameter); (2) *flower spray endings*—the rings or coils of smaller (6 to 9 μ) myelinated (secondary) afferent fibers; and (3) small (3 to 7 μ) *efferent* fibers—the myelinated endings that terminate in end-plates on the striated portion of the intrafusal fibers. The afferent endings of the muscle spindle are so arranged in the muscle that neural impulses are generated by mechanical distortion whenever the muscle is stretched, rather than contracted; hence the name, *stretch afferents*.

The *Golgi tendon organ* consists of a number of tendon fasciculi enclosed in a cylindrical capsule supplied by one or two myelinated afferent nerve fibers. Within the capsule, the fibers lose their myelin sheaths and terminate in numerous smaller branches that serve the entire tendon bundle. The Golgi organs are located at the junction of a tendon with muscle fibers requiring great strength, for example, the calf and eye muscles in man. Whenever the tendon is stretched, either passively or by an active muscular *contraction,* the afferent endings are displaced or distorted, and this mechanical action provides the adequate stimulus for the discharge of the receptor cells. Thus, the tendon endings are the principal organs for indicating muscle contraction.

In addition to the muscle spindle and Golgi tendon organ, the kinesthetic receptors include the joint organs: the *Pacinian corpuscle* (ovoid in form; 1 to 2 mm in length) (see Figure 4-9) and free nerve endings (in the blood vessels serving the

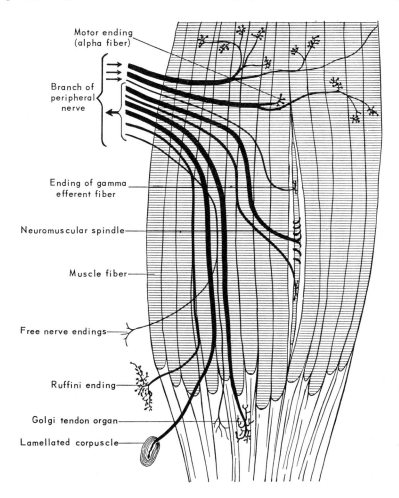

Figure 4–9. A schematic representation of a muscle and its nerve supply. Arrows indicate direction of conduction. Each muscle fiber has a motor ending from a large myelinated (alpha) fiber, and the muscle fibers within a spindle have motor endings from small myelinated (gamma) fibers. Muscle nerves have many sensory fibers. Some are large myelinated fibers coming from primary sensory (annulospiral) endings in spindles, from neurotendinous spindles (Golgi tendon organs), and from lamellated corpuscles (Pacinian corpuscles) in the connective tissue between muscle fibers or external to the muscle as a whole. Smaller myelinated fibers arise from proprioceptive endings (such as Ruffini endings) in the connective tissue in and around muscle, or in joints. Finally, there are small myelinated and nonmyelinated fibers that form free endings (presumably for pain) in the connective tissue in and around muscle. (After Denny-Brown, from E. Gardner, *Fundamentals of neurology,* 4th ed., Philadelphia: W. B. Saunders Company, 1963.)

muscles and tendons). These receptors respond to the mechanical pressure exerted upon them by the movement of a joint. Since the Pacinian corpuscles lie deep within the tissues under the skin, they are probably more important than the muscle receptors in detecting the passive movements or spatial position of the arms and legs.

The afferent nerve fibers of the kinesthetic receptors are of the large, myelinated type, with cells in the posterior root ganglia for those entering the spinal cord. The ascending branches form the dorsal funiculi; the fibers from the lower spinal nerves are located more medially, while those from higher levels are located more laterally in the dorsal segment of the spinal cord as shown in Figure 4-10. Some

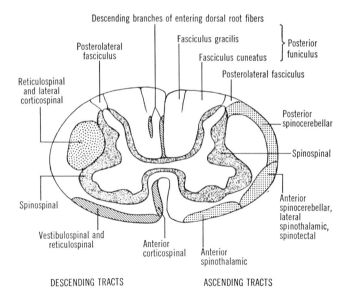

Figure 4–10. A diagram of the main tracts of the human spinal cord. Afferent, ascending tracts are shown on the right side; efferent, descending tracts are shown on the left side. In the spinal cord, however, both afferent and efferent fibers are found on either side. (From E. Gardner, *Fundamentals of neurology,* 4th ed., Philadelphia: W. B. Saunders Company, 1963.)

of the afferent fibers enter descending rami, pass down the cord for one or two segments, and make reflex connections. The ascending fibers entering the spinal cord below the midthoracic segment terminate in the *nucleus fasciculus gracilis* of the medulla oblongata; those that enter above this level, terminate in the *nucleus fasciculus cuneatus.* Neurons of the second order (*internal ascuate fibers*) relay the kinesthetic impulses from these nuclei through the medial lemniscus of the opposite side to the ventral nucleus of the thalamus. From here, the impulses pass to the region of the posterior central gyrus and to adjacent parts of the frontal and parietal lobes. Some ascending fibers do not form synaptic junctures at the nucleus gracilis and cuneatus but continue uninterrupted through the medulla oblongata to the *cerebellar cortex*. In the cerebellum, coordinating efferent branches arise that descend into the reticular formation of the midbrain and the spinal cord. These pathways are related to muscular coordination, but not to sensation.

The Vestibular System.   The *vestibular system* includes a specialized receptor organ which for some may not even be known to exist. The effects of stimulating this organ are so moderate under normal conditions that no appreciable sensations are produced. Furthermore, the organ is completely enclosed within the skull and its presence is not externally visible. The vestibular system consists of two functional parts: (1) the *positional receptors* that are responsible for *static* sensations produced by the position of the head at rest with respect to the pull of gravity, and (2) the *dynamic receptors* that are responsible for *kinetic* sensations related to accelerative or decelerative movements of the head. Given information about head position and head movement, organisms are able to make compensatory adjustments in bodily posture through the action of reflexive mechanisms. The sense organs and portions of the nervous system that must be stimulated to elicit these responses are called, collectively, the vestibular system.

The vestibular system, presented in Figure 4-6, which may be considered as part of the inner ear since it is appended to the organ of hearing, is supplied by part of the acoustic nerve. The inner ear of man (the *labyrinth*) lies within the petrous portion of the temporal bone in the base of the skull. There are two major divisions of the labyrinth: the *osseous* labyrinth, which is the outer bony capsule, and the *membranous* labyrinth, which lies protected within the osseous labyrinth. The space between the osseous and the membranous labyrinths is filled with *perilymphatic fluid,* while the space within the membranous labyrinth is filled with *endolymphatic fluid.* Thus, the end organs of the vestibular apparatus, together with the cochlea, lie enclosed within the petrous bone in which a series of cavities and canals has been formed.

The largest and most centrally placed of these cavities is the *vestibule,* with a volume of approximately 72 cu mm in the adult. Attached to and lying in front of the vestibule is the cochlea, with its base opening into the vestibule. Lying behind and above the vestibule are three *semicircular canals* (*superior, lateral,* and *posterior*), oriented at right angles to each other. Each canal forms two-thirds of a circle and has an enlarged portion at one end called the *ampulla*. The bony canals are approximately 18 mm long and 1 mm in diameter and the ampulla, approximately 2 mm in diameter. The ampulla of each canal connects directly to the bony vestibule. There are two other primary openings in the vestibule: the *oval window,* to which the stapes is attached by means of a circular ligament, and the *round window,* which is covered by a fibrous membrane and is located behind and below the oval window. The importance of these two openings, however, is in relation to hearing and not to body posture or movements. It should be noted, nevertheless, that the perilymphatic fluid which surrounds the membranous labyrinth of the semicircular canals and fills the vestibule is continuous and engulfs the cochlear duct of the inner ear. In hearing, it is the perilymphatic fluid in the scala vestibuli of the cochlea that is disturbed by the action of the stapes at the oval window.

The portion of the membranous labyrinth lying within the vestibule is not one large compartment, but is divided into two parts called the *utricle* and the *saccule*. Thus, the utricle, the saccule, the semicircular canals with their ampullae, and the membranous portion of the cochlea form continuous portions of the membranous labyrinth enclosed by the bony labyrinth. The larger utricle occupies the upper and posterior portion of the vestibule, while the smaller saccule occupies the lower and anterior portion of the vestibule. The ampullae of the semicircular canals open directly into the utricle. A small tube (*utriculosaccular duct*) connects the utricle to the saccule and a short canal (*ductus reuniens*) at the lower part of the saccule connects the saccule with the cochlear duct. The ductus reuniens is the only anatomical connection between the vestibular and auditory organs. The utriculosaccular duct is joined by the *endolymphatic duct,* through which endolymph is drained from the membranous labyrinth and passes through the cranial cavity, escaping into the subdural space.

The part of the vestibular mechanism concerned with *head position* includes the utricle and saccule. Part of the epithelium forming the walls of these two sacs is specialized for stimulation; this epithelium (*macula*) is located on the floor of the utricle and on the medial surface of the saccule. Each macula consists of two kinds of cells, *hair cells* and *supporting cells,* as shown in Figure 4-11. The hair cells are pear-shaped, with their rounded basal ends lying between the supporting cells and their free ends being truncated and ciliated. A network of nerve filaments derived from a fiber of the vestibular nerve surrounds each hair cell. The ciliated ends of the cells are covered by a layer of gelatinous substance (the *cupula*); on the free surface of this substance, small ovoid crystals of calcium carbonate (lime salts) are imbedded that form an organic structure known as the *otoliths.*

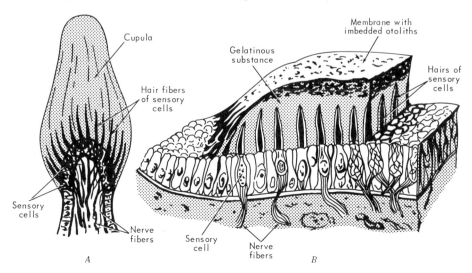

Figure 4–11.   Left, the crista and cupula present in the ampulla of each semicircular canal. Right, the maculae of the otolith organs (utricle and saccule). (After Geldard, 1953.)

As the resting or static position of the head changes, the macula is tilted and the otoliths tend to "fall" with gravity. This distorts the hair cells and stimulates the nerve fibers woven around the cell bodies. When the head is in the normal erect position, minimal stimulation occurs in the maculae of the utricles and saccules. As the head is tilted to one side, stimulation increases in the maculae of that side (the otoliths hang more directly from the cilia) and decreases in the maculae of the opposite side. Since the maculae of the utricles are horizontal, while those of the saccules are sagittal and face laterally, macular surfaces are provided for each of the three planes in space.

The part of the vestibular mechanism concerned with changes in the *angular movement* (acceleration or deceleration) of the head includes the three semicircular canals (see Figure 4-6). The ampulla of each canal contains a small ridge on which the *crista ampullaris* is found, consisting of a patch of ciliated cells and supporting cells, as in the maculae (see Figure 4-11). The clusters of hair cells in the cristae are covered by a layer of gelatinous material. When the head is turned suddenly, there is a relative displacement between the structures attached to the membranous labyrinth and the endolymphatic fluids in the semicircular canals. This displacement, due to frictional resistance within the small membranous canals and the marked tendency of the fluids to remain at rest, produces a flow of endolymph past the cristae and disturbs the gelatinous layer. This action distorts the hair cells, which in turn excite the terminations of the vestibular nerve surrounding the cells (Sand, 1938). The strongest stimulation is set up in the canal most nearly in the plane of rotation, but the other canals will also be stimulated to some degree. If rotation is maintained so that the canals and contained fluid have the same angular movement, no stimulation will occur, although the effects of centrifugal force or other disturbances may be experienced. If, after rotation, the head is suddenly stopped, an illusion of movement in the opposite direction will be experienced since the endolymph will continue to move due to its inertia. Violent and repeated stimulation of the cristae will induce motion sickness which, through the reflex connections of the vestibular nerve, will produce vomiting, sweating, and related symptoms.

The nerve fibers from the maculae and cristae pass through numerous tiny pores of the temporal bone and enter the internal acoustic meatus. The cell bodies of these nerves form the vestibular ganglion, which lies in the meatus, while the axons form the *vestibular* portion of the acoustic (VIIIth cranial) nerve, or more briefly, the *vestibular nerve*. The vestibular nerve, together with the cochlear portion of the VIIIth cranial nerve and the facial (VIIth cranial) nerve, traverses the internal meatus and enters the cavity of the skull where it reaches the corner formed by the pons, the medulla oblongata, and the cerebellum. On entering the medulla, the vestibular fibers divide into ascending and descending fibers. The ascending fibers constitute the direct vestibular tract to the cerebellum. The descending fibers terminate in the vestibular centers within the brain stem. Numerous secondary fibers run from the vestibular nuclei to the cerebellum. There is some evidence that connections are also made to the temporal lobe, thalamus, and hypothalamus, with tertiary fibers projecting to the cortex. Using the evoked potential technique in which the vestibular portion of the VIIIth nerve was stimulated electrically, Walzl and Mountcastle (1949) identified a small, sharply circumscribed area of the cortex as the cerebral projection for the vestibular apparatus. In the cat it is in the region of the suprasylvian sulcus and is adjacent to the cortical projections from the cochlea. The projection to the cortex is principally contralateral, but stimulation of the ipsilateral nerve activates a part of the same region. The vestibular system is largely a reflexive system that, in addition to the vestibular nerve, integrates the position and movements of the eyes, head, and body through the oculomotor nuclei of the IIIrd, IVth, and VIth cranial nerves in the midbrain.

The Cutaneous System for Pain

The sensory mechanisms of the skin, sometimes called the *proximoceptors,* provide information on changes in the physical environment immediately external to the living organism. This information usually supplements that provided by vision and audition. *Somesthesis* is the general psychological term applied to body sensibility and it includes the senses of pain, pressure, warmth, and cold but excludes the sensibility in the muscles, tendons, and joints which is called *kinesthesis.* Since the sense organs for pain, pressure, warmth and cold are located primarily in the skin, these senses are often called the *cutaneous* or *minor* senses. It should be pointed out, however, that certain types of specialized receptor cells found in the skin are located within the viscera of the body as well, and provide information regarding the internal environment of the organism (*interoceptors*). In this section, we will be concerned only with the cutaneous receptors of pain and will not consider the role of the interoceptors in relation to biological drives, such as hunger and thirst. Thus, we will not become involved with the pressure-pain patterns in the stomach, sometimes called "hunger pangs," or with the somesthetic sensations of dryness in the mouth and throat that are experienced as thirst.

Although pain has been included as a cutaneous modality that can be adequately stimulated by mechanical pressure, this classification is an arbitrary one. It is now known that, in addition to mechanical pressure, pain sensations can be elicited by a wide range of electrical, chemical, and thermal stimuli, whether in the form of high or low temperatures. However, the exact characteristic that excites the receptor cells in each case is still undetermined. Apparently the pain receptors are not specialized to react to a single form of energy. At one time it was believed that the adequate stimulus for pain was anything capable of producing damage to the tissues. This *intensive hypothesis,* or *overstimulation hypothesis,* has been refuted by considerable evidence, such as the elicitation of pain responses by electrical stimulation at intensities that do not damage the tissue. Cattell and Hoagland (1931) have shown that overstimulation of the sensory organs for touch and pressure does not produce pain. Also, some areas on the skin surface are capable of eliciting only one kind of sensory experience—that of pain, regardless of the magnitude of the applied stimulus. It must be concluded that pain is a unique sensory experience associated with the excitation of a particular receptor mechanism that is capable of responding to mechanical, thermal, electrical, and chemical stimuli. Thus, the notion of an adequate stimulus applies in only a limited manner to the sense of pain.

It is generally agreed that the sensory end organs for pain are the *free* or *diffuse nerve endings* that are widely distributed throughout the body (see Figure 4-8) (Gerard, 1960). They are most numerous in the skin but can also be found in the fascia, muscles, tendons, and joints, as well as in the connective tissue of many visceral organs. The pain sensations aroused by the stimulation of the receptors in these different body locations are called, respectively, superficial or cutaneous pain, deep pain, and visceral pain. Free nerve endings are formed by the repeated division of small myelinated fibers as they approach the epidermis, lose their myelin sheath, and branch into extensive unmyelinated plexuses in the deeper portion of the dermis and immediately beneath the epidermis. The arrangement of the free nerve endings is *plexiform;* a true nerve net is formed by the interconnections of the branchings of a single axon, which may extend over as much as 50 square centimeters. The nets from different axons overlap and interlock but do not connect protoplasmically. From the subepithelial plexus, tiny fibers penetrate the epithelium and, after dividing repeatedly, terminate in bead-like thickenings (*intraepithelial endings*) below and among the cells of the deeper layers of the epidermis. In the cornea, however, the intraepithelial endings may reach the surface of the eye. Terminal arborizations of free nerve fibers are also found in the tympanum (eardrum) and in the teeth. Similar arborizations may be found wherever pain responses may be elicited, whether the free nerve endings are intraepithelial, intramuscular, or intrafascicular.

The primary neurons of the pain system consist of unmyelinated, or slightly myelinated, fibers that enter the spinal cord in the lateral part of the dorsal root and form a longitudinally running tract (Lissauer's Tract) (*posterolateral fasciculus* in Figure 4-10). These neurons, like all other primary sensory fibers of the spinal cord, divide into short ascending and descending branches with appropriate collaterals. The ascending and descending fibers of Lissauer's Tract run for a segment, or slightly more, along the spinal column and terminate in the *substantia gelatinosa* of Rolando (gray matter), which is the primary receptive center of the cord. Secondary neurons arising in the gelatinosa either end as intermediate, intrinsic neurons of the cord or give off axons, some of which run diagonally through the gray matter, cross the median line of the cord, and reach near to the surface of the cord on the opposite side (ventrolateral part of the white matter). Here they form the *lateral spinothalamic tract,* which runs rostrally and enlarges as it ascends, due to the addition of fibers it receives from the thoracic and cervical segments of the cord which it passes along the way. Part of the fibers go directly to the thalamus, but many terminate in the reticular formation of the pons and the medulla oblongata, thus reaching the thalamus by several relays. Third-order neurons connect the thalamic centers with the general somasthetic sensory area of the cerebral cortex, located in the posterior, central, and adjacent gyri.

The Receptor Systems for Thermal Energy

In man, the receptor systems for thermal energy are those systems that mediate the sensations of cold and warmth. By studying the spike activity of single nerve fibers, it has been determined that there are specific cold and warm nerve endings which respond to cooling and warming but which are unaffected by mechanical stimulation. Although there is little question about the presence of thermal receptors, the morphological structure of the receptors is still largely unknown. Histological examination of excised human skin taken from beneath experimentally determined cold and warmth spots has failed to reveal the identity of the thermal receptors. However, by mapping the cold spots on the cold-sensitive periphery of the cornea, and then dropping methylene blue into the eye, the high correlation between the cold spots and the blue-stained end bulbs has led to the conclusion that the *Krause end bulbs* are the receptors for cold (see Figure 4-8). The end organs in the prepuce have been studied by a similar mapping technique in which methylene blue was injected intra-arterially (Bazett, McGlone, Williams, and Lufkin, 1932).

In addition to finding good agreement between the location of the cold spots and the Krause end bulbs, the distribution of warm spots agreed fairly well with the location of *Ruffini end organs*. Thus, it seems fairly well established that the Krause end bulbs are the receptors for cold, and the Ruffini end organs the receptors for warmth, at least in the areas of the body investigated in these studies. However, it is still uncertain whether these types of receptors are present in other skin areas. It has recently been proposed that the universal receptors are the unencapsulated nerve endings that are located at different depths in the skin (Lele, Weddell, and Williams, 1954). Those endings just beneath the epithelium are reduced in temperature and stimulated whenever the skin is cooled; those endings located deeper in the epithelium and closer to the blood vessels are heated by the blood and produce a positive temperature gradient between the nerve ending and the axon, resulting in a sensation of warmth.

This latter view on the nature of the thermal receptors is in agreement with data on the depth of the thermal nerve endings. By studying the rate of transmission of a temperature wave through the skin, and also by measuring the reaction time of subjects stimulated by thermal sources, data have been obtained which indicate that the cold receptors lie closer to the surface of the skin than the warm receptors. However, this fact does not negate the theory of specialized receptors, since the average depth of the Krause end bulb and the Ruffini type of end organ have been estimated to be approximately 0.17 mm and 0.3 mm, respectively. The conclusions on the depth of the receptors, based on subjective reaction times in which reaction time for warmth is consistently longer than that for cold, have been confirmed by more exact neurophysiological techniques involving the recording of spike potentials in specific nerve fibers.

The thermal fibers in man enter the spinal cord via the dorsal roots and form a lateral division in the dorsolateral fasciculus (Lissauer Tract). The fibers ascend from one to three segments and then terminate in the substantia gelatinosa Rolandi. In the substantia gelatinosa Rolandi, the axons of small cells cross the cord in the anterior gray commissure and ascend in the lateral spinothalamic tract. The spinothalamic tract fibers, which form part of the trigeminal nerve, enter the brain stem and terminate in the posteroventral nucleus of the thalamus. The exact location of the third order thermal neurons within the thalamus is not known. Nevertheless, the sensory body surface from the thalamus is projected upon the postcentral gyrus. This projection in the somesthetic area of the cortex is such that the spatial relations are preserved, but in a direction opposite to those in the thalamus where the head is represented posteromedially, the back superiorly, and the feet inferiorly.

Numerous studies have been performed to determine the distribution of cold and warm spots in the skin and mucous membranes of man. The usual procedure has been to systematically apply adequate or electrical stimuli over a small circumscribed region of the skin or mucous membrane, noting those locations or "spots" that give rise to cold or warm sensations. In this way, the number of cold and warm spots per square centimeter of skin surface can be experimentally determined. In general, there are far more cold spots than warm, but the relative density varies considerably for different bodily locations. The highest density of thermosensitive spots is found in the facial areas, for instance, approximately 17 cold spots/sq cm in the lips as compared with approximately 3 cold spots/sq cm in the palm of the hand. The eyelids and lips are especially sensitive to thermal stimulation. The forehead, on the other hand, is not particularly sensitive to warmth but is highly sensitive to cold. The mean density for warm spots is usually less than 2 warm spots/sq cm, the fingers and parts of the face being most sensitive, while the hairy parts of the head, tongue, and chest are only slightly sensitive to warmth.

While there are several unusual characteristics of the temperature modality, such as paradoxical sensations, thermal after-sensations, and sensations of "burning heat," it appears that there are three primary factors governing the occurrence of a thermal sensation. These are (1) the absolute intracutaneous temperature, (2) the rate of change of the intracutaneous temperature as a function of time, and (3) the areal extension of the stimulated cutaneous region. In physical terms, these conditions of excitation constitute a system of mutually dependent thermal-spatial-temporal factors which are to some extent interchangeable, that is, a decrease in one factor may be compensated for by an increase in some other factor. A sensation of cold, for example, can be produced by providing a low level of intracutaneous temperature, an appropriate rate of cooling, and a certain area of stimulated cutaneous surface.

Although the interaction of these three factors controls the character of the thermal sensation, the excitation mechanism of the thermal receptors does *not* depend upon the exchange of thermal energy. This has been demonstrated by observing a distinct discharge of impulses from a layer of thermal receptors in which the temperature was in a state of equilibrium, both spatially and temporally. In other words, the spatial and temporal temperature gradients between the two sides of a layer of receptor cells were both zero. It has been suggested that the receptor processes are probably chemical in nature, dependent upon temperature but not upon the external exchange of energy in the skin. These processes, one excitatory and the other inhibitory, are held to interact in a manner that can account for the frequency of the steady discharge of cold receptors at constant temperatures (Hensel and Zotterman, 1951).

The Receptor Systems for Chemical Energy

The Gustatory System

In man, the sense of taste is related to the *taste buds*. These are specialized receptor organs located in the mouth, particularly along the edges and dorsum of the tongue and in the surfaces of the epiglottis, soft palate, and pharynx. Taste buds are found in the fungiform papillae (3 to 4 taste buds per papilla), in the foliate papillae arranged in folds at the side of the tongue near its base, and in the dozen or so circumvallate papillae arranged in the form of an inverted V on the dorsal surface at the base of the tongue.

A schematic representation of the human tongue showing the distribution of circumvallate papillae and a cross-section of a taste bud are given in Figure 4-12. The taste buds in the epithelial layer are clusters of onion-shaped cells containing a small pore opening on the surface of the mucosa. The taste buds vary in size, but approximate 70 μ in length and 40 μ in width at their thickest part. Within the taste buds, the cells appear to be differentiated into two types: (1) the slender gustatory cells, each with a tiny hair-like tip projecting into the taste pore, and (2) the somewhat thicker supporting cells that help to maintain the vertical configuration of the cluster.

It has been estimated that an adult man possesses approximately 10,000 taste buds. From puberty to about 45 years of age, the number of receptors remains essentially constant through a continuous balance in the processes of atrophy and growth. In old age, however, there is a marked atrophy of the taste buds in the circumvallate papillae (Arey, Tremaine, and Monzingo, 1935).

From the subepithelial network of nerve fibers, two or three fibers may enter a taste bud, each fiber connecting to one or more receptor cells. The branchings from the entering nerve fibers make contact with both the gustatory and supporting cells. The afferent taste fibers from the anterior two-thirds of the tongue form part of the lingual nerve, which also contains fibers for touch, pain, and temperature. These fibers associated with taste are bundled together (*chorda tympani nerve*) and pass through the cavity of the middle ear near the tympanum; they enter the brain stem as part of the facial (VIIth cranial) nerve. The afferent fibers from the posterior region of the tongue are contained in the glossopharyngeal (IXth cranial) nerve and those from the larynx and pharynx travel in the vagus (Xth cranial) nerve. The taste fibers of these three cranial nerves terminate in the tractus solitarus and in its nucleus in the medulla. No primary cortical projection

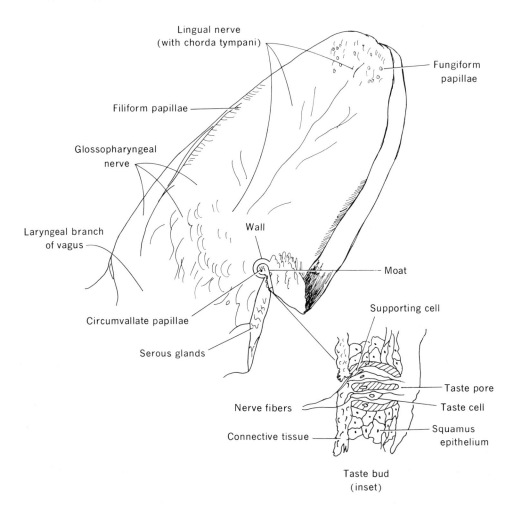

Figure 4–12. A schematic representation of the human tongue showing the distribution of circumvallate papillae and a cross-section of a taste bud (inset).

region with exclusive gustatory functions has been found in man, although there is some evidence that taste may be localized interiorly to the facial somatosensory area (Patton, 1950).

Although there are four primary taste qualities (salty, sweet, bitter, and sour), electrophysiological evidence in the cat indicates that the taste receptors can *not* be classified so simply into four corresponding neural types (Pfaffmann, 1941). The sensory cells for taste are sensitive to chemicals in general, with single cells possessing varying degrees of reactivity to several different kinds of chemical stimuli. Thus, while the individual cells are differentially sensitive, they cannot be separated into four distinct classes, since many of the chemical stimuli to which they respond fall into two or more categories of the basic taste classification. Also, the available evidence seems to indicate that man, unlike the cat, dog, pig, and rhesus monkey, does not have a specific water taste (Zotterman, 1959), but that the regulation of water intake is dependent upon various physiological conditions such as cellular dehydration.

The Olfactory System

The receptor organ for the sense of smell in man consists of the olfactory mucosa lying in the dorsal and posterior part of the nasal cavity. The olfactory mucosa, yellow-brown in color, extends over a total area of approximately 240 sq mm and covers the upper parts of both the lateral wall of the nasal cavity and the nasal septum. The general extent of the olfactory mucosa is shown in Figure 4-13, which also depicts the human olfactory structures.

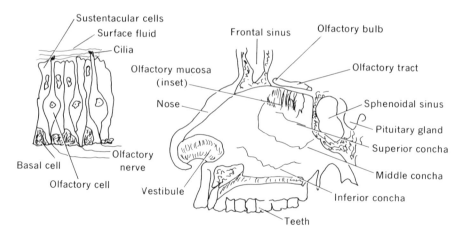

Figure 4–13. A schematic drawing of the nasal cavity, olfactory structures, and olfactory epithelium (inset).

During normal breathing, inspired air passes through the nose primarily via the interior and middle meatus without coming into contact with the olfactory mucosa. However, the flow of air may be altered, for example, by sniffing, which sets up eddying currents of air that move into the upper olfactory region. The olfactory receptors cannot be stimulated unless the odorous material is in some way brought into contact with the olfactory epithelium.

A schematic view of the olfactory mucosa with its olfactory (bipolar and oval) receptor cells is presented in the inset of Figure 4-13. The receptor cells, as viewed under an electron microscope, possess numerous small distal swellings and are characterized by the protrusion of up to 1000 hairs per cell (Bloom and Engstrom, 1952). Each hair is approximately 1 to 2 μ in length and 0.1 μ in diameter.

Each receptor cell appears to have its own associated nerve fiber. The olfactory (Ist cranial) nerve fibers associated with the hair cells penetrate the ethmoid bone to collect on the surface of the olfactory bulb and then enter into the formation of glomeruli within the bulb. The typographic arrangement of the olfactory epithelium seems to hold for the projection pattern at the level of the bulb; the upper and lower part of the epithelium project to the upper and lower part of the bulb. From the glomeruli, some 60,000 axons of second-order neurons (*mitral cells*) are collected into the lateral olfactory tract and travel to the primary olfactory cortex. An alternate route is taken by the finer axons of second-order neurons (tufted cells) which pass from the glomeruli into the anterior limb of the anterior commissure to reach the opposite bulb where they synapse with deeper (granule) cells. The higher-order neurons from the bulb travel to the *amygdala* where the stria terminalis arises; the stria terminalis passes to the hypothalamus where it partially ends. More direct connections probably exist between the amygdala and the hypothalamus, as well as the septum, through the diagonal band of Broca. The hypothalamus then establishes connections with the thalamic nuclei, where further relays pass via the fornix bundles beneath the corpus callosum to the hippocampal formation. Ultimately the nerve fibers reach the midbrain tegmentum via the entorhinal area and the stria medullaris. For the beginning student, this intricate pathway of olfactory fibers may be summarized by indicating that the olfactory bulb is brought into neural contact with certain structures of the rhinencephalon and certain regions of the diencephalon and midbrain.

II
Quantitative Methods in Psychological Research

Chapter 5

THEORIES, MEASUREMENT, AND BEHAVIOR

Orientation

This chapter is logically a continuation of Chapter 1 and could, perhaps, have been included in Part I of this book. However, the presentation of ideas to be found in this chapter has been delayed intentionally to provide the student with the opportunity of mastering the subject matter that is fundamental to the scientific study of human behavior, particularly sensory and perceptual behavior. Now we are ready to learn about the philosophic frame of reference that places psychology among the sciences (Kantor, 1963) and to explore, in the following chapters, some of the experimental methods and types of research designs that are used to study particular problems in psychology.

In Chapter 5 we are extending our concept of the philosophy of science by reviewing some general considerations related to scientific theories, experimental evidence, and problems of measurement indigenous to the study of behavior. We have already learned that the accumulation of knowledge is one of the aims of science and that all knowledge starts with observation. Controlled observation in the form of experiments provides the groundwork upon which all science is built. As scientists, psychologists manipulate conditions and events in order to observe what happens under a given set of circumstances. From these planned observations, the psychologist seeks to discover new facts and to derive statements of regularities or laws that apply to that particular situation. How do psychologists, or scientists in general, know what events should be observed or what factors should be manipulated? How are the changes that take place to be measured? What is the meaning or significance of the results that are obtained in an experiment? These are the kinds of questions that are explored in the present chapter.

How are we, as psychologists, to proceed in the world of science? What direction shall we follow? One possibility is to survey the various sciences and to follow that approach which over the years has proved to be the most successful. This takes us to physics, the most advanced of the natural sciences. The methods and techniques of physics are more accurate and more reliable than those of any other science; the predictions derived from theoretical physics have been strongly confirmed by experimentation. The "Theory of Theories," which deals with the logical structure of scientific theories, has been established mainly according to the example of the physical sciences (Frank, 1961, p. ix). It seems reasonable, therefore, to adopt physics as the prototype of psychology, although there are widely divergent opinions on this matter among contemporary psychologists.

Those who are concerned with the role of theories in psychology seem to fall into two major camps: one camp favors the approach commonly called the hypothetico-deductive method which, crudely speaking, proceeds from hypotheses to data (Burt, 1958; Burt and Gregory, 1958; Hull, 1951); the other, favors a descriptive approach which, crudely speaking, proceeds from observations to the induction of general hypotheses or principles (Skinner, 1950; Wrigley, 1960). This textbook advocates the first approach, but this is not to deny that important contributions in psychology have been made, and will undoubtedly continue to be made, by alternative approaches, nor is it proposed that everyone is in complete agreement as to the specific logical stages contained in the hypothetico-deductive method. In fact, the lack of agreement has been highlighted by a series of recent articles (Burt and Gregory, 1958; Pilkington, 1958; Pilkington, 1960; Taylor, 1958; Willis, 1958). Nevertheless, the tremendous advances made in the physical sciences by means of the hypothetico-deductive method provide ample evidence of the utility of this approach for those seeking to create a science of human behavior.

In this chapter, we will study the logical structure of physical theories and analyze the interrelationships that exist between theories, hypotheses, and experiments. Since the experiment underlies the method of modern science, we need to understand the nature of the connections between empirical events and theoretical concepts. The student must learn to distinguish between statements about observations, statements of logical conclusions, and statements that merely introduce new words or rules for the construction of propositions within some theoretical framework. The understanding of such distinctions is a prerequisite for clear thinking and the effective communication of ideas. Progress in science does not depend merely upon the performance of new experiments; the facts established by these experiments must be integrated by older theories or by the formulation of new theories. This chapter, then, is intended to provide the student with a more thorough appreciation of the nature of scientific theories and acquaint him with the problem of obtaining empirical evidence in support of these theories in the field of human behavior. Other writers have also recognized the need for imparting this kind of information (Whitrow, 1956).

Indeed, it is already gradually dawning on many of those whose duty it is to teach future scientists and technologists in an age when science and technology are tending to replace

the humanities as the intellectual foundations of our civilization, that the deliberate culti-
vation of critical standards is no less essential for the student of science than for the
student of literature. It has usually been assumed that students need only be taught facts
and techniques of science and that they should be left to discover for themselves intuitively
how to think and how to express themselves. The study of *the method and mode of presentation*
of the classics of science has usually been neglected while attention has been concentrated
solely on the results obtained and their place in the general body of knowledge: the
finished product, rather than the process of manufacture, has been the object on which
the student has been encouraged to focus his attention. Instead, I would suggest that the
educational curriculum of the future scientific research worker should include the study
of critical analyses, made by philosophers of science, of selected classics of scientific investigation (p. 198).

Some Characteristics
of Models and Theories

Models

In Chapter 1, some consideration was given to the place of psychology in the
world of knowledge. It will be recalled that in one schema presented for the
classification of areas of knowledge into an orderly and systematic arrangement,
science was divided into two major categories: formal sciences and material
sciences. This distinction tends to emphasize that the domain of science, when
looked at from a broad point of view, consists of two different types of activities,
one logical and the other observational. These two types of activities are related,
but conceptually separable; the practical procedures employed in obtaining
scientific results should not be confused with the theoretical formulations that are
designed to explain them. The dominant approach to the understanding and
explanation of events in the natural sciences has been through the use of *models*
and *theories*. The term model, however, has multiple meanings that need to be
clarified (Lachman, 1960) and the role models play in the construction of theories
should be examined (Hutten, 1954). Each will be considered in turn.

In science, the two most common meanings of model are (1) a *visual representation* and (2) an *analogy*. A model as a visual representation refers to anything that
can be seen; thus we ordinarily speak about a model *of* something, for example,
of an airplane or the Statue of Liberty. The model may be a three-dimensional
representation of an object and it may be larger than, smaller than, or equal in
size to the original. Consider, for instance, a plaster model of the human eye, a
souvenir model of the Empire State Building, and a wooden meterstick. Sometimes the representation is two-dimensional, as in a diagram or a cross-sectional
view. Whether the representation is two- or three-dimensional, the model is
intended to show the relations that exist among the various parts of the original
object. In some respects, a globe looks like the earth.

The field of engineering psychology has made increasing use of models or
replicas in the form of mock-ups, simulators, training devices, mannikins, and
workspace layouts. These representations, however, are not ordinarily referred to
as models. By using these representations or models of control rooms, aircraft

cockpits, spaceship cabins, and other complex work areas, engineering psychologists have been able to resolve many intricate problems of equipment design without endangering human lives and risking the potential destruction of extremely expensive equipment. Models of this type are also frequently used for teaching specific operational skills.

The second meaning of the word model is that in which the representation serves more than a visual function; the representation is a model *for* something. It shows how something functions or it *explains* how something happens by providing a sequence of temporally-related events, that is, a process. There is a likeness between the process, event, or structure being modeled and the significant aspects of the model itself. This can be clarified by the following quotation:

> . . . the set of phenomena A is like the set of phenomena B with respect to properties x, y, and z. And again A, in addition, is known to possess w. Now, does B also possess w? The question comes from the analogy, but the answer must come from further theoretical and experimental investigation . . . Success consists either in finding evidence that B does possess w or that B does not possess w (Turner, 1955, p. 238).

Nineteenth century physics was filled with models. Among others, there were purely mechanical models of balls, rods, springs, and flywheels; there were models of elastic bodies, models of the movement of ocean currents, and models of atoms sharing electrons in chemical reactions. Thus, there were mechanical, electrical, and hydrodynamical models, in pure and combined form, but with the advent of modern physics it became increasingly evident that a model need not necessarily be constructed in physical form. It was also apparent that some concepts such as Einstein's "finite but unbounded" space could not even be physically imagined. Such concepts could only be expressed mathematically. Mathematical formalisms, that is, mathematical models, now function in some respects like the mechanical models in the earlier stages of physics.

Gregory (1953) has pointed out that "much current work in psychology takes the form of looking for appropriate physical models with which to describe, by analogy, the findings of experiment and observation" (p. 192). What sort of mechanism, for example, could perform the tasks undertaken by the central nervous system as an organism learns a skill or translates a written passage into a foreign language? Perhaps the best-known example of an analogy in psychology is that in which an electronic computer is said to constitute a model of the brain, or its electrical processes. "What happens in the brain is interpreted in accordance with what happens in a computing machine" (Götlind, 1961, p. 59). Although analogies such as this may stimulate the generation of new ideas and the formulation of new functional relations which are both quantifiable and testable (Miller, 1955), they may also be misleading and erroneous.

The problem arises when we tend to identify the model with the objects or events that it is intended to represent. Consider, for example, the common statement that the "human eye is like a camera." While the analogy is correct in certain respects, for example, both are light-sensitive devices, there are many ways in which they differ. Perhaps the most obvious is that in a camera we adjust the focus by changing the distance between the lens and the photographic film; in the human eye, the lens changes its shape to produce a clear image of relatively near objects. Models are useful because they are familiar to us and can serve as aids in the explanation of unfamiliar events or processes. However, caution must be observed to insure that misleading or erroneous ideas are not fostered or propagated. A model may or may not be suitable, but even when it is appropriate there is the danger that overgeneralizations from the model may occur.

In science, the major significance of a model, whether physical or conceptual, lies in its *logical* function. The model may be characterized by a set of mathematical or symbolic statements that may be used to represent certain aspects of the objects, processes, or events being modeled. Figure 5-1 is a symbolic model of the tracking system for controlling depth in a fleet type of submarine. The

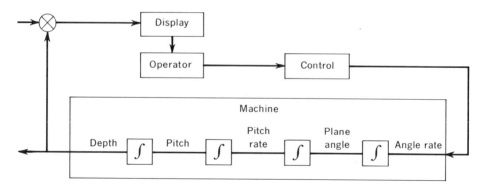

Figure 5–1. A symbolic model of the tracking system for controlling depth in a fleet-type submarine. (From Ely, Bowen, and Orlansky in *Human engineering guide to equipment design* by Morgan *et al*, copyright © 1963, McGraw-Hill Book Company. Used by permission.)

position of the operator's (planesman's) control device directly affects the rate of change of the control surface (plane angle); plane angle affects the acceleration of pitch; and pitch affects the rate of change of depth. The planesman in effect controls the fourth derivative of depth, that is, there are four integrations between the output of the operator and that of the machine. Since depth information (output) is fed back into the display of the system, the model is that of a closed-loop tracking system. Notice that the model does not pictorially resemble a man and a submarine. The lines and arrows symbolize the flow of information through the elements of the system and the primary components of the system are shown as boxes. The movement of the submarine through the water is symbolized by the mathematical function represented by the series of integral signs.

As symbolic systems, models have two characteristics which may be called (1) *formal rules* and (2) *pointers* (Hesse, 1953). The formal rules refer to the internal structure of the model in terms of axioms and rules of mathematical inference—in the example, differential and integral calculus. The pointers refer to generalizations and modifications of the model that are suggested by and consistent with the mathematics itself. It would be possible, for instance, to eliminate one integration by redesigning the machine so that the operator controls plane angle directly, rather than controlling plane angle rate. From a practical viewpoint, models may provide assistance in the design of man-machine systems; from a scientific standpoint, they may suggest new relationships that were not immediately apparent without the use of the model.

Now we will consider the relation of models to theory. As we have indicated, a model may be considered as an analogy and, as an analogy, it helps us understand complex processes or events; the familiar and simpler elements of the model are used to interpret the unfamiliar and more intricate aspects of some other process or event. The explanation of the more complex situation is tentatively offered in the form of a scientific theory. The *theory* is a formalized conceptual system that attempts to specify the variables that are relevant to the occurrence of a particular class of natural phenomena and to describe the nature of their interrelationships. In contrast with a model, a theory is broader and can account for a wider range of phenomena since it ordinarily includes a greater number of variables. A theory of human tracking behavior would extend far beyond the type of tracking depicted in the model of Figure 5-1. This model is restricted to a small portion of the domain of tracking behavior and as such is called an *auxiliary model*, since it specifically encompasses a limited range of events in a broader theory. A *main model* is considerably more comprehensive and serves as a basis for a whole theory. In physics, an example of an auxiliary model is that of describing heat as an oscillatory motion of atoms; a main model is found in the planetary model as the basis for the classical Bohr theory of atoms. In psychology, it is sometimes relatively easy to detect the particular model that is used as the source of inferential principles by noting the specific terms that are applied when the investigator refers to his own work, for example, *statistical* model of learning (Estes, 1950), *quasilinear* model of manual tracking (Licklider, 1960), and *genetic* determinants of behavior (Hirsch, 1962). Notice that in each of these examples an independent system lies outside the structure of the theory with which the investigator is primarily concerned.

Now let us be more precise. Theories (of certain types) consist of two major parts: (1) a formal *calculus*, that is, a set of terms (or a *vocabulary*) and statements (*postulates, axioms,* or *equations*) that describe the presumed relationships among the terms of the vocabulary, and (2) an interpretation that links the set of terms to observational statements (experiments) (Hutten, 1954). A model is a *separate* system frequently functioning as an analogy, but this need not be so. It is an ordered system independent of the theory and more than one model may be used in relation to a theory. The model contains an organization of concepts, laws, or relationships that are brought to bear upon the phenomena encompassed by the theory. The model, as an external organization or system, contributes to the construction, application, or interpretation of the theory. Thus the point is made that *the model serves to interpret the formal calculus of the theory.* The theoretical terms, symbols, and formulae are made intelligible by giving them meaning within the context of the model. From the basic concepts, relationships, and principles of the model, certain conclusions may be deduced, usually by applying mathematical argument or the formal rules of logic. This, in turn, may lead to an extension of the theory, or may suggest new relationships among the theoretical variables that need to be tested by experiment.

> The billiard ball model of gas molecules, for instance, consists of a collection of balls moving at random and colliding with each other and with the walls of the vessel, and the behavior of such a system is already known and expressed in a mathematical theory, independently of the experimental results about gases with which it is compared. This means that further ramifications of the theory of colliding billiard balls can be used to extend the theory of gases, and questions can be asked such as "are gas molecules like rigid balls or like elastic ones? . . ." Progress is made by devising experiments to answer questions suggested by the model (Hesse, 1953, p. 193).

We have seen, then, that models have both a heuristic and a logical function. Those models that function primarily as visual representations have a limited value and for the most part should be avoided. In dealing with such models we are likely to forget their limitations and may be drawn into a useless stream of experimental effort. Models that provide a logical function or establish the rules of logical inference leading to the prediction of certain outcomes may play an important part in the development of a theory but such models should be carefully evaluated.

One of the considerations in the evaluation of a model is the range of phenomena it encompasses. The broader the scope of the model, the greater the number and extent of the facts that may ultimately be brought together under a theory generated by that model. Many different models may provide varying degrees of interpretation in a given area of study, just as a single term may occur in a number of different models. Consider the notion of "atom," for example, as it occurs in the mechanical model (kinetic theory), in the vector model (quantum theory), and in terms of probability distributions (quantum mechanics). A given term may have multiple interpretations and different models may overlap, at least in part. Other things being equal, the broadest model is in general to be preferred.

Another criterion to be applied in evaluating a model is the degree to which the consequences of a theory are derived unequivocally from that particular model and its associated rules of inference. The model forms a link between theory and experiment; consequently, we require one that permits us to test the theory in terms of that model, with little or no uncertainty about the theoretical meaning or interpretation of the results obtained in a given experiment. Models that permit contradictory deductions foster research that is unlikely to contribute anything of significance to the general body of scientific knowledge. Whether or not a model we have adopted is applicable in a given situation will depend upon its success in practice. In science, the criterion for success is quite direct—the model must permit accurate predictions. The accuracy of the predictions will indicate whether the model "fits" the situation or whether the model that is successful in a narrower context is being applied beyond its intended domain of explanation.

Theories

In the preceding discussion, it was emphasized that models may assist the investigator who in interested in theory construction by providing two types of aid: representational and logical. In the history of science both types have assisted investigators in discovering new findings and in formulating new theoretical relationships. Miller (1955), for example, has proposed a general theory for the behavioral sciences based upon the electronic model of a computer. The use of models, however, is *not* a *requirement* in the development of scientific theories. We have already indicated that their use may be experimentally detrimental, but their acceptance may also limit the suppleness and freedom of thought so essential to scientific discovery. Some of the most ingenious theories in the physical sciences were, in fact, propounded only *after* the restrictive mode of thinking imposed by a model was abandoned, as, for example, in Maxwell's electromagnetic theory of light. The bulk of our scientific knowledge has been generated by the use of theory; models in science are optional, but theories are indispensable. We will now examine the meaning of theory in more detail.

All scientific theories have their origin in observation and are evaluated ultimately in terms of observation. From casual situations in everyday life, from clinical studies and field surveys, and from controlled experiments, there gradually emerges a collection of observations. Associated with these observations, is a group of ideas that attempts to interpret these observations. A classic example is Newton's supposed observation of a falling apple and his ideas about gravity; another is Pavlov's observation of his salivating dog and his ideas about a conditioned reflex. The commonality of observations suggests the subject matter to be systematized by the theory, for example, whether the theory will deal with falling bodies or with conditioned responses. A scientific theory, then, deals with the objects, events, or situations that are found in nature and that, as natural phenomena, belong to a particular class with specifiable characteristics. These classes form the traditional subject matter areas of science, such as astronomy, chemistry, and psychology; the observations may also be considered to represent subclasses of phenomena within these areas. The *scope* of theory is directly related to the range of phenomena encompassed.

Given a particular set of phenomena that need to be explained, the theorist establishes a set of basic terms (a *vocabulary*) he believes to be sufficient and indispensable for describing the phenomena of interest to him (Bergmann, 1960). These terms refer to physical objects, events, or situations and are *descriptive* or *referential;* they have a *denotative* meaning in the sense of "pointing toward" something or some property. Accordingly, descriptive words may be divided into *proper names* and *character words*. Proper names refer to things that can be pointed at, such as a memory drum or an audiometer, while character words refer to properties of objects or events, such as red or mammal. The term "concept" is frequently used as a synonym for character word. Notice that in the examples of character words there is a difference in the complexity of the characters. Simple characters like red may be considered as *undefined* descriptive terms; we are directly acquainted with the property named. A *defined* descriptive term names a complex character such as mammal; the complex character is specified by a definition that indicates how simple characters combine into a complex one. Character words may also be divided according to another classification: *relational* and *nonrelational*. We have already considered the nonrelational words—those naming properties, as for example, green. The relational words are exemplified by two or more objects, such as, the cat is *under* the table, the post office is *between* the hospital and the high school.

Proper names and character words, however, comprise only part of the theory-builder's vocabulary. Some words, called *logical* words, do not name anything. These include, for example, "and," "not," and "all"—words that play an important role in science and theory construction whenever logical or deductive inferences are made.

The point of this discussion is that the theorist must have a vocabulary with which to communicate in an unambiguous manner. The words he uses must be precise and have meaning within the framework of a scientific language. Thus, one of the primary aspects of theory construction is to specify the concepts (variables) that are relevant to the phenomena under consideration, and to introduce these concepts into the theory in such a way that there is no misunderstanding concerning any statement made within the context of the theory.

Once the scientific vocabulary has been established, the second portion of the theory may be developed. This requires a set of rules; in the physical sciences these rules are usually mathematical and establish the kinds of relationships that may be admitted to the theoretical system. By observing these rules, a set of *postulates* (axioms or equations) are generated which assert the presumed relationships among the physical phenomena as represented by the basic terms of the theory. In other words, this portion of theory construction provides a statement of the assumed functional relations between or among the variables that were identified as operative in the given situation.

An example of a postulate is that given by Hull (1943, p. 344):

Postulate II

The momentary effective reaction potential ($S\overset{\cdot}{\overline{E}}R$) must exceed the reaction threshold (S^LR) before a stimulus (S) will evoke a given response (R).

It is of historical interest that Hull's original theory of behavior (1943) contained a total of only sixteen postulates, each of which was stated both verbally and mathematically.

The first two portions of the theory (the vocabulary and the postulates) are said to comprise the *calculus* of the theory. The third portion of the theory consists of the *theorems* that are derived by deduction from the postulates and that explicitly portend new knowledge (Hull, 1951). The development of the theorems depends upon rules of inference that allow one sentence to be derived from another. The theorems, however, unlike the hierarchical classification of increasingly complex concepts (the vocabulary) or the hierarchical arrangement of increasingly general propositions (the postulates), must be tested by experiment before they can be accepted into the theory. We will consider this problem in detail in the next section of this chapter.

The type of theory we have described is commonly called a *hypothetico-deductive theory*. The classical example of this kind of theory is that of Isaac Newton. The theory consists of (1) seven definitions that include the concepts of matter, motion, and so on, and (2) a set of postulates (that became established as his three famous laws of motion), from which were derived (3) a set of seventy-three formally proved theorems and a large number of appended corollaries. The theorems and corollaries were related to such observable phenomena as the shape of planets and their orbits, the flowing of the tides, and so on. We need not stress the elegance of the theory and its tremendous success in predicting events involving the principle of gravity.

Given a hypothetico-deductive theory or axiomatic system, are there criteria that may be applied to determine whether, in principle, the system is acceptable? Ordinarily, a system is acceptable if the axioms fulfill three conditions: (1) the axioms must be as few as possible, (2) they must be consistent with each other, and (3) they must be sufficient to permit the deduction in the form of theorems of all facts falling within the domain of the theory (Woodger, 1937).

The criterion that the axioms should be as few as possible is primarily inserted for reasons of verbal and logical economy, although some writers (for example, Battig, 1962) have argued that the *law of parsimony* as applied to theory tends to handicap the psychologist by emphasizing simplicity rather than the complexity of the behavioral phenomena we are trying to understand and explain. Nevertheless, if the axioms are mutually independent, one axiom cannot be derived from another; but, if they are not, one axiom may be derived from a combination of the remaining axioms in the system. The nonindependent or superfluous axiom could then be considered as a *consequence* of the theory and, if such an axiom were included in the original set of axioms, it could be removed and inserted among the theorems. This would reduce the original number of axioms by one. In any theory there is no way of knowing how many axioms will be required to make a complete system. Sometimes superfluous axioms are not discarded, since they make the theory appear less complicated, thereby providing a practical advantage.

If the axioms are consistent with each other, the system will contain no *contradictions*. In such a case, if the rules of the system are correctly applied, it will be impossible to deduce two theorems concerning the same situation which suggest two different outcomes. There is no way of knowing beforehand whether or not the axioms are inconsistent, but the alert theorist will be aware of this possibility. Should there be any evidence of inconsistency, an experimental test should be run to determine which, if either, of the predicted outcomes actually agrees with the observation. The inconsistent axiom would then be discarded or rephrased to remove the erroneous implication.

Of the three criteria for the acceptability of an axiomatic system, the *principle of sufficiency* is the most critical. It implies that one can derive a theorem for each and every possible outcome that can occur under those conditions contained within each axiom or under those conditions implicit in any or all combinations of the axioms. Again, there is no way of knowing by the mere inspection of a set of axioms whether the set is complete. In principle, one could derive theorems one by one and determine by observation whether agreement was or was not obtained.

Although the next section of this chapter is devoted entirely to the experimental significance of physical theories, it should be apparent from the preceding discussion that physical theories have intrinsic characteristics that attract the support of scientists. We need only mention at this point that one of these characteristics is "intellectual economy." Starting with a large number of apparently disparate facts, empirical laws are derived; from these general expressions, a vast number of individual cases may be reconstructed. This first-order economy is redoubled when laws are integrated into theories. For example, the law of refraction can account for innumerable facts of refraction, but a theory of optics can account for a whole universe of light phenomena. Optical theory condenses all the known laws of light phenomena into a small number of principles. From these principles, and knowing how to calculate, one can extract any law of light and deduce any theorem within the context of that theory.

Physical scientists have in general tried to present their theories in the form of strict deductive systems consisting of definitions, axioms, and theorems; these attempts, however, have not been completely successful. This is to be expected, since science progresses slowly, and knowledge in a given area of study is modified to reflect the acquisition of new facts. A logic-tight representation of a theory can, then, be anticipated only after most of the facts have been collected and the theory representing these facts has been completed. In the meantime, the construction of a system must remain tentative and provisional. There is no a priori way of knowing when all the facts are "in," or whether some new facts may be discovered which cannot be described by the system.

In the early stages of theory construction, it is unlikely that sufficient data will be available to permit the complete formalization of the theory. Nevertheless, an attempt should be made to state the theory in a formal manner. Some fear that a premature statement of the theory may lead to the fixation of ideas or to their misdirection, but the history of science has shown that the logical clarity achieved by the formalization more than compensates for any potential psychological dangers. No bells or whistles signify the proper time to attempt the formal reconstruction of a physical theory; only the end results by trial will reveal whether an adequate theory has been propounded. Beginning with a few preliminary concepts and some tentative principles, the theorist starts to build a system that can account for the facts in a given area of inquiry. In the later or more advanced stages of the theory, the preliminary concepts may take the form of definitions, while the tentative principles constitute the axioms or postulates.

The axioms chosen as part of a theory are statements generated by the scientist that may have been suggested by, or derived from, observation. It should be realized that several different theories, each with its own particular set of axioms, may be able to describe the same set of natural phenomena. In formulating a theory, it is a matter of individual choice as to the set of axioms that will form the base of the theory. If the theorems derived from the theory are subsequently found to be in agreement with the observations of the natural phenomena to which they refer, the theory is held to be valid. The acceptance of the theory implies the acceptance of its axioms.

In the early evaluation of a theory, the axioms are in the form of hypotheses. Hypotheses are initially conceptual in nature; they are developed by reasoning based on past observations but they do not simply reflect objects and events. ". . . There can be no set of rules given for the procedure of scientific discovery—a hypothesis is not produced by a deductive machine by feeding experimental observations into it: it is the product of creative imagination . . ." (Hesse, 1953, p. 198).

Hypotheses contain conceptualized relationships or elements that fall within the theory such that, assuming the truth of the hypothesis, certain empirical consequences may be expected to follow. The consequences or implications of the hypotheses constitute the theorems of the theoretical system; these theorems must be substantiated by experimental evidence, if the conceptual aspects of the hypotheses are to be considered as supported or confirmed. Sometimes, in speaking loosely, scientists will use the term "hypothesis" to include in this single concept both the assumptions and postulates and the derived theorems of a system, and may even implicitly refer to the empirical situation for testing the theorem. Such use of the term should be avoided since it leads to a confusion of the logical and empirical elements of a physical theory. Sometimes, also, ro distinction is made between the two terms "hypothesis" and "theory." Although the two terms involve logical concepts aimed at explaining natural events, they are not interchangeable. A theory is considerably more general than a hypothesis, which postulates certain elements or relations in a limited segment of inquiry encompassed by the theory. A single theory may contain a large number of hypotheses, especially if the theory purports to explain a wide range of diverse phenomena. In this case, the theory may be considered as composed of a collection of noncontradictory and supplementary hypotheses, logically welded into a comprehensive conceptual system which is designed to account for a certain sphere of natural events.

Before an empirical test is conducted in which observations are collected that will tend to confirm or disconfirm a hypothesis, the theorem derived from the hypothesis, or combination of hypotheses, must be stated precisely. If this cannot be done, the basic hypothesis or hypotheses are likely to be ambiguous or conceptually inarticulate. Proceeding with an empirical test under these conditions is inadvisable. While there is always some possibility that a new fact may emerge from any experiment, to undergo the time, expense, and effort required to carry out an experiment under such adverse circumstances would represent poor judgment. A theoretical interpretation of the results obtained in such an experiment would be essentially impossible.

In an ideal system the theorems are derived mathematically from the set of postulates (tentative) and from the definitions previously formulated, thereby insuring an accurate and an exact statement of the theorem. However, in the early stages of theory formation, this may not be possible; the theorist is still attempting to arrive at a suitable set of postulates. These postulates are generated by formulating principles that extend beyond the specific findings of previous studies, by examining through logical analysis those factual situations or natural phenomena for which no adequate explanation has been proposed, and by applying his own personal skills and intellectual functions in the attempt to construct potentially successful hypotheses within the framework of a theory. Hypotheses must be accurately verbalized if the theorems following from them are to be unambiguous.

Prior to setting up an empirical test to determine the extent of agreement between a theorem and the observation of the natural phenomenon, a formal statement is usually constructed that combines the hypothesis and the theorem. This may take the form of an "if-then" statement, as follows: If hypothesis (H) is true, then under a set of conditions (E) certain consequences (R) will occur. The dependent clause in this sentence contains the hypothesis to be investigated; the independent clause contains the theorem. Provided the hypothesis is true, the implications (R) contained in the theorem should follow, given the proper set of conditions (E). The hypothesis is not directly tested, but its adequacy can be determined by examining the results of the experiment, assuming that the relationship between hypothesis and theorem is logically sound and that the implications of the theorem, if present, could be observed in the particular experimental test contrived. Until the hypothesis is supported by factual evidence, it remains as pure speculation, a guess, or "hunch," with no scientific import.

The empirical test of the consequences logically derived from the hypothesis must satisfy the conditions stated in the theorem. The elements in the test must be related in exactly the same way as the elements of the theorem, which means in effect that the investigator must be certain he is testing the theorem he thinks he is testing and not some other. At first glance, such a precaution seems hardly worth mentioning, but there are numerous instances in which this type of error has been made in the field of psychology. One of the difficulties, as well as one of the advantages, in setting up an empirical test is that a wide variety of situations can be evolved that will adequately represent the variables, conditions, or relationships contained in the theorem. A particular theorem, for example, might be tested by an experiment in vision or audition—but consider the vast differences in laboratory requirements and techniques, in the two cases, even though the empirical test involves the same theorem. The only experimental requirement is that the consequences contained in the theorem must be demonstrable in whatever setting is provided. Whenever the relations expressed in the theorem are appropriately interpreted in the factual situation, the nature of the relationship is identical in the two representations and a valid empirical test has been devised. If it is impossible to find a factual situation that encompasses the conditions of the theorem, the theorem is untestable.

We see, therefore, that there are two requirements for the verification of a hypothesis: (1) the testing situation must appropriately interpret the theorem, such that the variables or relationships contained in the theorem are allowed to function in the testing situation, and (2) the collected observations must agree with the consequences expressed in the theorem. If the observations do not agree with the expected consequences, there are several steps in the chain of events leading to the theorem that should be rechecked by the investigator. Probably the first thing he would do would be to reexamine the manner in which the conditions of the experiment are assumed to be related to the conditions of the theorem.

Although the procedures that have been described for confirming hypotheses are widely held in contemporary psychology, the critical approach to science espoused by Popper (1959) and his followers (Bunge, 1964) suggests another alternative. Simply stated (although logically complex), this approach argues that the verificationist approach to the confirmation of hypotheses must give way to a falsificationist approach. This means, among other things, that in testing a scientific "hypothesis" there should be ingenious and honest attempts to show that the hypothesis is false. The severity of testing will, in part, be dependent upon the ingenuity of the experimenter, his scientific integrity, technical competence, and so on. According to Popper, an empirical hypothesis is not verifiable but falsifiable; the reason for this is that falsity is transmitted from the conclusions to at least one of the premises, but truth is not. Thus, if the conclusion of a scientific inference is verified, it contributes nothing to our knowing whether the premises are true or not. In Popper's view, only when data are applied to try to "disprove" a hypothesis are we applying the scientific method. Whether the critical approach to science and philosophy will supplant that of verification and logical positivism remains to be seen. Marks (1964) is among the first in psychology to suggest that in developing better theories "progress will not be made until we . . . direct (our) attention to situations in which the indicated relationships fail demonstrably" (p. 794).

Scientific Evidence
and the Confirmation of Hypotheses

The task of the scientist is to construct adequate theories, that is, theories that permit testable theorems to be formulated. These theorems should be sufficient to describe a particular class of phenomena. The extent of agreement between the predicted outcome as stated in the theorem and the obtained experimental results determines the extent of confirmation or nonconfirmation of the underlying hypothesis. We will now examine this situation more thoroughly.

Begin by restating the various steps leading from the hypothesis to the observations. These are: (1) the postulation of a specific hypothesis, (2) the deduction of certain consequences or implications from the hypothesis, (3) the statement of these consequences or implications in the form of a theorem, (4) the interpretation of the elements, variables, or relationships of the theorem in terms of an empirical testing situation, and (5) the collection of observations within this situation. If the observations (Step 5) show complete agreement, within a small margin of error, with the implications of the theorem (Step 3), we have confirmed the hypothesis. If, on the other hand, there is complete disagreement between the outcome of Step 5 and the implications of Step 3, we have failed to confirm the hypothesis, that is, the hypothesis is disconfirmed. Usually, however, the results are not so clearcut; the predicted values (Step 3) and the empirical results (Step 5) are only in partial agreement. Then it depends upon theoretical and practical considerations whether or not we consider the experiment as supporting the hypothesis. It should be observed, however, that regardless of which of these three possible outcomes is actually obtained, valid inferences from the observations to the hypothesis may only be made provided the relationships implicit in Steps 1 through 5 are properly maintained. Any failure in logic or empirical interpretation invalidates any conclusion that involves the hypothesis.

Notice that at no point in this discussion have we used the expression "proved the hypothesis." The notion of proof carries with it the concept of "absolute truth" or certainty of a proposition; this cannot be applied to a scientific hypothesis. A hypothesis is a singular statement from a more general theory; it contains conceptual elements and relationships that are assumed to represent elements and relationships in the physical world. Although a particular test of the implications of a hypothesis may in fact support the hypothesis, another test could possibly produce some negative evidence; thus, the best that a scientist can do is to state that "It is probable that. . . ."

Judging the results of an experiment is a technical task in which the scientist uses a set of logical rules carried out by statistics to assist him in deciding whether the hypothesis is or is not confirmed by the evidence. There are a large number of inferential statistical methods, but most of them attempt to ascertain whether the results obtained in testing a hypothesis could have been due to "chance," that is, the operation of a large number of unknown factors. If chance factors can be ruled out, the scientist places more confidence in the adequacy of the conceptual hypothesis in the face of positive evidence. *How much* evidence does an investigator require before he is willing to state that a hypothesis is confirmed? This will depend in part upon the personal characteristics of the investigator and in part upon the seriousness of the error that is made when an adequate hypothesis is rejected as being unconfirmed. If the investigator is conservative, not wishing to be found in an error of this type very often, and if the consequences of rejecting an adequate hypothesis are critical, then the investigator will very likely require a high degree of probability in concluding that the results obtained are evidence in support of the hypothesis being considered.

One writer (Rudner, 1954) has stated this problem in the following way:

> Since no scientific hypothesis is ever completely verified, in accepting a hypothesis on the basis of evidence, the scientist must make the decision that the evidence is *sufficiently* strong or that the probability is *sufficiently* high to warrant the acceptance of the hypothesis. Obviously, our decision with regard to the evidence and how strong is "strong enough"

is going to be a function of the *importance,* in the typically ethical sense, of making a mistake in accepting or rejecting the hypothesis. Thus, to take a crude but easily manageable example, if the hypothesis under consideration stated that a toxic ingredient of a drug was not present in a lethal quantity, then we would require a relatively high degree of confirmation or confidence before accepting the hypothesis—for the consequences of making a mistake here are exceedingly grave by our moral standards. In contrast, if our hypothesis stated that, on the basis of some example, a certain lot of machine-stamped belt buckles was not defective, the degree of confidence we would require would be relatively lower. *How sure we must be before we accept a hypothesis depends on how serious a mistake would be* (pp. 32–33).

The scientist is assisted in reaching a decision about his hypothesis by using certain statistical procedures of logical inference. These procedures permit him to assert in a mathematical statement the probability that chance factors might have accounted for the results obtained. By choosing a high level of confidence— one which gives a low probability value to a chance effect—the scientist may be relatively certain that the data confirm his hypothesis, provided there are no invalid connections in the formal steps previously described. *Relatively* certain, however, is not the same as *absolutely* certain; scientific hypotheses can never be *proved* since there is always an element of doubt or probability. Accordingly, the empirical evidence can only serve as a source of confirmation, not proof, of a hypothesis. In the hypothetico-deductive method, the most convincing experiment is that in which not only is a particular hypothesis confirmed, but *the chief rival alternative hypotheses are discredited.*

Those psychologists who use statistics as a means for making inferences from whatever data have been collected have been identified as falling into two groups (Nelson and Bartley, 1961). One group consists of those who look upon statistics primarily as a *convenient basis of inference.* For this group, statistical analyses provide a means of discussing the degrees of relation that exist among diverse sets of data and establish standards for making inferences based upon such data. Statistical evidence, according to this view, is a convenience that must be treated as only part of the evidence available in a given situation. Any conclusion based on the results of a statistical analysis must be "accepted, rejected, or ignored *only* in the light of other considerations, and only when the researcher has adequate reasons for doing so" (p. 195).

The other group consists of psychologists who regard statistics as an *infallible basis for inference.* For this group, the results of tests of statistical significance take precedence over all other considerations when conclusions are to be reached regarding the acceptability or nonacceptability of a particular hypothesis. This procedure makes the conclusions, in effect, as dependent upon the mathematical model underlying the statistical design as it does upon the observed natural events. Also, it places a literal interpretation on the theory of probability, with the implication that statistical tests reveal "how events really do occur." The objection to the approach that uses statistical theory as an infallible basis for inference is that "individuals poorly informed with respect to sciences in general and all but unacquainted with the persistent problems of a discipline can be transmuted into theorists. And others, fundamentally inept in designing experiments and incompetent as observers, conduct research from this platform" (p. 197).

If on weighing the evidence (whether that of verification or falsification) the hypothesis is confirmed, the hypothesis may then be considered to represent new knowledge that can be expressed in the form of a probability sentence. The hypothesis was originally a guess about certain elements or relationships that might have been expected to occur in nature; confirmation of the hypothesis, in turn, changed the guess about the unknown to a statement of the known, though known only in terms of probability. Given the known situation, the hypothesis may be offered as an "explanation" of the situation. The hypothesis contains the conceptual elements and relations needed to provide a systematic organization of the previously unordered empirical elements, the relationships of which had not previously been established. By detecting the potential relationships and showing the order inherent in the natural phenomena, the hypothesis invests them with meaning and incorporates the findings in a meaningful way into the broader conceptual framework of a scientific theory. In this way, confirmed hypotheses serve as explanations.

Whether or not a hypothesis is confirmed, the formulation of hypotheses serves a number of different functions within science, although it is apparent that the most significant function is that of providing a basis from which to deduce theorems. One of the extraneous functions served by hypotheses is that their formulation *fosters research*. The scientist becomes accustomed to thinking in terms of testable theorems as he searches for the solution to some problem; from a careful scrutiny of seemingly vague and indefinite problems he is oftentimes able to extract the critical variables likely to be operating in that situation and to express a tentative solution to the problem in the form of a specific hypothesis. Once the potentially critical variables have been identified and a theorem has been deduced from the hypothesis, the task becomes one of implementing the empirical test.

This leads to a second function of hypotheses—the testing of their consequences provides a guide to the *methodology* to be employed by the investigator. The methodology is usually implicitly contained in the interpretation of the theorem. After the investigator has carefully analyzed the interpretation, he is generally able to prescribe the appropriate procedure for the test, including both the type and accuracy of instrumentation required and the kind of statistical procedures to be employed. Sometimes adequate instruments or necessary experimental designs are not available; obviously these must be provided before the empirical test can take place. Consequently, whether or not the hypothesis is ever confirmed, the necessity of testing the hypothesis may lead to a scientific contribution by the introduction of a new technique (Turner, 1959), a new apparatus (Corso, 1955), or a new statistical procedure (Eisler, 1964).

Aside from the various functions of hypotheses already discussed, the confirmation of hypotheses forms the cornerstone of science as it makes possible a *self-correcting system*. This feature of science distinguishes it from all other disciplines, religious and philosophic. A scientific theory is never ultimate, since evidence contradictory to a hypothesis demands that the hypothesis or theory be modified, and observation suggests the direction or form this modification should take. The corrigibility of science allows us not only to check empirically the implications derived from a hypothetico-deductive system, but also to change the system or to abandon it completely if the evidence so requires. If we wish to take advantage, as we probably do, of what we have learned from earlier experiments, our new theory will be constructed so that it contains within it the validated notions of the previous theory and, again, the new theory will be open to experiment. As before, some successes and some failures will ensue and the next cycle of corrections will be started. In this way, science proceeds in a series of approximations to better and better theories, guided by hypotheses and corrected through experiments.

We should also recognize that it is possible for different theories dealing with the phenomena in a given field to be quite differently constructed and still give rise to similar predictions; furthermore, the theories might be equally effective in explaining various aspects of the phenomena, or capable of integrating the phenomena within the same field (Götlind, 1961). At any given time we seldom, if ever, have simply one theory that is in agreement with the observed facts; usually there are several competing theories that are in partial agreement with the facts, and it is our task to develop, in effect, a theory that is a compromise among them. The "final" theory will have to represent adequately most of the observations and must be "simple" enough to be usable. Such a theory will, on the basis of past and present facts, permit us to predict future events.

Experimental Data
and Levels of Measurement

Observables

In discussing the requirements for testing a theorem, we stressed that it was necessary to collect empirical evidence in order to determine the adequacy of the hypothesis from which the theorem was deduced. The theorem is a statement containing words that designate things or describe the properties or characteristics of objects and events in the physical world. Sometimes these words are called *observable* constructs, as differentiated from *theoretical* constructs. *Rules of correspondence* are then used to bridge the gap between the theory and the level of observation. The rules indicate how the constructs contained in the theorem are to be identified in subsequent observations or experiments. In the terms of Chapter 2, *substantive* constructs (proper names) refer to stimulus objects, while *adjectival* constructs (character words) refer to the stimulus properties associated with the object.

At a higher level of theoretical abstraction, the basic constructs may enter into new relations that have not previously been specified. For example, mass is defined as the ratio of force to acceleration. This is an example of an *analytic* or *constitutive* *definition*. To be scientifically useful, all constructs in a theory must possess constitutive meaning; the terms must bear some relationship to one another. All theoretical terms defined by rules of correspondence (operational definitions) or established by constitutive definitions represent the *observables* of the system. In part, these terms form the empirical foundation of science since they derive their meaning directly or indirectly from observation.

When the observable constructs are combined with the relational terms according to certain *semantic rules* and in logical accordance with the axioms of a theory, *synthetic sentences* (theorems) are formed. A synthetic sentence is a statement that has a factual meaning that can be checked for its truth or falsity by making appropriate observations. This introduces the need for measurement. Consider, for example, the statement that simple reaction time to sound is faster than to light. The truth or falsity of this assertion can only be known after an appropriate set of measurements has been taken and a statistical analysis of the data has been performed.

Measurement

What, then, is involved in the process of measurement? Measurement is "the assignment of numerals to represent properties of material systems . . ." (Campbell, 1938, p. 126). It consists of two components: (1) *observation* which specifies the construct to be measured, and (2) *operations* which produce the mathematical value to be assigned to the construct. When both components, observation and operations, are present and completed, we may say that the measurement itself is completed. When the results of the measurement are in agreement with the implications (predictions) of a testable theorem, the collected observations are taken as evidence in support of the hypothesis. As psychology has developed, there has been an increasing emphasis on the need for the measurement of properties or variables in research in order that more rigorous descriptions and explanations may be provided. The statistical and mathematical treatment of psychological data is now commonplace and mathematical models are no longer novelties in the psychological literature.

The foundations of a quantitative psychology lie in measurement. The advantages of measurement over the primitive notion of simply designating classes of properties have been explicitly presented (Hempel, 1952). These advantages may be succinctly summarized. (1) With measurement, there is the possibility of making *finer distinctions* among the members of a class than without measurement; for example, given a class of men, some may be designated as "tall" and others as "short" by using the construct of length. (2) The potential exists for *ordering* different objects on the basis of a given quantitative concept; for example, a man 72 inches in height is *taller than* one of 60 inches. (3) It becomes possible to formulate general laws in a flexible way; for example, a law using the notion that the volume of a gas becomes larger with increases in temperature could not be stated if the terms of the law were restricted to classificatory (qualitative) concepts. (4) The opportunity occurs to introduce and to apply the concepts and theories of higher mathematics; for example, $f = ma$. In view of these advantages, there is little question that measurement should be used in psychology wherever and whenever possible. It is through measurement that we expect ultimately to establish the laws (equations) and theories of human behavior.

The empirical relationships or laws in which psychologists have been interested may be summarized as follows (Spence, 1948):

$$1.\ R = f(R)$$
$$2.\ R = f(S)$$
$$3.\ R = f(O)$$
$$4.\ O = f(S)$$

where R refers to response variables: measurements of behavior properties; S refers to stimulus variables: measurements of the properties of the physical and social environment; and O refers to organismic variables: measurements of neuroanatomical or neurophysiological properties of the organism.

Type 1 laws are laws that state the association of behavior properties. Sometimes these are called correlational laws and represent the type of relationships often studied in the field of psychological testing. Type 2 laws concentrate on past and present environmental events, both physical and social. Laws in this class would relate to the regularities of perceptual discrimination, learning, secondary motivation, and so on. Contemporary behavioristic psychologists have been concerned primarily with these types of laws, but increasing concern is now evident with respect to Type 3 and Type 4 laws which involve physiological and neurophysiological variables. These latter types of law may be expected to be established as additional research is performed in the area of sensory processes.

The specific aspects of the process of measurement will now be considered. Measurement, we have indicated, is the process by which numerals are assigned to objects or events to represent certain relations among these objects or events with respect to some designated property. The term "numerals" is used in this definition since a "numeral" simply means a symbol. It could refer, for example, to the assignment of "A" to all test scores above 90 percent, the use of I, II, and III to denote three groups of subjects, each of which is given a different treatment in an experiment, or to the number printed on the card of an automatic scale reading "168" pounds. Although symbols other than numbers can be used in certain kinds of measurement, numbers are preferred since the four fundamental arithmetic operations of addition, subtraction, multiplication, and division (except by zero) can be performed in the rational number system (positive, negative, and fractional numbers). All types of measurements are thus possible.

Before we can use a number system in measurement, however, we must make an assumption; this assumption states that the relations between the properties of the natural objects or events being measured are isomorphic (that is, they are in one-to-one correspondence) with the characteristics inherent in the number system being used. This is another way of saying that our mathematical model must adequately describe the properties of the natural system. If we did not believe this, then we would have little or no confidence in the interpretation of experimental data or in the accuracy of our results. The isomorphic assumption permits us to assign numbers to objects or events, since the properties of the numbers will reflect the properties of the objects or events on which the measurements are made.

If we examine the rational number system, we will note certain features of the system which, as will be shown, lead to different levels of measurement. These features may be summarized as follows:

1. The series has a specific *origin* designated by the number "zero." (Within the system, the operation of division by "zero" cannot be performed.)

2. The numbers are *ordered*. (The numbers are arranged in a sequence such that, as we move away from zero, each succeeding number is larger than the number which preceded it.)

3. The *distance* or *differences* between numbers are ordered. (Given any two numbers, their difference will be less than, equal to, or greater than the difference between any other two numbers in the system.)

These three features of numbers are not rigorously presented, but it should be evident that starting with these considerations, a complete axiomatic system of numbers can be developed; our rational number system is one of these. The properties of the numbers within this system have been given in the form of nine postulates based on the concepts of *equality, inequality,* and *addition* (Campbell, 1938). When we assign numbers to the properties of objects or events, the numbers assigned may reflect some, but not necessarily all, of the relations present in the number system. The measurement of certain properties, for example, beauty, permits judges to *rank order* the entries in a beauty contest, but there is no basis for saying that the winner (number 1) is four times as beautiful as finalist number 4, according to the way contestants are ordinarily judged. Also, we cannot identify a contestant or anyone else who has a value of "zero" with respect to the property of beauty. Thus, a distinction can be made among scales of measurement depending upon the degree to which the assigned numbers reflect none, one, two, or all three of the characteristics listed for numbers in the preceding paragraph.

On the basis of such criteria, four general levels of measurement have been distinguished (Stevens, 1951). These four levels of measurement, proceeding from lowest to highest, give rise to nominal, ordinal, interval, and ratio scales. As we move from lower to higher levels, more and more restrictions are placed on the manner in which the numbers can be assigned to the properties under study; this implies that for the higher level scales, more of the basic postulates must be satisfied. The significance of these restrictions, according to Stevens, is that they place certain limitations on the mathematical and statistical operations that can be performed on the numbers derived from the different levels of measurement. Consequently, the higher the level, the greater the diversity of permissible operations, since the operations that can be performed at a given level include all those ascribed to scales of lower order, as well as certain operations permissible only for that particular type of scale. The implication of this view is that, in research, the investigator must know not only the specific question or questions his data are intended to answer, but the kinds of scales on which to measure his variables. The kinds of scales will then determine the statistical measures and procedures that can be appropriately employed in the treatment of his data.

While some writers have adhered to the position expressed by Stevens (see Senders, 1958; Siegel, 1956), the position has not been generally endorsed in the field of psychology. In fact, the Stevens' strictures have been openly challenged (Burke, 1963). The prevalent view appears to be that the characteristics of scales of measurement should not be the prime determiners of statistical practices (Gaito, 1960). These characteristics should serve as guides, and the "context, mathematical assumptions of statistical procedures, and the results of research concerned with failure to satisfy assumptions should be the ultimate determiners of the choice of statistical techniques" (p. 278). Kempthorne (1955), for example, has shown mathematically that the choice of a scale of measurement has little effect upon the level of significance of the analysis of variance test for differences between treatments. The important requirement in this test is not that the data have certain scale properties, but that the assumptions of independence and homogeneity of errors must be met and that the data can be related to the normal distribution.

There is, however, little doubt that the Stevens' position on levels of measurement is theoretically important. The opposition contends, nevertheless, that not only is there no specific mathematical requirement expressed in the assumptions of tests of significance regarding specific scale properties, but that a rigid adherence to the Stevens' position is wasteful of data (Gaito, 1959). While such adherence does not lead to erroneous analyses, it does severely limit the statistical resources of the experimenter and leads to an overemphasis on the ultility of nonparametric techniques in psychological research. Clearly, the acceptance of the Stevens' position would lead to the probable rejection of the vast majority of experimental studies published in the literature prior to 1950.

With these reservations before us, we will consider each of the four basic types of scales and review the arithmetic operations and associated statistical measures which, according to Stevens, are permissible for each type.

Nominal Scales.   The most basic operation in measurement is that of identifying objects that are alike with respect to some property or combination of properties. When two objects are alike or similar in some respect, they may be designated as belonging to the same class or category, and the members of a given class may be identified collectively by a numeral, for example, group 1, class A. This level of measurement establishes a nominal scale; a numeral is used as the label for a class or category of objects. All members within a class are regarded as being equivalent in some manner, while members outside this class are regarded as being different. Each class differs from the other. When numerals are assigned to classes for purposes of identification, they are assigned in an arbitrary manner and could be interchanged without affecting the distinction between or among classes. The only rules to be followed in assigning numerals in this case is that all members of a given class must be given the same numeral and that the same numeral shall not be assigned to two or more classes.

In a nominal scale, the numerals assigned to the various classes are merely labels. When numbers are used in the numeral assignment, the formal rules of arithmetic cannot be applied to the numbers to perform the operations of addition, subtraction, multiplication, and division. The only permissible operation is that of *counting*. We can count the number of objects or cases within each class. Statistically, this limits us to the determination of the frequency of occurrences within classes and to the computation of measures derived from frequencies, for example, the mode of the distribution of classes and certain coefficients of correlation.

The nominal scale merely denotes the presence or absence of one or more properties among objects; it does not establish the amount or extent of the property or properties under consideration. Hence, nominal-scale measurement involves only the basic postulates of equality. There are three postulates: (1) either $a = b$ or $a \neq b$ (where $\neq$ means "does not equal"); (2) if $a = b$, then $b = a$, and (3) if $a = b$ and $b = c$, then $a = c$. These postulates are called, respectively, the postulates of *identity, symmetry,* and *transitivity.* A nominal scale is established when numerals are assigned to objects in such a manner that these three postulates are satisfied. Given a nominal scale, the only meaningful statements that can be made in comparing the scaled objects are those which implicitly or explicitly convey the idea or ideas contained within the three postulates.

Ordinal Scales.   It is oftentimes possible not only to classify objects on a nominal scale, but to rank order the classes in terms of the property, or properties, upon which the classification is based. Each class has *more* of the property or properties than the immediately preceding class, but the ranked categories are not to be considered as necessarily equally spaced on the scale, that is, that there are equal intervals between ranks. A common example of a rank-order scale is the grading system which utilizes the numerals A, B, C, D, and E or F. The basic rule that must be followed in assigning numerals on an ordinal scale is that the inherent order of the formal numeral system must correspond to the order established among the classes by some empirical procedure. The most common numerals assigned to ordinal scales are numbers and letters of the alphabet. The conventional order of the numbers or letters must correspond to the order of distinguished classes of objects possessing different amounts of the property, or properties, being scaled.

When numbers are assigned to ordered classes, only the ordered relation of the numerals is important. No operations can be performed on the absolute values of the numerals or on the differences between them. All the statistical measures that can be utilized at the level of nominal measurement are also appropriate at the level of ordinal measurement. In addition, those measures that do not depend on the absolute value of numerals may also be used. These include medians, centiles and interpercentile ranges, and rank-order coefficients of correlation.

To establish an ordinal scale certain postulates must be satisfied. These are:

(1) if $a < b$, then $b \not< a$ (where $\not<$ means "is not less than"); and (2) if $a < b$ and $b < c$, then $a < c$. These two postulates are called the postulates of *asymmetry* and *transitivity*, respectively. An ordinal scale is established whenever numerals are assigned to properties of objects in such a manner that these two postulates, and all preceding postulates, are satisfied.

Interval Scales.   Interval scales, sometimes called equal-unit scales, are those in which a unit of measurement has been established. In interval scale measurement, numbers are assigned to the properties of objects according to the rule that states that empirically equal differences must be denoted by numerically equal differences. For example, if two objects are given the numbers of 10 and 20 to represent the magnitudes of their property, and two other objects are given the numbers 50 and 60, then the two former objects are as far apart on the scale of measurement as the two latter objects. Symbolically, $x - w = z - y$, where $w = 10$, $x = 20$, $y = 50$, and $z = 60$. Likewise, since the units on the interval scale are equal, we can say that the distance from x to y, plus the distance from y to z, is equal to the distance from x to z. Notice that in each of these cases, the *distances* on the interval scale, and not the numbers, have achieved the property of *additivity*. In other words, $(y - x) + (z - y) = (z - x)$.

Although distances (differences) on the scale are additive, the addition of the numbers assigned on the scale has little meaning. This is due to the lack of a zero point on the interval scale that corresponds to the lower limit of the scale, that is, the point at which the property vanishes. The sum of the absolute values of the assigned numbers on an interval scale will vary, depending upon the location of the beginning point of the scale. This beginning point is placed in some arbitrary manner. For example, the calendar year is an interval scale. We can subtract years to compute our present age in a meaningful way; but, given the year of our birth and our present age we cannot meaningfully add the two to obtain the present year, *unless* we assume that time began at year 1 A.D. Changing the beginning point of time will obviously yield a different sum. In dealing with interval scales only the distances or differences between numbers may be treated as absolute amounts, and all arithmetic operations may be applied appropriately to these differences. Nearly all common statistical procedures may be employed in treating numbers on interval scales; these include the computation of means, standard deviations, Pearson product-moment correlation coefficients, and other statistics derived from these values.

The property of additivity in an interval scale requires that four postulates be satisfied. These are: (1) the *commutative* property: if $A + B = C$, then $B + A = C$; (2) the possibility of *summation*: if $A = Q$ and $B > 0$, then $A + B > Q$; (3) the *axiom of equals*: if $A = Q$ and $B = R$, then $A + B = Q + R$; and (4) the *associative* property: $(A + B) + C = A + (B + C)$. An interval scale is established when numbers are assigned to properties of objects in such a manner that these four postulates, and all preceding postulates, are satisfied.

Ratio Scales.   The assignment of numbers on a ratio scale requires that two conditions be met: (1) that all the postulates previously stated are satisfied, and (2) that the scale have an absolute zero point where zero denotes none of the property represented by the scale. The zero point is absolute, as in the Kelvin scale of temperature, and is not arbitrary. If these two conditions are met, one class of objects can be compared to another in terms of ratios. For example, if one object X has been shown to weigh twice as much as some other object Y, then the number assigned to X must be twice as large as that assigned to Y. The rule by which numbers are assigned in a ratio scale states that the number assigned to the property of an object must be proportional to the absolute size of the class of objects it represents. Ratios of numbers on this type of scale can be equated meaningfully. Given the ratios % and ⅓, it may be stated that the same relation obtains between the measured properties of the two pairs of objects represented by the two ratios. Since the ratio scale has a true zero point and equal units of measurement, the numbers in this scale may be appropriately utilized in all arithmetic operations and in all statistical procedures.

Sensation and Perception as Behavioral Events

Within the area of psychology, the application of the rules expressed for the different levels of measurement are most often evidenced in psychophysical research. *Psychophysics* may be narrowly defined as the study of the relationships that obtain between the various sensory attributes, for example, the pitch of a tone, and the dimensions of the physical objects or events with which these attributes are associated, for example, the frequency and intensity of the tone. Sometimes the term "sensation" is used in describing the "psycho" portion of the term psychophysics. This immediately sets the stage for numerous methodological and systematic arguments, since many will then contend that psychophysics deals with *phenomenological* events and utilizes a *subjective* terminology—all of which is intended to imply that such work is nonscientific (Kantor, 1962); others will debate the basis for the distinction between sensation and perception as psychological constructs or processes (Burt, 1961). It is, of course, true that terms such as "loud," "red," and "hot" are used in sensory experiments, but these terms are not taken as phenomenal reports nor as experiential data; the terms are simply labels that tie certain stimulus variables to particular discriminatory responses made by the observer under a given set of experimental instructions. In psychophysics, the so-called mentalistic or introspectionistic terms are introduced in accordance with the methodological ideal described earlier in this chapter: operational definitions from a physicalistic basis. The definition is contained in the operational procedures specified for a given experimental situation. As one psychologist has stated it, "What we can get at in the study of living things are the responses of organisms, not some hyperphysical mental stuff, which, by definition eludes objective test. Consequently, verifiable statements about sensation become statements about responses—about differential reactions of organisms . . . the term *sensation* denotes a construct that derives its meaning from the reactions, verbal or otherwise, made by an organism in response to stimuli. I know nothing about your sensations except what your behavior tells me" (Stevens, 1958, p. 386).

The psychologist, like every other scientist, is attempting to determine the empirical laws, that is, the functional connections, that hold between or among the variables in his area of inquiry. For the psychophysicist, the aim is to specify quantitatively the order that prevails between the reactions of sensory systems and the configurations of energy comprising the physical environment. At the present time, the behavioristic assumption is that response, whether psycho-physical, perceptual, or any other, is a function of certain specifiable variables; on this assumption, a general behavior function has been proposed within which psychophysics is held to be a special case (Graham, 1950). The general relation is given by:

$$R = f\ (a,b,c,d \ldots n \ldots t \ldots x,y,z).$$ (5-1)

where R refers to the response; $a,b,c,$ and d refer to specified properties of stimuli; n refers to the number of stimulus presentations; $t,$ to time; and x, y, z refer to specified conditions of the organism, such as physiological conditions, the inferred effects of instructions, and so on.

The variables contained in Equation 5-1, when viewed within the framework of an experiment, are usually designated as *independent* and *dependent* variables. The *independent* variables, placed to the right of the equal sign, are those aspects of the experimental situation controlled by the experimenter, physically, statisti-cally, or by specific selection procedures; the *dependent* variable or variables, placed to the left of the equal sign, are those changes in behavior produced by, or de-pendent upon, the independent variable or variables under consideration. Thus, the scientific objective is to determine the nature of the function that obtains between these two groups of variables. A formal statement of such a relationship, preferably in the form of a mathematical function, comprises a scientific principle or empirical law.

If in Equation 5-1 only the stimulus variables $(a,b,c,d \ldots)$ are considered, singly or in combination, while the remaining independent variables are held constant, then the experiment is considered to be a psychophysical one. In such a case, the general equation may be simplified to:

$$R = f(a,\ x),$$ (5-2)

where R denotes a response class such as brightness, a represents the variable of stimulus energy, and x refers to a particular set of instructions for a given experi-ment.

Other expressions may also be derived from Equation 5-1 to designate experi-ments other than those in psychophysics. Learning may be represented by $R = f_1\ (n)$, where n refers to the number of repetitions of constant stimulus condi-tions; motivation reduces to $R = f_2\ (y)$, where y refers to a deprivation state of the organism. In these and other instances, the task of the experimenter is to establish the order of relations between behavior (R) and the various classes of variables (stimulative, situational, and organismic). This is the primary objective; notice, however, that little, if anything, is gained by classifying a given experiment as "psychophysical," "perceptual," "learning," or "motivational." It may well be that such a classification tends to limit the investigator's perspective in a given problem, resulting in his lack of consideration of other variables which might be involved in that situation. Equation 5-1 provides a general theoretical framework within which the behavioral scientist may orient his thinking and, also, within which problems of sensation and perception may be subsumed as behavioral events.

Attempts to clarify the meaning of the two terms, *sensation* and *perception,* can be traced throughout the entire history of psychology (Boring, 1942). For some time, it was held that sensations, or the attributes of sensation, were the simplest elements from which an individual's "mental life," "conscious experience," or "awareness" could be reconstructed. Perception, then, was taken as that aspect of experience resulting from the combination of these simple elements. Since introspective evidence has failed to reveal the assumed substrate of sensory elements, this view has in general been abandoned. More recently, it has been proposed (Hebb, 1958) that the two terms, sensation and perception, be retained to distinguish between two theoretical processes. Sensation, in this view, is regarded as an afferent process bound to receptor-organ activity, with its associated neural representation in a cortical sensory area, while perception is defined as a mediational central process initiated by sensation, but not completely determined by it. Thus, sensation is directly and completely controlled by environmental factors; perception is only partially under environmental control and, consequently, may be affected by other relevant variables, that is, by those commonly designated as motivational, clinical, and personal.

If it is accepted that a behavioral sequence includes a complex chain of events proceeding from a stimulus through afferent neural activity, central neurosensory activity, central decision events (in certain types of behavior), central neuromotor events, efferent neural activity, and observable motor responses, then the terms sensation and perception are used in an attempt to delimit the number of phases of activity under consideration in a given situation. The terms encompass a class or a limited number of classes of variables affecting behavior in the initial phases of activity. The distinction between sensation and perception is a conceptual or theoretical one, not a substantive one (Corso, 1967). There are no differences in the fundamental operations of an experiment that can form the basis for a clear distinction between sensory discrimination and perceptual discrimination. Sensation and perception are convenient terms in everyday language and are cloaked in the garments of an honorable historical heritage, but their distinction as separate systematic concepts has not been established in the scientific vocabulary. While there are numerous theories that more or less independently encompass the so-called sensory and perceptual variables, there is a need in contemporary psychology for broader theories of perception that will integrate and organize the abstract concepts and empirical relations traditionally viewed as belonging to sensation. This would provide a more comprehensive approach from which the general study of "sensation and perception" as a unified behavioral concept could be initiated within psychology.

A Closing Remark

In the preceding sections of this chapter, we have stressed, among other concepts, the notions of hypotheses and measurement as critical aspects of science. Although the relationship between these two notions has been indicated at various stages of the discussion, the point should be clearly made that whenever possible a hypothesis should be expressed in quantitative terms, or at least be amenable to mensuration. Other things being equal, a quantified hypothesis is to be preferred to a nonquantified hypothesis.

It should be recognized, however, that in psychology we have a young and relatively immature science, and while it is noted that quantitative hypotheses are preferred, it is immediately apparent that such expectations cannot be realized in some areas of inquiry at the present time, for example, in personality theory, and psychoanalytic theory. A more advanced science of behavior will eventually produce fully quantified, empirical generalizations, but for the present a rigid adherence to the doctrine of quantification may be unrealistic and unattainable with respect to certain complex behavior, as formulated within the context of available theories. In many sciences, including physics, botany, and physiology, however, considerable progress has been attained in the early stages by methods classified as purely observational and qualitative. It should be recalled, however, that in our discussion of measurement even qualitative variables may be effectively treated by appropriate statistical procedures. Thus, while the higher levels of measurement are the most powerful mathematically, some degree of exactitude may be effected by utilizing the lower levels of measurement.

While "we cannot hold up immediate scientific advancement until after a compendious logical analysis is made of each psychological concept" (Newbury, 1958, p. 192), we can strive for the quantification of hypotheses as the desired goal of a scientific psychology. To attain this goal, it is necessary that in the final analysis vague and loosely constructed theories of behavior be reexamined and reformulated to permit the introduction of the sequence of activities we have already described: from theories to hypotheses to experiments. Measurement is an integral part of this sequence; it permits the discovery of functional relations among variables, the establishment of order, and the statement of regularities or laws of nature. In the older and well-developed sciences, when empirical laws are discovered, they are organized into a single deductive system by theories that provide for the integration of previously unrelated phenomena; but, in a newer science like psychology, theories play a somewhat different role and are utilized to assist in the discovery and formulation of such laws. Thus, for maximal effectiveness in developing a science of behavior, theories should be amenable to mathematization.

Chapter 6

EXPERIMENTAL DESIGN
AND THE TESTING
OF HYPOTHESES

Orientation

In Chapter 5, we considered the topics of theories, measurement, and behavior and indicated the sequence of logical steps that are involved in the experimental testing of a hypothesis. We did not, however, consider the precise nature of a psychological experiment nor did we describe any specific experimental designs that might be employed in the testing of hypotheses. That is the purpose of the present chapter.

Up to this point, we have considered the testing of hypotheses primarily in relation to the empirical verification of an explicitly stated theory, such as Hull's systematic theory of behavior or Estes' theory of learning. In the later chapters of this book, we will consider some specific and mathematically rigorous theories dealing with sensory and judgmental processes. Whenever such theories are available in a relatively advanced area of psychology, considerable effort is usually directed into research activities that are intended to reveal the predictive adequacy of all competing theories. In each instance, the investigator tries to design a study in such a way that a given set of results will confirm one theoretical formulation, while negating some other. The experienced investigator realizes, however, that no single experiment is very likely to dethrone a prevalent theory since alternative interpretations of the obtained results are often plausible, and a minor expansion or modification of the competing theory may easily encompass the apparently unreconcilable findings. Theories become accepted only when the mass of empirical data swings the balance in their favor. The evidence is usually experimental, but it may be derived from other empirical procedures, such as naturalistic observation, correlational techniques, and paper-and-pencil assessments.

While such activities reveal one facet of research, it should be recalled that in Chapter 1 some attention was given to the so-called basic versus applied issue in research. This issue implies that research may be undertaken for purposes other than theory-testing or the quest for "pure" knowledge. Some research is directed toward the solution of practical problems. Nevertheless, such research also involves the formulation of a hypothesis which, if supported by the empirical evidence, may be taken as an adequate answer to a particular problem. The point to be understood is that regardless of the source of motivation behind the scientist's endeavor, research involves the testing of hypotheses, and the most rigorous basis for accepting or rejecting such hypotheses is found in experiments. The purpose of the present chapter, therefore, is to present the concept of an experiment and to review some of the more common, elementary forms of research designs. Regardless of the initial motivation that leads to it, research must be judged by its quality and content (Pierce, 1960); a necessary condition for quality in research is a thorough understanding of experimental design both in principle and in practice.

Fundamental Concepts of Experimentation

Variables

The concept of a *variable* has already been introduced in Chapter 5; a variable, it will be recalled, is any property of an individual, situation, or event that is abstracted for observation and measurement in a given experiment. The investigator seeking to test a hypothesis plans a formal set of conditions; from these, the systematic observation of designated variables is intended to yield evidence relevant to the hypothesis or hypotheses under consideration. A psychological experiment, then, consists in part of the systematic observation of variables in a setting staged by the investigator, who seeks to determine the effects of certain conditions upon some characteristic of a particular group of subjects, as predicted by an empirical hypothesis.

Each observation of a variable provides a *value* of the variable, and the concept of a variable implicitly contains the notion that there are at least two possible classes of observation. Furthermore, these two classes must be mutually exclusive. Thus, objects or events that are alike on a particular variable are assigned to one category, while different objects or events are assigned to another category. Such observations are at the level of nominal measurement; sometimes, however, the variable observed is said to be a *qualitative* variable, since there are no ordered relations between or among the various classes of observations. In a recent study, for instance, "meaningful" figures, such as an arrow, a running man, and a jumping deer, were presented on a viewer in a dark room to determine the direction of autokinetic movement (an illusion of apparent movement). The subjects reported whether there was movement after a short period of visual fixation and, if so, they indicated the direction in which the figure seemed to be moving, that is, up or down, left or right, or in some other direction. These responses represent qualitative differences or mutually exclusive classes of observations. It was found that the autokinetic movement occurred to a large extent in the "meaningful" direction (Toch, 1962).

Within a class of observations, the values of a variable may also be obtained by higher levels of measurement, as discussed in Chapter 5. In these cases, we are clearly dealing with a *quantitative* variable, the measurement of which reveals that differences between classes of observations are differences in the amount or degree of the variable being studied. Quantitative variables may be further distinguished as *continuous* or *discrete*. A continuous quantitative variable is one which, theoretically, can assume a value within a range of values by infinitesimal changes in magnitude, increasing or decreasing; the value of the variable cannot be determined by counting, but must be obtained by higher order measurement. The value of a quantitative variable is always approximate and depends upon the fineness and precision of the measuring instrument. An example of a continuous quantitative variable is body weight.

Whenever the value of a quantitative variable is assigned by counting, the variable is said to be *discrete*. Quantitative data of this type are also called enumeration data or frequency data. No approximations are involved in discrete data and the numerals assigned are considered *exact*, assuming that no errors have been made in counting. An example of a quantitative discrete variable is the number of books in the Library of Congress. Sometimes in the treatment of data, a discrete variable may be used to represent an underlying continuous variable, or vice versa. The first case is reasonable if there is no experimental need for more precise observations, but the "vice versa" case needs to be treated with considerable caution.

It should be noted that qualitatively different responses may be measured either as quantitative continous variables or as quantitative discrete variables. In one experiment, for instance, the accuracy of two qualitatively different measures, reaction time and verbal report, were compared in the detection of a 5msec darkening of an otherwise steadily illuminated square of light. After delays varying from 0 to 75 msec, two adjoining (masking) squares on either side of the test square were illuminated for 100 msec. The subject's task in one instance was to depress a telegraph key as soon as possible after the test square of light was extinguished; in the other instance, he judged whether the masking lights alone, or the test stimulus (center light off for 5 msec) plus the masking lights, had been presented. Notice that reaction time is a quantitative continuous variable, while the verbal report is a quantitative discrete variable (two categories). It was found that at certain critical delays of the masking (side) lights, the verbal detection of the test stimulus (center light off) was little above chance accuracy, but reaction time was not affected by the delayed presentation. Compared with the verbal report, reaction time provided a far more accurate measure of the presence of the masked stimulus event (Fehrer and Biederman, 1962).

In a psychological experiment, the variables contained in the hypothesis fall into two classes: (1) the *independent* variable or variables and (2) the *dependent* variable or variables. As we indicated in Chapter 5, *independent* variables refer to the set of conditions or treatments controlled by the experimenter and physically manipulated according to a particular plan called an *experiment*. The purpose of the experiment is to determine the effects of the treatments, or stimulus variables, on some predetermined behavioral property of a particular living organism— animal or human. As the independent variables are imposed on the subjects of the experiment, the investigator observes and measures the response variables to determine whether they are affected by, or associated with, the experimental variables he has introduced into the situation. The variables denoting the effects are called *dependent* variables, or *criterion* variables; oftentimes, these variables indicate the frequency, latency, accuracy, or speed of a response. In the previous example on the detection of masked stimuli, the independent variable was the duration of the time delay in the illumination of the masking squares that adjoined the test square. The dependent variables were reaction time and the accuracy of verbal report. The variables studied in an experiment may pertain to the stimulus situation, the characteristicts of the organism, or to behavioral events. The designation of these variables as independent or dependent must be made in terms of the specific arrangement for a prescribed experiment.

Randomization

In the preceding section, we indicated that the purpose of a psychological experiment is to determine the effect, if any, of certain independent or treatment variables upon some chosen dependent variable, or to test a hypothesis about a postulated effect of the treatment variable. In any experiment, however, there are many extraneous factors present that may affect the results, aside from the primary experimental variable. If it is known that certain extraneous factors have an effect on the dependent variable to be studied, these factors should be removed from the experimental situation, whenever possible. In Chapter 2, it was pointed out that the elimination of extraneous variables was often accomplished by the use of specially designed testing chambers. Even with such precautions, every observation noted yields a value that depends upon the characteristics of each individual subject in the experiment and reflects, in addition, the influence of a large number of uncontrolled factors which, acting jointly, produce a certain bias in that particular observation. Thus, these two sources, intersubject differences and extraneous factors, produce an error of unknown magnitude in the observational measurement and an unknown directional effect on the dependent variable, either inflating or deflating its value. Consequently, the experimental effect obtained in a given study must be considered only as an estimate of the supposed "true" effect, that is, the effect that would have been obtained in an experiment with "perfect" control of all variables present. In a well-designed and well-conducted experiment, it is possible to obtain an *unbiased estimate* of the effect of the treatment variable and a quantitative description of the precision of this estimate (*error estimate*). Both of these estimates must be present if the statistical significance of the obtained results is to be determined appropriately.

It is seen, therefore, that in an experiment the variability (differences) in the dependent measures among all of the subjects (total variance) is attributable to several classes of factors, that is, they may arise from a number of different sources. These are: (1) the experimental treatments; (2) the extraneous factors that are known to the experimenter and controlled in all treatments by holding them *constant;* and (3) the extraneous, uncontrolled factors or "errors." The "error" factors may or may not be known to the experimenter; in some cases where they are identifiable, the cost, time, and effort required to control them might be prohibitive. Their effects, however, can in a sense be controlled in the experiment by the process of *randomization.* As an integral part of an experiment, randomization is a procedure that enhances the likelihood that the distribution of errors over all observations will occur in a random manner. In an experiment where the treatments have no "true" or real effect on the dependent variable, this procedure will lead to a random set of results. The details of randomization vary from experiment to experiment, but the general notion is that subjects are selected randomly from a particular population, and a particular observation represents a random combination of the treatment, the subject, and the particular situational factors attendant in the measurement. For optimal randomization, a table of random numbers should be used in setting up the experiment.

Randomization is critical in an experiment since it minimizes the possibility of the experimenter's personal bias affecting the data of an experiment, and it insures that a particular statistical model may be utilized in evaluating the significance of the obtained results. A test of the significance of the treatment effects is essentially a comparison of the variance due to treatments with that (variance) due to "error," and it involves a conclusion as to whether the treatment effects may be attributable to the uncontrolled sources of error.

One of the extraneous situational factors frequently encountered in psychological experiments is that of *order;* this factor is involved whenever the experimental design requires that each subject be tested under two or more treatments. Unless order effects are controlled, they will bias the results, since it is often the case that the effect of a given treatment will depend upon the particular sequence in which the treatments are administered. For example, in an experiment comparing the effects of two drugs on psychotic behavior, if drug A is always administered first to each subject and then, after a given period of treatment, drug B is administered in a similar manner, the obtained results may be due to the fact that drug B interacted with the residual effects of drug A. The order effect has confounded the treatment effect and has produced a result for drug B either greater or smaller than would have been obtained for drug B, had it not been influenced by the residual factor of drug A. *Confounding* is present since there is no way of knowing the real effect of drug B alone, without the influence of the order effect.

The experimental technique for controlling the order of presentation of the treatments is called *counterbalancing.* In an experiment with two treatments, A and B for example, counterbalancing is accomplished by having half the subjects randomly selected receive the treatments in the order A B, and the other half of the subjects in the order B A. Very often the sequence A B B A is adopted for half the subjects, and the order B A A B, for the other half. In either counter-balancing arrangement, the contaminating order effect is removed and an assessment of the size of the order effect may be obtained by comparing both the average A and B values for the two sequences. A combined A B B A *and* B A A B arrangement, however, has an additional advantage and is to be preferred, since the effects of a given order sequence, for example, A B, can be evaluated both near the beginning and near the end of the series of experimental trials.

If it is desired, a counterbalanced design can also be analyzed in such a way as to yield information on the significance of the *interaction* between treatments and order effects. A test of interaction will indicate whether the effectiveness of one treatment relative to another depends upon its order of appearance, that is, whether it is administered first or second in the experiment, and its relative effectiveness depends upon a "carry-over" effect. A counterbalanced design, then, will permit the evaluation of (1) treatment (main) effects, (2) order effects, and (3) the treatment by order interaction. In principle, counterbalancing may be accomplished in the manner described even when the number of conditions in an experiment is large, but in such cases it is often more feasible to use an advanced experimental design.

Sample, Population, and Generalizations

In performing an experiment, the investigator creates a situation in which known conditions are present and in which the events that occur can be systematically observed. While an experiment has numerous advantages because it entails controlled observation, certain precautions must be taken by the investigator to insure the validity of his conclusions and to permit him to make inductive inferences about people or treatments not directly involved in the particular experiment he performs. In order to permit such inferences, the investigator must be certain that the subjects, treatments, and conditions of observation involved in his experiment are representative of the entire universe of events about which he would like to make inductive inferences.

The psychological investigator planning an experiment must decide upon and specify the *subject* (observer) *population* he is going to study. A *subject population* is a group of individuals or animals that possess at least one designated property in common. For example, a population might be specified as all kindergarten children in the United States in a given year, as all men who have played or will ever play college football, or as all widows of World War II veterans. A given population may be *finite* (large or small) or *infinite* in number.

Since it is neither feasible nor required that the investigator test every individual in the population in a given experiment, the investigator selects by certain procedures a *sample* of individuals to serve as subjects. A *sample* is a selected number of cases taken from a specified population according to a prescribed sampling procedure. A sample is always smaller in number than the population from which it is drawn. When some measure is derived from observations of the sample, the obtained measure is called a *statistic,* for example, mean, standard deviation, frequency, or proportion. Statistics are computed to describe the data obtained in the sample (*descriptive* statistics) and to estimate or test hypotheses about certain characteristics of the population (*inferential* statistics). When similar measures, such as the mean, are computed from observations of a *complete* population, they are called *parameters*. Parameters, however, are seldom computed directly; they are usually *estimated* from an obtained sample statistic according to certain rules. In some cases, the best estimate of a parameter is the value of the statistic obtained for the sample, for example, a mean or median. The statistic is called an *unbiased* estimate of the parameter when there is no tendency for the statistic to be consistently too large or too small as computed from successive samples. The investigator plans his experiment in such a way that, knowing the results for his sample, he is able to make certain inferential statements about the population from which the sample was drawn.

To insure the validity of the *generalization* from the sample to the population, the sample must be *representative* of the *parent* population from which it was drawn. The most common technique for obtaining a representative sample is by drawing the sample at random. A *simple random sample* is one that has been drawn in such a manner that every member of the population has had an equal and independent probability of being selected to participate in the given study. The logic of random sampling is that all variables inherent in the population will be appropriately represented in the sample. In some instances, the representativeness of the random sample may be checked by computing statistics on certain variables and comparing them with published data, for example, educational levels according to census data. If the principle of representation by random sampling is rigorously followed, generalizations may legitimately be made from the sample of subjects to the parent population.

If the investigator is interested in generalizing about treatments or experimental conditions, rather than about subject populations, he must insure that the treatments are representative samples from all possible treatments in that class. The experimenter must randomly sample the experimental conditions. For example, if a study is intended to answer the question whether, in general, hand reaction time is faster to light or to sound, then all possible light conditions and all possible sound conditions should be represented in the experiment by random selections from the two populations of treatment conditions. If, for instance, only a red light and buzzer are used in the experiment as stimulus conditions, generalizations to other lights or sounds would not be valid. Although maximal generality is desired from the results of any experiment, in most situations there is no simple way of knowing either the number or the range of possible conditions from which the sample treatments should be drawn. The experimenter must usually base his design upon his own experience and his personal knowledge of the situation he is studying. Also, in actual experimental work, treatments are almost never randomly selected from some larger population; they are selected because they are of particular interest to the experimenter. This will, of course, limit the generalizations about treatments, but it does provide the experimenter with the opportunity to obtain the specific answer he is seeking.

The Logic of Testing Statistical Hypotheses

You will recall that in Chapter 5, considerable attention was directed to the logical relations involved in proceeding from a theory, to a hypothesis, and finally to an experiment. An *experiment* was described as a formally contrived empirical situation within which the testing of a theorem occurred in such a manner that the hypothesis from which the theorem was deduced could be said to be confirmed or disconfirmed on the basis of the obtained evidence. Attention was also given to the set of conditions that must be present before the testing situation could be considered to adequately represent the needs of the theorem, namely, that the variables and conditions of the theorem be interpreted in appropriate empirical terms, and that they be permitted to function in their usual manner. Now we are interested in knowing more precisely the procedures that are followed in an experiment which would permit a conclusion as to whether the experimental data collected are favorable to the theorem and, hence, support the hypothesis. In the preceding chapter we have already stressed that such a conclusion assumes that no logical or other errors have been committed up to this point in the given experiment.

In the early portion of this chapter, the major objectives of experimental design were delineated. These included: (1) the generation, control, and measurement of the experimental variables represented in the theorem; (2) the control of extraneous factors in the testing situation by direct means, such as holding the value of a factor at a constant level for all treatments; (3) the control of extraneous factors in the testing situation by indirect means using randomization and counterbalancing, (4) the selection of subjects by a particular sampling procedure and the random assignment of subjects to treatments as prerequisites for generalization; (5) the systematic observation and recording of the selected behavioral changes designated as qualitative or quantitative dependent variables; and (6) the possibility of performing an objective test of a specific hypothesis concerning the "true" treatment effects. We now need to consider the logical steps involved in testing a statistical hypothesis which, in turn, by inductive inference, permits us to arrive at a conclusion about the tenability of the hypothesis underlying the theorem tested. Simply stated, we need to know the steps by which we evaluate the statistical data of an experiment to determine whether or not our hypothesis is confirmed.

One of the simplest types of experimental designs takes the following general form: (1) the investigator obtains two groups of subjects which, through random sampling or some other technique, are considered to be equal in all respects; (2) having selected an appropriate dependent variable, the investigator imposes one treatment on one randomly assigned group and another treatment on the other randomly assigned group, measuring the responses for each group separately. (If the "treatment" administered to one group is "*no* treatment" that group is called the *control* group, the other group is called the *experimental* group); (3) the mean response value is computed for each group and a test of significance is performed to determine whether the *difference* between the group (sample) means could be due only to the presence of sampling errors—this is formally expressed in the *null hypothesis* which states that there are no real treatment differences; (4) if the null hypothesis is rejected, the investigator concludes that the treatments imposed were responsible for producing a significant difference between the sample means; and (5) the experiment is considered as having yielded scientific evidence confirming the empirical hypothesis under consideration.

Steps 3 and 4 in the preceding paragraph require a more detailed and sophisticated exposition if the full meaning of these steps is to be grasped. An understanding of the logic involved is critical for understanding the nature of an experiment. It is also emphasized that the statistical analysis of an experimental design is often predicated upon a number of statistical assumptions, for example, randomness, additivity, homogeneity of variance, normality, and so on. Consideration of these matters lies outside the scope of the present chapter, but the student is cautioned against the "blind" application of statistical techniques. Now we will consider how the testing of a *statistical* hypothesis leads to a conclusion about the *empirical* hypothesis an investigator has structured in the form of an experiment.

A *statistical hypothesis* is a statement about a statistical population, for example, means or variances, that an investigator tries to support or refute on the basis of the data obtained in an experiment. The decision about the statistical hypothesis is reached by employing a set of rules called a *statistical test*. The statistical test involves, among other factors, a statement indicating the probability of making the correct decision when different conditions are true in the population to which the hypothesis has been applied. These probability statements that are associated with the decision rules represent predictions of the expected results if the same experiment were to be performed a large number of times. The procedural steps involved in performing a statistical test and the order in which they must be performed will now be considered.

(1) *State the statistical hypothesis.* In psychological research this is often the *null hypothesis* about means and is designated as H_0; the null hypothesis states that the mean of the dependent measure is the same for each treatment population. It is a hypothesis of no differences, and when the data tend to contradict it, the investigator is actually demonstrating what he set out to establish by performing his experiment. In other words, every experiment involves not only a null hypothesis but also an *alternative hypothesis,* H_1, which bears directly on the *empirical* hypothesis under consideration. H_1 involves the prediction contained in the empirical hypothesis as derived from a theory, from certain observations, or even from mere guesses. Whenever the null hypothesis (H_0) that $m_1 = m_2$ is rejected, the alternative hypothesis (H_1) that $m_1 \neq m_2$ may be accepted where the symbol m represents the population mean. A null hypothesis stated in this form is said to involve a *two-tail* test of significance, since the empirical hypothesis (H_1) which predicts a difference in values does not state the *direction* of the difference, that is, whether m_1 will be larger or smaller than m_2.

If the empirical hypothesis predicts that m_1 will be greater than m_2, then the appropriate hypotheses are as follows:

$$H_0: m_1 \leqq m_2 \text{ and } H_1: m_1 > m_2.$$

If the empirical hypothesis predicts that m_1 will be less than m_2, then the appropriate hypotheses are as follows:

$$H_0: m_1 \geqq m_2 \text{ and } H_1: m_1 < m_2.$$

The null hypothesis in these two latter cases is said to involve a *one-tail* test of significance, since H_0 can only be rejected if, in fact, the direction of the difference in means is identical to that stated in the hypothesis *before* the experiment is performed.

(2) *Select a statistical test.* The selection of a specific statistical test for evaluating H_0 involves at least two fundamental considerations: the numerals assigned to the values of the dependent variable in the experiment must satisfy the measurement requirements of the statistical test, and the statistical model from which the test is derived must closely approximate the conditions of the experiment. Other considerations are also involved but these have been omitted in the present treatment, since we are concerned primarily with the logic of testing a statistical hypothesis and not with the mechanics. The student should be aware, however, that, for nearly every research design, there are alternative statistical tests that might be appropriately used. Also, many statisticians do not agree that the measurement requirement imposes a restriction in the selection of a statistical test. "The processes of statistics do not depend upon how our measures are obtained" (Games and Klare, 1967, p. 478).

(3) *Establish a level of significance and the size of the sample.* The *level of significance* (α) (read as "alpha") of a statistical test specifies the probability which the experimenter will consider as being too small to warrant support of the statistical hypothesis under test. The choice of a level of significance is arbitrary, but depends upon certain considerations about making erroneous decisions, as discussed in the preceding chapter. Values of α that are often used are 0.05 and 0.01. At this point in the procedure, we assume the statistical hypothesis being tested to be true and proceed to reject H_0, if the probability associated with the occurrence of the particular value yielded by the statistical test is equal to, or less than α. Rejection of H_0 is equivalent to supporting H_1, the statement logically connected to the empirical hypothesis, which is one of the possible alternative hypotheses that has not been contradicted by the data.

The decision rules in a statistical test concern the rejection or nonrejection of H_0. The rejection of H_0 leads to the decision to accept H_1; the nonrejection of H_0 leads to the decision not to accept H_1. It is evident that some errors will be made in the rejection or nonrejection of H_0. If, in fact, H_0 is true and it is rejected, this will lead to an erroneous decision; such an error is called a Type I error and the probability of making such an error is limited by the value of α. The Type I error is under the direct control of the experimenter and is fixed by his decision regarding the level of significance (α).

If, in fact, H_0 is false and it is not rejected, this will also lead to an erroneous decision; such an error is called a Type II error and the probability (β) (read as "beta") of making such an error is determined by α and the size of the sample. For any given sample size, the smaller α, the larger β, since α and β are inversely related. However, if the sample size is increased and α remains fixed, then the Type II error will be reduced.

The *power* of a statistical test is defined as the probability of rejecting H_0 when in fact it is false, that is, power $= 1 - \beta$, where β is the probability of a Type II error. Since the probability of committing a Type II error decreases as the sample size becomes larger, the power of a test correspondingly increases with sample size. This discussion of Type I and Type II errors is summarized in Table 6-1, which also indicates the kinds of decisions that can be reached in testing a statistical hypothesis.

Table 6–1   Decisions and Types of Errors in Testing a Statistical Hypothesis

		Conditions Present in Treatment Populations	
		H_0 is true and H_1 is false	H_0 is false and H_1 is true
Decisions Reached	Reject H_0 and accept H_1	Type I error (α)	Correct decision
	Do not reject H_0 and do not accept H_1	Correct decision	Type II error (β)

(4) *Determine or assume the sampling distribution of the test statistic, assuming H_0 to be true.* A *sampling distribution* of a test statistic is a theoretical distribution that indicates the probability of occurrence of each possible value of the test statistic under the assumption that H_0 is true. These probability values are usually given in *tabular* form as cumulative frequencies, cumulative relative frequencies, or cumulative probabilities that indicate the probability of occurrence of a value *as extreme as,* or *more extreme than,* the particular value of the test statistic under H_0. This means, for example, that the tables of t, χ^2, and F, as found in most statistical textbooks, are based on the integral form of the distribution function for that particular test statistic. Sampling distributions are usually derived mathematically from theorems, but they could be determined empirically by constructing a frequency distribution of a given statistic computed from a large number of samples (for example, 100,000), each having the same size and drawn randomly from a specified population.

(5) *Define the region of rejection on the basis of the foregoing considerations.* The region of rejection refers to a portion of the sampling distribution. The general idea is that if under H_0 the test statistic has a relatively high probability of occurring, as determined from the sampling distribution, the decision is made that the data do not contradict the statistical hypothesis. If, however, the probability of the test statistic is relatively low when H_0 is true, the decision is that the data tend to contradict the statistical hypothesis. The region of rejection consists, then, of a set of possible values so extreme that the probability of the observed sample having yielded a value that is among them is very low (α), assuming H_0 to be true.

As indicated under Step 1 of this testing procedure, the precise statement of H_1 which the investigator is trying to establish will determine H_0 and locate the region of rejection. For a two-tail test, the region of rejection is divided between the two ends of the sampling distribution, for example, with $\alpha = 0.05$, the region of rejection is 0.05 of the total area, with 0.025 of this located at each end of the sampling distribution.

As an illustrative example, Figure 6-1 shows the t distribution function (the sampling distribution of the t statistic) for a sample with 25 *degrees of freedom (df)*.

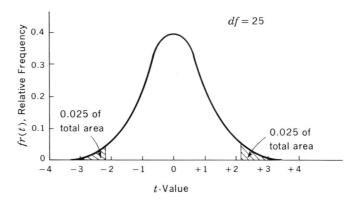

Figure 6-1. The t-distribution function for 25 degrees of freedom (df), showing the region of rejection for a two-tail test of significance of the null hypothesis $m_1 = m_2$ against the alternative hypothesis $m_1 \neq m_2$, with the level of significance set at a probability of 0.05. (Adapted from *Quantitative methods in psychology* by D. Lewis, copyright © 1960. Used by permission of McGraw-Hill Book Company.)

(This statement implies that there is not a *single* t distribution, but many such distributions, with the form of each one dependent, in part, upon the number of elements in the sample. The number of degrees of freedom for each t distribution is computed from the number of elements in the sample that are used to estimate the population variance.) The region of rejection for a two-tail t test with the level of significance set at a probability of 0.05 is shown by the shaded area under each tail of the distribution. Of the total area under the curve, 0.025 of the area lies to the right of $+2.060$ and 0.025 of the area lies to the left of -2.060. For 25 *df*, any value of t equal to a greater than ± 2.060 will fall in the region of rejection.

For a one-tail test with H_0: $m_1 \leq m_2$ and $\alpha = 0.05$, the region of rejection is 0.05 of the total area, with all of this located under the right tail of the sampling distribution. With H_0: $m_1 \geq m_2$ and $\alpha = 0.05$, the region of rejection is 0.05 of the total area, with all of this located under the left tail of the sampling distribution.

(6) *Reach a decision.* The final step in testing a statistical hypothesis is to reach a decision regarding H_0. The rule is stated simply. Whenever the observed test statistic, for example, t, falls in the region of rejection for the particular hypothesis tested, H_0 is rejected. The types of decisions that can be reached and the types

of errors that can be made have already been summarized in Table 6-1. Whenever it is concluded that H_0 is false, that is, H_0 is rejected according to the predetermined value of α, we say that the observed value of the test statistic is "significant." A "significant" value is one that has a probability of occurrence as shown by the sampling distribution, equal to or less than α, assuming H_0 to be true. Whenever a significant result is obtained in testing a statistical hypothesis, the investigator concludes by inductive inference that the data of the experiment are in support of the empirical hypothesis, that is, the experiment has confirmed his prediction.

Some Representative Experimental Designs with a Single Independent Variable

Simple Randomized Design
(Statistical Test: The t test for
independent means)

The basic plan of a simple, randomized experimental design with a single independent variable has already been presented in the preceding section of this chapter. To summarize briefly, this is the simplest possible experimental arrangement. It involves two groups of subjects randomly selected from a specified population; each group is assigned to a different condition or treatment in a random manner. The two conditions or treatments involve different values of the designated independent variable, or one group is given "no treatment" while the other is administered a particular treatment. The "no treatment" group is called the *control* group; the treatment group is called the *experimental* group. In either arrangement, the individuals in each group are measured on a specific dependent variable and a statistical hypothesis is tested in accordance with the steps outlined in the preceding section. A decision is then reached about the significance of the results and an inductive inference is made about the effectiveness of the imposed treatments on the dependent variable.

A computational example of the t test used in evaluating the statistical significance of the difference between the means of two groups in a simple randomized design is presented in Table 6-2. Consider that we are interested in the effects of music on the learning of meaningful material. The question we are attempting to answer is whether music facilitates, hinders, or has no effect upon, the learning of meaningful material, for example, the learning of vocabulary words in a foreign language.

For expository purposes, suppose that the experiment was appropriately designed and implemented so that fifteen subjects (experimental group) learned vocabulary words in the presence of music, while fifteen subjects (control group) learned the same list of words in quiet. After a given number of trials has been administered to each group, we obtain the scores presented in Part A of Table

6-2, where the higher the score, the better the learning. The test of the null hypothesis and the necessary computations for t with independent measures are presented in Part B of Table 6-2. Since the null hypothesis is rejected, the results of this hypothetical study indicate that the type of music used in this experiment does have a significant effect on the learning of meaningful material, that is, vocabulary words in a given foreign language.

Table 6-2 Example of a Simple Randomized Design with Two Independent Groups

Part A: Criterion Scores (Fictitious Data)

Control Group (Group 1)		Experimental Group (Group 2)	
Subject	Score	Subject	Score
1	15	1	12
2	15	2	10
3	13	3	13
4	11	4	17
5	16	5	9
6	12	6	8
7	20	7	10
8	14	8	7
9	12	9	9
10	15	10	14
11	11	11	12
12	17	12	11
13	13	13	9
14	12	14	8
15	10	15	12
$n_1 = 15$	$\Sigma X_1 = 206$	$n_2 = 15$	$\Sigma X_2 = 161$
	$M_1 = 13.7$		$M_2 = 10.7$
	$\Sigma X_1^2 = 2928$		$\Sigma X_2^2 = 1827$

Part B: t test of the Null Hypothesis
($H_o: m_1 = m_2$ with $H_1: m_1 \neq m_2$; $\alpha = 0.05$)

1. Computational Formula:

$$t = \frac{M_1 - M_2}{\sqrt{\dfrac{(\Sigma X_1^2/n_1) - M_1^2}{n_1 - 1} + \dfrac{(\Sigma X_2^2/n_2) - M_2^2}{n_2 - 1}}}, \quad df = n_1 + n_2 - 2 \qquad (6\text{-}1)$$

2. Solution:

$$t = \frac{13.7 - 10.7}{\sqrt{\dfrac{(2928/15) - 13.7^2}{15 - 1} + \dfrac{(1827/15) - 10.7^2}{15 - 1}}}$$

(Table 6-2 cont.)

$$= \frac{3.0}{\sqrt{\frac{(195.2 - 187.7)}{14} + \frac{(121.8 - 114.5)}{14}}} = \frac{3.0}{\sqrt{\frac{7.5}{14} + \frac{7.3}{14}}}$$

$$= \sqrt{\frac{3.0}{0.54 + 0.52}} = \frac{3.0}{\sqrt{1.06}} = \frac{3.0}{1.03}$$

$t = 2.91,\ df = 15 + 15 - 2 = 28.$

3. Conclusion:

From the t table, $t_{0.05} = 2.048$ for 28 df.

Since the obtained t is larger than the tabular value, reject the null hypothesis.

Simple Randomized Design with Matched Subjects (Statistical Test: The t test for related means)

One of the difficulties involved in the simple randomized design is that the two groups in the experiment are *assumed* to be equal in all respects through the process of random sampling. Random sampling randomizes subject variations, but there is no assurance that the two groups are, in fact, equal, since subject differences are controlled only by randomly assigning subjects to groups. It is possible, therefore, that "by chance" we established two unequal groups with respect to those factors that might affect the dependent variable. Such an eventuality would, of course, invalidate the conclusions drawn from our experiment.

One way to minimize the possibility of nonuniform random samples is to use a large number of subjects in each group. When the groups are large, they are more likely to be similar. Another technique for insuring that the subjects in the two groups are more nearly alike than is possible through randomization is to provide for the *matching* of subjects.

There are three basic procedures that can be used to effect the matching on a particular variable. In each of these three procedures the experimenter begins by randomly selecting from a specified population all of the subjects to be used in the experiment. The matching of subjects between groups is then accomplished by setting up pairs of subjects who are as nearly alike as possible. The pairs may be established (1) by pretesting all subjects on the dependent variable under uniform conditions, and by assigning to each pair those subjects whose scores are identical or as close together as possible; or (2) if it is not feasible or appropriate to pretest on the dependent variable, by matching the subjects on the basis of some other variable or variables known to be related (*correlated*) with the dependent variable, or (3) by having the subjects serve as their own controls, that is, by testing each subject under both (or all) treatments of the experiment.

In the last plan (treatments by subjects design), counterbalancing of the order of presentation of the treatments is specifically required; the reasons for this requirement and the techniques for implementing a counterbalanced design have been discussed earlier in this chapter. It should also be clear that regardless of the procedure used for matching, the subjects will be more or less comparable only on the variable matched; they may still differ considerably on the very large number of other variables on which they were not matched.

After the pairs of subjects have been established, one member of each pair is assigned randomly to one treatment and the other member, to the second treatment. Finally, the treatments are imposed on the two groups of matched subjects, with counterbalancing being used when necessary.

The general intent of the three matching procedures is to establish two groups of subjects that are essentially identical before the treatments are imposed; in addition, the pairing is an attempt to insure that a high correlation will obtain between the scores of the two groups after the treatments have been imposed. If the scores on the dependent variable are positively correlated, then the standard error of the difference between the means of the two groups, as contained in the denominator of the t statistic, will be reduced, and the t value will be larger. Therefore, for a given sample size, a smaller difference in the means of the two treatment groups is likely to be significant, in contrast with the simple randomized design.

All three procedures for matching subjects reduce the probability of a Type II error, provided the correlation on the dependent variable is positive and fairly high; of the three, the treatments by subjects design is usually far more precise than either of the other matched designs, or the simple randomized design. No part of the difference in treatment means can be attributed to intersubject differences, although intrasubject differences (chance errors of measurement) might, nevertheless, favor one treatment over the other. In using the treatments by subjects design, the experimenter must be reasonably certain that the effect of a given treatment is independent of, or unaffected by, the previous administration of the other treatment to the same subjects, unless counterbalancing is introduced to control for order effects.

One other caution should be advanced. In an experiment with matched groups, the number of degrees of freedom associated with the t statistic is only one half as large as that for random (independent) groups. Thus, the correlation on the dependent variable for the matched groups should be positive and quite high in order to offset the loss in degrees of freedom, particularly when the size of the sample in the experiment is rather small. Figure 6-2 shows the minimal value of the correlation coefficient (r_{12}) between the two groups on the dependent variable that should obtain for a given sample size, if the matched subjects design is to be preferred over the randomized design. For example, with ten subjects in each group, the expected correlation coefficient should be at least 0.20 for a matched subjects design to be preferable.

In analyzing the data of a matched subjects experiment, it is not necessary to compute directly the correlation coefficient between the two sets of scores on the dependent variable before testing the null hypothesis. Although computation of the correlation coefficient is appropriate, if its underlying assumptions are met, and the value of the coefficient can be introduced in certain formulae for determining the standard error of the difference between the correlated means, such a

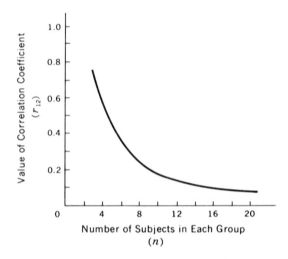

Figure 6-2. The functional relationship between the number of subjects in a sample and the value of the correlation coefficient between two groups on a dependent variable which determines whether a matched subjects design is to be preferred over a randomized design. When the expected value of r_{12} exceeds the value obtained from the curve for a given n, select the matched subjects design, other things being equal. (From F. J. McGuigan, *Experimental psychology: a methodological approach,* copyright © 1960. Reprinted by permission of Prentice-Hall, Inc., Englewood Cliffs, New Jersey.)

procedure may be avoided. When the criterion scores are paired, a much simpler formula for the standard error is available which is derived from the mean difference between paired scores; the mean difference between paired scores is equal to the difference between group means. Thus, when the direct-difference method is used to compute the t statistic, the standard error in the denominator of t is the standard error of the mean difference; this is equal numerically to the standard error of the difference between correlated means. Since the direct method is much simpler computationally, it is preferred to the more tedious formula involving the correlation coefficient, unless the investigator is interested in knowing the specific value of the correlation coefficient. The direct-difference method takes into account the correlation between the two matched groups, but does not require a separate computation of the correlation coefficient.

Suppose, for example, that we are interested in knowing whether there is any difference in the visibility of a blue light and a green light that are being considered for installation in a particular situation. For a preliminary study, we randomly select ten subjects from a specified population and appropriately test each subject's ability to correctly identify each light. Since each subject has been tested under both conditions, that is, under each of the lights, we can pair the number of correct identifications made by each subject. A set of fictitious data for such an experiment is presented in Part A of Table 6-3; Part B of Table 6-3 contains the necessary computations for testing the null hypothesis by the direct-difference

Table 6-3 Example of a Simple Randomized Design with Matched Subjects

Subject	Part A: Criterion Scores (Fictitious Data)			
	Blue Light (1)	Green Light (2)	Difference (D)	D^2
1	24	26	-2	4
2	19	18	1	1
3	29	28	1	1
4	32	27	5	25
5	21	23	-2	4
6	25	28	-3	9
7	31	28	3	9
8	40	35	5	25
9	28	32	-4	16
10	36	34	2	4
$n = 10$	$\Sigma X_1 = 285$	$\Sigma X_2 = 279$	$\Sigma D = 6$	$\Sigma D^2 = 98$
	$M_1 = 28.5$	$M_2 = 27.9$	$(\Sigma D)^2 = 36$	

Part B: t test of the Null Hypothesis
(H_0: $m_1 = m_2$ with H_1: $m_1 \neq m_2$; $\alpha = 0.05$)

1. Computational formula:

$$t = \frac{M_1 - M_2}{\sqrt{\dfrac{\Sigma D^2 - (\Sigma D)^2/n}{n(n-1)}}} , \quad df = n - 1 \tag{6-2}$$

2. Solution:

$$t = \frac{28.5 - 27.9}{\sqrt{\dfrac{98 - (36/10)}{10(10-1)}}} = \frac{0.6}{\sqrt{\dfrac{98 - 3.6}{90}}} = \frac{0.6}{\sqrt{\dfrac{94.4}{90}}}$$

$$= \frac{0.6}{\sqrt{1.05}} = \frac{0.6}{1.02}$$

$$t = 0.588, \quad df = 10 - 1 = 9$$

Conclusion:

From the t table, $t_{0.05} = 2.262$ for 9 df.
Since the obtained t is not larger than the tabular value, do not reject the null hypothesis.

method of the t test for related measures. The results of this hypothetical study indicate that there is no difference in the visibility of a blue and a green light under the given set of experimental conditions.

Randomized Design With More Than Two Groups
(Statistical Test: The F ratio in the analysis of variance)

In the preceding paragraphs, we described the application of the t test to problems of research in which the difference between the means of *two* samples was evaluated for statistical significance. Two cases were reviewed: in one case the means were considered by design to be independent; in the other case, they were considered by design to be nonindependent or related. Such simple experimental plans as these, however, are not too frequently encountered in the psychological literature, although they serve as excellent pedagogical devices for presenting the basic idea of an experiment and for delineating the critical steps in the testing of a statistical hypothesis. We will now consider a technique that can be used to test the significance of the difference between three or more means in a given experiment; the technique is known as the *analysis of variance* and is one of the most frequently used approaches in psychological research.

In the simple randomized design with three or more groups, the treatments may be differences in the amounts, intensities, or durations of a single experimental variable, for example, the amount of sleep expressed in hours, the intensity of noise in a factory, or the duration of a conditioned stimulus. This type of treatment classification is often called a *"single-factor"* classification.

The treatment classification, however, could be a different general type: for example a *"categorical"* classification. In a classification of this type there are numerous variables operating within the several treatments, making them complex and unordered with respect to particular variables. Consider, for example, an experiment designed to yield information about the design effectiveness of three different desk calculators. It would be a relatively simple matter to perform such an experiment, and it might be found that Calculator A required the shortest period of time for learning its operation and produced the fewest number of errors on a standard set of computational problems. Calculator A might clearly be superior on each of these two criteria, but the variable or variables responsible for this superiority might not be readily identifiable, for example, larger keys, special symbols, special operations, slant of keyboard, and use of "memory" devices. In any situation where there are numerous, unordered factors, or combinations of factors, operating on the dependent variable, the experimental treatments fall into the *categorical* classification.

A single-factor experiment involving the analysis of variance may be performed (1) to determine whether the treatments administered in the experiment produce any "effects" on the subject's behavior as indicated by the dependent variable, or (2) if the treatments do affect the dependent variable, to determine the form of the functional relationship obtaining between the values of the dependent and independent variables, assuming the treatments have been ordered in some meaningful way. It is seen, therefore, that a two-group design (two values of the independent variable) could be used to achieve the first purpose; but, if the form of the relationship between the two classes of variables is to be established, at least a three-group design (three values of the independent variable) must be used in the conduct of the study. Whenever an investigator employs three or more groups in a single-factor study with *ordered* treatments, he not only is able to specify the type of relationship between the independent and dependent variables, but he has also increased the likelihood of accurately determining whether a given independent variable affects the dependent variable.

Detailed consideration of the use of analysis of variance in establishing functional relations, however, lies beyond the scope of this textbook, and the present account will be limited to the more basic purpose of analysis of variance, that is, to test for the significance of the differences among all the means in a given experiment. Some examples of studies that might be performed using the randomized type of design include the influence of different sensory cues on maze learning, the influence of early sensory deprivation on visual discrimination, the influence of noise exposure on auditory thresholds, the influence of temperature on the sending of telegraphic messages, and the influence of ambient lighting on industrial production.

The basic procedure in applying a randomized design with two or more groups is to select the appropriate values or categories of the independent variable according to the intended purpose of the experiment. When only two groups are to be used in a single-factor experiment, it seems advisable to choose values of the independent variable that are "reasonably" far apart on the given continuum. Extreme separations in values should generally be avoided, since it is a difficult matter in psychology to establish a lawful relation that will hold except within relatively narrow limits; conversely, values too close together should also be avoided, since this tends to reduce the probability that a significant effect will be discovered.

If three or more groups are to be used to determine the form of the functional relation between the independent and dependent variables, the values of the independent variable should be ordered and selected in terms of the function that is expected to be present. If the anticipated relationship is linear, then three or four equally spaced values will probably suffice; if the anticipated relationship is curvilinear, then, in addition to the two end points of the function, sufficient values should be interjected to describe accurately the function that obtains. In particular, an effort should be made to include values of the independent variable where the slope of the anticipated curve is expected to change.

There are no precise rules for denoting the values or categories of the independent variable that should be used in an experiment; the selection is made by the experimenter in terms of his hypothesis and expectations, his familiarity with the subject matter of the experiment, and his knowledge of previous experiments performed in the same general content area.

After the values or categories of the independent variable have been selected, either by design or in a random manner, a group of subjects selected randomly from the same parent population are assigned at random to each value or category. There will be as many groups as there are different values or categories of the independent variable. Usually the number of subjects per group is the same for all groups but this is not a necessary condition for this design.

Each group is then administered its prescribed treatment, that is, each group is exposed to its predetermined value or category of the independent variable in accordance with the overall plan of the study. For example, in an experiment to investigate the comparative psychology of learning in the earthworm, the following plan was used to determine the influence of sensory control on the learning of a T-maze:

> Three groups of earthworms, numbering 12 each, were studied. The animals were selected at random from the stock colonies. For Group SS, the bar of the T had a smooth floor, as it did in the pilot experiments. Half of the animals were trained with the right arm correct, and the others with the left arm correct; for the remaining two groups, SG-C and SG-U, the floor was differentiated: that of one arm was smooth and that of the other was gravelled. Half of the animals in Group SG-C were trained with gravel on the left, and half with gravel always on the right; that is, tactual and spatial cues were confounded. Three Ss were trained to gravel-left, three to gravel-right, three to smooth-left, and three to smooth-right. For Group SG-U, tactual and spatial cues were unconfounded—the position of the gravel was varied systematically from trial to trial . . . and the problem became a pure tactual discrimination. The smooth arm was positive for half the Ss, and the gravelled arm was positive for the remaining Ss. All groups had 10 days of training with 5 trials per day and an intertrial interval of 5 min (Datta, 1962, p. 536).

Whenever the earthworm went to the positive arm of the maze, he escaped into his home container fitted at the end of the arm; whenever the earthworm made an incorrect turn at the choicepoint of the T-maze, it received a moderate shock. The criterion measure of performance was the mean number of correct initial choices in ten days of training under each of the three conditions; these were found to be 32.4 for Group SS, 30.5 for Group SG-C, and 29.1 for SG-U. It was concluded on the basis of an analysis of variance that "contrary to expectation, tactual differentiation did not improve performance, even in the confounded group."

In the analysis of variance of a randomized design, the hypothesis that is tested is that the criterion means of the several treatment populations are identical. This is an "overall" null hypothesis, since we are concerned *simultaneously* with *all* of the treatments, and not simply with specific null hypotheses between single *pairs* of treatments. The treatment populations are hypothetical populations, since each treatment may be regarded as having been generated from some parent population through the administration of a particular value or category of the independent variable. Conceptually, there are as many hypothetical populations as there are treatment groups. The overall null hypothesis in the analysis of variance refers to a statement of no differences among the means of the several treatment populations. Having set up a null hypothesis, we will reject the hypothesis, or fail to reject it, on the basis of an appropriate statistical test, the *F* test.

Table 6-4 presents a set of illustrative data for a single-variable randomized design, in which $N = 18$ subjects have been assigned at random to one of $k = 3$ treatments with 6 subjects in each treatment. For each of the three treatments, each entry in Table 6-4 represents the criterion score made by a given subject.

Table 6–4   Example of a Single Variable Randomized Groups Design with Three Treatments

Treatments:	Criterion Scores (Fictitious Data)		
	1	2	3
	8	8	15
	10	9	14
	7	13	9
	6	11	12
	12	7	8
	7	7	6 Grand Totals
	$\Sigma X_1 = 50$ $\Sigma X_2 = 55$ $\Sigma X_3 = 64$ 169		
	$\Sigma X_1^2 = 442$ $\Sigma X_2^2 = 533$ $\Sigma X_3^2 = 746$ 1721		

The first step in the analysis is to compute the *total sum of squares* for the 18 observations, disregarding the treatment classification. The total sum of squares (SS_T) is obtained from the equation

$$SS_T = \Sigma X^2 - \frac{(\Sigma X)^2}{N}, \tag{6-3}$$

where $N = n_1 + n_2 + \ldots + n_k$, or the total number of observations, and X is the criterion score. For the data of Table 6-4, Equation 6-3 yields

$$SS_T = (8)^2 + (10)^2 + (7)^2 + \ldots + (6)^2 - \frac{(169)^2}{18}$$

$$= 1721 - \frac{(169)^2}{18} = 1721 - 1586.7$$

$$SS_T = 134.3$$

The next step is to compute the *sum of squares between groups* or the *treatment sum of squares* (SS_B). SS_B is based upon the squared deviation of each group mean from the grand mean, that is, the mean for all observations considered together. Each squared deviation is weighted by the number of observations in its group, and the weighted squared deviations are added to give SS_B. Stated in equation form,

$$SS_B = \Sigma n_g (M_g - M_{tot})^2, \tag{6-4}$$

where n_g is the number of observations in a given group, M_g is the mean for that group, and M_{tot} is the mean of the total number of observations.

This is equivalent to:

$$SS_B = \frac{(\Sigma X_1)^2}{n_1} + \frac{(\Sigma X_2)^2}{n_2} + \ldots + \frac{(\Sigma X_k)^2}{n_k} - \frac{(\Sigma X)^2}{N}. \tag{6-4a}$$

For the data of Table 6–4, the solution of Equation 6-4a gives

$$SS_B = \frac{(50)^2}{6} + \frac{(55)^2}{6} + \frac{(64)^2}{6} - \frac{(169)^2}{18}.$$

$$SS_B = 1603.6 - 1586.7 = 16.9$$

(The student is encouraged to show that Equations 6-4 and 6-4a are algebraically equivalent by obtaining this same value through the solution of Equation 6-4.)

The final sum of squares that is needed is the *sum of squares within groups* (SS_W). Sometimes this component is called the *within treatments sum of squares* or the *error sum of squares*. The SS_W component is a combined sum of squares based on the variation of the measures (observations) in each treatment group about their respective means. SS_W is a pooled sum of squares within the separate treatment groups. That is

$$SS_W = \Sigma x_1^2 + \Sigma x_2^2 + \ldots + \Sigma x_k^2, \tag{6-5}$$

where $\Sigma x_1^2 = \Sigma X_1^2 - \frac{(\Sigma X_1)^2}{n_1}$ and the remaining terms are computed in a similar manner. Each term in Equation 6-5 is simply an expression of the variabilty within that particular group. For the data of Table 6-4, we have

$$SS_W = \left[442 - \frac{(50)^2}{6}\right] + \left[533 - \frac{(55)^2}{6}\right] + \left[746 - \frac{(64)^2}{6}\right]$$

$$SS_W = 25.3 + 28.8 + 63.3 = 117.4$$

It should be observed that SS_B plus SS_W is equal to SS_T; this is always so. Thus, SS_W could have been computed by subtraction by

$$SS_W = SS_T - SS_B. \tag{6-6}$$

For the present example, we have

$$SS_W = 134.3 - 16.9 = 117.4.$$

However, it is suggested that SS_W be computed directly, since the summation of SS_W and SS_B will indicate a computational error if the total does not equal SS_T. Also, no SS term can ever have a negative value; if it does, an arithmetical error has been made and recalculations must be performed to detect the source of the error.

We have seen, now, how the total sum of squares may be partitioned or analyzed into separate components: between groups and within groups. The magnitude of the between groups sum of squares depends upon the differences between the several group means. The larger the differences among means, the larger will be the between groups component. The within groups component depends upon the extent to which the subjects in each group differ, that is, intragroup variability. The more the subjects in each group differ among themselves, the larger the within groups component and the larger the "error" variance in the experiment. If all the subjects in each group were exactly alike at the time of the experiment, and if the respective treatments were imposed, all subjects within each group would obtain the same score on the dependent variable. There would be no variation among the scores of each group and SS_W would be equal to zero. SS_T, in such a hypothetical case, would be accounted for entirely in terms of the variability between groups.

Likewise, if the treatments had no real effects, the means of the several groups would all be identical and equal to the grand mean; there would be no SS_B and all of SS_T would be accounted for by SS_W. Rarely, however, is either SS_B or SS_W equal to zero, and the problem becomes one of deciding whether the differences among the group means may be attributed to the effects of the treatments, when SS_W is used to provide an estimate of the "error" variance in the experiment. The following will show how this is done.

If, in a randomized groups design, there are k samples, each drawn at random from normal populations with identical variances, then each of the samples will provide a separate estimate of the same population variance. These separate estimates can be combined to yield a single estimate of the population variance. It can be shown algebraically that this single estimate is equal to the sum of squares within groups, divided by its associated number of degrees of freedom. For SS_W, the associated df equal $N - k$, and the obtained quotient is called the *mean square within groups* (MS_W). Thus,

$$MS_W = SS_W/df_w. \tag{6-7}$$

Again, if there are k samples each drawn at random from normal populations with identical means or from the same normal population, then each of the samples will provide a separate estimate of the same population mean. These separate estimates can be combined to yield a single estimate of the population mean; this estimate will then be equal to the overall (grand) mean of the kn measures in the experiment. The squared deviation of each sample mean from the overall mean is then weighted (multiplied) by the number of observations in that sample and a summation is made for all samples. The result is, as before, SS_B. By dividing SS_B by its associated degrees of freedom ($k - 1$), the *mean square between groups* is obtained and provides another independent estimate of the common population variance. Thus,

$$MS_B = SS_B/df_B. \tag{6-8}$$

It should be observed that just as the total sum of squares can be partitioned into two parts, so can the total degrees of freedom (df_T) in the experiment. The degrees of freedom for the total number of observations in the experiment are equal to $k - 1$. Since $df_B = k - 1$ and $df_W = N - k$, it is seen that

$$df_T = df_B + df_W. \tag{6-9}$$

For Table 6-4, $df_T = 18 - 1 = 17; df_B = 3 - 1 = 2; df_W = 18 - 3 = 15$.

The test of significance in the analysis of variance is the F test. Recall that MS_B and MS_W are two independent estimates of the same population variance. When we compute the F statistic, we divide MS_B by MS_W. If the null hypothesis is true, then the numerator of the ratio should not exceed the denominator except as the result of random sampling.

On the assumption that the sample variances are homogeneous, a significant F ratio will be obtained whenever the sample means are more variable than might be expected due to random sampling fluctuations from populations with identical means. Whenever samples are drawn randomly from populations with identical means or from the same population, the differences in sample means should vary only within such limits. Whenever the samples are drawn randomly from populations with different means, the variability among sample means will be increased such that MS_B will tend to be larger than MS_W. If the F ratio is significant, it is concluded that the population means are not equal, that is, evidence is obtained which indicates that the treatments produce real effects on the dependent variable.

In the randomized groups design, the F ratio is given by

$$F = MS_B/MS_W, \tag{6-10}$$

with $k - 1$ df for the numerator and $N - k$ df for the denominator. The solution of Equation 6-10 for the data of Table 6-4 yields

$$F = \frac{8.45}{7.83} = 1.08,$$

with 2 df for the numerator and 15 df for the denominator.

In referring to the table of F in a standard reference or textbook, we find that, with $\alpha = 0.05$, the critical value of F for 2 and 15 df is equal to 3.68. Thus, we see that our obtained value of $F = 1.08$ is not significant with $\alpha = 0.05$, that is, the obtained value does not exceed the tabled critical value. We cannot reject the null hypothesis that there are no differences between the three sample means, that is, we have no reason to believe that the three sample means are not estimates of a common population mean.

The usual form of summarizing the results of the analysis of variance in an experiment is to present the data in a table. For our worked example, the summary is contained in Table 6-5.

Table 6-5 Summary of Analysis of Variance

Source of Variation	Sum of Squares	df	Mean Square	F
Between Groups	16.9	2	8.45	1.08
Within Groups	117.4	15	7.83	(Non-significant)
Total	134.3	17		

If the null hypothesis had been rejected, which it was not, we would probably have been interested in knowing more about the mean differences. It might occur to us, for example, that a significant difference might obtain between the means of Groups 1 and 2 and Groups 1 and 3, but that it might not between the means of Groups 2 and 3. Rejection of the null hypothesis indicates that there is at least *one* significant difference between the group means; we might like to know specifically which means are significantly different and which are not. There are several ways of determining this, but these techniques extend beyond the scope of the present discussion and the reader is referred to other sources (Duncan, 1955; Ryan, 1959).

The critical values of F presented in the F table can be meaningfully applied in the analysis of variance only if certain assumptions are satisfied. These are: (1) that each of the k populations from which the various groups in the experiment were drawn are normally distributed; (2) that the variance values for the k populations are equal (homogeneous); and (3) that the subjects tested in the experiment have been drawn independently and at random from their respective parent populations. Although tests are available to determine whether the assumptions of normality and homogeneity of variance seem to be met in a given experiment, a discussion of these techniques extends beyond our present needs. Whenever the assumptions underlying the F test are not met, the values presented in the F table are no longer exact. Whether the violation of the parametric assumptions will have negligible or serious effects upon the tabular probabilities will depend upon a multiplicity of factors (Bradley, 1959). It is fallacious to accept the unqualified generalization that parametric tests are insensitive to the violation of the fundamental assumptions that underlie t and F.

Sometimes, when it has been determined that the assumptions of analysis of variance have not been met, it is possible to overcome such difficulties, for example, nonhomogeneity of variance or nonnormality of distribution, by a *transformation* of the criterion scores (Mueller, 1949). The transformation of the original scores to a new scale of derived scores may improve the tenability of the underlying assumptions. These are several commonly used transformations, but the selection of the transformation to be performed will depend upon the particular difficulty that has been encountered. If, for example, it is found that there is a correlation between the variances and the means of the treatments, this indicates the departure from normality and, very likely, the heterogeneity of variance. In such a case, each criterion score (X) could be transformed into the measure $\sqrt{X} + \sqrt{X + 1}$ (Freeman and Tukey, 1950). Unfortunately, valid transformations are not always possible; this occurs, for instance, whenever the treatments produce differences in the variance of the criterion measures but not in the means, or whenever the distributions are homogeneous in variance but differ in form. The careful research worker attempts to avoid such difficulties by selecting, from several alternative criteria which may often be appropriately employed, that criterion measure most likely to satisfy the basic assumptions of the analysis of variance.

Since at an earlier point the classification of scales of measurement into nominal, ordinal, interval, and ratio categories was discussed in detail, it should be indicated that one of the current controversies in psychology relates to the matter of whether subinterval type of data may be appropriately utilized in the analysis of variance. Several writers (Gaito, 1960; Jarrard, 1960) believe that the level of significance of the analysis of variance test for differences between means is affected only slightly by the choice of a scale of measurement; the important consideration seems to be that the data must be related to the normal distribution and that the fundamental assumptions of the analysis of variance must be met. Although the scales of measurement determine the appropriateness of certain *descriptive* statistics, it is held that the mathematical requirements of *inferential* statistics, as in the analysis of variance, are contained in the assumptions, with no specific mention of particular scale properties.

The Factorial Design: Two or More Independent Variables

In the preceding section, we presented the simplest form of the analysis of variance and indicated the logic involved in establishing an F test of the null hypothesis. The design presented involved the testing of a hypothesis about the differences in population means for an experiment involving several groups but only one independent variable. With a few extensions of the basic procedures already described, it is possible to analyze an experiment in which two or more independent variables are involved.

A *factorial* design is one in which two or more independent variables, or *factors*, are studied in an experiment to determine their separate and interactive effects on a dependent variable. The *levels* of a factor refer to the number of different values assigned to that variable in a given study. For example, a factorial experiment might be performed to determine the effects of two independent variables, temperature and relative humidity, on simple hand reaction time to a visual stimulus. There might be three levels or values of temperature used in the experiment, and two levels or values of relative humidity. Such an experiment would be commonly referred to as a 3×2 factorial experiment, indicating that there are two factors with three levels of one factor and two levels of the other.

In this example, the total number of treatments would consist of all possible (different) combinations of one level from each factor; in the conduct of the experiment all six treatment combinations could be administered, one treatment for a given group with an equal number of observations per treatment. Such an experiment would be called a *complete factorial experiment with equal replications*. However, a more complicated design could be used in which some treatment combinations might be omitted, or in which the number of observations per treatment combination might be unequal.

There are several advantages of the factorial design which make it preferable to the single-variable design we have already considered. First of all, the use of different levels of a variable makes it possible to determine simultaneously the relative effectiveness of these various levels in a single experiment rather than performing, say, three separate experiments, each with a different value of the independent variable. The factorial design is, then, economical in terms of time, cost, and effort.

Furthermore, there are numerous instances in which the separate effects of the independent variables, for example, temperature and relative humidity, may not be of primary concern. The separate or main effect of a given independent variable indicates whether that variable alone influences the values of the dependent variable. In our example, the main effect of temperature would indicate whether temperature affects simple hand reaction time, and the main effect of relative humidity would provide a similar indication. However, there is the possibility that while temperature and relative humidity may separately affect simple hand reaction time in a given direction, the two variables may interact to produce certain unique effects. In a recent study, for example, it was found that rats exposed to either random vibrations from 5 to 800 cps or to 18,000 ft altitude conditions had a mortality rate of less than 8 percent. However, when the vibration factor was combined with the altitude factor, the resulting interaction was so critical that it increased the mortality rate to about 80 percent (Megel, 1962).

In an experiment with two independent variables, *interaction* is said to exist between the two variables if the value of the dependent variable resulting from a given level of one independent variable is determined by the particular value held by the other independent variable. Assume, for example, that there is an interaction between temperature and relative humidity in an experiment on simple hand reaction time. Assume further that the main effect of temperature is statistically significant, such that there are real differences between the means corresponding to the three levels of temperature, disregarding the relative humidity classification. The means indicate that the fastest reaction time is obtained with the lowest temperature and that the slowest reaction time is obtained with the highest temperature. A significant interaction between temperature and relative humidity would indicate that the superiority of low temperature depends upon whether it is combined with a low relative humidity or with a high relative h·:midity.

As shown in Figure 6-3, a treatment combination of low temperature and high relative humidity yields a faster reaction time than a low temperature and low relative humidity; but, a high temperature and high relative humidity yields a slower reaction time than a high temperature and low relative humidity. In

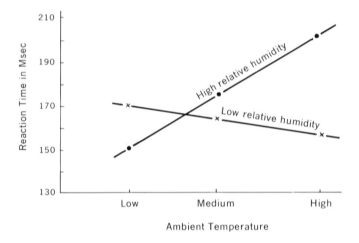

Figure 6-3. Fictitious data for a 3 × 2 factorial study on simple hand reaction time to a visual stimulus.

other words, whether a given temperature yields a slower or faster reaction time depends upon the particular value of relative humidity with which it is paired. Relative humidity combined with temperature does not produce a constant effect on reaction time; the two variables interact to produce a differential effect on one of them at different levels of the other.

In the general case of a factorial design, several factors or treatment classifications, each with a number of different levels, could be appropriately employed. A 3 × 2 × 2 factorial design, for example, would indicate that there are three independent variables, since there are three numbers given, and that one variable has been assigned three values, another, two values, and the third, two values. Multiplication of the three numbers indicates the total number of possible experimental conditions—in this case, twelve. The subjects to be used in such an experiment would be randomly selected from a specified population and would then be divided randomly into twelve treatment groups, usually equal in number. Each group would then be administered its particular treatment combination in a controlled setting, and measures of the dependent variable would be obtained for each subject within the respective groups.

The dependent measures would then be analyzed by the technique of analysis of variance in much the same manner as described for the randomized groups design. We will not go into the details of this analysis, but will simply indicate that for our 3 × 2 reaction time experiment, the total sum of squares would be partitioned into a between-treatments and a within-treatments component. The sum of squares between treatments could be further subdivided into three parts: between temperature conditions, between relative humidity conditions, and the interaction between temperature and relative humidity (temperature × relative humidity). Thus, in a 3 × 2 factorial design four sum of square terms can be computed and, hence, four mean squares. Since in our experiment we selected particular values of each independent variable and did not arrive at them by random sampling from a larger population, we are dealing with *fixed* variables, and the correct error term for all F tests to be run is the *within groups mean square*. Since we are dealing with a *fixed model* in the analysis of variance, we cannot generalize our findings to other values of temperature and relative humidity; we must restrict our conclusions to the specific values of the two variables employed in the study.

If the levels of each factor had been selected at *random* from all possible values, that is, from populations of temperature and relative humidity, we would be dealing with a *random model* of analysis of variance. In this case, the significance of the interaction would be tested by using the within groups mean square as the error estimate (denominator of F); each of the between groups mean squares would then be tested for significance by dividing by the *interaction mean square*. Significant results in this design could be appropriately generalized beyond the particular levels of the two variables used in the study.

The results of the analysis in our example would indicate: (1) whether there are significant differences between the means of the three temperature levels, that is, whether the *main* effect of temperature is significant when averaged over the two levels of relative humidity; (2) whether there are significant differences between the means of the two relative humidity levels, that is, whether the *main* effect of relative humidity is significant when averaged over the three levels of temperature; and (3) whether there is a significant interaction between the two independent variables. The finding in each of these three instances would, of course, depend upon whether the associated null hypothesis had been rejected or not rejected on the basis of the calculated F ratio.

Chapter 7

PSYCHOPHYSICAL
METHODS

Orientation

In the preceding chapter we considered the matter of experimental design and indicated how certain designs could be utilized to determine whether a particular independent variable had the capability of producing a significant effect upon the dependent variable. The decision regarding the effectiveness of the independent variable was shown to rest upon the outcome of certain statistical hypotheses that were tested in accordance with specific rules. It was also indicated that, if significant results were obtained, the nature of the functional relationship between the independent and dependent variables could be established, provided certain features had been incorporated into the experimental design.

The purpose of this chapter is to present some experimental methods which, unlike the statistical methods already described, begin with the presupposition that lawful relations obtain between a given independent variable and a particular dependent variable. The problem is not one of isolating variables that may or may not affect behavior but, instead, one that involves establishing the individual's sensitivity to certain dimensions of the stimulus situation or determining the nature of the relationship between two sets of variables, one physical and the other psychological. This is the area of experimental psychology called *psychophysics*. Experiments are performed to determine the lawful relations that exist between the qualitative or quantitative characteristics of a stimulus and particular aspects of sensory or perceptual behavior. The procedures used in such experiments are designated as *psychophysical methods*.

While there are only a few *basic* models that differentiate among the fundamental procedures of data collection and statistical analysis in psychophysical experiments, there are as many variants of the psychophysical methods as there are techniques for establishing relationships between physical and subjective variables. Most of the basic methods are adapted or revised by the individual investigator to suit his particular needs; consequently, a given method is seldom used strictly in accordance with classical or well-established doctrine. However, the modification of a method presumes a thorough understanding of the fundamental principles and procedures of psychophysics. Furthermore, psychophysical methods have been found so effective in research that their use is no longer restricted to traditional problems in sensory and perceptual psychology. In fact, they are now widely employed in all areas of psychological research, from problems of clothing and equipment design to the study of perception as a function of personality variables. A consideration of psychophysical methods is, therefore, an integral part of the study of experimental psychology.

Aspects of Psychophysical Theory and Types of Problems

Before proceeding with detailed material on psychophysical methods, we should consider some aspects of psychophysical theory, otherwise we might become so preoccupied with the methods that the issues and problems with which psychophysics is concerned would tend to be ignored. In Chapter 2, we stressed the physical environment and indicated how stimuli could be specified and measured in physical terms. In Chapters 3 and 4, emphasis was directed toward man's receptor systems and associated neurocortical structures which permitted the environmental forces to initiate or maintain certain types of behavior. Now we are ready to consider both of these factors as the background against which to develop certain theoretical notions of psychophysics.

The Basic Theoretical Structure of Psychophysics

We will begin with a particular characteristic of a physical stimulus which varies continuously along some dimension, for example, the frequency of a pure tone in cycles per second, or the luminance of a surface in foot-lamberts. Designate this dimension or physical continuum by the letter S and indicate specific values of the stimulus by the symbols $S_1, S_2, \ldots S_j, \ldots S_n$. Let each of these stimuli be presented to the same individual (observer) for a given number of times in a predetermined order and in a predetermined time pattern.

Each time the stimulus is presented, certain physiological or neurophysiological events will occur within the appropriate sensory system of the observer. These events may be associated with the processes of *peripheral* structures, such as the retina of the eye, or they may refer to *central* processes, as in the occipital lobe of brain. Taken collectively, the peripheral and central events comprise a sequence of sensory activities that are initiated by the stimulus and terminate in a particular response. These events, however, are of primary concern to the psychophysiologist rather than the psychophysicist. For the psychophysicist, the events that mediate a particular response are associated with a subjective or inferred continuum, such as pitch or brightness. The task of the psychophysicist is to determine the nature of the relationships that exist between continua of this type and continua of corresponding stimuli. The notion of a sensory continuum may refer, therefore, either to the physiological events or to the inferred subjective events; ordinarily the context in which the term is used will provide an adequate basis for determining the specific meaning that is implied.

Now, when the same stimulus, S_i, is presented to the same observer on different occasions (trials), it will not always produce the same magnitude of the subjective variable on the sensory continuum. Thus, there is a small amount of variability in the magnitudes associated with each stimulus. The implication is that for each stimulus there is (1) a *"true"* or *correct* magnitude which corresponds to that stimulus, (2) a *particular* magnitude which is the one actually associated with that stimulus on that particular occasion, and (3) an *error* or *deviation,* which is the difference between (1) and (2). Assume that these errors or deviations vary at random and are unrelated to one another and to the "true" magnitude; assume further that the sum of the errors for a given stimulus is zero. For simplicity, we will describe the subjective distributions associated with $S_1, S_2, \ldots S_j, \ldots$ and S_n as normal and equally variable.

Finally, we need some indicant of the magnitude of the subjective variable, so we must specify a third continuum. This is a judgmental (behavioral) continuum. The judgment may be in the form of a verbal report or it may involve some other symbolic response, such as depressing a key to indicate "I hear it." It is possible, therefore, by making certain assumptions about the nature of the relationship between the judgmental continuum and sensory continuum, to specify the magnitude of a subjective variable as a function of the magnitude of the stimulus. The basic data that are required to accomplish this are the judgments of the observer.

Figure 7-1 is a schematic representation of the ideas developed to this point. The three continua are designated as S (stimulus or physical continuum), P (physiological, subjective, or inferred continuum), and J (judgmental continuum). Each stimulus presented to an observer produces a *discriminal process* on the P continuum, according to Thurstone (1927). However, fluctuations in the observer's sensitivity, or changes in the experimental situation, prevent a given stimulus from always producing the same discriminal process on repeated presentations. As a result, many discriminal processes are associated with each stimulus, and a frequency distribution of discriminal processes is generated. Each distribution of the discriminal processes for each stimulus is called a *discriminal dispersion.* The standard deviation of each discriminal dispersion is commonly taken as the measure of variability of the distribution and the mode of the distribution is considered to be the "true" subjective magnitude for that stimulus. The modal value is called the *modal discriminal response.*

Notice that the physical continuum in Figure 7-1 is the longest of the three. There are stimuli at both ends of the physical continuum that fail to register on the subjective continuum, but the terminal points of the subjective continuum are not absolutely fixed. Hence, the dashed lines are called *zones of transition.* The

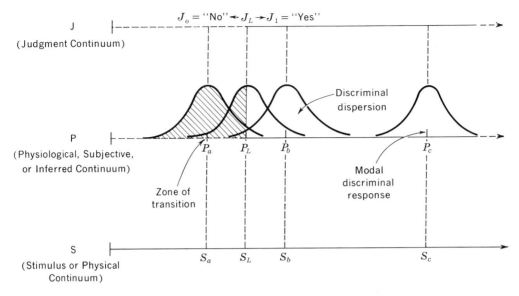

Figure 7–1. A schematic arrangement of the three continua underlying contemporary psycho-physical theory. Four discriminal dispersions are shown on the subjective (P) continuum corre-sponding to four stimuli, one of which defines the absolute threshold (S_L).

schematic arrangement in Figure 7-1 represents a typical psychophysical prob-lem—that of the absolute threshold. For a given physical variable and a given observer, what is the value of the stimulus that corresponds to the point of transi-tion on the sensory continuum, such that stimuli above this value lead to a be-havioral (judgmental) response, while those below this value lead to no response?

To answer this, we begin by assuming that there is a perfect linear correlation between the J and P continua. The J and P continua increase from left to right, as does the S continuum. Let the stimulus quantity S_L indicate the stimulus limen (absolute threshold) for a given sensory modality with respect to a particular stimulus dimension. On the P continuum, there will be a quantity P_L which is the modal discriminal response for S_L. Since there is an assumed perfect correla-tion between P and J, there will a point J_L on the J continuum which corresponds to P_L. If a particular psychophysical method is used, the observer will be per-mitted two categories of judgment, for example, "yes" and "no." The observer uses one of the categories each time a stimulus is presented. Whenever P exceeds P_L, the observer will use the J_1 or "yes" category; whenever P does not exceed P_L, he will use the J_0 or "no" category.

It may be seen that stimulus S_c will always elicit an affirmative judgment, since the distribution of discriminal processes is completely above the critical point, P_L. Hence, S_c cannot be the threshold stimulus, if this is defined as the value of the stimulus that elicits a response on half the trials. S_b, however, has a dispersion, part of which is above P_L and part below P_L. The proportion of judgments in the J_1 region is represented by the area under the curve of dispersion to the right of

P_L, while the proportion of judgments J_0 is given by the area to the left of P_L. Since the discriminal distribution is assumed to be normal, the distance between P_b and P_L on the P scale can be expressed in terms of a unit-normal-deviate (standard z-score measure) taken from a table of the normal curve. A similar process may be used for S_a. The stimulus we are seeking is S_L; this is the value of the stimulus that yields 50 percent judgments J_1 and 50 percent judgments J_0. In practice, it is extremely rare that a particular stimulus would be used in an experiment that would yield these exact proportions. However, by linear interpolation between two stimuli, for example, S_a and S_b, in accordance with certain psychophysical procedures, it is possible to establish the value of the absolute threshold.

Types of Psychophysical Problems

The absolute threshold is only one of a number of problems that may be investigated by means of the psychophysical methods. Stevens (1948) has identified seven categories of problems in psychophysics; this list, which includes the absolute threshold, is summarized below.

1. *Absolute threshold.*   What is the value of the stimulus which, for a given dimension, marks the point of transition between a behavioral response and no response on the part of an observer?

   Example: What is the least amount of acoustic energy at a frequency of 1000 cps that will be heard by a normal observer?
   (*Answer:*   About 5 db SPL for a young adult.)

2. *Differential threshold.*   What is the smallest change in a stimulus that can be detected by an observer?

   Example: How many grams must be added to a weight of 200 grams in order for the observer to report that it feels heavier?
   (*Answer:*   About 4 grams.)

3. *Equality.*   What values must two different stimuli have in order to appear equal to an observer with respect to some designated attribute?

   Example: Given a particular intensity of green light, what intensity must a particular red light have if it is to appear equally bright?
   (*Answer:*   The physical intensity of the red light must be about eight times that of the green light.)

4. *Order.*   Given a series of stimuli, what is the order in which they are ranked by an observer with respect to some designated attribute?

   Example: What is the order of eminence of nine particular composers born before 1870?
   (*Answer:*   As judged by 120 college students, from highest to lowest: Beethoven, Bach, Chopin, Mozart, Wagner, Brahms, Tchaikovsky, Handel, and Liszt.)

5. *Equality of intervals.*   What set of stimuli produces a set of judgments which are successively equidistant on the scale of some attribute?

Example: What is the duration of a particular electrical stimulus that is midway between the unpleasantness of stimulus durations of 0.18 sec and 1.72 sec?
(Answer: It is not a duration of 0.95 sec as you might suppose, but approximately 0.56 sec.)

6. *Equality of ratios.*   What stimuli produce a set of judgments which bear constant ratios to one another?

Example: When will the brightness ratio of two lights of different intensity equal the loudness ratio of two tones of different intensity?
(Answer: The two ratios will appear equal when the same physical ratio exists between the intensities of the two sounds and the intensities of the two lights.)

7. *Stimulus rating.*   What is the accuracy and reliability with which an observer can judge the physical value of a stimulus?

Example: How accurately can an observer judge the physical magnitude of a standard time interval?
(Answer: A standard duration of 25 sec will be judged to have a duration of only about 20.6 sec.)

These are some of the types of problems that can be studied by the conventional psychophysical methods. Whatever the psychophysical problem may be, it is possible to conceptualize the solution of the problem in terms of the elements identified in Figure 7-1. It should also be noted that although some of the problems that have been listed involve organismic sensitivity, for example, absolute threshold, differential threshold, equality, and stimulus rating, others such as order, equality of intervals, and equality of ratios, are fundamentally problems in scaling subjective magnitudes. For the latter type of problems, the answers that were provided for the illustrative examples were derived from particular psychophysical scales. The properties of these scales are consistent with the criteria specified in Chapter 5 for the various levels of measurement.

Representative methods for investigating problems of organismic sensitivity and for deriving scales of sensory magnitudes will be described in the following sections of this chapter. In the first half of the chapter, we will present three basic psychophysical methods dealing with organismic sensitivity: the method of limits, the method of constant stimulus differences, and the method of average error. In the latter half, attention will be given to two selected psychophysical scaling methods: the ratio method of fractionation and the method of direct magnitude estimation.

The Method of Limits

The Problem

The *method of limits* (sometimes called the method of minimal changes or the method of serial exploration) is one of the most frequently used methods for determining the *absolute threshold*. In psychophysics, the absolute threshold, or *stimulus limen,* is given an operational definition that corresponds to the value of the stimulus that is detected and reported by an observer on 50 percent of the trials.

The fundamental notion, as shown in Figure 7-1, is that in any psychophysical study there are three quantitative variables involved. One of these variables is on a *physical* or *stimulus* continuum; the second, on a *subjective* continuum, and the third, on a *judgment* continuum. It is assumed that the latter two variables are linearly and perfectly correlated. This means that, given certain data on the judgment continuum, implications may be drawn concerning the nature of the occurrences on the subjective (sensory) continuum. These implications or inferences have, in part, been described with reference to Figure 7-1.

It has also been pointed out that a given physical continuum usually extends from an infinitely small value (theoretically, the lower limit is zero) to some finitely large magnitude. The range of this continuum is, therefore, so great that the organism is incapable of responding either to the exceedingly small quantities of the property under consideration, or to the exceptionally large quantities (see Chapter 2). Thus, the subjective continuum may be considered to be shorter than the physical continuum at both ends.

The concept of the absolute threshold applies to the lower end of the physical continuum. It is the value on the physical continuum which separates the stimuli that are not capable of eliciting a behavioral response from those that are. At the upper end of the physical continuum, the *terminal stimulus,* or *terminal limen,* is a value on the continuum which separates the stimuli that are capable of eliciting a behavioral response from those that are not. In either case, there is an underlying zone of transition on the subjective continuum which leads to a change in the type of behavioral response made by the observer.

The notion of a *zone of transition* implies that the exact location of the absolute threshold varies from moment to moment as measured over a given portion of the physical continuum. The variations may be due to a large number of factors, such as extraneous "noise" in the nervous system, fluctuations in attention, changes in the criterion of response, and so on. The result is that random variations in sensitivity are invariably observed in psychophysical experiments. Consequently, a number of observations must be made in determining the threshold value; this generates a distribution of observations that encompasses the transition zone. On the basis of this distribution, the stimulus limen is given a statistical definition; it corresponds to the central tendency (usually the arthimetic mean) of the distribution of observations.

As we have already stated, the *absolute threshold* is conventionally defined as that stimulus quantity which has a probability of 0.50 of arousing a behavioral response. Stimuli above the absolute threshold are reported more than half the time; stimuli below the absolute threshold are reported less than half the time, as depicted in Figure 7-1.

The Procedure

A basic requirement of the method of limits is that the stimulus must be variable in small discrete steps of equal physical magnitude. This requirement is easily met, for example, in the determination of absolute thresnolds for tones, lights, temperature, pressure, odorous gases, and gustatory substances. The experimenter presents a series of stimuli, each differing by a small amount from the preceding one; for each stimulus in the series, the experimenter records the response of the observer. If the observer gives a positive response, for example, "Yes," "I hear it," or some equivalent coded response such as raising a finger or depressing a response key, the experimenter records a "+" for that trial. If the observer gives a negative response, for example, "No," "I don't hear it," or fails to raise his finger or to depress the key, the experimenter records a "−" for that trial.

In the determination of an absolute threshold, two kinds of stimulus series are generally employed: (1) an *ascending series* and (2) a *descending series*. In the ascending series, the initial stimulus of the series is presented well below the threshold and, on each succeeding trial, the experimenter increases the magnitude of the stimulus by a constant small step until the observer detects the presence of the stimulus and gives a positive response. In the descending series, the initial stimulus of the series is presented well above the threshold and, on each succeeding trial, the experimenter decreases the magnitude of the stimulus by constant small steps until the observer can no longer detect the presence of the stimulus and gives a negative report. Each series is stopped as soon as the observer's report changes from "+" to "−" or from "−" to "+," depending on the direction of the series.

In determining a threshold value, the experimenter usually employs several ascending and several descending series. These two types of series are either presented in alternation, for example, descending, ascending, descending, ascending, or they are presented in a prearranged sequence, with the total number of ascending trials being equal to the total number of descending trials.

The use of both ascending and descending trials tends, in the computation of the absolute threshold, to cancel out two constant errors which may occur in the method of limits. These are (1) the *error of habituation,* in which the observer tends to give the same response for too many trials within a given series, for example, "Yes" in a descending series and "No" in an ascending series, and (2) the *error of expectation,* in which the observer prematurely changes his response from negative to positive, or from positive to negative, because he thinks a change should have occurred in view of the number of trials or the amount of time that has elapsed since the beginning of that particular series.

In presenting the ascending and descending series of trials, it is advisable to vary the length of each series. The length of the series refers to the number of steps through which the stimulus must be changed in order to reach the threshold. Sometimes a given series starts a large number of steps above or below threshold; sometimes it starts only a few steps above or below threshold. By varying the length of the series in a predetermined manner, the experimenter is able to minimize the observer's tendency to respond in terms of the *number* of presentations in a given series rather than in terms of his sensory ability. If the length of the series were not changed, the observer could count the number of trials in which he gave a particular response, for example, a positive response in a descending series, and in subsequent descending series, he could respond the same way for exactly the same number of trials, regardless of whether the stimulus was actually detected.

The Computations

To illustrate the computation of the absolute threshold in the method of limits, suppose that an experiment has been performed to determine the threshold for pressure on the back of the hand. Assume that by means of an aesthesiometer a series of graduated pressures was applied to the skin in accordance with the requirements of the method of limits. Assume also that the point of application of the force on the back of the hand was always constant and that the force was always applied at a constant rate over a constant area of stimulation. Sufficient time, for exmple, 10 sec, was permitted to elapse between successive applications of the stimulus to minimize the effects of adaptation to pressure.

Assume that the results for one observer in such an experiment are contained in Table 7-1, in which the magnitude of the stimulus is specified in grams per square millimeter. The "+" sign indicates a positive or "yes" report, the "−"

Table 7-1   Determination of the Absolute Threshold for Pressure by the Method of Limits

(Fictitious Data)

Stimulus in grams per square mm	Series Order					
	Descending	Ascending	Descending	Ascending	Descending	Ascending
21	+					
20	+					
19	+				+	
18	+				+	
17	+				+	
16	+				+	
15	+		+		+	
14	+		+		+	
13	−		+	+	+	
12		+	+	−	−	
11		−	+	−		+
10		−	+	−		−
9		−	−	−		−
8		−		−		−
7		−		−		−
6		−		−		
5				−		
Threshold / series	13.5	11.5	9.5	12.5	12.5	10.5

Descending Threshold = (13.5 + 9.5 + 12.5) / 3 = 35.5 / 3 = 11.8

Ascending Threshold = (11.5 + 12.5 + 10.5) / 3 = 34.5 / 3 = 11.5

Absolute Threshold = (11.8 + 11.5) / 2 = 11.65 gm/sq mm

sign indicates a negative or "no" report. There are three descending and three ascending trials presented in alternation. Each series yields a threshold value; this value is taken as the midpoint between the stimulus magnitude which terminates a series and the stimulus magnitude immediately preceding it. For instance, in the first descending trial in Table 7-1, the absolute threshold is taken to be 13.5 grams per square millimeter. However, a more reliable estimate of threshold may be obtained by averaging the values obtained in each of the six series. A common procedure for doing this is to average the threshold values for all descending series to obtain a *descending threshold,* and to average the threshold values for all ascending series to obtain an *ascending threshold.* The absolute threshold is then obtained by finding the mean of these two estimates.

It is also possible to compute the standard deviation (σ or SD) for all the data, as well as a standard deviation for each type of series, either descending or ascending. The standard error of the mean (σ_M or SE_M) can then be computed for the absolute threshold and for the ascending and descending thresholds by the usual formula:

$$\sigma_M = \sigma \text{ sample } \sqrt{N-1} \tag{7-1}$$

A summary of the means, standard deviations, and standard errors of means is presented in Table 7-2 for all the data and for the descending and ascending series.

Table 7-2 Summary of Means, Standard Deviations, and Standard Errors of Means in a Hypothetical Pressure Limen Experiment

	All Data	Descending Series	Ascending Series
M	11.65	11.80	11.50
SD	1.34	1.70	0.81
SE_M	0.60	1.20	0.57

Mean difference between series = 0.3 gm/sq mm

The difference in means of 0.3 gm/sq mm between the descending and ascending series is also shown in Table 7-2. The significance of this mean difference, with $\alpha = 0.05$, can be evaluated by a t test for related measures. The use of this statistic assumes that it is appropriate to pair the threshold values for the first descending and ascending trials, the second descending and ascending trials, and so on. The computations of t are similar to those shown in Chapter 6, Table 6-3, Part B, in which the direct difference method was demonstrated. For the data in Table 7-2, the obtained t is 0.179, with $n - 1 = 2$ df. The obtained t is nonsignificant at the 0.05 level and the null hypothesis cannot be rejected. We conclude, therefore, that the means for the descending and ascending series were drawn from a single population of thresholds, and that the obtained difference in means could have arisen by random sampling. Thus, this experiment indicates that the effects of the constant errors of habituation and expectation tended to cancel out. One effect was not excessively greater than the other. Also, since the thresholds obtained under the descending and ascending series were found to be homogeneous, we are justified in combining all the data of the experiment to obtain a single, final estimate of the absolute threshold (11.65 gm/sq mm).

If a larger number of series had been presented in this hypothetical experiment, for example, 10 descending and 10 ascending series, other possible constant errors could have been appropriately investigated. For example, we could have compared the thresholds obtained in the first 10 series with those in the last 10 series to evaluate the effects of learning and fatigue. Learning would tend to reduce the thresholds in the later trials, as shown in a study by Corso and Cohen (1958), while fatigue would tend to increase the thresholds in the later trials. A comparison might also have been made of the short series versus the long series of trials. It is also suggested that if sufficient data are available, the results of an experiment may be more effectively treated by analysis of variance in a factorial design (Guilford, 1954). With two serial orders (descending and ascending) and two time blocks (first half and second half of the judgments), a 2 × 2 factorial analysis could be performed.

The Method of Constant Stimulus Differences

The Problem

In the preceding section, a hypothetical psychophysical experiment was described in which the method of limits was used to determine the absolute threshold for pressure. What happens, however, as we proceed to increase or decrease the value of the stimulus along a particular dimension once the absolute threshold has been passed? Is every minute change in the stimulus detected and reported by the observer? Numerous studies have shown that this is not the case—there are definite limits in the resolving power of the various human senses. For any physical dimension associated with a discriminable subjective attribute, it is possible to select two stimulus values that are so close together that an observer presented with the two stimuli cannot reliably report which is greater. If the two stimuli lie extremely close together on the continuum under consideration, the observer will be correct in his judgments only at the chance level, that is, he will report correctly on one half of the trials. However, as the difference between the two stimuli increases, the probability of a correct response will increase accordingly (see Figure 7-1).

As in the case of the absolute threshold, there is a zone of transition, a *range of uncertainty*, associated with differential judgments. This range extends from a difference between two stimuli in which the greater stimulus is *never* judged to be greater, to a difference between two stimuli in which the greater stimulus is *always* judged to be greater. The *difference limen, DL,* (sometimes called the differential threshold, *DT*, or the "just noticeable difference," *jnd*) is located within the range of uncertainty. The *DL*, defined statistically, is generally taken as the stimulus difference that is reported correctly 75 percent of the time, that is, halfway between chance guessing (50 percent) and perfect discrimination (100 percent), when the observer is permitted only two categories of judgment, for example, greater or smaller.

The *DL* is experimentally determined from a set of operational procedures, like those in the method of constant stimulus differences. The method of constant stimulus differences is considered to be the most accurate of all the psychophysical methods for answering the question: "What is the smallest difference between two stimuli that can be correctly judged by an observer in a specified percentage of the trials in which it occurs?"

The Procedure

The basic procedure in determining the *DL* by the constant method involves the presentation of a comparison stimulus (S_v) simultaneously with, or in temporal sequence with, a given standard (S_s) and the task of the observer is to report which member of the pair appears to be "larger" or "smaller" than the other. Sometimes "equal" or "doubtful" judgments are permitted; however, the case of three categories of judgment involves numerous controversial and theoretical issues with respect to the analysis of data. Consequently, the restriction of judgments to two categories is usually preferred.

The comparison stimuli to be used in an experiment are selected after some preliminary judgments have been made. The stimuli are usually selected so that the smallest stimulus difference is correctly judged "smaller" approximately 95 percent of the time, while the largest stimulus difference is judged "larger" approximately 95 percent of the time. The number of comparison stimuli is fixed after the preliminary investigation; this number ordinarily ranges from four to seven. A comparison stimulus equal to the standard is often included and the final series of comparison stimuli represents a set of values that are systematically arranged around the standard stimulus in equal, symmetrical steps. In a pitch discrimination experiment with a standard of 1000 cps, a typical set of comparison stimuli might be 994, 996, 998, 1000, 1002, 1004, and 1006 cps. The constant stimulus difference is 2 cps.

In presenting the stimuli for judgment, the experimenter presents, simultaneously or successively, a pair of stimuli consisting of the standard stimulus and one comparison stimulus. On each trial, the same standard stimulus is always used as a member of the pair. The comparison stimuli, however, are included in the various pairs according to a prearranged plan unknown to the observer. Each comparison stimulus is paired with the standard a large and constant number of times, for example, 100. The observer's task is to judge the second stimulus as "larger" or "smaller" than the first, if the members of the pair are presented successively. If the members of the pair are presented simultaneously, the right or left member is always judged in comparison with the other. In both cases, a counterbalanced order must be used to cancel the effects of the constant errors of time and space. In the case of successive presentations, the standard is presented as the first member of the pair in one half of the trials and as the second member of the pair in the remaining half of the trials. In the case of simultaneous presentations, the standard is presented as the right member of the pair in one half of the trials and as the left member of the pair in the remaining half of the trials. The experimenter records the observer's juugment after each trial, either directly, for example, "larger" or "smaller," or in coded form, for example, "+" or "−".

The Computations

The computations that are usually performed in the method of constant stimulus differences will be illustrated with reference to a pitch discrimination experiment. Assume, as already suggested, that a standard stimulus (S_s) of 1000 cps has been selected and that seven comparison stimuli (S_v) were fixed after preliminary exploration. Suppose the comparison stimuli were set at 994, 996, 998, 1000, 1002, 1004, and 1006 cps and that all tones were presented at a *sensation level* of 40 db, that is, 40 db above the absolute threshold. Assume, further, that the experiment has been conducted according to the procedures required by the constant method. Consider that each comparison stimulus has been paired 100 times with the standard stimulus in a counterbalanced order and that the successive method of presentation was employed.

A set of hypothetical data for one observer is presented in Table 7-3. In order to obtain the values to be entered in the table, the experimenter must review the observer's raw data and tabulate the number of times each comparison stimulus is judged both higher and lower in pitch than the standard, assuming that only two categories of judgment have been used. The tally of frequencies for each comparison stimulus must equal the number of times that each comparison stimulus was paired with the standard. The sum of these totals will equal the total

Table 7-3 Experimental Data for One Observer in a Pitch Discrimination Experiment Showing the Frequency and Proportion of Each Type of Judgment for Each Comparison Stimulus Paired with a Standard Stimulus of 1000 Cycles Per Second

(Fictitious Data)

S_v	Frequency of Judgments			Proportion of Judgments		
	Higher	Lower	Total	Higher	Lower	Combined
994	4	96	100	0.04	0.96	1.00
996	12	88	100	0.12	0 88	1.00
998	32	68	100	0.32	0.68	1.00
1000	56	44	100	0.56	0.44	1.00
1002	69	31	100	0.69	0.31	1.00
1004	89	11	100	0.89	0.11	1.00
1006	96	4	100	0.96	0.04	1.00

Total = 700

number of judgments made by each observer in the experiment. In the present example, the total for each comparison stimulus is 100 and the total number of judgments for one observer is 700.

Each obtained frequency is then converted into a proportion by dividing the frequency of the given judgment by the total number of judgments for that particular comparison stimulus. Since in our example each comparison stimulus was presented 100 times, the proportions are readily obtained and are entered in Table 7-3.

At this point in the analysis of data, several possible procedures might be followed in order to obtain the experimental values in which we are interested. Each procedure has its own theoretical justification and some procedures are mathematically more rigorous than others. It is possible, for instance, to fit an ideal function to the data, such as the cumulative normal curve, before computing the threshold values, but the particular function that is chosen represents a specific theoretical position regarding the nature of the sensory discriminatory process (Corso, 1963a). Since this question poses one of the issues in contemporary sensory psychology, a complete exposition of the two major theories will be presented in Chapter 8; hence, the treatment of the data in our example will follow the procedure of plotting *empirical* psychometric functions.

A *psychometric function* is a graphical plot which indicates the proportion of times that each comparison stimulus is judged to be in a given category when compared with the standard stimulus. In the present example, there will be two psychometric functions, one for the judgment category of "higher," and the other for the judgment category of "lower." The two functions are shown in Figure 7-2, in which the data points have been connected with straight lines with no attempt being made to fit a particular theoretical curve to the points. This graphical procedure is much less precise than several other techniques, but it will suffice to convey the fundamental concepts that are an integral part of the method of constant stimulus differences. If we assume that any two adjacent points on a psychometric function are joined by a straight line, the graphical solution for the desired constants will yield a set of values identical to those computed by the process of *linear interpolation*.

Our first concern in Figure 7-2 is to consider each of the psychometric functions separately. Since there were only two categories of judgment permitted in the experiment, the observer would have been able to judge each comparison stimulus correctly in one-half of the trials by chance alone, that is, by guessing. Hence, a judgment criterion of 0.50 would indicate essentially nothing about the observer's discriminatory ability. For the two-category case, therefore, the criterion of differential discrimination is generally set at a proportion of 0.75; this is half (50 percent) of the distance between chance performance and perfect discrimination.

Accordingly, in Figure 7-2, a horizontal dotted line has been drawn through the two psychometric functions at a value of 0.75, the third quartile Q_3. The stimulus values of the two functions at the points of intersection with the dotted line are denoted by arrows on the abscissa, that is, x-axis of the graph. For the lower psychometric function, the lower threshold (L_l) is approximately 997.3 cps;

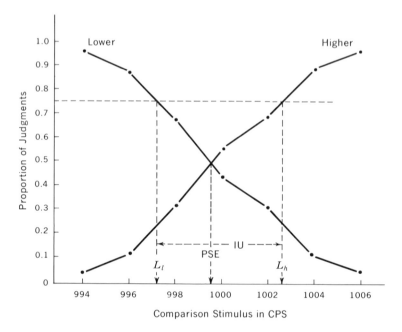

Figure 7-2.   A hypothetical set of psychometric functions obtained in a pitch-discrimination experiment with two categories of judgment.

for the higher psychometric function, the upper threshold (L_h) is approximately 1002.6 cps. These are the values of the comparison stimuli that are judged correctly as "lower" and "higher," respectively, 75 percent of the time when compared with a standard stimulus of 1000 cps.

Notice that the lower threshold (997.3) which is located at Q_3 of the lower psychometric function is equivalent to the first quartile Q_1 (proportion 0.25) of the higher psychometric function. Thus, it is possible to obtain all of the desired constants either graphically or by linear interpolation from the data for *one* set of judgments in a two category experiment. To illustrate the computation of the upper threshold (L_h) by linear interpolation, the following general formula may be used:

$$L_h = S_b + \frac{(S_a - S_b)(C - p_b)}{p_a - p_b},\qquad (7\text{-}2)$$

Where S_a = the stimulus value immediately above the upper threshold;
$\quad\ \ S_b$ = the stimulus value immediately below the upper threshold;
$\quad\ \ p_a$ = the proportion of "higher" judgments for the stimulus value immediately above the upper threshold;
$\quad\ \ p_b$ = the proportion of "lower" judgments for the stimulus value immediately below the upper threshold;
$\quad\ \ C$ = the proportion of judgments defining the threshold criterion.

Using the data presented in Table 7-3, we have for the upper threshold

$$L_h = 1002 + \frac{(1004 - 1002)\,(0.75 - 0.69)}{0.89 - 0.69}$$

$$= 1002 + \frac{(2)\,(.06)}{0.20} = 1002 + 0.6$$

$$L_h = 1002.6$$

Equation 7-2 may also be used to compute the lower threshold (L_l) by simply changing the meanings of the symbols to refer to L_l rather than L_h. The computed value of L_l is 997.3.

The interval of uncertainty (IU) is taken as the distance in stimulus units between the higher and lower thresholds.

$$IU = L_h - L_l \qquad\qquad (7\text{-}3)$$

For our data, $IU = 1002.6 - 997.3 = 5.3$. Given only the higher psychometric function, it is seen that the interval of uncertainty is equivalent to the *interquartile* range, $Q_3 - Q_1$, that is, $1002.6 - 997.3$.

The interval of uncertainty may also be computed from the *lower* and *higher* *differential thresholds*. The lower differential threshold (L_{DL}) is given by

$$L_{DL} = S_s - L_l \qquad\qquad (7\text{-}4)$$

and the higher differential threshold H_{DL} is given by

$$H_{DL} = L_h - S_s. \qquad\qquad (7\text{-}5)$$

For the data shown in Figure 7-2,

$$L_{DL} = 1000 - 997.3 = 2.7$$

and

$$H_{DL} = 1002.6 - 1000 = 2.6.$$

The interval of uncertainty may, therefore, be redefined as

$$IU = L_{DL} + H_{DL}, \qquad\qquad (7\text{-}6)$$

which, for the data in Figure 7-2, yields $IU = 2.7 + 2.6 = 5.3$. This is the same value that was obtained by solving Equation 7-3.

The mean DL is taken as one-half the interval of uncertainty. That is

$$\text{Mean } DL = IU \,/\, 2, \qquad\qquad (7\text{-}7)$$

but, since the interval of uncertainty is equal to the interquartile range $(Q_3 - Q_1)$ of one distribution of judgments, the mean DL is also equal to the *semi-interquartile range* (Q), for example, of the higher psychometric function:

$$\text{Mean } DL = Q = \frac{Q_3 - Q_1}{2}. \tag{7-8}$$

For our data, the mean $DL = \dfrac{5.3}{2} = 2.65$ by Equation 7-7 and the

$$\text{Mean } DL = \frac{(1002.6 - 997.3)}{2} = \frac{5.3}{2} = 2.65$$

by Equation 7-8. This is the difference in cps which is required between a comparison stimulus and a standard stimulus of 1000 cps in order for the observer to report a just noticeable difference in pitch (higher or lower) at a criterion level of 0.75.

Finally, the point of subjective equality (PSE) is defined as that value of the comparison stimulus which is equally likely to be judged as higher or lower. The PSE is the value of the comparison stimulus that is subjectively equal to the standard stimulus, given the particular conditions of the experiment. The PSE is located at the stimulus value at which the two psychometric functions intersect. For two categories of judgment, the two functions will intersect at a judgment proportion of 0.50, which locates the median (Q_2) of each distribution. In Figure 7-2, the PSE is estimated to be 999.5 cps, suggesting the possibility of a constant error of 0.5 cps.

Inspection of the two curves in Figure 7-2 will reveal that the steepness of a psychometric function depends on the observer's differential sensitivity. For a very sensitive subject, the function will have a steep slope, that is, the proportion of judgments will increase markedly from one stimulus value to the next; for an observer with poor sensitivity, the function will have a much smaller slope, that is, the proportion of judgments will increase relatively little from one stimulus value to the next. The result, therefore, is that the interval of uncertainty will be smaller or larger depending on the observer's discriminatory ability and the mean DL will, accordingly, have a smaller or larger value.

Finally, it is reiterated that the calculations described in this section on the method of constant stimulus differences are not the most precise techniques available. The more refined techniques, however, are based on certain assumptions about the form of the theoretical distribution underlying the psychometric function. The present technique suffices, however, for providing an estimate of the mean DL, even though it does not incorporate all of the data collected in the course of the experiment. Also, at best, the technique can provide only a crude estimate of the standard error of the difference limen. Thus, it is not advisable to test for the significance of the difference between the PSE and the value of the standard stimulus by means of a t test. Nevertheless, the technique that has been presented is an acceptable one and provides an excellent introduction for some of the more complex concepts to be introduced in Chapter 8.

The Method of Average Error

The Problem

It is commonplace that stimuli that are identical in their physical character-istics are often judged as being different; likewise, stimuli that are different physi-cally are often judged as being the same, that is, identical or equal. There is no reason to expect, however, that all stimuli that are physically equal will be judged to be subjectively equal, since the presence of apparently extraneous fac-tors may interact in such a way as to affect the judgment under consideration; in a similar way, the presentation of two physically identical stimuli may well elicit a response of "different."

In the method of constant stimulus differences, we were primarily concerned with the problem of detecting small differences between stimuli; now we are concerned with the equivalence of stimuli. Under what conditions are two stimuli judged to be equal with respect to a particular sensory attribute? What is the extent of the physical "error" that is present when equality judgments are made with respect to that attribute? These are questions that involve the point of sub-jective equality (*PSE*) which was introduced in the analysis of the data in the method of constant stimulus differences. Although the constant method may be used to determine the *PSE*, a more efficient method may be used for this purpose. This is the method of *average error* (sometimes called the method of reproduction or the method of adjustment). As a method it provides an experimental design that supplies data from which the point of subjective equality (*PSE*) and other constants may be readily determined.

The Procedure

Since the aim of the experiment in which the method of average error is em-ployed is to determine the subjective equivalence of two stimuli, the observer is provided with a standard stimulus (S_s) and a comparison stimulus (S_v). The com-parison stimulus (S_v) is continuously variable with respect to the attribute being judged. For a given trial, S_v is presented at a value that is distinguishably different from S_s, and the task of the observer is to adjust S_v until it appears equal to the standard on the given attribute. The adjustment of the observer is his judgment of S_s as measured on a physical scale; each judgment, therefore, provides a meas-urement of the *point of subjective equality* (*PSE*). To provide a more *reliable* estimate of *PSE*, a number of judgments are made by the observer and the central ten-dency (usually the arithmetic mean) of the distribution of *PSE* values is taken as the physical value equal to S_s for that particular set of experimental conditions.

The method of average error may be applied in any experimental situation in which the observer (or the experimenter) can manipulate the variable stimulus to produce a continuous change in the attribute of the variable stimulus that is being judged. The method would be appropriate, say, in the study of lengths of lines, in the measurement of visual illusions, for example, Müller-Lyer illusion, in the study of visual brightness, in matching colored papers to a "shade" of gray, in equating the pitch or loudness of tones, in matching the heaviness of objects differing in color but identical in both size and shape, and in reproducing the extent of arm movement under a given set of conditions. Although the classical procedure requires that the adjustment of the variable stimulus be made by the observer, there are some modifications of this method in which the changes are actually made by the experimenter and the observer simply reports when S_s and S_v appear to be equal.

When collecting data by the method of average error, there are several precautions that must be observed, otherwise the data will be biased or there will be a limitation in the extent of the generalizations that may be made. (1) The starting value of S_v should be varied randomly or in accordance with a counterbalanced plan such that S_v is sometimes larger and sometimes smaller than S_s by greater or lesser amounts. This permits an evaluation of the *constant error of movement*. Randomization or counterbalancing insures that the direction of adjustment will vary from trial to trial and that the amount of adjustment required to achieve equality will also vary from trial to trial. Sometimes the observer will notice that at the beginning of a trial S_v is considerably greater than S_s and will decrease S_v by a large amount to produce a judgment of "equal"; at other times the observer will notice that S_v is only slightly smaller than S_s and will increase S_v by a small amount to achieve equality.

In a counterbalanced design, the number of "decrease" (D) trials will exactly equal the number of "increase" (I) trials; the two types of trials will, however, occur in a fixed order. In making his adjustment on a given trial, the observer will typically go beyond the point of equality and may be allowed to attain equality by a series of successive approximations or "bracketing" movements. Such a procedure, however, becomes excessively time-consuming, particularly for certain types of observers, and destroys in effect the planned sequence of the "decrease" and "increase" trials. It may be wise, therefore, for the experimenter to instruct the observer that reverse corrective movements will not be permitted. In either case, the observer is permitted, within reasonable limits, to take his own time in making his adjustment.

(2) The spatial arrangement of S_s and S_v, or the temporal order in which S_s and S_v are presented, should be varied systematically in order to take into account the possibility of the *constant errors of space and time*. Whenever S_s and S_v are presented simultaneously for judgment, half the observations should have S_s on the observer's left and half on his right. If S_s and S_v are presented successively, half the observations should have S_s presented first and half, second.

(3) The experimenter must insure that there are no extraneous cues present in the judgmental situation that may be utilized by the observer. This is one reason for starting each trial at a different value of S_v. This forces the observer to make

the judgment that is appropriate for the given experiment rather than a judgment, for example, based on the angle of rotation of a given knob or the distance over which a string has been pulled. The use of extraneous cues may often lead to a set of consistent judgments by the observer but, unfortunately for the experimenter, the judgments will not necessarily represent repeated measurements of the point of subjective equality.

The Computations

To illustrate the method of computation in the method of average error, suppose that we have performed an experiment in which we have collected data to determine the point of subjective equality for the angular velocity of a moving target under a given set of conditions.

Assume that the subject was presented with a visual display, as shown in Figure 7-3, which consisted of two black dots; each dot moved in a circular pattern, but

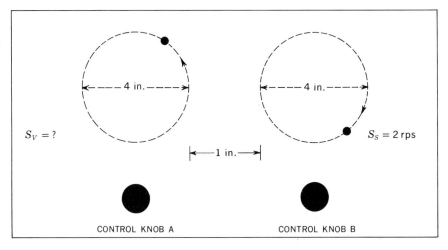

Figure 7-3. Schematic illustration of the visual display employed in a hypothetical experiment on judgments of angular velocity. For this particular trial, the standard stimulus (S_s) is placed on the right; the comparison stimulus (S_v) is placed on the left. The task of the observer is to adjust the angular velocity of S_v by turning Control Knob A so that the two dots appear to be turning at an equal rate, although in opposite directions.

the two dots moved in opposite directions. One dot moved clockwise, while the other moved counterclockwise. The diameters of the two circles were equal, for example, 4 in., and the centers of the circles were displaced horizontally, for example, 5 in., so that the paths of the two dots did not overlap. The standard stimulus always moved with a constant angular velocity that made two revolutions per second (rps). The angular velocity of the comparison stimulus was continuously variable by means of a control knob located on the display board a few inches below the circumscribed path of the "target," that is, the black dot. On half the trials, S_v was placed to the left of S_s; on half the trials, to the right of S_s. These are designated as L and R space arrangements, respectively. On half the trials, the turning rate of S_v was greater than that of S_s; on the other half, the turning rate of S_v was slower than that of S_s so that the observer had to "slow down" or "speed up" the moving target accordingly. These are designated as D (decrease) and I (increase) movement conditions, respectively. For simplicity, we will assume that the experimenter did not vary the direction of movement of S_s; S_s always turned clockwise.

A set of data for this hypothetical experiment is presented in Table 7-4. Assume that, in all, 40 judgments were made by a given observer and that a completely counterbalanced design had been arranged for space (R and L) and for movement (D and I). Assume that there were five judgments for each combination in the following sequence: LD, RI, RD, LI, RI, LD, LI, RD. Within each block of five judgments, slow, medium, and fast rates of rotation of S_v had been randomly selected as starting points for the various trials. Each entry in Table 7-4 repre-

Table 7-4 Example of the Method of Average Error in a Hypothetical Experiment on the Judgment of Angular Velocity

		Space Condition (C)						
		S_v on Right (R)		S_v on Left (L)				
Movement Condition (R) — Increase S_v (I)		1.9	1.6	2.1	1.6			
		1.8	1.7	2.1	1.9			
		2.1	2.2	1.9	1.6			
		2.0	2.2	1.8	2.1			
	For Columns	1.8	2.1	1.8	1.8	For Row (I) ΣX_r M_r ΣX_r^2		
	ΣX_{rk}	19.4		18.7		38.1		
	M_{rk}		1.94		1.87		1.91	
	ΣX^2_{rk}		38.04		35.29			73.33
Decrease S_v (D)		1.8	1.6	1.7	1.6			
		1.8	1.9	1.7	1.8			
		2.0	1.8	1.8	1.6			
		1.7	1.8	1.6	1.7	For Row (D)		
		2.1	1.7	1.9	1.8	ΣX_r M_r ΣX_r^2		
	ΣX_{rk}	18.2		17.2		35.4		
	M_{rk}		1.82		1.72		1.77	
	ΣX_{rk}^2		33.32		29.68			63.00
		For Column R ΣX_k M_k ΣX_k^2		For Column L ΣX_k M_k ΣXk^2		For Both Rows (I and D) ΣX_r M_r ΣX_r^2		
		37.6		35.9		73.5		
			1.88		1.80		1.84	
			71.36		64.97			136.33

sents one trial, and the number is the setting in rps at which the observer judged that S_v was rotating with the same angular velocity as S_s, that is, both black dots were rotating at the same rate.

The first step in the analysis of the data in Table 7-4 is to determine whether the four sets of judgments (RD, RI, LD, and LI) can be considered to have been drawn by random sampling from the same population of judgments. If either of the differences, that is, between R and L, disregarding the movement classification, or between D and I, disregarding the space classification, is statistically significant, we will have to conclude that at least two populations of observations are involved. A significant difference between R and L will indicate the presence of a constant space error, while a significant difference between D and I will indicate the presence of a constant error of movement. If neither the difference between R and L nor the difference between D and I is significant, we may conclude that the four sets of judgments came from the same population and may be combined in the calculation of the point of subjective equality (PSE). The mean of all the judgments (M_j) will be taken as the measure of PSE, in accordance with common practice.

Inspection of the format of Table 7-4 indicates that the study may be considered as a 2×2 factorial design (Guilford, 1954). There are two factors (space and movement) and each factor is represented by two categories (R and L; D and I). Thus, the technique of analysis of variance may be employed, following the procedures indicated in Chapter 6. In this example, there are two columns ($k = 2$), two rows ($r = 2$), and 10 judgments in each set of treatment conditions ($n = 10$). The total number of judgments (N) for the entire experiment is 40. For each of the four conditions, Table 7-4 contains the sum of the judgments, the mean of the judgments, and the sums of squares that will be needed in the analysis of variance and in subsequent computations of the constant errors.

The total sum of squares is computed using Equation 6-3:

$$SS_T = \Sigma X^2 - \frac{(\Sigma X)^2}{N}$$

$$= 136.33 - \frac{(73.5)^2}{40} = 136.33 - 135.05 = 1.28$$

The equation for computing the sum of squares between columns (SS_C) is the same as that for computing the sum of squares between groups (Equation 6–4):

$$SS_C = \frac{(\Sigma X_1)^2}{n_1} + \frac{(\Sigma X_2)^2}{n_2} + \cdots + \frac{(\Sigma X_k)^2}{n_k} - \frac{(\Sigma X)^2}{N}.$$

This may be rewritten as

$$SS_C = \frac{\Sigma(\Sigma X_k)^2}{nr} - \frac{(\Sigma X)^2}{N}. \tag{7-9}$$

For the data of Table 7-4, we have

$$SS_C = \frac{(37.6)^2 + (35.9)^2}{20} - 135.05 = 135.19 - 135.05 = 0.04.$$

The sum of squares between rows (SS_R) is given by an equation that is logically similar to that for computing the sum of squares between columns.

$$SS_R = \frac{\Sigma(\Sigma X_r)^2}{nk} - \frac{(\Sigma X)^2}{N} \tag{7-10}$$

$$= \frac{(38.1)^2 + (35.4)^2}{20} - 135.05 = 135.24 - 135.05 = 0.19$$

The sum of squares computed between the four sets of judgments (SS_{BS}) is given by

$$SS_{BS} = \frac{\Sigma(\Sigma X_{kr})^2}{n} - \frac{(\Sigma X)^2}{N} \tag{7-11}$$

$$SS_{BS} = \frac{(19.4)^2 + (18.7)^2 + (18.2)^2 + (17.2)^2}{10} - 135.05$$

$$= 135.31 - 135.05 = 0.26.$$

The sum of squares for the $R \times C$ interaction is given by

$$SS_{R \times C} = SS_{BS} - SS_R - SS_C \tag{7-12}$$

Since the three terms on the right-hand side of the equation have already been computed, we have

$$SS_{R \times C} = 0.26 - 0.19 - 0.04 = 0.03.$$

The sum of squares from *within* the four sets of judgments (SS_{WS}) is given by

$$SS_{WS} = SS_T - SS_{BS}. \tag{7-13}$$

Substituting the values we have already computed, we have

$$SS_{WS} = 1.28 - 0.26 = 1.02.$$

As a partial check on the accuracy of the solution of Equation 7-13, it should be observed that SS_{BS} should equal $SS_C + SS_R + SS_{R \times C}$.

The results of the analysis of variance for the data in Table 7-4 are summarized in Table 7-5. The number of degrees of freedom for each of the variance components is as follows: df for between rows $= r - 1$; df for between columns $= k - 1$; df for interaction $= (r - 1)(k - 1)$; and df for within sets $= N - rk$. Note in particular the significance or nonsignificance of the F ratios, with $\alpha = 0.01$ as set before the beginning of the experiment. Of the three F's computed, none is significant at the 0.01 level, although the F for movement (between rows) approaches significance. On the basis of the results of the analysis of variance, therefore, we do not reject the hypothesis that these data came from the same parent population of judgments. This permits us to legitimately combine data, as necessary, across the four sets of judgments in order to compute the various constant errors in which we are interested experimentally.

Table 7-5 Summary of Analysis of Variance in a Hypothetical Experiment on Judgments of Angular Velocity

Source of Variation	Sum of Squares	df	Mean Square	F	Significance
Space (C)	0.04	1	0.04	1.43	$p > 0.05$
Movement (R)	0.19	1	0.19	6.78	$0.05 > p > 0.01$
Interaction ($R \times C$)	0.03	1	0.03	1.07	$p > 0.05$
Within Sets	1.02	36	0.028		
Total	1.28	39			

The first such computation to be performed is the one that will indicate whether the observer has any systematic tendency to overestimate or underestimate the rate of rotation of the standard stimulus. Given a standard stimulus of 2 rps, what is the rate of rotation of the comparison stimulus that appears to be equal to that of S_s?

The best and most reliable estimate of this point of subjective equality is the arithmetic mean of the total number of judgments. If there is a significant difference between the value of S_s and the mean value of S_v, that is, the average adjustment or *PSE*, this indicates that a *constant error* exists. This is the *primary* or *main* constant error in the experiment. It indicates that some condition or conditions are present that tend to influence the individual judgments in such a way as to produce a deviation from S_s in a particular direction and in a given amount. Whenever the mean judgment (M_j) for all trials is significantly larger than the value of the standard stimulus, that is, $M_j - S_s$ gives a *positive* difference, this indicates that the standard stimulus has been *overestimated*. If, however, the mean judgment is significantly smaller than the standard, that is, $M_j - S_s$ gives a *negative* difference, this indicates that the standard stimulus has been *underestimated*. Whether the mean judgment is significantly larger or significantly smaller than the standard stimulus must be determined by an appropriate statistical test.

The primary constant error (E_c) is given by

$$E_c = M_j - S_s = PSE - S_s. \tag{7-14}$$

For the data of Table 7-4 we have

$$E_c = 1.84 - 2.00 = -0.16$$

To determine whether the mean judgment differs significantly from the standard stimulus with $\alpha = 0.05$, we need to test the hypothesis that the sample of judgments was taken from a population of judgments having a mean of 2.00. The test will be a two-tail test of significance since, before the experiment, we had no basis for predicting a directional effect of the independent variable on the dependent variable.

An appropriate test in this situation is the t test (Lewis, 1960). The null hypothesis states that $M_j = m_{\text{population}}$ or $M_j - m_{\text{population}} = 0$; the alternative hypothesis is that $M_j \neq m_{\text{population}}$. The t may be computed from

$$t = \frac{M_j - m}{\sqrt{S^2/(N-1)}} \text{ , with } N - 1 \ df \tag{7-15}$$

where M_j is the mean of the judgments in the sample, S^2 is the variance, and N is the number of judgments in the sample. However, as we have already computed the mean square from within sets (MS_{WS}), and it is known that the mean square for within sets (groups) is an unbiased estimate of the common variance of the treatment populations (Lindquist, 1953), we may use

$$t = \frac{M_j - m}{\sqrt{MS_{WS}/N}}, \text{ with } N - rk \ df. \tag{7-16}$$

Solving Equation 7-16, we obtain

$$t = \frac{1.84 - 2.00}{\sqrt{0.028/40}} = \frac{-0.16}{0.026} = -6.15.$$

Since our t with 36 df is significant at the one percent level, we must reject the hypothesis that the mean of the sample of judgments is equal to the mean of the population of judgments, that is, we reject the hypothesis that $M_j = m_{\text{population}}$. Thus, we conclude that there is a main (primary) constant error present in this experiment and, as the difference $(M_j - m)$ is negative, we may further conclude that the standard stimulus has been underestimated.

Our concern now turns to the *secondary* constant errors of space and movement. We would ordinarily not expect to find significant differences between the means for the R and L trials, nor between the D and I trials. The results of the analysis of variance, as shown in Table 7-5, confirm our expectations. It is possible, however, that such secondary constant errors might occur in the method of average error. Conventionally, the magnitude of the constant space error (E_s) is given by

$$E_s = \frac{M_R - M_L}{2}.$$ (7-17)

Consideration of the relative magnitudes of M_R and M_L as obtained in a particular experiment will indicate which space mean is larger than M_j and which space mean is, conversely, smaller than M_j. The space error computed by Equation 7-17 indicates the magnitude of the differences between M_R and M_j, and between M_L and M_j.

The magnitude of the constant error of movement (E_m) is given by

$$E_m = \frac{M_D - M_I}{2}.$$ (7-18)

As in the case of the space error, consideration of the relative magnitudes of M_D and M_I will indicate which movement mean is larger than M_j and which movement mean is, conversely, smaller than M_j. The movement error computed by Equation 7-18 indicates the magnitude of the difference between M_D and M_j, and between M_I and M_j.

Sometimes, in the method of average error, we are interested not only in the constant errors, but in the observer's ability to produce *consistent* judgments from trial to trial in the experiment. If all of the observer's settings of S_v at equality are quite similar, the spread of the distribution of judgments will be small; if the settings are highly dissimilar, the spread will be large. The *variable error* around the mean of the judgment (M_j) is measured by the standard deviation (σ_v) of the combined data, that is, the judgments for the total number of trials.

The variability which is present in a given situation may be due to a large number of factors. From moment to moment, the condition of the organism may be altered so as to modify his sensitivity in relation to the required discrimination; one condition may favor the performance of a fine discrimination, while another condition may be unfavorable. As the experiment proceeds, the observer's attitude may shift or his interest may wane; such changes of interest and attitude will be reflected in the observer's judgments.

In addition to these organismic changes, there may also be changes in the physical situation, including changes in the stimulus. Regardless of the degree of control an experimenter may exercise in the instrumentation of a study, there is always some degree of fluctuation in the values of the physical variables, even though this fluctuation may be remarkably small in certain types of research. These and other factors serve to produce differences in the observer's judgments from trial to trial; a distribution of judgments is, therefore, generated. The mean of this distribution (M_j) forms the basis for determining whether there is a *systematic* tendency on the part of the observer to overestimate or underestimate the magnitude of the physical stimulus; the variable error (σ_v) of the judgments around this mean reveals the degree to which the judgments differ from trial to trial. The study of constant and variable errors is an important aspect of the field of engineering psychology (Chapanis, 1949).

General Approaches
to Psychophysical Scaling

In the preceding sections of this chapter, three fundamental problems were introduced and certain appropriate methods for resolving these problems were presented in detail. The problems dealt with the psychophysical concepts of the absolute threshold, the differential threshold, and subjective equality; the methods were, respectively, the method of limits, the method of constant stimulus differences, and the method of average error.

The reader should be aware, however, that the application of each method is not restricted to the single problem to which it has been applied in this chapter. For instance, in addition to locating an absolute threshold, the method of limits may be employed to determine a differential threshold or to establish the point of subjective equality for a particular situation. Obviously, the experimental procedures in these three cases will be somewhat different, but the three techniques would be classified under the general heading "method of limits," since each utilizes a limiting procedure as exemplified in the ascending and descending series. It should also be clear that there are other procedures which have not been included in this chapter, but which could also be appropriately applied to solve these same problems. In the preceding sections, only the more commonly used techniques were presented. We turn now to the problem of scaling.

The Concept of Scaling

The problem of scaling concerns the assignment of scale values to a psychologically (subjectively) discriminable attribute. The problem encompasses both the rationale involved in the construction of a scale and the properties of measurement that can be ascribed to that scale. In Chapter 2, we considered the physical environment and learned about the various scales that are available for measuring stimuli; our task at this point is to consider how psychological scales may be constructed for measuring sensory magnitudes.

It will be recalled that, in Chapter 5, we reviewed the three characteristics of numbers that are related to the properties of a scale of measurement: specifically, the characteristics of *order, distance,* and *origin.* Depending upon whether none, one, two, or all three of these characteristics were present in a scale, four types of scales were designated: nominal, ordinal, interval, and ratio. All four types may be found in psychology, but since the ratio scale is the most powerful (with a true zero point and equal scale units), our consideration of the scaling problem will be limited primarily to that type of scale.

A considerable number of experimental procedures have been developed in psychology that yield data from which scales of subjective measurement may be constructed. Some of the procedures require that a related and measurable physical continuum be available; these procedures are sometimes classified as *psychophysical methods,* since the end results provide subjective values that are related to *physical* scales. That is, a functional relationship is established between the magnitude of a sensory attribute and the magnitude of its underlying physical dimension. The search for psychophysical laws is based upon the application of psychophysical methods (Stevens, 1962).

Other scaling procedures in psychology do not ordinarily require that a measurable physical continuum be available; these procedures are sometimes classified as *psychological methods*, since the end results provide subjective values that cannot be related to a designated physical continuum. The construction of psychological scales ordinarily makes use of stimuli that cannot be measured or calibrated with respect to a physical dimension, for example, an attitude scale on atomic warfare. In both the psychophysical and psychological methods, the systematic variation in the judgments of the observer is held to be a function of the differences that are present in the stimuli with respect to the attribute under consideration.

The Indirect Approach

Unidimensional scaling methods may be considered to fall into two distinct groups: (1) the *variability methods* and (2) the *quantitative judgment methods* (Torgerson, 1958) or, as they are often called, the indirect and direct methods, respectively. The distinction between these two groups of methods lies in the rationale that is adopted for obtaining the *unit of measurement* in constructing a scale with interval or ratio properties. In the variability approach, the task of the observer is to differentiate stimuli on the basis of order, for example, which is higher in pitch, stimulus A or stimulus B? If stimulus A is judged higher than stimulus B more than 50 percent of the time, it is concluded that stimulus A is higher than stimulus B with respect to the designated attribute, that is, pitch. Regardless of the particular psychophysical procedure used to establish the proportion of times that stimulus A is judged higher than stimulus B, the rank order will be essentially invariant.

Given the obtained proportions for all stimuli in the set, the specific analytical procedures that should be followed to establish the scale values will depend upon the particular theoretical approach that has been adopted. One of these approaches bases the equality of scale intervals on the definition of equality of just noticeable differences. The notion is that the proportion of times in which a difference between two stimuli is noticed depends only upon the magnitude of the psychological difference (distance) between them, regardless of the portion of the psychological continuum in which this difference occurs. If, for instance, stimulus B is just noticeably higher than stimulus A, and stimulus C is just noticeably higher than stimulus B, then the distance on the psychological continuum that separates B and A is assumed to be equal to the distance that separates C and B.

Now, in the method of constant stimulus differences, we learned how to obtain experimentally the value of a *jnd*, that is, a *DL*. This is one procedure by means of which we can proceed to devise a scale that expresses the functional relationship between the physical magnitude of a stimulus and the psychological magnitude of the corresponding subjective variable. As we have indicated, the unit of measurement is the *jnd* and *jnds are assumed to be equal* throughout the psychological continuum under consideration, according to the advocates of this technique of scaling. Once we have experimentally determined that stimulus *B* is one *jnd* greater than stimulus *A*, we can proceed to establish that stimulus *C* is one *jnd* greater than *B*, *D* than *C*, and so on. If we then assign successive integers to each of the stimuli in the set, for example, $A = 1$, $B = 2$, and $C = 3$, we will have constructed a scale with equal interval properties. If, further, we are willing to accept the absolute threshold as the origin of the psychological continuum under consideration, we will have arrived at a scale with ratio properties, since we have specified the origin of the scale and have a unit of measurement.

An example of a *jnd* scale of psychological magnitude is presented in Figure 7-4. The scale has been derived mathematically (Lewis, 1960) from a set of data in which *DLs* for pitch were determined from 31 to 11,700 cps at a sensation level of 5 db (Shower and Biddulph, 1931). Since the differential thresholds for pitch discrimination vary as a function of sensation level, the values of the curve in Figure 7-4 are restricted to that particular level and to the particular testing conditions of that study.

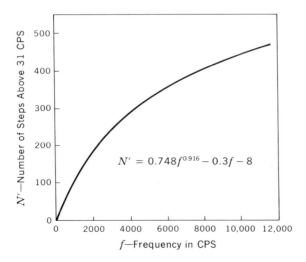

$$N' = 0.748f^{0.916} - 0.3f - 8$$

Figure 7-4. The psychophysical magnitude function for the pitch of pure tones derived from the integration of just noticeable differences. (From *Quantitative methods in psychology* by D. Lewis, copyright © 1960, McGraw-Hill Book Company. Used by permission.)

The curve in Figure 7-4 denotes graphically the number of *jnd* steps in pitch that a designated frequency is above the reference frequency of 31 cps. If a mathematical solution is desired to obtain the number of steps which a given frequency is above the reference frequency (31 cps), the inset equation for the curve may be used. It should be noted that the equation and the curve in Figure 7-4 are based on the assumption that the number of *jnd* steps in pitch is equal to zero when the frequency is equal to 31 cps. This is equivalent to stating that the pitch scale has its origin at 31 cps or that frequencies below 31 cps have no pitch. Since this is an assumption and has not been established for these particular data, the *jnd* scale in Figure 7-4 should be regarded in a strict sense as an interval scale of pitch rather than a ratio scale. The total number of steps between the limiting frequencies of 31 cps and 11,700 cps has been calculated to be 467.

In constructing a scale by the differential sensitivity method, it is not necessary to determine experimentally each individual *jnd* over the entire range of stimuli in which we are interested. For example, the obtained *jnd* function in Figure 7-4 was derived mathematically from only ten experimentally determined *DL* values. These ten values were used in a curve-fitting procedure which, in conjunction with the assumption about the origin of the scale, yielded the equation shown in the inset of Figure 7-4.

Another commonly used indirect method of scaling is that based on Thurstone's model, as shown in part, in Figure 7-1. Although the details of the method are too involved for consideration at this level, the general nature of the approach may be outlined. The significant point is that the variability of judgments with respect to each stimulus (or stimulus combination) is used to derive the unit of measurement of the subjective scale. It will be recalled that, according to this view, a given stimulus does not always excite the same discriminal process on the sensory continuum. Repeated presentations of the stimulus generate a frequency distribution of discriminal processes; this distribution is assumed to be normal. The standard deviation of the distribution is a measure of the subjective variability associated with that stimulus.

In this approach, the scale value of a particular stimulus is the value of the corresponding modal discriminal response on the subjective continuum. However, the discriminal process which is generated by each presentation of the stimulus is unknown, and it is held that the observer cannot report directly in terms of these values. Since the discriminal dispersions cannot be obtained directly from the observer, the stimuli must be scaled by an indirect method. This method is based on the fact that the observer can provide judgments about the *relations among stimuli*, for example, $A > B$, just as in the case of the differential threshold. These judgments yield a matrix of proportions for a given set of stimuli which, on the basis of certain simplifying assumptions, can be converted into a corresponding matrix of z-scores. The final scale values for the experimental stimuli are computed from the latter matrix, following one or another of the several equations deduced from Thurstone's model. The simplest solution assumes that the discriminal dispersions are all equally variable and that the variability is equal to unity; the variability of the discriminal dispersions is then taken as the unit of the subjective scale.

One of the problems in deriving scale values by the Thurstonian method is that the method does not establish an absolute zero point. Since the computations are based only on the judgments of differences between stimuli, the location of the stimuli on the subjective continuum is with respect to one another only.

The origin or zero point of the scale must be chosen arbitrarily; usually, for typical psychophysical dimensions, it is located at the absolute threshold.

The Direct Approach

In recent years, the use of the variability (indirect) methods in the construction of scales has been gradually replaced by the direct methods of quantitative judgment. There are several reasons for this change in the approach to scaling problems. First of all, it was found that, for certain physical dimensions, different subjective scales were obtained with different methods of measurement. In other words, the numbers assigned on the subjective scale for some dimensions of objects or events were not independent of the particular procedure employed in the scaling process. This suggests that either one of the methods is producing invalid or biased scale values, or the different methods are operationally measuring different dimensions. The proponents of the direct methods have argued for the first alternative and have rejected judgments of equal intervals and judgments of order (comparative judgments) for psychological scaling purposes. Scales derived from the indirect methods are often called "confusion scales" and the validity of the scales derived from the direct methods are based upon the arbitrary acceptance of the validity of ratio judgments.

Secondly, it was found that the assumption of equality of *jnds* is not valid for all psychological attributes. For loudness, it has been determined that the *DLs* are not subjectively equal, but tend to increase in psychological magnitude with increases in the physical magnitude of the stimulus (Stevens, 1936). For pitch, however, it has been concluded "that all *jnds* . . . are essentially equal in subjective size" (Stevens and Volkmann, 1940a). Whether *jnds* are equal thus seems to depend upon the particular attribute involved. Those continua of the first type, for example, loudness and brightness, are called *prothetic* continua; those of the second type, for example, pitch and visual inclination, are called *metathetic* continua (Stevens, 1957). It is suggested that the physiological process underlying the sensory discrimination of prothetic continua involves the *addition* of neural excitation to excitation. For metathetic continua, the process is believed to involve the *substitution* of excitation for excitation, that is, a change in the locus of the excitation. The *power function* (Stevens, 1964) appears to be the general law that relates subjective and physical magnitudes for prothetic continua, but the function does not seem to hold for metathetic continua (Stevens, 1961). There is some evidence, however, which indicates that *individual* psychophysical functions do not follow the power law, although averaging data for groups of observers does yield a power function (Freides and Phillips, 1966; Pradhan and Hoffman, 1963).

Finally, the question has been raised concerning the appropriateness of using the value of the absolute threshold as the natural origin of the sensory scale (Corso, 1963a). Whether the indirect or direct methods are used, the obtained subjective scale must have a "true" origin if ratio properties of measurement are to hold. Stimuli smaller than the statistically defined absolute threshold do produce finite subjective magnitudes greater than zero. For subjective scales pertaining to ranges of stimuli well above the minimal detectable level, the use of the absolute threshold as the origin introduces a negligible error; but, for small stimulus values, the error becomes proportionately larger and should be avoided.

The *direct* methods of scaling have been developed primarily by Stevens (1957) and his co-workers. In this approach, the unit of measurement is obtained directly from the quantitative judgments of the stimuli with respect to a particular dimension. In this situation, the observer is required to do more than simply differentiate between stimuli on the basis of their order. The observer must not only judge that $A > B$ on a designated continuum, but he must specify a particular relationship among subjective distances or ratios in accordance with specific instructions, for example, adjust stimulus B so that it is subjectively ½ as large as stimulus A.

The basic rationale of the direct methods is that the subject is instructed, either explicitly or implicitly, to base his judgments on an equal-interval scale of the subjective continuum under consideration. This assumes that the stimuli vary along some discriminable dimension and that the observer is capable of making direct quantitative judgments in accordance with the instructions. The judgments may be referred to an arbitrary starting point or to an absolute reference point, depending on the specific experimental method. Any variability in the judgments associated with a particular stimulus is treated as experimental error and the observer's judgments are, otherwise, considered to yield direct scale values of the stimuli on a linear subjective continuum. The specific scale values are obtained through a straightforward averaging procedure. Notice that in the indirect methods, the variability of the observer's judgments provides the basis for the unit of measurement on the subjective scale, whereas in the direct methods, the variability is treated as error. Consequently, in the direct methods, the attempt is made to introduce rigorous controls in the experimental situation so that judgmental variability is minimized.

The specific nature of the direct methods will be presented in the next two sections of this chapter. The two quantitative judgment methods which we will consider are: (1) the *ratio method of fractionation* and (2) the *method of direct magnitude estimation*.

The Ratio Method of Fractionation

The Problem

The problem in scaling may be stated quite simply: to determine the quantitative relationship between a designated psychological attribute and the corresponding physical dimension with which it is associated. The objective is to construct a subjective magnitude function, a psychophysical scale, from which the value of any stimulus lying within the range of the scale may be obtained. Given a series of objects or events along a physical continuum which is capable of initiating psychological activity, how are numbers to be assigned to the various sensory magnitudes which are elicited by the particular values of the stimuli within this continuum? Since the ideal type of scale is the ratio scale, how are the numbers to be assigned to generate a scale with ratio properties?

The Procedure

The fundamental assumption in the ratio method of fractionation, as in all fractionation methods, is that the observer is able to perceive and to indicate the magnitude of a *sense ratio*. A sense ratio is defined as the ratio between two subjective magnitudes on a given psychological continuum. It is seen that the task of the observer in the fractionation methods is more stringent than any of those we considered in the preceding sections of this chapter. The observer does more than merely report the presence or absence of a sensory variable, or equate psychological magnitudes, or differentiate among stimuli on the basis of their relative order of magnitude. In the fractionation methods the observer must be able not only to detect the order of sensory magnitudes, but to indicate the quantitative relationships that obtain among the psychological distances associated with given stimuli.

The typical task in the ratio method of fractionation requires the observer to indicate when the sensory magnitudes associated with two stimuli stand in a specified ratio. One stimulus is the standard and remains fixed throughout a series of judgments; the other stimulus, the variable, is adjusted or selected by the observer. The task of the observer is to adjust or to select the variable so that the resulting sensory magnitude provides a subjective ratio of the variable to the standard that is equal to the ratio prescribed by the experimenter. The observer, for example, might be required to adjust the variable stimulus so that it appears to be *one half* as bright as the standard.

The task imposed on the observer, therefore, assumes that certain requirements are met regarding the stimulus continuum on which the psychological attribute is based. First of all, the stimulus continuum must be scalable by physical procedures; this permits the assignment of a numerical value to the magnitude of the physical attribute under consideration for each of the stimuli in the series for a given experiment. In short, it is assumed that the precise location of a stimulus on a particular continuum can be determined. Second, since the observer is required to adjust or to select the value of the variable stimulus, the adjustment or selection must encompass the entire range of stimulus values appropriate for a given experiment. This insures that the observer will have available a value of the stimulus that can satisfy the prescribed judgment ratio. If these two requirements are met, and if the observer can reliably indicate the prescribed ratio, a subjective magnitude function can be constructed from the collected judgments (Ekman, 1961).

There are several techniques that may be used for obtaining the required judgments in the ratio method of fractionation. One of the most common techniques is the method of average error, in which the observer adjusts the variable stimulus until it stands in the proper relation with the standard, that is, the prescribed ratio has been attained. This method is sometimes modified so that the experimenter adjusts the variable according to the observer's instructions until the observer makes a judgment of the prescribed ratio. In another modification of this method, the experimenter places the standard stimulus and a set of comparison stimuli before the observer and, after having experienced the standard stimulus, the observer is required to select the comparison stimulus that appears to satisfy the prescribed ratio, for example, is judged half as large as the standard.

Regardless of the specific psychophysical method used to obtain the estimates of the prescribed ratio, whether it involves the method of average error, the method of limits, the constant method, or some other, it is necessary that repeated estimates (judgments) be obtained for each standard due to the extreme variability of the estimates. The repeated estimates may be obtained by testing a large number of observers for relatively few trials, or by testing a few observers for many trials. Of course, if conditions permit, it is permissible to test many observers for many trials. If the intent of the experimenter is to construct a scale that is to be generalized to a particular population, the usual precautions of random sampling must be followed in the selection of observers and a large sample is desirable. If, however, the scale is to be constructed for a given individual, or for a specific group of individuals, randomization is not required and a small sample may be used. Whether or not the observers selected for the study should be trained (experienced) or naive, or should be given preliminary training prior to the criterion trials in an experiment, will depend upon the anticipated application of the obtained results. There should be some correspondence between the kinds of observers employed in the construction of the scale and the kinds of individuals on which the scale is intended to be used.

In the fractionation methods, there is no fixed number of standard stimuli that should be employed in the construction of a scale. The number varies from one experiment to another and depends upon the particular situation and the personal inclination of the experimenter. Since the final scale will probably be a complex function, there should be sufficient data points to accurately describe the function and to reveal any discontinuities or irregularities that may exist. It would seem, therefore, that no fewer than five standards should be employed and that they should be distributed throughout the stimulus range under consideration. Whenever possible, a larger number of standard stimuli is to be preferred, with a maximum of ten or so.

The experimental conditions of the study should insure that the possibility of constant errors has been considered and that the results obtained will not be contaminated by the biasing effects of extraneous factors. Appropriate counterbalancing procedures should be adopted to control for space and time errors. If the judgments are being collected by the method of average error, the setting of the variable stimulus should be altered from trial to trial, as described in the preceding section on this method. If the method of limits is being used, the starting points and the lengths of the ascending and descending series should be systematically altered as previously described. These procedures will tend to minimize the bias associated with the particular set of variable stimuli that is employed in a given experiment.

To minimize the effects of order, such as practice, learning, fatigue, and so on, the standard stimuli should be presented in a different order from trial to trial or from observer to observer. This may be accomplished by a systematic pre-arrangement of the standards, or by randomization. Although it is generally recognized that the particular distribution of the variable stimuli selected for an experiment, as in the method of constant stimuli, produces a bias in the judg-ments, this context effect (Garner, 1954) has not been fully explored and tech-niques for controlling it remain to be determined. The spacing of the variable stimuli, however, seems to have a negligible effect on the scale values obtained by the direct estimation of sensory magnitudes, at least for loudness and for grouped data (Stevens, 1956).

The Construction of the Scale

The construction of a scale by the ratio method of fractionation will be pre-sented in terms of a set of reported data (Ekman, 1958). It will be noted that the construction of the scale occurs in two phases: (1) the use of a psychophysical method to provide the estimates of all the variable stimuli in the experiment that bear the prescribed ratio to the standard, and (2) the actual construction of the scale in terms of the obtained estimates.

As part of a broader study, five observers were required to make judgments of the subjective size of various circular surfaces. Two illuminated circular surfaces were presented side by side on a translucent screen. The distance between the centers of the surfaces was 160 mm and the distance from the observer's eyes to the screen was 750 mm. The observer was able to vary the size of the variable circular surface by turning a knob. The position of the variable surface was counterbalanced in the right and left position, and the ascending and descending judgments were also counterbalanced. Five standard surfaces were employed: their areas were 5.3, 11.9, 21.2, 33.2, and 47.8 sq cm. The task of the observer was to adjust the variable surface until it appeared half as large as the standard. Each observer made ten adjustments for each standard. The order of presentation of the standard stimuli was randomized.

The results of this part of the study are shown in Table 7-6. The left-hand

Table 7-6 Data in the Ratio Method of Fractionation

Standard Stimulus (Area in sq cm)	Stimulus judged as half (Area in sq cm)	Scale Value (In psychological units)
5.3	2.3	1.0 (arbitrary)
11.9	5.3	2.0
21.2	9.5	3.4
33.2	14.5	4.8
47.8	21.4	6.6

Source: G. E. Ekman, Two generalized ratio scaling methods, *J. Psychol.*, 1958, **45**, 287–295.

column in the table gives the values of the standard stimuli and the center column indicates, for each standard, the value of the variable stimulus that was adjusted to be half as large as the standard. The "half-judgments" are based upon the combined data for all five observers. In the general case, the average of the estimates for each standard may be taken to be the arithmetic mean, the geometric mean, or the median. The particular measure of central tendency that should be used will depend upon the type of scale on which the measurements were made and upon the form of the distribution of judgments. For a normal distribution with measurement at least at the interval level, the arithmetic mean is most often used. For a skewed distribution with ordinal or higher-level data, the median may be used; the geometric mean may also be applied to correct the skewness of a set of data, provided measurement is at the ratio level (Stevens, 1955). It should be stressed, however, that when data are averaged over observers, there is the danger that the form of the psychophysical function for the *group* may not necessarily reflect the form for *individuals*. Pradhan and Hoffman (1963) have shown, for example, that averaging data (arithmetic mean) for groups of observers in a study on lifted weights yielded a power function, although only one of six individuals produced a psychophysical function that followed the power law.

The specific measure used in the present example was not reported, but it seems reasonable to assume that it was the arithmetic mean. The values in the right-hand column of Table 7-6 are the subjective scale values associated with each of the standards. These values were derived from the psychophysical scale shown in Figure 7-6.

The construction of the scale by the common graphic procedure begins with the plotting of the "half-judgments" as a function of the standard stimuli expressed in physical units. This plot is usually made on log-log paper, since in many instances the log-log function will be approximately linear. In the present example, the plot of the values in Table 7-6 has been made on a graph with a linear set of axes. The result is an almost perfect straight line as shown in Figure 7-5. The function in Figure 7-5 permits us to determine the size of the area judged half as large as any given stimulus area contained within the limits of the function.

The next step is to develop the psychophysical scale in which we are interested; this is, the scale that relates subjective magnitude to the physical magnitude of the corresponding stimuli. First of all, the unit of the subjective scale must be specified. This is an arbitrary matter and is achieved by assigning any positive number to any one stimulus. We shall define the unit of subjective area as the visual area perceived when an observer views an illuminated circular surface of 5.3 sq cm at a distance of 750 mm, and we shall call the unit a *surf*. Thus, by definition, a physical stimulus of 5.3 sq cm corresponds to a subjective area of 1 surf. Any other positive value could have been assigned to the stimulus of 5.3 sq cm, or to any one of the remaining stimuli without affecting the general form of the scale, since we are dealing with the ratios of numbers. We are now ready to construct the surf scale of visual area, as shown in Figure 7-6.

In Figure 7-6, the abscissa is scaled in linear units of stimulus area expressed in sq cm; the ordinate is scaled in linear units of subjective area expressed in surfs.

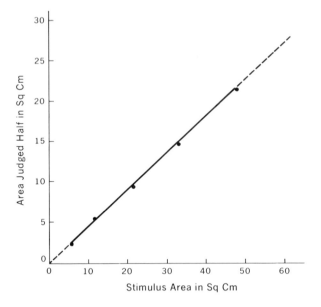

Figure 7–5. The "half-judgment" plot for an experiment on the subjective size of circular surfaces. (From Ekman, *J. Psychol.,* 1958.)

Since we have assigned a subjective value of 1 to a stimulus of 5.3 sq cm, we may plot the first point in Figure 7-6 at (5.3, 1). By referring to Figure 7-5, we see that for a stimulus of 5.3, the area judged half as large is 2.3 sq cm. Since a physical stimulus of 5.3 has a subjective magnitude of 1, and since a stimulus of 2.3 was judged half as large as the stimulus of 5.3, it follows that the subjective magnitude

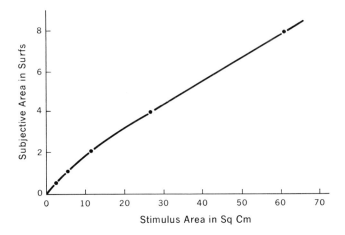

Figure 7–6. The psychophysical magnitude function for the size of circular surfaces as constructed from the half-judgment function in Figure 7–5. (Adapted from Ekman, *J. Psychol.,* 1958.)

of the stimulus of 2.3 must be 0.5, that is, half as large as the magnitude for 5.3. We thus enter a second point in Figure 7-6 at (2.3, 0.5).

Now reconsider Figure 7-5. Locate 5.3 on the ordinate and from the straight line function determine the physical value of the stimulus for which 5.3 was judged to be half. This stimulus is found to be approximately 11.9. Since a stimulus of 11.9 is subjectively twice as large as a stimulus of 5.3, or four times as great as a stimulus of 2.3, the subjective magnitude of this stimulus (11.9) is 2. A third point may be entered in Figure 7-6 at (11.9, 2). Again, referring to Figure 7-5, we find the value of the stimulus for which 11.9 was judged to be half, that is, locate 11.9 on the ordinate and read the value on the abscissa as determined from the linear function. This stimulus is approximately 26.9. Since 11.9 has a subjective magnitude of 2, and the stimulus of 26.9 was judged twice as large, it follows that the subjective magnitude of 26.9 is 4. A fourth point is entered in Figure 7-6 at (26.9, 4). To obtain the fifth and final point to be plotted, locate 26.9 on the ordinate and, by extrapolation of the linear function, determine the value of the stimulus for which 26.9 would be judged to be half. This stimulus is approximately 60.7 and has a scale value of 8. The final point (60.7, 8) is entered in Figure 7-6. Extrapolation of the linear function was necessary in this case to insure that the obtained subjective scale would extend over the entire range of stimulus magnitudes for which "half-judgments" were obtained.

The subjective scale in Figure 7-6 is obtained by connecting the empirical points with a smooth curve. This curve is the psychophysical magnitude function or the psychophysical scale in which we are interested. Given this function, the subjective scale value for any stimulus within the limits of the physical continuum encompassed by the scale can be determined. The scale values for the five standard stimuli used in the present example are given in the right-hand column of Table 7-6. Extrapolation of the subjective magnitude function beyond the experimental range is permissible, but the resulting estimated scale values should be accepted with caution, as in the extension of the function to its point of origin. It would, of course, be possible to construct the scale by means of algebraic procedures (Ekman, 1958), but such refined techniques are not generally employed.

Method of Direct Magnitude Estimation

The Problem

The problem in which the method of direct magnitude estimation is used is identical with that for the method of fractionation: to establish a scale of subjective magnitude. The nature of the problem was amply described in the preceding section, but some further insights may be gained from the following quotation:

> By a scale of subjective magnitude we mean a quantitative scale by which we can predict what people will say when they try to give a quantitative description of their impressions. Since we are concerned with how people judge stimuli, we must rely on one form or another of verbal report. Consequently, the construction of a representative scale of sensation

involves a process not unlike public-opinion polling, and as every pollster knows there are good ways and bad ways of asking questions. The problem in subjective measurement is to arrange the conditions and the task in such a way that O can assess his impressions and communicate them to E in a quantitative language with as few biasing cues, suggestions, and constraints as possible. The fact that a person can be influenced in what he reports does not mean that he has no impressions, or that they are not quantifiable, but only that the task is a difficult one; O behaves like a sensitive galvanometer. He is sensitive not only to the stimuli he is trying to gauge but also to a host of adventitious influences that in varying degrees can warp his reactions. Nevertheless, under optimal conditions the typical individual is able to make direct ratio estimations of relative subjective magnitude over wide ranges—as much as a billion to one (90 db) in physical intensity, which corresponds approximately to a thousand to one in subjective ratio. These estimates provide important corroboration of the subjective scales generated by other procedures such as fractionation. In particular they demonstrate clearly that loudness is a power function of the stimulating intensity (Stevens, 1956, pp. 2-3).

The Procedure

The usual procedure in the method of direct magnitude estimation is one in which the experimenter selects a particular single stimulus on a given physical continuum and assigns a number to its subjective magnitude. The observer is then presented in turn with the members of a set of variable stimuli and is instructed to assign to each variable stimulus a number (whole number, fraction, or decimal) which seems to him to be proportional to its subjective magnitude as compared to the standard. The judgments are expressed in terms of subjective magnitudes and the psychophysical scale is, therefore, obtained directly.

As in all psychophysical experiments, extreme care must be taken to minimize the effects of extraneous factors on the judgments that are made in a given setting. For judgments of loudness by magnitude estimation, the following suggestions have been offered (Stevens, 1956, pp. 5–6):

(1) Use a standard whose level does not impress the O as being either extremely soft or extremely loud, i.e., use a comfortable standard—one that O can "take hold of."

(2) Present variable stimuli that are both above and below the standard.

(3) Call the standard by a number, like 10, that is easily multiplied and divided.

(4) Assign a number to the standard *only,* and leave the O completely free to decide what he will call the variables. For example, do not tell O that the faintest variable is to be called "1," or that the loudest is to be called some other number. If E assigns numbers to more than one stimulus, he introduces constraints of the sort that force O to make judgments on an interval rather than on a ratio scale.

(5) Use only one level of the standard in any one session, but use various standards, for it is risky to decide the form of a magnitude function on the basis of data obtained with only one standard.

(6) Randomize the order of presentation. With inexperienced Os it is well, however, to start with loudness ratios that are not too extreme and are, therefore, easier to judge.

(7) Make the experimental sessions short—about 10 min.

(8) Let O present the stimuli to himself. He can then work at his own pace, and he is more apt to be attending properly when the stimulus comes on.

(9) Since some estimates may depart widely from those of the "average" O, it is advisable to use a group of Os that is large enough to produce a stable median.

A careful review of these nine experimental recommendations will reveal that they are not all specific only to judgments of loudness. Many of these recommendations hold in general for the method of direct magnitude estimation and should be observed, or at least considered, in the performance of experiments in which this method is used.

An illustrative example of a representative procedure that may be employed in the method of direct magnitude estimation is taken from a recent report (Mashhour, 1962). The study relates to estimates of velocity. In this study, the stimulus display consisted of two identical green, luminous spots which appeared to be moving from left to right on a vertical, gray, circular plate. The linear paths traversed by the spots were located one above the other. Actually, the spots were small segments of the electronically activated spikes on the screen of an oscilloscope. The speed of each of the moving spots could be varied continuously from a slow rate to a very high rate. From this range of values seven stimuli (V_1 to V_7) were selected. The velocities of these seven stimuli are presented in Table 7-7;

Table 7-7 Velocities of the Stimuli and the Numbers Assigned in an Experiment Involving the Method of Direct Magnitude Estimation

Stimulus:	V_1	V_2	V_3	V_4	V_5	V_6	V_7
Mm/sec	12.38	20.74	33.18	49.26	80.81	118.75	189.81
Stimulus relative to V_1	1.00	1.67	2.68	3.98	6.53	9.59	15.33
Standard	V_1	V_2	V_3	V_4	V_5	V_6	V_7
Assigned number	1	10	10	10	10	50	100

Source: M. Mashhour, *A comparison of the method of ratio estimation and the method of magnitude estimation,* Rep. Psychol. Lab., University of Stockholm, 1962, **110**, 1–14. By permission of the author.

the slowest stimulus (V_1) had a velocity of 12.38 mm/sec and the fastest stimulus (V_7) had a velocity of 189.81 mm/sec. The stimuli were always viewed at a constant distance of 215 cm and each stimulus was used in turn as a standard. The order of presentation of the stimuli in the variable series was randomized and the lower-upper positions were counterbalanced. The number assigned to each stimulus by the experimenter is given in Table 7-7. The standard was shown before each judgment.

Ten observers were used in the study and each observer was presented with the series of variables four times for each standard in four sessions on four days, with the exception that for standard V_4 the variables series were estimated seven times. The order of presentation of the standards was counterbalanced. The instructions to the observers for standard V_4 were as follows:

. . . This is the standard and I call its velocity 10. What would you call the velocity of the other spot in comparison with the standard? Try to give the appropriate number to each velocity regardless of what you may have called the previous stimuli. If, for example, the variable seems to you twice as fast as the standard, say 20. If it goes one tenth as fast, say 1, if one fourth, say 2.5, etc. As you know there are infinite numbers above as well as below 10. You may use decimals, fractions, or whole numbers. . . . (Mashhour, 1962, p. 5).

The Construction of the Scale

The results obtained in the study described in the preceding section are presented in Table 7-8. For each observer, the estimates for each variable were pooled to provide a mean score; a median for the group was then computed based on the ten individual means. To make the scales comparable, that is, to have all scales begin at the same scale value of unity, the median estimates of V_1 were taken as the units of the scales.

The construction of the subjective magnitude function, as shown in Figure 7-7, will be described for standard V_4 with an assigned value of 10. The function will be plotted in terms of both linear and logarithmic units. The plot of the data in logarithmic units will provide an immediate indication regarding the general form of the magnitude function. If the form of the magnitude function is a power function, that is, of the form $Y = aX^b$, as has been found in numerous other psychophysical experiments, the plot of the logarithm of subjective velocity as a function of the logarithm of physical velocity will approximate a straight line. The linear plot, on the other hand, should yield an increasing monotonic function with negative acceleration.

The empirical data points to be plotted are given in row V_4 of Table 7-8. The values in row V_4 are values on the ordinate of Figure 7-7; the values on the abscissa corresponding to each of these points are indicated by the columnar headings of Table 7-8, designated V_1 to V_7. The physical magnitudes of these variable stimuli in relative units are given in row 2 of Table 7-7. For example, the first point to be plotted in linear units in Figure 7-7 is at (1.00, 1.000); the second point is at (1.67, 2.000); the third point is at (2.68, 3.200), and so on for the remaining four pairs of values. For the logarithmic plot, the logarithms of these same pairs of values are determined and entered into Figure 7-7.

Table 7-8   Summary of Velocity Scales* Derived by the Method of Direct Magnitude Estimation

Standard Stimulus	Variable Stimuli						
	V_1	V_2	V_3	V_4	V_5	V_6	V_7
V_1	1.000	1.595	2.350	3.183	4.265	5.425	9.280
V_2	1.000	1.151	1.959	2.815	3.253	4.595	7.778
V_3	1.000	2.156	2.646	3.431	4.220	7.870	13.161
V_4	1.000	2.000	3.200	4.000	6.000	8.380	16.000
V_5	1.000	1.583	2.468	3.596	4.255	6.553	12.822
V_6	1.000	1.913	3.105	4.046	5.545	6.274	9.640
V_7	1.000	1.528	2.417	2.799	5.151	7.035	8.606

Source: M. Mashhour, *A comparison of the method of ratio estimation and the method of magnitude estimation,* Rep. Psychol. Lab., University of Stockholm, 1962, **110**, 1–14. By permission of the author.

* All scale values are based on the medians of 10 individual means; the median for the variable stimulus V_1 has been defined as the unit for each of the seven scales.

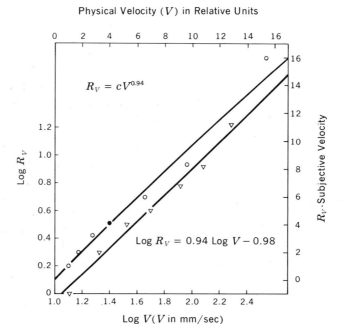

Figure 7-7. The psychophysical magnitude function for the velocity of moving spots of lights, plotted in terms of both linear (o) and logarithmic (△) units. The solid point represents the subjective magnitude of the standard V_4, which had an assigned value of 10. (From Mashhour, 1962.)

After all the data points have been plotted, a smooth curve is fitted to each set of points by visual inspection or by means of more precise curve-fitting techniques. The straight lines in Figure 7-7 are the best-fitting functions computed for the linear and logarithmic plots. The inset equation in the upper left-hand corner of Figure 7-7 is the mathematical equation for the power function that describes the relationship between subjective and physical velocity in linear units, while the mathematical equation in the lower right-hand corner describes the same relationship in logarithmic units.

Notice that the fit of the power function to the empirical values is not particularly good; nevertheless, a subjective magnitude scale of velocity has been obtained and the objective of the experiment has been met. Given the subjective magnitude function in Figure 7-7, we are able to assign a scale value to the perceived velocity of a moving spot of light for physical movements up to approximately 190 mm/sec. Furthermore, since the scale has ratio properties, we are able to perform all arithmetic operations meaningfully with respect to the numbers assigned to the subjective magnitudes. The method of direct magnitude estimation and the ratio method of fractionation are, therefore, two different procedures for arriving at the same end result.

III

Classical Problems in Experimental Psychology

Chapter 8

ABSOLUTE
AND DIFFERENTIAL
THRESHOLDS

Orientation

In 1824, Herbart introduced the term "threshold" into psychology with his definition of the "threshold of consciousness." This was specified as that "boundary which an idea appears to cross as it passes from the totally inhibited state into some degree of actual ideation" (p. 341). The Herbartian tradition was continued by Lotze (1852), but it remained for Fechner (1860) to establish the quantitative meaning of the term by using it in a specific formula. Fechner was thoroughly familiar with the difficulties involved in measuring the absolute and differential thresholds and developed elaborate psychophysical methods for establishing the thresholds in statistical terms.

Much has been done, however, since Fechner's day. We now have new methods of research, new refinements of classical methods, and a better understanding of the interrelations that exist among the various methods. Nevertheless, the student or psychologist who deals with problems of threshold is working at Fechner's doorstep, although Fechner's primary interest was not with thresholds per se but with the measurement of "mental activity." He was interested in measuring the intensity of "mental activity" in terms of the underlying physical events.

One of the major links in the mathematical reasoning involved in Fechner's procedure of measurement was the concept of threshold or limen—a datum of everyday experience that, according to Fechner, had attracted little attention, but on which "the whole of the night side of mind depends." Thus, the first step in his psychophysical procedures was to establish a metric principle of sensitivity, that is, a measure of the organism's capacity to respond to stimulation or a measure of the degree of correspondence between "sensation" and the adequate stimulus. Sensitivity was measured, then, by measuring stimuli, not "sensations." Specifically, absolute sensitivity was measured by the inverse value of the absolute threshold, and differential sensitivity was specified either as the inverse value of the differential threshold (DL or ΔI) or as the inverse value of the relative differential threshold ($\Delta I/I$).

The psychophysical methods for determining these fundamental values were presented in Chapter 7 and as we learned, these procedures form the basis for the indirect approach to the scaling of sensory magnitudes. The classical Fechnerian formula, then, obtained a sensory scale by summing just noticeable differences, starting with the absolute threshold as the origin. By setting the value of the absolute threshold equal to unity, Fechner derived a metric formula which stated that "sensation is proportional to the logarithm of stimulus." In Chapter 7, we presented evidence which indicated that this relationship may well be a power function, rather than a logarithmic function. At this point, we are not discussing the relative acceptability of these two functions; rather, we are simply indicating that historically the concepts of absolute and differential thresholds were fundamental in the scaling of sensory magnitudes. In recent years, however, the advent of the direct approach to scaling has de-emphasized the use of thresholds. Nevertheless, the study of thresholds continues to be of importance in its own right. Consequently, while in the previous chapter we concentrated on the *methods* used in determining thresholds, in the present chapter we are concerned with the presentation of selected *experimental findings*.

The significance of this chapter, then, is both theoretical and applied. Theoretically, there are certain questions that relate to thresholds in general, that is, to thresholds in the various sensory modalities such as vision, audition, and olfaction. The question, for example, of the applicability of Weber's law is a well-known classical problem. Is the DL a constant fraction of the magnitude of the stimulus? This and other problems have been widely studied in sensory psychology in an attempt to derive S-R laws. Such laws are of theoretical importance, even though they may not hold for more than one sensory modality.

From a practical consideration, it is important to know the minimal amount of energy or change in energy that can be detected by an observer. Consider, for example, the detection of a radar pip in the presence of visual "noise." It may also be well to know that an observer's detection ability will vary with time, for example, over a tour of duty of several hours' duration, and that different individuals may have different thresholds for the same task. Knowledge of thresholds is critical in any military, industrial, or practical situation in which the absolute and differential sensitivity of a large number of individuals is likely to be involved.

This chapter presents a summary of selected threshold studies in the various sensory fields, and in some instances indicates the theoretical or practical significance of the experimental results.

The Visual System

Absolute Sensitivity for Vision

In Chapter 4, the receptor system for photic energy was described in consider-able detail. It was emphasized that (1) the visual system was capable of respond-ing to electromagnetic energy with radiation wavelengths ranging from about 380 to 760 mμ, and that (2) the retina of the eye contained two different kinds of light-sensitive cells, rods and cones. A fundamental question that follows from these facts relates to the sensitivity of the visual system: What is the minimum amount of photic energy needed to produce a behavioral response when the vis-ual system is activated?

In one experiment performed to answer this question (Hecht, Shlaer, and Pirenne, 1942), a small patch of light with a wavelength of approximately 510 mμ was adjusted to stimulate an area of the retina that contained an estimated 500 rods, located outside the macula. The exposure time was held constant at 1 msec and, as the amount of energy was manipulated on successive trials with an optical wedge, the observer's task was to report whether or not he saw the mo-mentary flash of light. The average energy required to produce a just visible flash was then computed for a large number of trials. For different observers, this value varied from 21 to 57 hundred billionths of an erg.

Some further calculations were then made. It is known that the amount of energy in the stimulus outside the eye is considerably greater than the amount that ultimately reaches the receptor cells in the retina. About 4 percent of the incident light is lost due to the reflection from the cornea. For a wavelength of 510 mμ, about 50 percent is lost by scattering and absorption in the ocular media between the outer surface of the cornea and the retina. Finally, about 80 percent of the energy arriving at the retina fails to be absorbed by the rhodopsin of the rods. Thus, the best estimate is that only about 10 percent of the incident light at the cornea actually stimulates the receptor cells. Since the light energy at thresh-old, expressed in terms of quantum calculations at the corneal surface, was 58 to 148 quanta, and only 10 percent of these were ultimately absorbed by the retinal rods, it is seen that the visual response was produced by about 5 to 14 quanta. With 5 to 14 quanta distributed over 500 rods, it was considered highly improb-able that any single rod would receive more than one quantum. Thus, it appears that only a single quantum needs to be absorbed by each of 5 to 14 rods in order to produce a visual response. More recent evidence indicates that under certain conditions the response is produced by the absorption of only two light quanta (Bouman, 1955; Smith, Cutchshaw, and Kincaid, 1958).

Spectral Sensitivity of Rods and Cones

In the preceding section, the problem of absolute sensitivity was considered for a particular homogeneous segment of the visible spectrum, 510 mμ. The question, however, may be extended to cover the entire spectrum and may include not only a retinal location containing rods, but one containing a concentration of cones. In this way, the spectral sensitivity of the human eye to the entire visible spectrum may be established. Such experiments have already been performed, although the results have not ordinarily been expressed in quantal terms; instead, the data have taken the form of *relative luminosity curves* (or, as sometimes called, spectral visibility curves or spectral sensitivity functions).

In a classic experiment (Hecht and Williams, 1922), 48 observers with an average age of 25 years were tested to determine the relative brightness of lights of different wavelengths when viewed under conditions of monocular dim-light vision. Each observer was seated in a dark chamber for at least one-half hour to allow his eyes to become adapted to the darkness. Then a test figure was presented about 20 degrees from the fovea, and the observer was required to judge when the two segments of the figure appeared equal in brightness. One portion of the test figure consisted of a constant white light which was very near to the absolute threshold of visibility; the remaining portion of the figure allowed light of a given wavelength to pass through from a spectrometer. The intensity of this light was varied by passing the beam through a pair of Nicol prisms and changing the angle between them. (The intensity of the light transmitted by this arrangement is proportional to the square of the cosine of the angle between the two prisms.) When a perfect match was obtained by the observer, the two portions of the test figure were no longer discernible and the entire figure appeared uniform in brightness. Brightness matches were made at each of the following wavelengths: 412, 455, 486, 496, 507, 518, 529, 540, 550, 582, 613, and 666 mμ.

A similar experiment was performed by other investigators under conditions of bright-light vision (Gibson and Tyndall, 1923). Fifty-two observers were tested after they had been adapted to daylight levels of illuminance. The test patch was restricted to a size falling well within the fovea, and monocular observations were made at selected wavelengths. The results of these two experiments have been plotted on a single graph, as shown in Figure 8-1. For the dim-light experiment, the data are plotted as the *scotopic curve;* for bright-light vision, as the *photopic curve.*

Four major facts can be derived from the curves in Figure 8-1: (1) neither the rods nor cones are uniformly sensitive to the entire visible spectrum; (2) the region of maximal sensitivity is 554 mμ for cone vision and 511 mμ for rod vision; (3) the rod function lies below the cone function, indicating that throughout most of the spectrum the rods require less energy for vision (have a lower threshold) than the cones; and (4) the rods and cones are about equally sensitive to radiant energy in the long wavelength (red) end of the spectrum.

An additional point of significance is that visual stimulation at scotopic levels does not produce color vision anywhere along the spectrum. Color vision is possible only with light levels sufficient to activate the cone system. When only the rods are functioning, all wavelengths are seen as a series of lighter or darker grays; it is not possible to discriminate between wavelengths on the basis of color or chromatic vision. Weak lights are visible, but *hue* is absent. The interval between the absolute threshold of visibility (*scotopic* curve) and the initial appear-

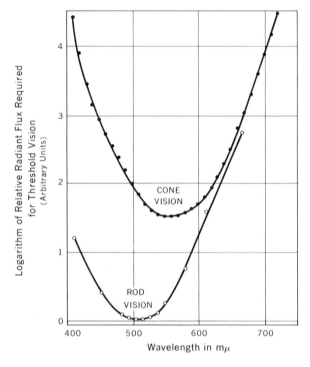

Figure 8-1. Relative amounts of radiant flux for threshold vision under conditions of dark adaptation (rod vision) and light adaptation (cone vision). (From Chapanis, in *A survey report on human factors in underseas warfare*, National Research Council Committee on Underseas Warfare, 1949.)

ance of hue for a given homogeneous wavelength (*photopic* curve) is called the *photochromatic interval*. The photochromatic interval is largest at the short wavelength end of the spectrum and smallest (near zero) for the very long wavelengths (above about 665 mμ). *Mesopic* vision occurs at intermediate levels of luminance, where rods and cones are believed to work together.

Experimental data, such as those presented in Figure 8-1, indicate that whether the eye is dark-adapted or light-adapted, the various parts of an equal-energy spectrum do not appear to be equally luminous to a normal observer. For photopic vision, the most luminous part of the spectrum occurs at approximately 554 mμ; for scotopic vision, at approximately 511 mμ. Accordingly, data as in Figure 8-1 are usually presented in the form of photopic and scotopic *relative luminosity* (visibility or sensitivity) curves. Such curves are shown in Figure 8-2 and represent the photopic (V_λ) and scotopic (V'_λ) luminosity functions for the CIE (International Commission on Illumination) standard observer. Despite the gross differences in absolute sensitivity between rods and cones, the two functions may be plotted on the same graph by performing a simple arithmetic adjustment. For each curve, the reciprocals of the threshold values are computed; then the mini-

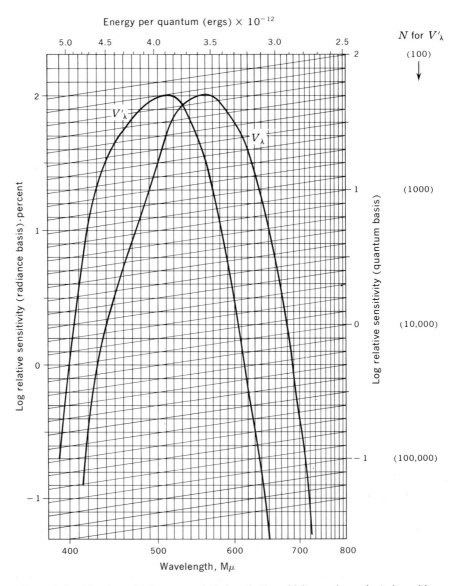

Figure 8-2. Visual sensitivity curves plotted so that sensitivity can be evaluated on either a reciprocal radiance basis (left-hand ordinate) or a reciprocal quantum basis (right-hand ordinate), as a function either of wavelength (bottom abscissa), or of energy per quantum (upper abscissa). The oblique coordinates refer to the right-hand ordinate. Shown are the photopic (V_λ) and scotopic (V'_λ) luminosity functions for the CIE standard observer. The values in parentheses on the right-hand ordinate apply to V'_λ and indicate the approximate number of quanta required to produce a threshold response. (From Boynton, 1963.)

mum threshold for each curve is taken as 100 percent and all other reciprocals are expressed as percentages of 100. Thus, the two curves indicate the relative luminosities produced by the various wavelengths in an equal-energy spectrum (that is, a spectral distribution characterized by equal flux per unit interval of wavelength). In Figure 8-2, the photopic (V_λ) curve has been lowered a vertical distance of about 1.6 logarithmic units to render it comparable to the scotopic (V'_λ) curve on an *absolute* basis (for a 1° diameter test field).

In Figure 8-2, the horizontal coordinates (left-hand scale) indicate the *relative spectral sensitivity* (luminosity) in terms of 100 percent at the peaks of the two functions; the scale values are logarithmic and are read from the points of intersection with the scotopic and photopic functions. For example, 10 percent relative sensitivity for scotopic vision is found at wavelength values of about 420 and 582 mμ; for photopic vision, 10 percent relative sensitivity is found at wavelengths of about 475 and 651 mμ. The left-hand scale is plotted in terms of the reciprocal of the *radiance* required to elicit a criterion response, such as a threshold probability of seeing, a brightness match, or an electrophysical response. The oblique coordinates (right-hand scale), however, are plotted in logarithmic units but indicate the relative spectral sensitivity on a *quantum* basis. Thus, if in addition to wavelength, the scale at the top of Figure 8-2 is used as a measure of the independent variable, relative sensitivity may be expressed in four ways: (1) reciprocal radiance as a function of wavelength; (2) reciprocal radiance as a function of energy per quantum; (3) reciprocal number of quanta as a function of wavelength; and (4) reciprocal number of quanta as a function of energy per quantum. Of these, the first is most commonly used.

The values in parentheses on the right-hand ordinate apply to the scotopic curve (V'_λ); they indicate the approximate number of quanta (N) entering the pupil of the eye that are necessary for threshold visibility under optimal conditions. This number is assumed to be 100 at the wavelength of peak sensitivity. To obtain, say, the number of quanta required for a threshold response at 400 mμ (at one percent sensitivity on the scotopic function), locate the appropriate horizontal coordinate (0) and follow the oblique coordinate to the right-hand side of the graph. It will be found that $N = 10,000$ quanta. Reading the graph in another way, it may be stated that any two points on the *scotopic* function which are intersected by one of the *oblique* lines can be projected downward to locate two wavelength values to which the eye is equally sensitive on a quantum basis. For example, follow the oblique coordinate labelled 1000 and read the wavelengths corresponding to the points of intersection on the scotopic function; these are approximately 420 and 576 mμ. This indicates that under dim-light conditions, wavelengths of 420 and 576 mμ are equally visible and require ten times the number of quanta at the peak of the curve (10×100 quanta $= 1000$) in order to produce a threshold response.

Any two points on *either* function which are intersected by a *horizontal* line can also be projected downward to locate two wavelength values to which the eye is equally sensitive on an *energy* basis. It should be noted that the given values of N

are not appropriate for the photopic function, but a rough approximation can be made by multiplying the given values of N by about 100.

Range of Effective Light Intensities

Numerous studies reported in the literature on vision, including those cited in the preceding sections of this chapter, indicate the duality of the visual receptor processes; they support the *duplexity theory of vision.* The rods function at low intensities and initiate colorless (achromatic) visual experiences; the cones operate at higher intensities and are responsible for mediating color responses. There is a tremendous range of intensities between the weakest light that can produce a threshold response in the rods and the strongest light that can be tolerated by the cones.

Expressed in terms of luminance, the minimal threshold for dark-adapted rods for a white light with a relatively long exposure is approximately 0.000001 millilambert (mL); for the cones, it is 0.01 mL. As the intensity level continues to increase above the cone threshold, the eye continues to respond until the *terminal threshold,* or the upper limit of visual tolerance, is reached. This occurs at about 16,000 mL, which represents a luminance level greater than that produced by new snow on a clear, sunny day. The range of effective light intensities is, then, about 1 to 10 billions or about 100 decibels (10 logarithmic units). The extreme range of light intensities to which the human eye can respond effectively is shown in Figure 8-3. The precise values for the absolute thresholds for rods and for cones are dependent upon the areal size of the stimulus, the location of excitation on the retinal surface, and the duration of exposure.

Discrimination of Light Intensity

The ability of an observer to detect differences in the intensities of light sources is called *differential* or *contrast discrimination.* This ability is measured by determining the minimum difference in the luminance of two areas that can just be distinguished as different in brightness a given percentage of the time, that is, by determining the *differential threshold for brightness* or the *contrast* threshold. This is usually expressed as a fraction:

$$\frac{I' - I}{I} = \frac{\Delta I}{I} \tag{8-1}$$

where I' is the luminance of the test object, I is the luminance of the background or field, and ΔI is either an increment superimposed on the background or a decrement in the luminance of the background. When $(\Delta I + I > I)$ we have *positive contrast;* when $(\Delta I + I < I)$ we have *negative contrast. Contrast sensitivity* is expressed as the reciprocal of the fraction specified in Equation 8-1.

In the experimental determination of the contrast threshold, $\Delta I/I$ is sometimes

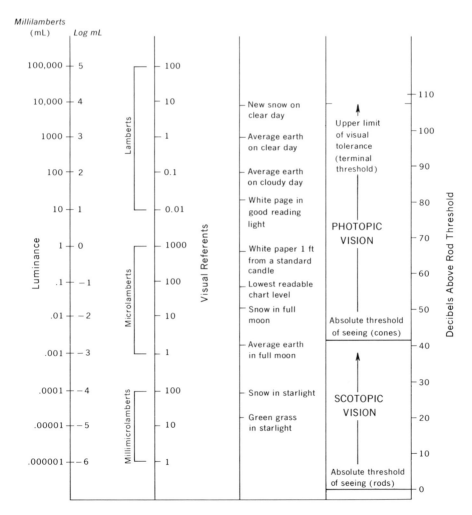

Figure 8–3. Range of effective light intensities for both rod and cone vision. (From Bartley, in Stevens, 1951, and from Baker and Grether, 1954.)

obtained by making a homogeneous test object lighter or darker than the surrounding background, and the surrounding background extends over the whole visual field. At other times, the test object is divided into two identical parts (fields) and the luminance of one half is altered systematically. In this case, the unaltered luminance is arbitrarily defined as the luminance of the background. The divided light field usually consists of a bisected disc or two concentric rings (a *disc annulus* arrangement). In the measurement of the positive contrast threshold, any luminance value may be used as the background from which to determine ΔI, except that value of luminance yielding maximal brightness.

In one experiment (Steinhardt, 1936) two subjects were successively adapted to 27 levels of retinal illuminance and, at each level, they reported the appearance of a boundary as the luminance of one half of the test field was varied. The experimental apparatus allowed one light (I) to illuminate the entire field, while another light added an increment (ΔI) to only a portion of the test field. The stimuli were two rectangles, the total area of which varied from 24° to 23½′. Monocular vision was used and over 6000 measurements were made. The results are given in Figure 8-4. For a given size of test object, as the background luminance (I) is increased, the value of $\Delta I/I$ decreases and approaches an asymptotic value at about 10^6 trolands.* Also, for the seven different sizes of test field, $\Delta I/I$ becomes progressively smaller as the size of the test field becomes larger.

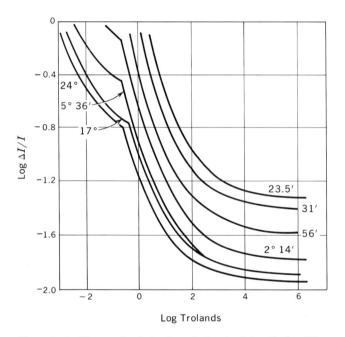

Figure 8–4. Human discrimination of stimulus intensity for different sizes of test field. (From Steinhardt. Reprinted by permission of The Rockefeller University Press, from *J. gen. Physiol.,* 1936, **20,** 185–209.)

Classically, the fraction $\Delta I/I$ was known as the *Weber fraction* and it was believed to be a constant (Weber's law). However, from Figure 8-4, it may be seen that the fraction for the discrimination of stimulus intensities is not constant. At the lowest intensities it is approximately ⅓ and at the highest intensities it decreases to about ⅟₆₇. Since both variables in Figure 8-4 are plotted in logarithmic units,

---

* The troland is a unit of retinal illumination that takes into account the size of the pupil as well as the intensity of the light source. The troland is defined as the retinal illuminance produced by viewing a surface having a luminance of 1 candela/sq meter through a pupil having an area of 1 sq mm. A retinal illuminance of 10 trolands is roughly equivalent to 1 mL.

each curve would be expected to be linear if Weber's law were to be supported. The curves are clearly nonlinear, thus failing to support the law. With the larger sizes of the test field, the curves show discontinuities at the low intensities and are taken as further evidence of the duality of the receptive process. Very small test objects (radii from 2 to 28 minutes of visual angle) stimulating the fovea do not, as expected, produce such discontinuities (Graham and Bartlett, 1940).

Discrimination of Wavelength

In Chapter 2, Figure 2-2, the visible portion of the electromagnetic spectrum was given as approximately 380 to 760 mμ. In this chapter, in the section on the spectral sensitivity of the rods and cones, it was indicated that color vision was present only when the light levels were sufficiently intense to activate the cone system. *Hue* is the sensory characteristic of visual experience which is related primarily to wavelength and which permits the various portions of the visible spectrum to be classified as reddish, greenish, yellowish, or bluish. This classification is a psychological one; hue is not a property of electromagnetic energy, but a characteristic or dimension of experience that depends upon the normal functioning of the visual system. Even when brightness differences are eliminated, the normal observer can discriminate about 180 segments of the spectrum that differ in hue.

The relation of hue to wavelength is shown in Figure 8-5. At the short wave-

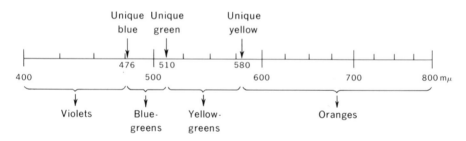

Figure 8-5. The relation of hue to wavelength in the visible spectrum. (From Boring *et al.*, 1948.)

lengths below 476 mμ, the violets or reddish blues are visible. From 476 to 510 mμ, the hues progress from blue to green; the yellow-greens (or green-yellows) form a series from 510 to 580 mμ. The oranges (or red-yellows) lie above 580 mμ and approach the "reds" at the long wavelength end of the visible spectrum. As shown in the upper portion of Figure 8-5, three unique, or "psychologically pure," hues may be observed which correspond to specific wavelengths. Unique blue is usually seen at about 476 mμ; unique green, at 510 mμ; and unique yellow, at 580 mμ. Unique red has no simple correlate on the wavelength continuum, but may be obtained by mixing a little spectral blue with spectral red (which is decidedly yellowish). Purples are also not evident in the spectral hues and must be obtained by mixtures of wavelengths from both short and long ends of the spectrum.

When the wavelength is increased or decreased by equal amounts, the resulting changes in hue are not equally different. The difference in wavelength needed to produce a just noticeable change in hue varies as a function of wavelength. The judgments for wavelength discrimination are obtained by having the observer report the just noticeable difference in hue between two halves of a test patch; brightness is equated for the two sides and saturation is maximal. One half of the test patch has a fixed wavelength while the other half is illuminated with a variable wavelength that can be adjusted by the experimenter. Under these conditions the threshold difference in some regions of the visible spectrum is less than one mμ; in other regions it is more than 4 mμ. The functional relation between the differential threshold for hue and wavelength is shown in Figure 8-6. Hue discrimination is best for all normal observers in the blue region between 480 and 490 mμ and in the yellow region between 580 and 590 mμ. In both regions the hue threshold is less than about 0.7 mμ. At 450 mμ (blue-violet) and 640 mμ (orange), the threshold is more than 3.0 mμ. Although the function for wavelength discrimination varies from individual to individual, the general form remains the same for normal observers.

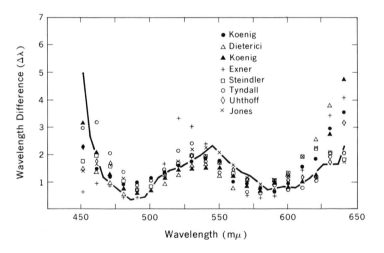

Figure 8-6. Wavelength discrimination, showing the difference in wavelength which can be just detected (Δλ) as a function of wavelength for the human eye. Data are shown for eight experimenters. (From Judd, *J. opt. Soc. Amer.*, 1932.)

Absolute Threshold for Saturation

In Figure 8-5 it was indicated that the visible spectrum contains many different wavelengths, each giving rise to a particular hue. Light which consists essentially of a single wavelength is said to be *homogeneous* or "spectrally pure." At the other extreme, "white" light (such as sunlight) contains luminous energy which is distributed at random among all wavelengths. Thus, its purity is zero or, stated differently, it is maximally *heterogeneous* and achromatic. Whenever the purity of a light stimulus changes between the extremes of complete homogeneity and maximal heterogeneity with luminance held constant, the color changes in grayness. The degree to which any stimulus possessing a hue differs from a gray of the same brightness is called *saturation*. Saturation is directly related to spectral purity. For example, a blue light at 480 mμ is composed of a single wavelength and is spectrally pure; it is highly saturated. Now, if the total luminance is held constant while other wavelengths are mixed with the blue, the light appears grayer, that is, the saturation becomes less. Notice, however, that the hue (blue) remains the same since the dominant wavelength is not altered.

The saturation of spectral wavelengths is measured in terms of the *minimal perceptible colorimetric purity* or, more simply, the *absolute threshold for saturation*. This measure is defined as the amount of a given pure (spectral) wavelength that must be mixed with white light to produce a just perceptible hue. The lower a light is in saturation, the greater the amount of the light that must be added to white to produce the perceptible hue. In measurements of saturation, the two halves of the test patch are maintained at equal brightness. For normal observers, the yellow region of the spectrum is less saturated than the red or blue regions. Approximately 0.05 percent yellow light must be added to white light to produce a perceptible hue, whereas only 0.001 percent of blue light and 0.005 percent of red light are needed (Chapanis, 1944).

The Auditory System

Frequency Limits of Hearing and the Threshold of Audibility

The human ear as a receptor mechanism is limited in its ability to respond to acoustic energy. While the acoustic spectrum is composed of a wide range of frequencies, the ear, like the eye, is sensitive to only a small part of this spectrum. Those sounds in the environment which lie beyond this range are inaudible to the human ear and are ineffective in providing acoustic stimulation. The exact limits of the audible frequency range are difficult to specify, since they depend in part upon the observer's willingness to be exposed to sounds of great intensity and upon his ability to determine whether h is hearing a "tone."

Another factor that must be considered is the method of presentation of the acoustic stimulus. The human auditory system may be activated by energy which is transmitted to the cochlea by either of two primary routes: (1) *air conduction* or (2) *bone conduction*.

In air conduction, the acoustic energy is conducted to the inner ear through the air in the external auditory canal that serves as the initial part of the pathway. This is the normal mode of hearing. When this technique is used in a laboratory setting, the acoustic stimuli may be transduced by either of two means, an earphone or a loudspeaker. Each of these leads to a specific type of measurement of the sound intensity at threshold. *Minimum Audible Pressure* (MAP) measurements specify the threshold sound pressure generated by an earphone that has been calibrated in a cylindrical volume (an artificial ear) of standard size, for example, 6 cc. From the calibration data it is possible to determine the equivalent sound pressure at the entrance of the ear canal, along the ear canal, or within one millimeter of the tympanic membrane (Pollack, 1949).

Minimum Audible Field (MAF) measurements specify the threshold sound pressure in terms of the intensity of the sound field in which the observer is placed. The procedure is to vary the intensity of the field until the observer's threshold has been reached and then to remove the observer from the field. The intensity of the existing field is then measured by inserting a microphone into the field at the location previously occupied by the observer's head. Since reflections and diffractions of sound will occur due to the observer's body, head movement, and clothing when he is in the field, MAF measurements are more variable than MAP measurements and the two types of measurements are not in perfect agreement. Threshold values for MAF are about 10 to 20 db lower than MAP values measured at the tympanic membrane.

The second route of acoustic transmission, bone conduction, involves the transmission of sound energy to the inner ear via the bones of the skull. In this procedure, the transducer is pressed firmly against the head, usually over the mastoid bone, with a pressure of about 200 to 400 gm. The mechanical properties of the human skull and cochlear capsule are such that auditory stimulation can produce at least two types of bone conduction: *translatory bone conduction* and *compressional bone conduction* (Wever, 1949). In *translatory bone conduction* it is postulated that all of the cochlear parts move in the same direction as the capsule is vibrated back and forth in reaction to the applied acoustic energy. However, due to their mass, the cochlear contents and the ossicular chain will exhibit a resistance to acceleration, or inertia, in the form of a time lag. Thus, relative motion is induced between the capsule and the cochlear contents and between the capsule and the ossicular chain. Although these two inertial forces operate in slightly different directions, the effect in each case is to produce a displacement of the basilar membrane which is capable of mediating an auditory response.

In *compressional bone conduction* it is postulated that the cochlear capsule expands and contracts as the sides of the head move in reaction to the rarefactions and condensations of the applied stimulus. Since the cochlear contents are incompressible under these conditions, the change in cochlear volume forces the fluids to be displaced in and out, primarily at the round window. In this process the basilar membrane is moved up and down, thereby initiating the neural action that is required for hearing.

The lower portion of the audible frequency range has been studied by a number of investigators who used the MAP technique. Their findings, as plotted in a single graph by Corso (1958a), are shown in Figure 8-7. It may be seen that the lower limit of hearing extends to 2 cps according to Békésy (1936) and that Corso (1958a) was able to obtain threshold data to 5 cps, which represented the lowest

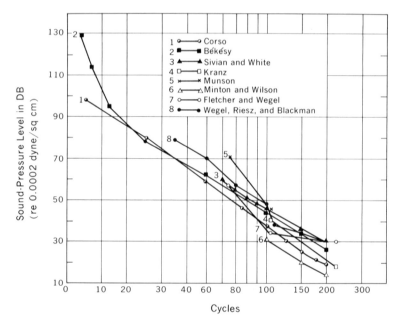

Figure 8-7. Absolute threshold curves for tones of low frequency as determined by various investigators. (From Corso, *Amer. J. Psychol.*, 1958.)

frequency tested in that particular study. While there are some differences in the relative positions of the various threshold functions in Figure 8-7, the slopes of the functions are quite similar, at least down to 10 cps. Additional data need to be collected to establish the slope of the audibility function and the threshold values beyond this point. In experiments of this type, the auditory signal below approximately 14 cps loses its tonal characteristic and appears to be "pulsating" or "throbbing" (Pollack, 1948).

Although it is recognized that auditory thresholds obtained from 125 to 8000 cps under MAP laboratory conditions are considerably more sensitive than those obtained in mass surveys under "field" conditions (Corso, 1958*b*), there is need for adopting a set of data to define *"normal hearing."* Normal hearing is conventionally called *audiometric zero* or the reference zero level for pure tone audiometers. By comparing an individual's hearing threshold level with this reference level, it is possible to establish the number of db by which the two differ, and in which direction. This information is important in making certain practical appraisals and for forming judgments related to the degree of hearing impairment, the time of onset of a hearing handicap, the social adequacy of hearing, and the effectiveness of otological operations, for example, fenestration.

The present American Standard for audiometric zero is based upon the U. S. Public Health Service survey of the population in 1935–36 (National Health Survey, 1938) and is embodied in the 1951 specification for audiometers for general diagnostic purposes (American Standards Association, 1951). However, several independent studies conducted over the past decade have indicated that the present standard is too lenient, that is, the threshold values are too high by about 10 db, and should be made more rigorous to approach the British Standard. The American Standard is now employed in the United States of America, Japan, and less systematically in several other countries; the British Standard is used in Great Britain and most European countries.

In 1955, the International Organization for Standardization (ISO) began an evaluative and critical review of all published data on the thresholds of normal hearing. Thirteen different studies from five different countries were examined, with four of them (Albright *et al.*, 1958; Corso, 1958*b*; Glorig *et al.*, 1956; Harris, 1954) from the United States (Harris, 1961). The agreement among the various studies was good and the results of the studies all differed substantially from the 1951 American Standard. Accordingly, the data were combined with those from several other countries to provide a proposed international standard for the uniform calibration of pure tone audiometers. This recommendation was published in 1964 by the ISO and will probably be adopted in the next revision of the American Standard for Audiometers.

The MAP reference zero levels for audiometers as published in 1951, and as recommended in 1964, are shown in Figure 8-8 from 125 to 8000 cps. On the average, the 1951 standard has been lowered by about 10 db; in addition, the adjustments have altered the shape of the audibility curve. The most sensitive

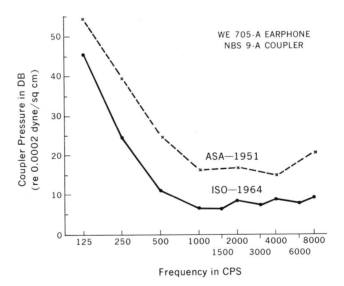

Figure 8–8. Comparison of the present zero reference level for audiometers (curve of normal hearing) of the American Standards Association (1951) with that recommended by the International Standards Organization (1964). (From Davis and Kranz, *J. Acoust. Soc. Amer.*, 1964.)

region of hearing in the 1964 contour is from 1000 to 1500 cps, with a small progressive rise in threshold up to 8000 cps. Below 1000 cps the curve rises sharply, going from about 8 db SPL at 1000 cps to about 46 db SPL at 125 cps. The ISO curve is based upon the threshold data of numerous young adults who were screened to exclude those with either a history of otologic disease, or visible signs of damage, and were tested by approved psychophysical methods under "audiometrically perfect" conditions.

The threshold of audibility for frequencies above 10,000 cps is not so well established as that for frequencies in the lower sonic region. This is due in part to the inherent difficulties of instrumentation and data collection. The determination of threshold values at high frequencies requires that an appropriate sound transducer be used in presenting the test tones to the observer. The earphones normally employed in clinical work and in certain laboratory situations are ineffective for two reasons: (1) they do not produce satisfactory high-level signals above approximately 10,000 cps, and (2) at such high frequencies they generate standing wave effects in the external auditory canal due to the mechanical coupling at the ear. These problems can be eliminated by utilizing a sound transducer of the free-field type and by making threshold determinations via the MAF technique. Such measurements, however, require that the testing room be *anechoic* (without echo) to avoid reverberation effects in the sound field.

In a study designed to establish the MAF air conduction threshold for pure tones in the upper sonic region (Corso, 1965), these precautions were observed and data were obtained on 36 men and 37 women, 18 to 24 years of age. Threshold determinations were made on the right ear only, and nine frequencies were tested from 6000 to 23,000 cps, inclusive. The results of the study are presented in Figure 8-9. While separate curves of audibility were obtained for men and women, the differences in the mean MAF values were not statistically significant at any frequency. The combined curve for men and women is shown in Figure 8-9 and is positively accelerated with slight "dips" at 12,000 and 20,000 cps. For comparison, the MAF curve of audibility of the American Standards Association (1942) is also shown in Figure 8-9. This curve, however, is based on binaural rather than monaural listening, which may account for the lower, (more sensitive) threshold values.

Of the 73 observers tested in this study, only 9 responded at 23,000 cps. Each observer was also presented with a test tone of 28,000 cps, but none responded. Thus, it may be concluded that the absolute upper frequency limit of hearing by MAF air conduction lies between these two limits, and that 23,000 cps may be taken as the limit for all practical purposes. This finding is in close agreement with Wever (1949) who contends that the upper limit of hearing lies in the region of 24,000 cps for young persons with unimpaired hearing; beyond this, nothing at all is said to be heard.

Although the air conduction characteristics of the human ear apparently impose an upper frequency limit of about 23,000 cps, several investigators have reported that the upper limit of hearing by *bone conduction* is considerably higher

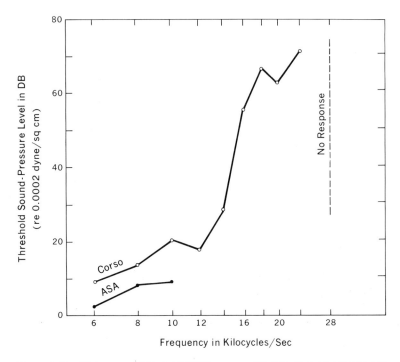

Figure 8–9. Minimum audible field (MAF) monaural threshold curve for men and women in the upper sonic region (upper curve) compared with the binaural MAF curve of the American Standards Association (lower curve). (From Corso, 1965.)

than that for air conduction. In a comprehensive study, Corso (1963*a*) tested 38 men and 37 women, all of whom were 17 to 24 years of age and showed no evidence of otological abnormalities or disease. Threshold data were obtained by a modified method of limits, with one descending and one ascending series of trials at each of twelve frequencies. Throughout the tests, the bone conduction transducer was pressed firmly against the mastoid bone of the observer's head by means of a specially designed headpiece.

The results of this study are shown in Figure 8-10. The bone conduction thresholds in db re 0.0002 dyne/sq cm are shown as a function of frequency for both men and women. The mean sound pressure levels at threshold are not markedly different for the two groups. From 10,000 to 20,000 cps the audibility function has a slope of approximately 50 db/octave; from 20,000 to 95,000 cps, a slope of approximately 15 db/octave. The results of this study clearly indicate that frequencies above the conventional upper limit of hearing by air conduction can produce auditory responses when presented by means of bone conduction. It appears, therefore, that the neural receptive processes are capable of responding by bone conduction to frequencies at least as high as 95,000 cps, but that the mechanical characteristics of the human ear impose a physical restriction on the transmission of air-conducted sounds beyond approximately 23,000 cps.

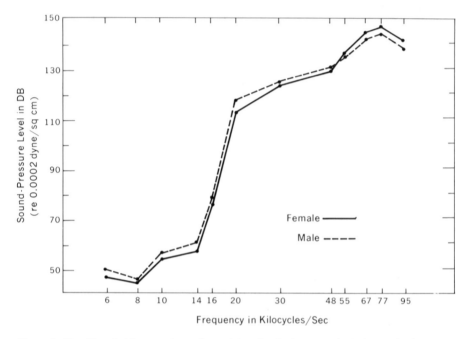

Figure 8-10. Threshold curves for males and females for bone-conducted tones in the upper sonic and ultrasonic frequency region. (From Corso, *J. acoust. Soc. Amer.,* 1963.)

Frequency and the Absolute
Threshold for Pitch

In the preceding section, it was indicated that the frequency limits of man's hearing depended upon the particular method used in presenting the acoustic stimulus and upon the observer's ability to discriminate between the presence or absence of a *tone*. A *tone* is a sound wave capable of producing an auditory response and is characterized as having a definite *pitch*. *Pitch* is an attribute in terms of which sounds may be ordered on a psychological scale extending from low to high. It depends primarily upon the frequency of the physical stimulus, but it also depends upon other physical variables, such as the sound pressure and the duration of the stimulus.

While the lower frequency limit of hearing has been measured down to 2 cps, there is some question whether these signals are characterized as having "pitch." Below 15 cps, what is heard is a series of "chugging" or "fluttering" sounds, probably containing harmonics generated by distortion in the ear itself due to the extremely high sound pressures. Above 15 cps, and certainly above 25 cps for most observers (Wever and Bray, 1937), a continuous tone is heard with a definite pitch, provided the sound pressure level is above 15 to 20 db. For sound pressures as low as 10 db SPL, tonality is not present until a frequency of approximately 60 cycles is reached. Since the lower limit of tonal recognition depends upon the intensity of the auditory stimulus, no single frequency value can be given as the point at which pitch emerges.

Similarly, the upper limit for pitch perception has not been clearly established. Some data have been collected for frequencies as high as 10,000 cps and 14,000 cps, but no exhaustive studies have been conducted on this problem. For observers with relatively little experience with pure tones, there appears to be no pitch characteristic for frequencies above approximately 5500 cps (Ward, 1954).

Regardless of the frequency of the tone which is presented to the observer, the tone must be of sufficient intensity and duration if it is to be heard as having a definite pitch. In one study (Pollack, 1948) it was found that from 125 to 8000 cps, inclusive, a given frequency had to be at least 5 db above its threshold of audibility (detection threshold) before a definite pitch emerged (*tonal threshold*). The intensity area between these two thresholds has been called the *atonal interval,* which is analogous to the photochromatic interval in vision. For stable pitch values, pure tones should have a duration of at least 0.5 sec (Ekdahl and Stevens, 1937).

In discussing the frequency limits of hearing, it was indicated that auditory responses can be produced by high intensity, bone-conducted sounds above the upper limit of hearing by air conduction. The question remains: What, if any, are the pitch characteristics of ultrasonic frequencies heard by bone conduction? To answer this, a study was conducted (Corso and Levine, 1963) in which the observers were presented with a standard stimulus at a *sensation level* (SL) of 5 db, that is, 5 db above the threshold of audibility, and a comparison stimulus that could be manipulated by the experimenter to produce continuous changes in frequency and intensity. The observers were tested individually on four frequencies: 14,000; 57,000; 64,000; and 94,000 cps and were required to match, if possible, the pitch and loudness characteristics of these tones with a bone-conducted sound in the sonic region. The results are presented in Table 8-1. The

Table 8-1   Pitch Matching Data for Sonic and Ultrasonic Frequencies

Standard Frequencies	Sonic 14,000 cps	57,000 cps	Ultrasonic 64,000 cps	94,000 cps
Number of Subjects	3	3	2	3
Mean of Judgments	14,084 cps	16,681 cps	17,656 cps	17,352 cps

Source: John F. Corso and M. Levine. The pitch of ultra-sonic frequencies heard by bone conduction. *Proc. Penna. Acad. Sci.,* 1963, **37**, 22–26. Reprinted by permission of the Pennsylvania Academy of Science.

mean match for 14,000 cps was 14,084 cps, which is quite accurate for this method and indicates that the observers can make accurate judgments. However, the three ultrasonic frequencies (57,000; 64,000; and 93,000 cps) were all matched to sonic frequencies in the region of 16,000 to 17,000 cps. It was concluded, therefore, that the pitch of bone-conducted, ultrasonic frequencies approximates that of bone-conducted pure tones in the region of 16,000 to 17,000 cps.

Discrimination of Frequency

The literature on psychophysical methods is filled with cautions that thresholds obtained by different methods will not necessarily be comparable in size. This has been clearly demonstrated in the determination of the differential threshold for pitch in which several investigators have obtained widely divergent results. In order to establish the maximal sensitivity of the observer, a method must be chosen that will tax the observer's discriminatory ability to the fullest extent and that will reflect minimally the effects of other variables, such as fluctuations of attention, changes in motivation, different amounts of practice, and so on. Furthermore, other controls must be incorporated into the experimental situation. The stimulus must be sinusoidal, without distortions or transients, and must be precisely prescribed; it must be of sufficient duration, a half-second or longer; and it must be turned on and off without perceptible noises or clicks.

Harris (1952) performed a study on monaural pitch discrimination in which these and other factors were taken into account. The results of this study are presented in Figure 8-11, together with those of several other investigators. Below

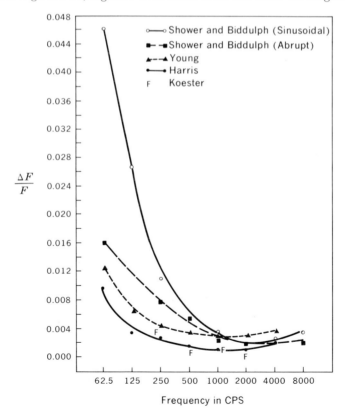

Figure 8-11. Values of the relative difference limen ($\Delta F/F$) for frequency discrimination as obtained by various investigators. (From Harris, *J. acoust. Soc. Amer.*, 1952.)

1000 cps the classic data of Shower and Biddulph (1931) show the poorest sensitivity. These differences, however, are probably due to differences in psychophysical procedures. Shower and Biddulph used a test tone that was frequency-modulated (sinusoidally or abruptly), whereas Harris used a steady tone in a modified method of constant stimulus differences. The *Weber fraction* (DF/F or $\Delta F/F$) is smallest for tones in the 1000–2000 cps region; as the frequencies depart from this region, both above and below, the Weber fraction becomes larger (except for the Shower and Biddulph curve). Thus, a smaller change in frequency must be added to a frequency of 1000 or 2000 cps for the change to be detected as a rise in pitch than for those frequencies located higher or lower on the physical continuum.

The curves in Figure 8-11 were obtained for tones at a medium intensity level, that is, about 30 to 40 db above the threshold of audibility. However, the differential threshold for pitch depends upon both the frequency of the standard tone (F) and its intensity (I). The *absolute differential threshold* for pitch (DL or ΔF) as determined by Harris is presented in Figure 8-12. Four curves are presented, one for each of four loudness levels in phons. (The *Loudness Level*, LL, of a sound, expressed in phons, is numerically equivalent to the sound pressure level of an equally loud 1000 cps tone expressed in decibels relative to 0.0002 dyne/sq cm.)

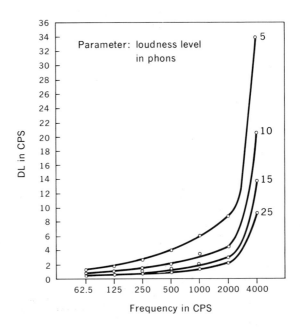

Figure 8–12. The absolute *DL* for pitch as a function of frequency at different loudness levels. (From Harris, *J. Acoust. Soc. Amer.*, 1952.)

For the lower frequencies, loudness level has little effect on the absolute *DL*, but for the higher frequencies it has a very marked effect. Decreasing the loudness level from 25 to 5 phons for a 62.5 cps tone increases the absolute *DL* by a factor of about three (0.5 to 1.5 cps, approximately), while the same decrease in loudness level changes the absolute *DL* of a 4000 cps tone by a factor of more than four (8 to 34 cps, approximately). Regardless of frequency, the greater the loudness level of a tone, the smaller the increment in frequency which is required to produce a just noticeable change in pitch. From Figure 8-12 it may also be determined that for a given frequency, the absolute *DL* decreases sharply from 5 to 10 phons and remains essentially constant as loudness level increases beyond this, except for 4000 cps, which reaches an asymptotic level at about 20 phons.

The classical studies on frequency discrimination, such as those already cited, used an isolated pure tone as the standard stimulus from which to determine the differential threshold. What if *two* harmonically related frequencies were to be presented simultaneously, would this affect the pitch discrimination of either component? Schodder and David (1960) presented three observers with a two-tone complex consisting of 500 cps and either 3500 cps or 5000 cps. The two tones were adjusted to a loudness level of 40 phons and, when they were presented simultaneously, were heard as individual tones rather than as a fused complex sound. The observers were presented with a standard stimulus, followed by a variable stimulus, or a variable followed by the standard in random order. The standard was a tone pulse consisting of either frequency by itself, or both frequencies together; the variable consisted of an increment (ΔF) added to each frequency in the standard tone. The observers were asked to judge whether the pitch of the second tone pulse was higher or lower than that of the first.

The results showed that the *DL* for the two-tone harmonically related complex was never smaller than the smaller *DL* of the single tones and was never larger than the larger *DL* of the single tones. In the same experiment, however, data on four observers tested with a two-tone complex of 4000 cps (variable) and 4100 cps (fixed) showed that the *DL* for 4000 cps was smaller in the complex than when presented alone. Thus, there is tentative evidence that, under certain circumstances, the discrimination of the pitch of a complex sound can be finer than that of any of its component tones taken in isolation.

Discrimination of Intensity

The classical data on the differential threshold for intensity ($\Delta I/I$) are those of Riesz (1928). Riesz avoided the problem of generating transient sounds due to the successive presentation of discrete tones by using the "beat" method. In this method, two tones that differed by 3 cps were permitted to sound together; this produced an effect which was heard by the observer as a single tone waxing and waning in loudness three times per second. The difference threshold was determined from the energy levels at the threshold of the beating signals. Maximal sensitivity (the smallest value of ΔI) was found in the region of 2500 cps.

For low sensation levels, the absolute differential threshold was rather large; for example, for 1000 cps at 5 db SL, the ΔI (*DL*) value was 3 db. Harris (1963), however, found that under optimal monaural listening conditions the *DL* was considerably smaller. He used two tones, each of which was 0.5 sec in duration, with a 40-msec rise-fall time and a 0.5 sec interstimulus interval. The judgments were made in accordance with the method of constant stimulus differences in which twelve variable steps (between +1.2 db and −1.2 db in 0.2 db intervals) were usually presented. The loudness levels from 5 to 80 phons for any session were selected at random for each frequency. In any one experimental session 60 to 90 judgments were made; each variable was presented at random until it was judged a total of 75 times over a period of several months. The observer was forced to judge the second of a pair of tones as "louder" or "softer" than the first; the tones were presented whenever the observer pressed a silent microswitch to indicate he believed he was in a maximally attentive condition.

The results of this study are presented in part in Figure 8-13. The *DL* values are considerably smaller than those obtained by Riesz (1928); the differences be-

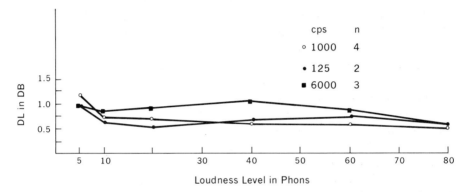

Figure 8-13. The mean difference limen *(DL)* in db for intensity discrimination under optimal conditions of judgment. (From Harris, *J. Speech and Hearing Disorders*, 1963, Monogr. Suppl. No. 11.)

tween the studies have been attributed primarily to differences in methodology and in the manner of presenting the stimulus. Under optimal conditions, the *DL* value is less than 1.5 db regardless of frequency or loudness level. At its most sensitive point, the most acute *DL* is approximately 0.5 db. It should be noted, however, that these data are for a few highly trained observers. For normative data on a larger number of men tested on an amplitude-modulated signal, the reader is referred to Tonndorf, Brogan, and Washburn (1955).

Discrimination of Wave Form

Timbre is the psychological attribute in terms of which an observer can judge that two complex tones with the same loudness and pitch are auditorily dissimilar. For example, an observer may hear two complex tones presented successively over a loudspeaker system; he judges the first tone to have been a clarinet tone and the second, a trumpet tone, even though both tones were equally loud and both instruments were playing Middle C. While at the level of casual observation it seems that the various instruments of the orchestra can be distinguished readily one from another, the facts indicate that this is not quite so easily done in the laboratory; also, the relevant physical cues for timbre have not been fully identified.

Two theories of timbre are now posited. The *classical theory* or *harmonic structure theory* of von Helmholtz (1862) asserts in its revised form that the musical quality of a tone depends upon the presence and strength of partial tones, their relative location along the frequency continuum, and their phase relations. In this theory the acoustic spectrum of a tone is considered to be the primary determinant of musical quality, or timbre. The physical correlate of timbre lies in the cross-sectional analysis of a tone as represented by the momentary duration of one cycle.

In Part A of Figure 8-14, the basic concept of the harmonic structure theory is represented in diagrammatic form. Three complex tones are shown: C_4 (Middle C) = 261.63 cps, C_5 = 523.26 cps, and C_6 = 1046.5 cps. The physical analysis of the tones shows fifteen partials in each tone (depicted as vertical bars along the frequency continuum) and indicates the relative intensity of these partials in decibels (depicted by the different heights of the vertical bars). In each case, the seventh partial is the strongest, regardless of the frequency at which it is located, and has the same relative intensity in each spectrum. The harmonic structure theory requires that the spectrum of each tone be exactly the same for all tones from the same source, no matter what frequency is selected as the fundamental (first partial).

The *formant theory* of timbre provides an alternative or supplement to the classical theory. The formant theory holds that the characteristic quality of a musical instrument depends upon the relative strengthening of partials which lie within a fixed, or relatively fixed, region of the frequency scale. This region is called a formant of that tone and any tone may have more than one formant. The partials nearest the formant region or regions are those that are strengthened in intensity. Unlike the harmonic structure theory which emphasizes the *fixed* spectrum of a tone, the formant theory relies upon *changes* in the spectral characteristics of a tone to produce constancy in musical quality. The perceived tonal quality is probably influenced not only by the formant frequency range, but also by the amount of energy in that range and by the width of the frequency band involved. It is believed that the strengthening of the partials in the formant region is due to the resonance of some part of the musical instrument being played, or to the resonance of the body of air enclosed within the instrument. This means that the formant need not be at a frequency that is harmonically (integrally) related to the fundamental of the tone.

Part B of Figure 8-14 shows the basic concept of the formant theory of tone quality. For Middle C (C_4), the seventh partial has the greatest relative intensity and the frequency region at approximately 1800 cps may be considered to be a formant region of that tone. Accordingly, the formant theory requires that for any other tone from the same source, the partial or partials falling in this region will be strengthened. For C_5, the third and fourth partials are shown as increased in strength, while the seventh partial has decreased in relative intensity. For C_6, the

(A) HARMONIC STRUCTURE THEORY

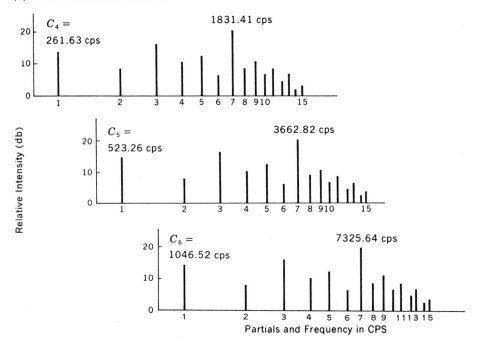

(B) FORMANT THEORY

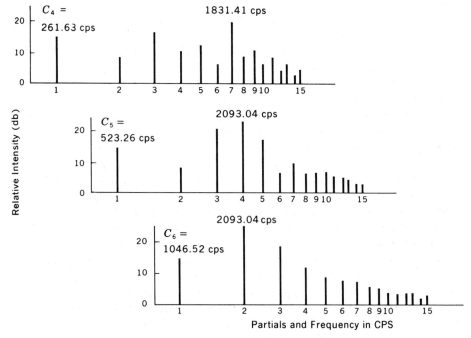

Figure 8–14. Diagrammatic representation of the harmonic structure and formant theories of timbre.

second partial (2093.04 cps) is strongest and the seventh partial is among the weakest. Whenever the fundamental frequency of a tone is raised or lowered, there is a change produced in the appearance of the spectrum, and the relative intensity of those partials falling in or near the formant region or regions will be increased.

In the revision of the Seashore Measures of Musical Talent (Saetveit, Lewis, and Seashore, 1940) data bearing on the harmonic structure theory were collected. The timbre test in this battery was designed to measure the observer's capacity for discriminating between complex sounds which differed only in harmonic structure. There were two series in the test (A and B) with each series consisting of 50 pairs of tones. In each series half the pairs were the same in harmonic structure, while the other half were different. The listener was instructed to judge whether the two tones of a pair were the same or different in timbre.

Each tone had a fundamental frequency of 180 cps and five additional partials. Changes in the harmonic structure of the tones were brought about by reciprocally alternating the intensities of the third and fourth partials. The standard tone had the greatest intensity in the third partial and, for purposes of plotting the acoustic spectrum in Figure 8-15, was assigned a value of zero db. Since the intensities of the other five partials were less than that for the third partial, their relative intensities are represented by negative numbers. The fundamental component is 8 db below the level of the third, the second is 6 db below, and the fourth, fifth, and sixth partials are -11, -12, and -14.5 db, respectively.

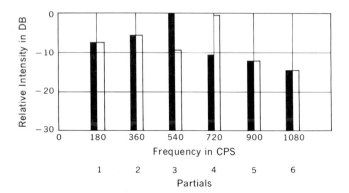

Figure 8-15. Acoustic spectrum of the standard tone (solid bars) and the variable tone (open bars) which differed most in harmonic structure from the standard. The ordinate shows the relative intensity of the six partials (harmonics) with the intensity of the third partial (540 cps) arbitrarily designated as zero. (From Saetveit et al., *Revision of the Seashore measures of musical talent,* University of Iowa Studies, New Series No. 388, University of Iowa Press, 1940.)

In addition to the standard tone, there were five different variable tones in Series A and five others in Series B. The particular variable tone that differed most in harmonic structure from the standard appeared in Series A and is shown by the open vertical bars in Figure 8-15. Table 8-2 presents a summary of the amounts in decibels by which the intensities of the third and fourth partials in the variable tones differed from their levels in the standard tone. Table 8–2 also shows the percentage of correct responses for the mean performance of different groups of observers at each level of difficulty.

Table 8–2 Summary of Characteristics of Variable Tones in Series A and B and the Percentage of Correct Responses

Series A

| Items | Increase in 4th harmonic | Decrease in 3d harmonic | Percentage of Correct Responses | |
			7th and 8th Grades	Adults
1–10	10.0	9.6	87.5	90.7
11–20	8.5	4.0	77.2	82.4
21–30	7.0	2.4	69.4	74.2
31–40	5.5	1.2	61.5	64.8
41–50	4.0	0.7	55.7	56.2

Series B

| Items | Increase in 4th harmonic | Decrease in 3d harmonic | Percentage of Correct Responses | |
			Unselected Adults	College Musicians
1–10	9.0	5.2	81.6	90.1
11–20	7.5	2.7	71.7	78.1
21–30	6.0	1.7	59.7	68.8
31–40	4.5	0.9	50.9	56.0
41–50	3.0	0.5	51.7	52.4

Source: J. G. Saetveit, D. Lewis, and C. E. Seashore. *Revision of the Seashore measures of musical talent.* University of Iowa Studies, New Series No. 388, No. 65, 1–62. Iowa City, Iowa; University of Iowa Press, 1940. Reprinted by permission of the publisher.

If the timbre threshold is taken as the stimulus value at which 75 percent correct responses are obtained, it may be seen in Table 8-2 that, in Series A, adults have a lower threshold than 7th and 8th graders and that in Series B, college musicians have a lower threshold than unselected adults. For the adults in Series A, an increase of approximately 7 db in the 4th harmonic and a decrease of approximately 2.4 db in the 3d harmonic produces a just noticeable difference in timbre; in Series B, college musicians can detect a threshold change in timbre when the 4th harmonic is increased by approximately 7.4 db and the 3d harmonic is decreased by approximately 2.5 db. These threshold values, however, are applicable only with reference to the particular structure of the standard tone used in this study and with a listening level of approximately 70 db SPL.

While two theoretical possibilities (harmonic structure and formant regions)

have already been proposed to account for our ability to discriminate among the various instruments of the orchestra, Saldanha and Corso (1964) have performed a study which suggests that other possibilities may exist. In this study, high-fidelity tape recordings were made of single tones from ten different instruments as played by college and professional musicians. Three tones were used: $C_4 = 261.6$ cps; $F_4 = 349.2$ cps; and $A_4 = 440$ cps. Each of these tones was played with and without vibrato. By appropriately splicing the original tape and rerecording, five types of tones were produced: (1) initial transients and short steady-state; (2) initial transients, short steady-state, and final transients; (3) initial transients, long steady-state, and final transients; (4) short steady-state; and (5) short steady-state and final transients. The final test tape contained 300 randomly ordered tonal stimuli (10 instruments × 3 frequencies × 2 playing styles × 5 types of tones). Twenty college symphony players were tested and retested on the final tape in two separate sessions, thereby providing a total of 12,000 judgments. The observers were provided with a reminder list of 39 instruments, grouped into orchestral classes, and were required to identify the particular instrument for each tonal stimulus.

Figure 8-16 shows the percentage of correct identifications for the ten different musical instruments used in the study. The clarinet, oboe, and flute are identified most easily; the cello and bassoon are the most difficult. The results indicate that there are marked differences among instruments in terms of their absolute identification based on auditory cues alone. In all, only about 40 percent of the abso-

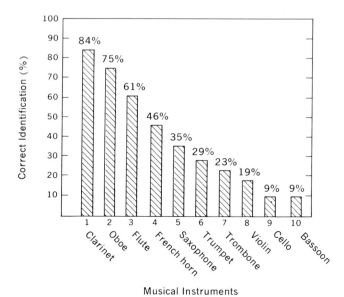

Figure 8-16. Bar diagram showing the percentage of correct identifications for ten musical instruments by the method of absolute judgments. (From Saldanha and Corso, *J. acoust. Soc. Amer.*, 1964.)

lute judgments were correct. These findings, however, may in part be affected by the particular instruments selected for the experiment; if the cello, for example, had not been included, the percentage of correct identifications for the violin might have been higher.

The data for the five types of tones are shown in Figure 8-17. Notice that there is only a 3 percent difference in discrimination between Type 2 and Type 3; these

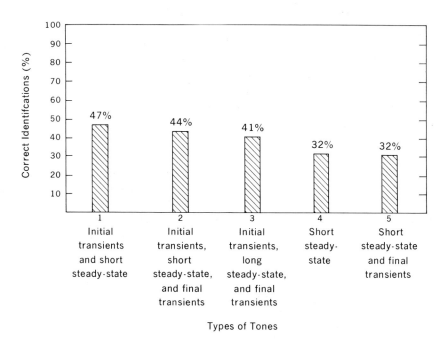

Figure 8-17. Bar diagram showing the percentage of correct identifications for five types of tones. (From Saldanha and Corso, *J. Acoust. Soc. Amer.*, 1964.)

two tones differed only in the duration of the steady-state. The entire tone with the long steady state was 9 sec in duration; the entire tone with the short steady state was 3 sec. From this it may be concluded that the duration of the tone has little if any effect on identification, provided some minimal duration has been exceeded. Optimal identification is obtained when the initial portion and short steady-state are presented (Type 1). Since the poorest identification is obtained when the short steady-state portion is presented alone (Type 4) or when it is followed by the final portion of the tone (Type 5), it appears to be the onset (beginning) of the tone that contains the auditory cues for the discrimination of timbre, not the ending. These cues may be in the form of short-duration, inharmonic *transients,* or they may be related to the *temporal order* in which the upper partials emerge in the tonal complex due to differences in *rise-time,* that is, differences in the rate at which the various partials reach a given level of intensity. Graphic analysis of the tones indicated that during the onset of the tone, the fundamental always appeared first, followed by the second, third, and fourth partials; during the stopping of the tone, the partials disappeared in the opposite order (from highest to lowest). Finally, the results of the study indicated that more correct identifications were obtained at F_4 than at C_4 or A_4, and that a vibrato tone was better identified than a nonvibrato tone.

The Tactile System

As described in detail in Chapter 4, the receptor cells of the tactile system are located in the skin, and are activated by mechanical pressures that are sufficiently large to deform the skin tissue. The significant variable for eliciting touch is tension (pressing or pulling) which creates a gradient of deformation with respect to the cutaneous surface.

Tactile Thresholds

The classic work on the stimulus threshold for pressure was performed by von Frey (Woodworth, 1938). He used a series of straight hairs, human or other, fastened to the end of light wooden handles; these were calibrated by pressing down on one pan of a sensitive balance. After the diameter of each hair was measured with the aid of a microscope, the force exerted per square millimeter was then computed. The threshold of a spot on the skin was established by determining the weakest hair in a graduated series that gave rise to a report of touch. It was found that the absolute threshold for pressure varies widely for different parts of the body. The data for one observer are presented in Table 8-3. It may be seen that the lowest thresholds occur on the tongue and fingers, and the highest on the loin and the thick parts of the soles of the feet. Compared with the eye

Table 8-3 Absolute Thresholds for Pressure in Various Regions of the Body

Bodily Region	Absolute Threshold (gm/sq mm)
Tip of tongue	2
Tip of finger	3
Back of finger	5
Front of forearm	8
Back of hand	12
Calf of leg	16
Abdomen	26
Back of forearm	33
Loin	48
Thick parts of sole	250

Source: R. S. Woodworth, *Experimental Psychology.* New York: Holt, Rinehart and Winston, Inc., 1938.

or the ear, the skin is relatively insensitive to stimulation and requires tremendously larger energy values to produce a positive report. The intensive threshold for touch is approximately 100 million to 10 billion times as large as that for vision or hearing.

In a more recent study, Hensel and Boman (1960), working with fully awake observers without the influence of anesthesia, recorded afferent impulses from thin preparations of the superficial branch of the radial nerve in the region between the thumb and forefinger. They found that the threshold for eliciting a single impulse in a single mechanosensitive fiber was the same as that for producing a report of touch, that is, approximately 0.15 to 0.6 grams applied with a perspex rod of 1 mm diameter. It is remarkable that a report of touch can be mediated by a single impulse in the nerve fiber associated with a hair receptor or, in a hairless part of the body, with a single mechanoreceptor.

The problem of the differential threshold for pressure has also been studied by the von Frey technique, as well as by more refined procedures that verified the earlier findings. The differential threshold for pressure, expressed as the Weber ratio $(\Delta I/I)$ as a function of I, is shown in Figure 8-18; the data are those of Gatti

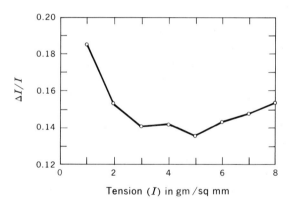

Figure 8-18. Differential threshold for pressure $(\Delta I/I)$ as a function of intensity level (I). (From Boring, *Sensation and perception in the history of experimental psychology*. New York: Appleton, 1942; after Gatti and Dodge, *Arch. ges. Psychol.*, 1929.)

and Dodge (1929) for a single pressure "spot" as published in Boring (1942). In this case, the pressure gradient was produced by traction, that is, lifting an object attached to the skin. It may be seen that the Weber ratio is not constant for values of I ranging from 1 to 8 gm/mm. The values of the ratio are large at either end of the scale and minimal in the mid-range of intensities; from 3 to 6 gm/mm, the Weber ratio is essentially constant.

These data on differential pressure sensitivity, as well as those on the absolute threshold, hold only for the particular conditions under which they were obtained. Among other factors, the locus of stimulation is crucial for the magnitude of the values obtained. In general, the parts of the body that are normally exposed, such as the lips and fingertips, have small absolute thresholds for pressure and small differential thresholds. These thresholds are related to the number of pressure "spots" that are found in a given area. If the surface of the skin is explored systematically with a weak pressure stimulus, it is found not to be uniformly sensitive to excitation. Pressure is felt at given "spots" or "points" on the skin that occur more frequently or in closer proximity in the skin regions with low thresholds. These "pressure points" are located near the base of the hairs on the skin (just to the side of the hairs away from which they are bent) and in the hairless regions in the vicinity of Meissner's corpuscles or free nerve endings. As the intensity of the probing stimulus is increased, the proportion of "points" responding in one square centimeter of cutaneous tissue increases in a sigmoidal manner until a stimulus intensity of 1.6 grams produces a response 100 percent of the time, regardless of the location at which the stimulus is applied on the back of the hand (Guilford and Lovewell, 1936).

A Note on Electrical Stimulation

In considering the potentialities of using the cutaneous senses for communication, some investigators (Geldard, 1960; Gilmer, 1961) have applied electrical stimuli to the skin, rather than mechanical stimuli. Hawkes (1961) determined the values of $\Delta I/I$ for stimulation at the fingertip for various combinations of intensity and frequency of alternating current. Although two different methods were used to present the electrical stimulus, it was found that the frequency of the current (100, 500, and 1500 cps) had no effect on $\Delta I/I$. Increases in the standard intensity (I), however, significantly reduced the size of $\Delta I/I$. The Weber ratio was found to vary from about 0.052 when the standard intensity was weak, that is, 120 percent of the absolute threshold, to about 0.036 at strong intensity, or, 200 percent of the absolute threshold. These values of the Weber ratio are smaller than those that have been reported for the mechanical stimulation of the cutaneous receptors (see Figure 8-18). It has been suggested by Hawkes that electrical stimulation may act directly on the cutaneous nerves, as well as the receptors, whereas a mechanical stimulus may normally act first upon the receptors alone.

The Proprioceptive Systems

The Kinesthetic System

Threshold for Lifted Weights.   Although it is common knowledge that a normal person with his eyes closed can tell the direction of movement and the position of his arms and legs, whether moved actively or passively, the kinesthetic system has not been extensively studied in the laboratory—except, of course, for studies on lifted weights. In one of these studies (Oberlin, 1936) five observers lifted different weights successively in one hand and judged whether the second member of each pair was lighter or heavier than the first. Six standard weights from 25 to 600 gm were used, with each standard being paired with its own set of five comparison stimuli. The *DL,* taken as the interval of uncertainty between the upper and lower differential thresholds, varied from about 3 gm for a standard of 25 gm to about 45 gm at a standard of 600 gm, with little change in the Weber ratio beyond 150 gm. These *DL*s are considered to be kinesthetic *DL*s and the differences in perceived weight are attributed to differences in kinesthesis. The greatest sensitivity to differences in weights was obtained when the weights were lifted primarily with shoulder movement; wrist movement produced the least sensitivity. The perception of differences in lifted weights is a function of the part of the arm used in the lifting motion.

Threshold for Movement of Body Parts.   The sensitivity of the limbs to movement has also been studied directly. Goldscheider made over 4000 observations and concluded that of nine bodily joints tested, the shoulder was the most sensitive to movement and the ankle the least (Boring, 1942). The threshold for passive movement of the shoulder at a rate of 0.3° per sec was between 0.2 and 0.4 degrees; for the ankle, the threshold displacement was somewhat larger, approximately 1.1–1.3 degrees. Sensitivity of the wrist and knuckle of the index finger is nearly as great as that for the shoulder, with values of 0.2–0.4 degree and 0.3–0.4 degree, respectively. Other studies tend to confirm these findings, and it may be concluded that movement of the larger joints, such as the shoulder and hip, is more readily detected than at the fingers or toes. If the movement of a limb is actively accomplished by the individual, the sensitivity is slightly greater than that for passive movement.

The passive movement of the human elbow joint has been studied by a number of investigators. The results of these studies are summarized in Table 8-4. From the table it may be seen that, although the speed of movement seems to have a direct effect on the threshold value, the specific relationship is not clearly defined. The data of Cleghorn and Dorcus do, nevertheless, reveal that the threshold for

Table 8-4   Summary of Threshold Values for Passive Movement of the Human Elbow Joint

Investigator	No. of Observers	Range of Speed of Movement (deg/sec)	Range of Threshold (deg)
Goldscheider (1889)	1	0.7–1.4	0.40–0.76
Pillsbury (1901)	3	0.33	0.43–0.85
Winter (1912)	7 (2)[a]	0.08–0.56	0.20–2.82
Laidlaw and Hamilton (1937)	60 (20)[a]	0.16	0.30–2.50
Cleghorn and Darcus (1952)	4	0.10–0.25	0.8–1.8[b]

[a] Figures in parentheses indicate number of observers for whom incomplete data were presented.
[b] The smaller value is for 80 percent correct detection of movement and the larger, for 80 percent correct identification of direction of movement at all speeds within the tested range.

the detection of the direction of passive movement is larger than that for simply detecting that movement has occurred. Also, both of these judgments are more efficient in extension than in flexion.

It is generally agreed that the perception of movement is mediated primarily by the receptors associated with the joints, and that the receptors in the muscles and tendons contribute to the feelings of kinesthetic strain whenever resistance to movement is present.

The Vestibular System

Threshold for Bodily Tilt. One of the most fundamental of the propriocep-tive processes is that which assists in maintaining the stability of the human body. The anatomical structures that perform this function are the *utricle* and the *sac-cule*, the two structures of the membranous labyrinth housed within the vestibule. In the laboratory, the effects of gravitational pull on the otolith organ are studied by placing a blindfolded observer in a so-called tilt chair or on a tilt table. By tilting the entire body away from the horizontal and vertical axes according to a predetermined plan, the thresholds of otolithic action have been determined. Under these static conditions, deviations of about 2 to 3 degrees from the vertical were detected in either the right-left or forward-back directions (McFarland, 1946), but, some observers required an angle of 14 degrees before the direction of tilt could be correctly distinguished.

The findings of this and other bodily tilt experiments, however, should be ac-cepted with caution. First, there are very large differences among individuals so that average thresholds are not too meaningful unless the observers are tested in large numbers. Second, extraneous cues are often elicited from the skin and mus-cles due to the presence of restraining straps and a head holder. The threshold for these excitations appear to be lower than those of vestibular origin and may act to mask the otolithic response. These factors contribute to the unreliability of threshold determinations that should be considered only in terms of order of magnitude, not as definitive values.

Thresholds for Linear Motion. The otolithic organs also provide information when an individual is exposed to linear acceleration and deceleration as in flying or riding in an automobile. Here there are changes in speed with no change in direction; this involves a positive or negative linear acceleration that may serve as an effective stimulus for the vestibular receptors. What is the absolute threshold for linear acceleration? This depends upon several factors, including the duration of the accelerative force and the direction of the force with respect to the vertical and horizontal axes of the body. The threshold of vertical acceleration ranges from 4 to 12 cm/sec/sec and that for horizontal acceleration from 2 to 20 cm/sec/sec (Armstrong, 1943); the range of values for the two directions of accelera-tion reflect not only the particular experimental conditions under which the measurements were made, but also the internal factors of individual differences.

In a study conducted with the observer sitting blindfolded in the rear cockpit of a two-place training plane (Clark and Graybiel, 1949), it was found that a positive acceleration of 0.02 g, that is, 2 percent of the acceleration imparted by a force equal to that of gravity, or 0.644 ft/sec/sec, produced a threshold feeling of backward tilt as in increasing altitude, while a deceleration of 0.08 g, or 2.576 ft/sec/sec produced a threshold feeling of forward tilt as in diving.

Thresholds for Angular and Radial Acceleration.   When an individual is not provided with visual information, sensory experiences may be induced that do not correspond with the prevailing environmental facts. In flying, aviators are well aware that the information provided by flight instruments is far more trustworthy than subjective impressions. This is illustrated in a study that involved the *semicircular canals* and combined the effects of *angular* and *radial acceleration* (MacCorquodale, 1948).

In this study, the subject sat blindfolded in the rear cockpit of an airplane and made judgments of the amount and direction of turning and tilting, in addition to estimating the magnitude of the accelerative forces. Six angles of bank were used: 10, 18, 30, 40, 50, and 60 degrees, and the angular accelerations over the different angles of bank varied, respectively, from 0.10 degree/sec/sec to 0.80 degree/sec/sec. The results showed that the perceived lateral tilt was grossly in error, ranging from 4.1 degrees for the 10-degree angle of bank to 11.9 degrees for the 60-degree bank. Also, the duration of the feelings of movement was on the average only about one-third the physical duration, for example, a turn lasting 60.3 sec was reported as lasting 20.9 sec.

The absolute threshold for the perception of turning is approximately a 15-degree bank, which is characterized by an acceleratory force of about 0.15 degree/sec/sec. Changes of direction and position are often not detected, especially for small angles, but may be unreported even for a banking angle as large as 60 degrees. For both turning and tilting there is a time lag of at least 5 sec in reporting the perceived change in conditions. The only condition in the present study accurately judged by the three trained observers was the magnitude of the g force. As the actual g force increased from 1.02 g (at 10-degree bank) to 2.00 g (at 60-degree bank), the mean reported g increased, respectively, from 1.00 to 1.95. The 50 percent threshold for the perception of acceleration was at a 24-degree angle of bank with an acceleration of approximately 1.10 g. Unfortunately, for practical purposes in flying, the ability to make accurate judgments of the magnitude of g forces is not particularly significant.

Threshold of Rotation.   The thresholds of human subjects for activities involving either or both the otolith organs and semicircular canals vary with the designated response indicator and the specific experimental method. The detection of bodily motion is a commonly used indicant, but the appearance of detectable *nystagmus* (oscillating movement of the eyeballs) during and after rotation, and the *oculogyral illusion* (apparent motion of a fixed, dim light) have also been employed in the study of proprioception. The *threshold of rotation* as measured by compensatory eye movements seems to be lower than that measured by perceived bodily motion for blindfolded subjects. Of the various response indicators, the oculogyral illusion appears to be the most sensitive, with a threshold value of approximately 0.12 degree/sec/sec for both positive and negative acceleration

(Graybiel, Kerr, and Bartley, 1948). There are many cues that combine to indicate the position and movement of our body and its parts in three-dimensional space; in addition to the interaction of cues from the proprioceptive systems, those from the eye and eye muscles are probably the most important.

The Cutaneous System for Pain

Distribution of Pain Receptors

As pointed out in Chapter 4, pain may be elicited by a number of different stimulus classes: mechanical, thermal, electrical, and chemical. Exploration of the surface of the body by mapping techniques shows that the receptors for painful stimuli, like those for pressure, have a punctiform distribution when the stimulation is weak. However, unlike the pressure receptors, the receptors for painful stimuli tend to decrease in density in passing from the base of a body limb to its extremity. The density of "pain spots" is approximately 224/sq cm at the bend of the elbow, 203/sq cm on the volar side of the forearm, 188/sq cm on the back of the hand, 95/sq cm on the radial surface of the middle finger, and 60/sq cm on the ball of the thumb (Strughold, 1924). A greater density is found at the back of the knee (232 "spots"/sq cm) and a smaller density on the tip of the nose (44 "spots"/sq cm).

Some parts of the body, such as the cornea of the eye and the tympanic membrane of the ear, are extremely sensitive to painful stimulation. Other parts, such as the mucous lining of the cheeks and the rear part of the tongue, are relatively insensitive to pain. The four classes of stimuli capable of activating cutaneous receptors do not evoke pain reactions when applied to the gallbladder, the alimentary canal, or to most other deep structures of the body. When one of the major body cavities has been opened under local anesthesia, surgical operations may be performed without eliciting pain even though excisions, crushing, or cauterization may be involved (Lewis, 1942). Nevertheless, overdistension or spasm of the hollow viscera may induce pain, as does traction on certain blood vessels. Also, striking, puncturing, or severely squeezing the periosteum, deep fascia, and the gonadal coverings produces pain. Vascular pain can be produced by puncturing the arteries or by injecting intra-arterially a small volume of a hypertonic electrolyte, such as barium chloride or sodium iodide (Lim, 1960). Unlike cutaneous pain which is acute and usually of short duration, vascular pain is diffuse and tends to persist.

Mechanical Stimulation

The classical technique for establishing the threshold for pain was to use *mechanical pressure* applied by means of an *algesiometer*, that is, an instrument with a needle-sharp tip which was pressed against the skin according to a calibrated series of weights. Table 8-5 presents some of the stimulus thresholds for pain obtained for mechanical pressure. It may be seen that the extremities of the limbs are relatively insensitive to pain from mechanical pressure, while the cornea is extremely sensitive.

Table 8-5 Absolute Thresholds for Pain by Mechanical Pressure

Bodily Region	Absolute Threshold (gm/sq mm)
Cornea	0.2
Conjunctiva	2
Abdomen	15
Front of forearm	20
Back of forearm	30
Calf of leg	30
Back of hand	100
Sole	200
Fingertip	300

Source: R. S. Woodworth, *Experimental Psychology*. New York: Holt, Rinehart and Winston, Inc., 1938.

Thermal Stimulation

The determination of the pain threshold for an intense *thermal* stimulus has been made by Hardy, Wolff, and Goodell (1940). The basic technique involves passing radiant heat from a 1000-W lamp through a condensing lens and controlling the exposure of the beam on the forehead of the subject by means of a pair of shutters. Stimulus duration is automatically fixed at 3 sec by the primary shutter, while the secondary shutter is operated manually just before the stimulus is presented. The intensity of the heat is regulated by a rheostat. With this technique, the mean pain threshold for the 3-sec exposure was found to be 0.206 gm cal/sec/sq cm (206 mcal) for a group of 150 normal observers. Inter- and intra-observer differences in pain thresholds show little variability.

The radiant heat technique was also used to determine the differential threshold for pain (Hardy, Wolff, and Goodell, 1947). From the absolute threshold (220 mcal for these observers) to 320 mcal, the Weber ratio ($\Delta I/I$) was found to be essentially constant at 0.03; above 320 mcal, there is an increase in the ratio. Over the range of stimulus values from 220 to 480 mcal, there were 21 *jnd* steps; thus, once the pain threshold has been obtained, the upper limit of pain tolerance will be reached when the stimulus intensity is approximately doubled. Stated in different terms, the thermal pain threshold on the forehead is 45.7°C, compared with a threshold of 44°C for human lips and 45°C on the cheek (Hardy, Wolff, and Goodell, 1952).

Some of us may have noted that many individuals drink hot liquids with considerable pleasure even though the temperatures are near the boiling point of water. This raises the question of whether the mouth is less sensitive to thermal pain than the lips, or the skin of the face, or of other parts of the body. Margarida,

Hardy, and Hammel (1962) studied this problem by individually fitting thin-walled aluminum thermodes to the roof of the mouth of four observers and rapidly alternating the circulation of hot water and water at 37°C. Each observer was exposed to 288 stimuli in six experimental sessions, with the hot water between 40°C and 49°C.

The results of the study are presented in Figure 8-19, in which the absolute

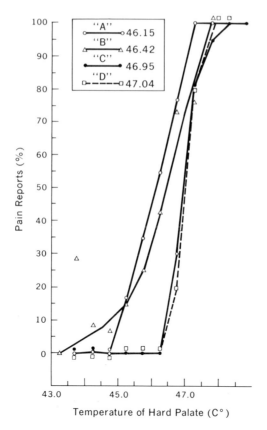

Figure 8–19. Percent reports of pain as a function of the temperature of the hard palate for four observers. (From Margarida et al., J. Appl. Physiol., 1962.)

threshold for thermal pain is taken as the temperature of the hard palate at which pain was reported 50 percent of the time. The threshold values for each of the four observers are shown in the box inset of Figure 8-19. The mean value for these observers is 46.6°C and does not differ significantly from the threshold value on the forehead. Why, then, is there a lack of pain when hot liquids are ingested? Further tests revealed that hot tea at 84°C could be sipped without pain if the observer first sipped air that effectively lowered the temperature of the palatal surface to about 23°C before the liquid came into contact with it. The hot liquid then raised the temperature of the palatal surface, but the momentary rise in temperature was insufficient to excite the thermal receptors, estimated to lie about 0.25 mm below the surface of the hard palate. Thus, "the sipping of air with small amounts of hot liquid maintains the tissue temperatures within tolerable limits" (p. 338).

Electrical Stimulation

In contrast with the various studies on thermal pain, Pattle and Weddell (1948) investigated the arousal of pain by the direct *electrical* stimulation of a peripheral nerve—the exposed digital nerve of Weddell's index finger. A pair of silver-silver chloride electrodes were clipped onto the nerve, and the skin was sutured in such a manner that the nerve and electrode were insulated by a sheet of rubber from the surrounding tissue. A steady DC (direct current) potential was then carefully applied to the nerve through a 6000-ohm resistor connected in series with the nerve. A threshold response was obtained at 7.5 volts, with the pain resembling that of a "wasp sting." The locus of the pain, however, was not at the exposed nerve but in the pad of the index finger where the nerve endings were located. This was so despite the fact that mechanical stimulation of the pad of the finger failed to produce a response. When separate shocks from a condenser were applied to the exposed nerve through a series resistor of 6000 ohms, the "wasp sting" response occurred at a value of 0.1 microfarad (μf), with a latency of about 1.27 sec. The same quality of pain was produced by condenser discharges up to 6.0 μf, but at 7.0 μf the discharge produced a marked change in the pain. At 7.0 μf the pain was severe, aching, and long-lasting; however, the latency of response remained the same. It appears, therefore, that between 6.0 and 7.0 μf a modified or different sensory process for pain is activated such that the experiential correlates are considerably different from those at lower values of the stimulus.

The Cutaneous Systems for Thermal Energy

Stimulation of the Receptor Systems

It is generally held that temperature sensitivity involves not one, but two systems: one for warmth and one for cold. This conclusion is based upon several sources of experimental evidence: (a) observers can reliably report subjective differences between warmth and cold; (b) temperature sensitivity is distributed in a punctiform manner, with some spots sensitive to warmth but not to cold; (c) the cutaneous tissue contains some receptors that discharge more rapidly as the temperature increases, while other receptors respond more rapidly as the temperature decreases; and (d) there is a difference in the latency of cold and warmth sensations that is correlated with the depth of specific receptors in the skin. However, while it may be tentatively concluded that there are two systems of temperature sensitivity, there are *not* two sets of stimuli which initiate thermal responses.

The adequate stimulus for both warmth and cold is the positive or negative transfer of physical energy in the form of heat. When the surface of the body absorbs heat from the surrounding air or by direct contact with objects of higher temperature in the environment, there is a positive transfer of heat; when the body loses heat to objects in the environment or to the surrounding air, there is a negative transfer. In both of these situations, it is the temperature of the skin at the depth of the thermal receptors, not the temperature of the object or air, that determines the characteristics of the thermal response. Objects having a temperature approximately equal to that of the skin do not feel as either warm or cold and are said to be at *physiological* (or psychological) *zero*. Physiological zero is the temperature of the skin at which a gaseous, liquid, or solid stimulus is judged as being thermally indifferent, neither warm nor cold. It differs for the various parts of the body and may cover a range of temperatures as large as 1°C. For the fingers at their normal temperature of 32°C, the range of indifference is approximately plus and minus 0.15°C. Stimuli above physiological zero feel warm and those below feel cold. Physiological zero also depends upon several other factors, including the temperature of the surrounding air, the state of thermal adaptation, and the health of the individual.

Thermal Thresholds

The determination of the *absolute* threshold for warmth and cold has been difficult and has not produced general agreement. Part of the problem centers around experimental methodology, with different procedures yielding different results; part lies in the changes in sensitivity of the receptors as a result of thermal adaptation. Nevertheless, some data are available. By using the radiant heat technique, Hardy and Oppel (1937a) found that the minimum thermal energy required to elicit a response of warmth was 0.00015 gm cal/sq cm/sec acting for three seconds on an exposed skin area of 200 sq cm. Compared with the threshold for pain (0.218 gm cal), the threshold for warmth is only about one-thousandth as large as that for pain. Stated differently, the threshold stimulus for warmth receptors is a rise in temperature of 0.001°C per sec for a continuous period of three seconds. For exposures of the entire body, warmth is experienced at an average skin temperature of 34°–35°C, regardless of the rate of temperature change (from 0.05° to 0.2°C per minute); an increase of less than 0.2°C per minute is sufficient to produce feelings of warmth.

For cold receptors, the threshold stimulus is a fall in temperature at the rate of 0.004°C per sec, continuing for three seconds. The threshold stimulus for cold decreases with an increase in the area of the exposed surface. By comparing the thresholds for warmth and cold, it may be seen that the sensitivity of the warmth receptors is four times as great as that for cold. If both types of receptors are stimulated with temperatures of greater magnitude, the warmth sense will produce pain at approximately 50°C, while the cold sense will produce pain at approximately 18°C. Considerable damage occurs to the tissues as the temperatures climb toward 70°C or fall below −10°C; beyond these limits, the receptors for warmth and cold probably fail to respond (Hardy and Oppel, 1937b).

The *differential* threshold for temperature depends upon the temperature at which the measurements are made and upon the part of the body being tested. The sensitivity of the face, for example, is much greater than that of the forearm or hand. Herget, Granath, and Hardy (1941) studied the discrimination of differences in heat intensity on the forehead for various temperatures above the normal temperature of the skin. A standard stimulus of a certain intensity was presented for two seconds and then a comparison stimulus was presented on an adjacent area of the forehead. There were successive presentations of the standard stimulus and the comparison stimulus; the comparison stimulus was increased in intensity until the observer could just distinguish between the two.

The results of the study are presented in Figure 8-20, which shows the size of the increment in heat intensity (ΔI) that is just detectable for a given value of the

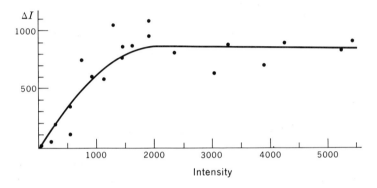

Figure 8-20.   Just noticeable increments in heat intensity (ΔI) as a function of the intensity of the stimulus (I) on the forehead. One "unit" is 10^{-5} gm-calorie/sq cm/sec. (From Herget *et al., Amer. J. Physiol.,* 1941.)

standard intensity of the stimulus (I). The best discrimination (smallest value of ΔI) is obtained when the standard intensity is close to the normal temperature of the skin; after a 2-sec exposure, a change in skin temperature of $0.002°C$ per sec can be detected. For standard stimuli approximately $0.2°C$ above the temperature of the skin, ΔI remains essentially constant at a value of $0.06°C$. This value holds even for stimuli removed by plus or minus $1.0°C$ from the temperature of the skin.

A Theoretical Note

Békésy (1962) has recently proposed that the skin, the basilar membrane of the ear, and the retina of the eye are all structures that exhibit similar phenomena due to lateral inhibition among nerve endings. These sense organs are alike in that they involve large surface areas with highly developed lateral interconnections that extend into neighboring end organs.

It is hypothesized that these lateral interconnections are responsible for lateral inhibition and other related phenomena. For example, when a "heat bulb" is applied above the skin, there is a distribution of heat along the surface that can be detected by the observer; then, if two bulbs are applied, the intensity of the heat increases and spreads out laterally, but when the separation between the bulbs reaches a certain size, the intensity of heat drops considerably. This leads to the conclusion that every sharply localized stimulus produces an excitation that is surrounded by a less sensitive inhibitory area. For small separations, the excitatory areas overlap and increase the intensity of the heat; when the critical separation is reached, the excitation falls in the inhibited area of the neighboring stimulus and the resulting intensity of heat is smaller than that of either stimulus acting alone. Beyond this separation, the two stimuli are independent. Although there are similarities in the phenomena exhibited by the skin, the basilar membrane, and the retina, there are, nevertheless, differences in the magnitudes of the effects that are produced.

The Gustatory and Olfactory Systems

The Gustatory System

Qualities of Taste.   The human observer normally can identify four distinct taste qualities: sweet, salt, bitter, and sour. All complex gustatory responses are a fusion of these four primary qualities augmented by various somatosensory and olfactory components. It is further established that the typical stimulus for sweet is common table sugar or sucrose ($C_{12}H_{22}O_{11}$); for salt, sodium chloride (NaCl), with both the positive (Na^+) and negative (Cl^-) ions taking part in inducing the salty taste; for bitter, quinine or caffeine, although many other substances may taste bitter under certain circumstances; and for sour, an acid such as hydrochloric acid (HCl) with a hydronium ion, but not all such acids are sour. The ability of observers to discriminate among these various types of stimuli provides some evidence in support of the notion that there are four basic qualities of taste.

Additional evidence for this generalization is found in the spatial distribution of the taste qualities over the surface of the tongue. Applications of pure solutions, such as those indicated in the preceding paragraph, reveal differences in the sensitivity of the tongue. The tip is particularly sensitive to stimuli for sweet and salt; the lateral edges are most sensitive to sour or acid, but also respond to salt; and the base of the tongue is most sensitive to bitter stimuli. The existence of these findings, when considered with the fact that some narcotizing drugs (for example, cocaine) selectively abolish the qualities of taste, argues in favor of four specific taste receptors. The experimental evidence, however, does not support this hypothesis.

Action potentials recorded from single afferent fibers reveal that most receptors respond to more than one type of taste stimulus. For example, a receptor that responds to salt (NaCl or KCl) may also respond to acid (HCl). This lack of specificity in the stimuli for taste receptors has led to several theories that attempt to specify the manner in which the sensory information for taste discrimination is encoded. Pfaffmann (1959) believes that the frequency pattern of excitation of a large number of receptors contains the discriminatory cues for taste; thus, taste does not depend merely upon the all-or-none response of particular fibers. Another hypothesis has been advanced by Adrian (1946); he has suggested that there is a topographical organization of the receptive area for taste within the cortex. Whatever the neural code may be for taste, it seems clear that the physiological data are altered by adaptation. The taste of water and other substances can be affected by sensory adaptation and solutions of NaCl can take on any one of the four primary tastes: salt, sour, bitter, or sweet (Pfaffmann, 1965).

Gustatory Thresholds.   The differential distribution of sensitivity on the surface of the tongue creates a problem for the determination of the absolute threshold for taste of a given substance; the threshold will vary from region to region. Quinine, for instance, has a threshold on the left edge of the tongue four times greater than that at the base of the tongue. This variability, which is also present when other pure stimuli are used, may account for the different values of threshold that are cited in the literature for the same substance. Other factors also need to be considered. Of these, temperature is one of the most important, since not all substances are affected in the same way by changes in temperature. The threshold for salt increases linearly with an increase in the temperature of the testing solution, but the threshold for HCl (a sour stimulus) is unaffected over a wide range of temperatures.

The amount of solution and the method of introducing the solution may lead to further variability in the absolute thresholds for taste even with the same observers; individual thresholds may vary by a factor of 50 to 1 for the same substance depending upon whether the drop method or sipping method is used. McBurney and Pfaffmann (1963) have also shown that the salt threshold in man is a function of the prevailing concentration of sodium in the saliva. Inasmuch as these and other variables are so crucial in determining the absolute gustatory threshold, data will be presented here only to indicate the relative magnitudes for the four basic substances of taste.

Table 8-6 presents the *absolute* thresholds for five representative taste stimuli. If saccharine is considered a sweet stimulus, the four basic qualities may be or-

Table 8-6   Absolute Thresholds for Taste

Substance	Percent Concentration (Approx.)	Molar Concentration
Sucrose	7×10^{-1}	2×10^{-2}
Sodium chloride	2×10^{-1}	3.5×10^{-2}
Hydrochloric acid	7×10^{-3}	2×10^{-3}
Saccharine (crystallose)	5×10^{-4}	2×10^{-5}
Quinine sulfate	3×10^{-5}	4×10^{-7}

Source: C. Pfaffmann, in S. S. Stevens (Ed.), *Handbook of Experimental Psychology.* New York: John Wiley & Sons, Inc., 1951.

dered from lowest to highest sensitivity in the following order: salt, sour, sweet, and bitter. This relationship holds whether the threshold is specified in percent concentration (number of grams of solute in 100 grams of solvent, usually 100 cc of water, as in this case) or in molar concentration (number of grams of solute divided by its molecular weight per liter of total solution).

The determination of the *differential* threshold for taste, like the absolute threshold, is affected by a number of experimental variables; perhaps the most important is the particular gustatory quality under study. In addition, the value of ΔI will be related directly to the concentration of the standard taste solution. Discrimination is generally poor at low molar concentrations. The particular testing method, the temperature of the solution, and the state of gustatory adaptation also have their effect on the differential threshold. In one study (Holway and Hurvich, 1937), the Weber ratio for various concentrations of salt (NaCl) up to 4 moles was found to vary from 0.24 to 1.25; the experimental procedure involved placing a single drop of the test solution on the outstretched tongue of the observer.

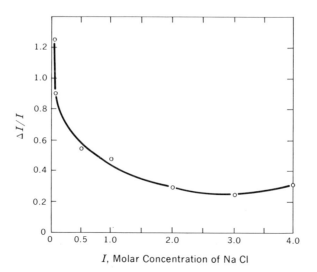

Figure 8-21. Differential sensitivity ($\Delta I/I$) for salt as a function of the molar concentration of the standard solution (I). (From Holway and Hurvich, *Amer. J. Psychol.*, 1937.)

The complete function for differential sensitivity to salt is given in Figure 8-21. The Weber ratio is large at low molar concentrations and becomes progressively smaller up to a concentration of approximately 3.0 moles; beyond this point, absolute sensitivity decreases (the Weber ratio becomes larger) and the tastes are extremely salty.

A Theoretical Note. Although we will not consider the theory of signal detection until Chapter 11, it may be well to indicate at this point that the applicability of the simple model of threshold underlying these studies on taste has recently been challenged. The classical studies assumed that all the responses of the observer were dependent only upon sensory events related to the values of the stimulus. Whenever the judgments of the observer failed to reflect the changes in the stimulus, it was asserted that the observer was inadequately trained or that he was not following instructions for one reason or another. In such cases, a "correction for guessing" was often introduced to compensate for these nonsensory effects. The work of Linker, Moore, and Galanter (1964) shows that the responses of the observers "bear orderly, but not necessarily direct, relations to the stimulating conditions" and that the simple model of threshold "is . . . inappropriate in the taste mode" (p. 66).

Nevertheless, the data presented in this section on taste fall within the general framework of classical psychophysical theory. As such, the data are representative of those studies on taste that presume the existence of a sensory threshold and that are intended to show the relation of the observer's sensitivity to changes in the values of a particular class of stimuli.

The Olfactory System

Characteristics of Odorous Stimuli.   The olfactory system is activated when an odorous stimulus comes into contact with the olfactory mucosa situated in the upper region of each nostril. It is commonly held that odor depends upon miniscule particles or molecules that are volatilized from solids or liquids and are carried into the nostrils by currents of air produced by normal respiration or by sniffing. *Volatility,* then, is a necessary condition for olfaction. If this were the only prerequisite, the relative efficiency of various substances to produce odors would be indicated directly in physical terms by *vapor pressure*—a measure of the relative ease with which a particular substance releases its molecules into the surrounding environment. While in general the more odorous substances or liquids do have high vapor pressures, there are some odorants, for example, musk, that are extremely powerful but relatively involatile. In contrast with this, distilled water is highly volatile, but odorless. This indicates that volatility is not a sufficient condition for eliciting odors.

In addition to having a high vapor pressure, an odorous substance must be *soluble.* The odorous particles or molecules must be soluble in water to be trapped by the mucous lining of the nostrils and must also be lipoid soluble in order to be able to enter the cells containing the olfactory nerve endings. The solubility requirement, however, has not as yet been definitely established, although it does appear to be a necessary condition. Compounds, like butanol (C_4H_9OH), which are soluble in both water and fat, have potent odors (like rancid butter, in this instance). Other compounds, like methyl alcohol (CH_3OH) and ethyl alcohol (C_2H_5OH), are readily soluble in water but not in fatty materials and give only weak odors, or none at all. There are, of course, exceptions to this generalization; acetone, for example, has a strong odor but low fat solubility. The relationship of water solubility, lipoid solubility, and perhaps the protein solubility of certain substances to the generation of odors needs to be explored in further research.

It has also been suggested that the *Raman shift* may be involved as a physical property of odorous substances. Many liquids possess the unique ability to alter an incident monochromatic light in such a way that the transmitted light contains waves that are both longer and shorter than the monochromatic beam. It is this difference in the lengths (or frequencies) of the incident and transmitted waves that is called the Raman shift. Substances producing shifts between 140 mμ and 350 mμ are believed to be odorous; some substances having similar odors have been found to have similar Raman shifts. Another possibility in the physical basis for odor lies in the absorption characteristics of odorous substances—some absorb waves from the infrared portion of the electromagnetic spectrum, while others absorb primarily from the ultraviolet portion. In summary, the specific physical characteristics of substances that are necessary and sufficient for the production of odors have yet to be determined, although some possible factors have been identified; these include *volatility, solubility,* and *electromagnetic reactions* to light.

Similar uncertainties are present in attempting to predict the odor of a substance from its chemical composition. Some compounds smell alike even though their structures are widely different; others smell differently, but possess identical molecular components that may vary only in their atomic arrangements (*stereoisomers*). Most odorous stimuli are organic rather than inorganic substances. Except for arsenic, which is odorous when heated to the point of vaporization, the inorganic elements that are found in a natural, free state are not odorous, unless they are combined to form a compound; the odorous elements, normally found in combined form, include phosphorous (P_4), oxygen (as ozone, O_3); and the halogen group: chlorine (Cl_2), bromine (Br_2), iodine (I_2), and fluorine (F_2). The supposition is that since these seven elements occur in groups 5, 6, and 7 of the periodic table, high valency is a factor in the production of odors. Also, those inorganic compounds that are odorous are known to be composed primarily of nonmetallic elements. However, the key to the factors that produce odors may lie in the organic compounds; with some exceptions, these always contain both carbon and hydrogen atoms, and are likely to include oxygen. There is little question that the physical origin of odors is in the chemical structure of substances, but whether valency, position in the electrochemical series, common elements, or other unknown factors, provide the basis for odors remains to be established.

Techniques of Olfactory Measurement.   The most common technique for measuring the absolute threshold for smell involves the use of an *olfactometer*. In the Zwaardemaker model, there is a single glass tube which is open at both ends. One end is inserted in the observer's nostril; the other end slips into a larger tube made of rubber or plastic. The inside of this larger tube is impregnated with an odorous material; as the observer inhales, air is drawn over the material, passes through the glass tube, and enters the nostril. A scale is etched on the inner glass tube in such a way that the length of the outer odor-bearing tube, through which the incoming air passes, can be read directly. The odor-bearing tube in the standard model has a total length of 10 cm and a volume of 50 cc; the standard "smell unit" is called the *olfactie* and is defined as the length (in cm) of the odor-bearing tube which is exposed at the absolute threshold for a given observer. For example, one olfactie of India rubber equals 0.7 cm. To minimize the difficulty in controlling the amount of odorous stimulation received by the observer in this method, some models of the olfactometer have been equipped with a continuous flow pump for moving a given volume of air at a certain rate for a given period of time.

The *blast-injection method* is another technique for measuring the olfactory threshold (Elsberg and Levy, 1935). In this method a small amount of odorous liquid is placed in a bottle containing a two-holed stopper. A short outlet tube passes through one hole in the stopper and terminates in a Y-shaped nosepiece which is inserted into the observer's nostrils; the inlet tube passes through the other hole and extends into the odorous liquid. Air may be forced into the bottle by means of a hypodermic syringe attached to the inlet tube; this action increases the pressure inside the bottle so that whenever a pinch clamp located on the outlet tube is opened, a blast of odorous vapor is delivered to the nostrils. The threshold is determined by varying the amount of air pressure and is specified in cubic centimeters as read from the scale of the syringe, that is, the volume of odorous vapor injected.

One of the major problems with this method is that the pressure variations within the bottle not only blast differing amounts of vapor into the observer's nostrils, but appear to affect the threshold as an uncontrolled variable. Consequently, threshold determinations of odor intensity are confounded with pressure variations, unless the method is modified to hold pressure constant during the stimulus blast. Jones (1954) has introduced a more elaborate version of the Elsberg olfactometer that overcomes this problem and permits the control of the pressure, volume, temperature, humidity, and duration of the stimulus blast. Such fine control of the stimulus variables is obtained with this device that it is possible to specify the stimulus concentration in molecular terms. Ough and Stone (1961) have also developed an olfactometer that delivers calculated amounts of an odorant to individual observers in a rapid and reproducible manner.

The use of the *olfactorium* in measuring olfactory sensitivity has already been described in Chapter 2. The olfactorium provides a completely controlled environment for studies in olfaction. The observer eliminates body odors by bathing and then, after donning a plastic envelope, enters the inner chamber of the olfactorium. Special devices permit the introduction of the odorous vapor that can be precisely controlled with respect to composition, pressure, temperature, and humidity.

Olfactory Thresholds. The odor thresholds for a number of different substances are presented in Table 8–7. Since the thresholds were obtained by several different techniques, the results are not directly comparable but the relative order of magnitude may be noted. The thresholds for the substances listed in Table 8–7 appear to vary by a factor of more than 60 million to one, from carbon tetrachloride to trinitro-tertiary-butyl xylene. Although some of the threshold values seem to be extremely small, the actual number of molecules at the threshold concentration of a given substance may be extremely large; a 20-cc "sniff" of a test solution might contain 10 trillion or more molecules, as in the case of mercaptan. It has been estimated that in terms of the concentration of molecules, the sense of smells is 10,000 times as sensitive as the sense of taste (Moncrieff, 1946).

Table 8-7   Absolute Thresholds for Some Odorous Substances

Substance	Odor	Threshold (Milligrams/liter of air)
Carbon tetrachloride	sweet	4.533
Methyl salicylate	wintergreen	0.100
Amyl acetate	banana oil	0.039
N-butyric acid	perspiration	0.009
Benzene	kerosiney	0.0088
Safrol	sassafras	0.0050
Ethyl acetate	fruity	0.0036
Pyridine	burned	0.00074
Hydrogen sulfide	rotten eggs	0.00018
N-butyl sulfide	foul, sulfurous	0.00009
Coumarin	new-mown hay	0.00002
Citral	lemony	0.000003
Ethyl mercaptan	decayed cabbage	0.00000066
Trinitro-tertiary-butyl xylene	musk	0.000000075

Source: M. A. Wenger, F. N. Jones, and M. H. Jones. *Physiological Psychology.* New York: Holt, Rinehart and Winston, Inc., 1956.

In a recent calculation similar to that followed in the analysis of visual threshold data, it was determined that the threshold of excitation for a single human olfactory cell is, at most, 8 molecules for secondary butyl mercaptan and certain other odorous substances. By analyzing the psychometric functions (frequency-of-smelling curves), it was further determined that at least 40 molecules are necessary to produce an olfactory response; this means that for appropriate substances, an odor will be detected if only 5 or 6 olfactory cells are excited (DeVries and Stuiver, 1961).

The *differential* threshold for odors has not been studied to any great extent. The available data indicate, however, that when the absolute threshold is low, the differential threshold is high. As in the case of gustation, the differential threshold decreases as the stimulus intensity increases; over the range from 10 to 40 olfacties for India rubber, $\Delta I/I$ decreases from 1.0 to approximately 0.2 (Zigler and Holway, 1935).

A Note on the Intensity of Odors.   Moncrieff (1957) believes there are three properties that are closely associated with the intensities of odors: (1) a low threshold concentration of the odorant, (2) a high vapor pressure, and (3) the ability of the odorant to mask the odors of other substances. There are, however, exceptions to this generalization. The mercaptans and pyridines have low values of threshold and intense odors, but other substances such as acetone have intense odors, despite their relatively high threshold values. The musks commonly added to perfumes, on the other hand, have extremely low threshold values but their odors are not intense, although they are "persistent and pervasive."

Some of the intense odorants such as ether, carbon disulphide, acetone, and chloroform have very high vapor pressures. At 20°C, these pressures range from 150 to 450 mm of mercury. However, other substances such as geranyl acetate and citral also have intense odors, but their vapor pressures are about 10,000 times lower. While high volatility is frequently associated with the intensity of odor, there is no evidence which indicates that this is the only factor upon which odor intensity depends.

Some substances have very intense odors and are capable of masking or obliterating the odors of other substances. Amyl butyrate, for example, is sometimes used to hide the unpleasant odors of certain industrial products. Most masking agents that have intense odors also have low concentrations at threshold, with variable volatilities. It appears, therefore, that the intensity of odors is a function of threshold concentration, volatility, and masking ability, but the exact functional relationship has not been determined.

Chapter 9

ADAPTATION
AND OTHER SENSORY
PHENOMENA

Orientation

For many psychological phenomena, time is a critical variable. For example, in order for a given stimulus to elicit a behavioral response, it must be presented for a minimal period of time; this period will, of course, vary from modality to modality. In vision the exposure time varies inversely with intensity, so that within threshold limits it is possible to compensate for reductions in intensity by increasing the duration of the stimulus (*Bloch's law*). In gustation, the chemical stimuli must act for 2 or 3 sec in order to produce a response; with a drop of solution at threshold intensity on the tongue, the latency of response is slowest for bitter, sour and salt are somewhat faster, and sweet is in between (Piéron, 1914). Other modalities show a similar requirement of a minimal time for excitation.

The time factor, however, extends beyond the relatively simple process of sensory excitation. In hearing, the differential threshold for intensity becomes considerably smaller as the duration of the stimulus increases from 1 to 10 sec; in vision, there is a similar influence of stimulus duration on the differential threshold, with the lowest intensive threshold being reached at approximately 0.6 sec for a stimulus of a given areal size.

In this chapter we will consider some of the sensory effects in which the temporal duration of the stimulus is a significant factor. What happens to a particular sensory magnitude as the duration of the stimulus is increased? Is there a "build-up" in sensory effect? If so, does this "buildup" continue indefinitely or is there a maximal period of stimulus effectiveness? As we will learn in Chapter 9, there is such a maximal period which varies according to the sensory system activated.

Then what happens? If stimulation is continued, is there a diminution of this response? Does *adaptation* occur? Again the answer is affirmative; continued application of a stimulus leads to a decrement in its effectiveness in generating a sensory excitation, but the process of adaptation varies widely in form from one sensory mechanism to another. What happens when the stimulation is terminated? Does the excitation stop abruptly or does it continue to persist for a short period of time? If it does persist, is the related verbal report the same as that given prior to the termination of the stimulus, or does it differ in some respect?

These are the kinds of questions for which we will be seeking answers in Chapter 9; accordingly, we will consider the process of *sensory adaptation* in detail. In addition, we will consider the process of *sensory recovery*. The lawfulness of both processes will be described and supporting experimental evidence will be presented. Finally, some attention will be given to sensory afterimages. As necessary, selected theoretical formulations on the various sensory systems will be included throughout the chapter to provide for a more complete understanding of these phenomena.

Stimulus Effectiveness as a Function of Time

Vision

In Chapter 8 it was shown that in order for a behavioral response to be elicited by a given stimulus, the stimulus had to be of sufficient magnitude to activate the particular system under study. The values of the absolute threshold were then given for different characteristics of the stimulus for each of the human senses. In each instance, it was understood that the absolute threshold was determined under conditions in which the duration of the stimulus was held constant at some fixed value. This value, as predetermined by the experimenter, is sufficiently long so that the stimulus elicits or does not elicit a response depending upon its magnitude, not its duration. (This assumes, of course, that the investigator is not attempting to establish a temporal threshold of some kind.)

The problem of reciprocity between time and intensity is an important one in vision, and attempts are currently being made to determine the generality of this reciprocal relationship. In photography, it is well known that if the light is dim, the exposure time must be lengthened. This is known as the *Bunsen-Roscoe law* which states that $It = C$, where I is the intensity of the light, t is the duration of the light, and C is some constant effect. This law underlies all photochemical processes and it has been proposed to hold for the visual process, since this process is initiated by photochemical reactions within the rods and cones.

The reciprocity relation is derived from the fact that the retina displays temporal summation of luminous energy within critical limits. The longer the duration of a visual stimulus, the greater will be the amount of energy entering the eye; below a critical duration, there is believed to be a complete integration of this energy. The distribution of the energy within the interval is not important. It is the *quantity* of luminous energy (It) that determines its effectiveness.

If the absolute threshold is taken as the constant effect, its value will be found not to depend upon the energy distribution in time up to 0.01 sec, provided the size of the test field is no larger than one degree. Under these conditions, if the duration of the test stimulus (target) is doubled, then the threshold intensity is correspondingly halved. Over a short range of durations, the increased time during which the stimulus is acting serves to compensate for the decreased intensity (Bloch's law). Intuitively, Bloch's law cannot be considered to hold over an indefinite range of durations, since this would lead to the conclusion that a light of any intensity would be visible, provided it were exposed for a sufficiently long time. Problems of instrumentation and measurement have up to this time precluded precise findings for temporal durations less than one millisecond.

For extremely small areas of retinal stimulation, the Bunsen-Roscoe law has been found to hold up to approximately 0.1 sec (Graham and Margaria, 1935). It remains constant up to this value, but for stimulus exposures longer than this critical duration, there is a rise in the magnitude of It. This indicates that beyond the critical duration, the only determiner of the effectiveness of a stimulus of this size is its intensity.

The applicability of the Bunsen-Roscoe law has also been tested with regard to the differential threshold for intensity. In one study (Clark, 1958), ΔI values were obtained for a circular target of about 18 min of arc against a background illuminance of about 10 ft-lamberts. The expected inverse relationship between target duration and the detection threshold was obtained up to approximately 0.02 sec. From 0.02 to 0.08 sec, duration continued to offset intensity but to a smaller and smaller extent; from 0.08 to approximately 0.17 sec, increased duration had no effect on the differential threshold. The course of the entire function is shown in Figure 9-1. Between approximately -3.0 log sec ($T = 0.001$ sec) and -1.0 log sec ($T = 0.1$ sec) there is a negative linear relationship between the detection threshold and target duration.

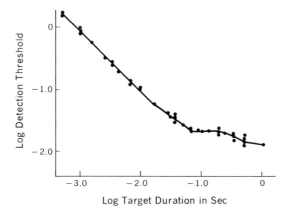

Figure 9-1. The visual detection threshold as a function of target duration. (From Dember, 1960; after Clark, 1958.)

In addition to the Bunsen-Roscoe law, other functional relations have been proposed for the dependency of the liminal quantity (It) on the duration of stimulation (t). In 1911, Blondel and Rey offered a linear law:

$$It = a + bt, \tag{9-1}$$

where It is the quantity of light at threshold, with I denoting the intensity and t the duration of stimulation; a and b are constants. Equation 9-1 indicates that the quantity of light at threshold consists of a certain fixed amount (a) to which is added a component (bt) that increases proportionately with time. Piéron (1920) presented a different law by pointing out that the quantity It is not strictly a linear function of time, but has a parabolic form near the beginning of the time scale. The function becomes linear only after a critical point on the time scale has been passed. *Piéron's law* is given as:

$$It = a \ t^n, \tag{9-2}$$

where I, t, and a have the same meaning as in Equation 9-1, and n is a fractional power of time with a different value for rod and cone vision.

The various types of relationships that have been proposed between the threshold quantity (It) and the duration (t) of the luminous excitation are shown in Figure 9-2. It may be seen that the functions for all laws converge on a single

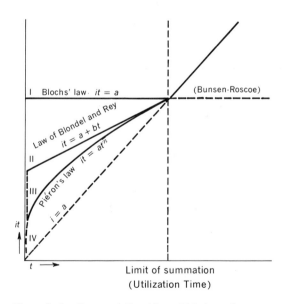

Figure 9–2. Some relationships which have been proposed between the threshold quantity (*It*) and the duration (*t*) of retinal stimulation. (From Piéron, *The sensations,* copyright © 1945. Paris: Editions Gallimard.)

point; this indicates that the temporal summation of excitation in the retina occurs only up to some finite value of *t*. Beyond this value, reciprocity of intensity and time cannot be expected to occur in any form. On the other end of the time continuum, the nature of the function is uncertain for durations below one millisecond. While the exact limits between which reciprocity may be expected to hold have not yet been determined, a gross approximation may be given as 10 to 100 msec. It should also be clear that the laws depicted in Figure 9-2 can not all be in accord with the facts of liminal action, nor need we expect that any one of the laws is necessarily correct in its present form. Additional research must be performed on this problem before a more definitive answer can be given.

An explanation of the reciprocity principle has been proposed by Boynton (1961). For threshold stimulation, the explanation lies in the phenomenon of neural summation. It is offered that (1) the neural elements of the visual system are capable of summating (integrating) the luminous energy up to some critical duration, and that (2) the summative effect does not appear to have a photochemical basis, as might be supposed.

There are several reasons offered for this position: (1) the speed of photochemical reaction within the receptors is so great that successive light flashes presented within the limits of Bloch's law would correspondingly transmit multiple impulses to the brain; (2) double flashes presented at two different retinal locations and separated in time produce complete summation even though different receptors are involved, thereby precluding a cumulative photochemical effect; and (3) at threshold, there is little likelihood that the minimal number of quanta required for a sensory response would be absorbed in the same receptor cell. While reciprocity at threshold seems to involve temporal neural summation, this explanation may not hold for intensive, temporal interactions above the visual threshold.

As in hearing, the longer the duration of a visible stimulus, the greater will be the magnitude of the resulting sensory response. For a stimulus of a given intensity, an increase in the time of exposure will increase the effectiveness of the stimulus. The sensory magnitude at first builds up very rapidly and then reaches a plateau. Various equations have been proposed to describe this functional relationship, but universal agreement on the precise form of the function is lacking. It does appear, however, that the magnitude of the sensory response is a negatively accelerated, increasing monotonic function of the exposure time of the stimulus. The function also differs for rod and cone vision; even within cone vision, there are differences in the function depending upon the wavelength of the particular stimulus.

Audition

Although it is necessary for a given stimulus to act upon a sensory system for a certain period of time before it can produce a stable response, there is some evidence that indicates that a stimulus of shorter duration is not completely ineffective. Such a stimulus is capable of producing a response, but the response varies as a function of the actual duration of stimulation. Ekdahl and Stevens (1937) have established this relationship for the pitch of a pure tone, as shown in Figure 9-3.

In Figure 9-3, the ordinate indicates the frequency of a tone lasting 1.5 sec which is judged equal in pitch to that of a 1000-cps tone, presented for the period

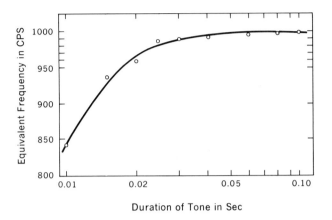

Figure 9-3. Pitch as a function of tonal duration. (From Stevens and Davis, *Hearing: its psychology and physiology,* 1938.)

of time indicated on the abscissa. For instance, a tone of 1000 cps presented for 0.015 sec sounds equal in pitch to a tone of 928 cycles presented for 1.5 sec. The function reveals that as the duration of the tonal stimulus is shortened, the apparent pitch of the tone is lowered. This relationship holds from 250 to 8000 cps. When the duration is decreased beyond approximately 10 msec, the signal sounds like a click with no definite pitch.

If the absolute time required for the establishment of a definite pitch is known for a given frequency, then by multiplying the duration by the frequency, it is possible to determine the minimal number of sound waves that are required for the establishment of pitch. Below 400 cps, tonality is clearly defined after seven or less waves are presented; at 1000 cps after 12 waves; and at 10,000 cps after 250 waves. (Bürck, Kotowski, and Lichte, 1935). The absolute time necessary for the establishment of "tone pitch" is smallest in the frequency region above 1000 cps, where it is approximately constant at 0.01 sec (Doughty and Garner, 1947).

As in the case of pitch, loudness also depends upon the duration of the acoustic stimulus. For very short tones, loudness is minimal; but as the duration increases, loudness likewise increases until it reaches a maximal value. From this it may be deduced that, within certain temporal limits, the threshold of audibility decreases as the duration of the auditory stimulus increases. This relationship at threshold is not so simple, however, that it can be expressed in the general form:

$$It = C, \tag{9-3}$$

where I is the intensity of the stimulus and t is its duration. This concept suggests that the auditory mechanism is capable of integrating the stimulus power over time. While this may be appropriate for certain frequencies and durations, it does not seem to hold beyond 100 msec. Accordingly, the hypothesis has been modified and expressed in the following form (Licklider, 1951):

$$(I - I_0) t = C, \tag{9-4}$$

in which I is stimulus intensity, t is time, and I_0 is a portion of the stimulus input that is diverted from the auditory excitation process and is not integrated. This is known as the *diverted input hypothesis*. It indicates that the acoustic stimulus impressed on the ear, minus a certain fixed portion of the power, multiplied by the duration of the stimulus, is a constant at threshold.

A more specific relation has recently been formulated between the threshold intensity of a tone and its duration (Miskolczy-Fodor, 1959). This relationship is shown in Figure 9-4 in which the data for 40 normal ears have been combined for

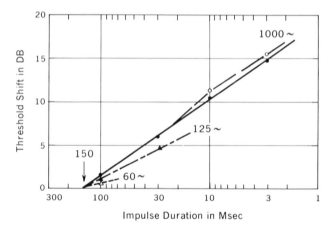

Figure 9-4.   Mean threshold change in decibels as a function of tonal-pulse duration. The solid line shows the data which have been averaged for three frequencies (250, 1000, and 4000 cps) and 40 normal-hearing ears. Separate curves are shown for the selected frequencies of 1,000, 125, and 60 cps. (From Miskolczy-Fodor, J. acoust. Soc. Amer., 1959.)

three frequencies (250, 1000, and 4000 cps). In this study threshold values were determined for tonal pulses presented monaurally at a repetition rate of 2/sec; the pulses for the reference threshold were 300 msec in duration. Threshold intensities were then determined as a function of different pulse durations, and the amount of change in threshold with respect to the 300-msec reference was computed for each pulse duration. Figure 9-4 shows the amount of threshold change in db re the 300-msec reference threshold for selected pulse durations. For each tenfold decrease in duration, there is a mean threshold increase of 8.92 db. This rate of change corresponds to the equation

$$C = n - a \log (T_0/T), \tag{9-5}$$

where C is the threshold constant, n is the threshold change in decibels, T_0 is the adjusting time of the auditory mechanism with an assigned value of 150 msec, a is the threshold change (8.92 db) for a tenfold decrease in pulse duration below 150 msec, and T is the actual pulse duration. Thus, by substituting the given numerical values where appropriate, Equation 9-5 may be rewritten as

$$C = n - 8.92 \log (150/T). \tag{9-6}$$

From this equation the amount of shift in the intensive threshold in decibels may be calculated for any pulse duration (T) between 3 and 300 msec.

Other Sensory Modalities

In gustation, the time required for a chemical stimulus to produce a taste sensation is longer than that for vision; also, the time varies according to the specific form of stimulation. Sweet stimuli require approximately 2 sec; salt, 3 sec, and bitter and acid, 3.5 sec. When the intensity of the stimulus is increased above the threshold, increasing the exposure time produces an increase in the magnitude of the sensory response. The maximal response for salt is reached in 4 to 5 sec; for bitter, in 8 to 10 sec; and for sweet, at some intermediate value. Limited data involving chemical stimuli in olfaction indicate that beyond a duration of 5 sec, time is probably no longer a significant factor in the reciprocity relationship at threshold.

The threshold phenomenon for thermal excitation produced by the radiant heat technique is similar to that for gustation, except that the limit of additivity is considerably longer, that is, up to 10 sec. Unlike gustation, however, in which the buildup time is approximately equal for different suprathreshold values of the stimulus, thermal responses for areal stimuli build up in time according to the intensity of the stimulus. For a stimulus approximately four times as intense as the threshold stimulus, the time required for the maximal buildup is nearly 30 sec, as contrasted with a 7- or 8-sec period for a stimulus twice that at threshold. Cold responses produced by a current of air striking the forehead involve reciprocity up to approximately 1.5 sec, while the curve of buildup has the same general form and values as that for gustation.

In each of these several modalities, the effects of uniform and continuous stimulation are quite similar with respect to threshold excitation. Reciprocity is present up to some given duration of the stimulus; a decrease in the duration can be offset by an increase in the intensity of the stimulus in order to produce a threshold response. When the stimulus is presented at an intensity greater than threshold, there is a rise in the magnitude of the sensory response as the stimulus is presented for longer periods of time, up to some critical value. Beyond the duration at which the buildup is maximal, the magnitude of the sensory response remains essentially constant. The specific form of the buildup function depends upon the particular receptor system activated and the specific characteristics of the stimulus. Several attempts have been made to express the form of these functions in mathematical terms, such as those indicated in Equations 9-1 through 9-6.

Adaptation and Recovery

The Generality of Adaptive Processes

In the preceding section, we considered the effects of time and intensity on a threshold response and on the magnitude of a sensory response for suprathreshold stimuli. We indicated that in the latter case the magnitude of excitation remained essentially constant when the duration of stimulation exceeded a certain critical value. In fact, however, this constancy is seldom obtained even when the external stimulus is held constant at some predetermined value. This is due in part to the decline in the excitation level of the receptor cells and in part to the decrease in the rate of recovery of the activated nerve fibers. The result of these two factors is that the rate of impulses in the afferent (sensory) nerve fibers declines under a condition of uniform and continuous stimulation.

For a given sensory system, the number of impulses per second depends upon several factors, among which are the energy of the stimulus, the length of time during which the stimulus has been acting, and the frequency with which the stimulus has been applied. The rate of neural discharge is initially high, and then becomes progressively slower until some stable value is reached that can be maintained for several minutes or hours. The decrease in the rate of discharge corresponds to a decrease in the magnitude of the sensory response. We say that at this point the sensory system is adapted. *Adaptation* is the process by which the sensitivity of a sensory system is modified due to the continuous presentation of a stimulus at a constant level of intensity. The term *adaptation* has a variety of meanings, and the reader should be aware that in the present context we are dealing with a process of sensory modification, and not with the evolutionary concept of adaptation. The latter notion is expressed in terms of the *learned* adjustments made by an organism as it copes with its environment in the course of its lifetime (Martin, 1964) and is irrelevant for the purposes of the present discussion.

Adaptation is a characteristic of sensory behavior that apparently is not modifiable by learning. It empasizes the fact of a *progressive change* in response as a function of stimulation. This change in response ordinarily affects the sensitivity of the particular receptor system; sometimes, however, as in olfaction, adaptation produces some changes in the *quality* of the sensory experience, and an odor that smelled pleasant prior to adaptation may become disagreeable after adaptation. While the physiological mechanism varies from modality to modality, adaptation as a general process occurs in each of the human senses under conditions of constant stimulation. Some senses show little adaptation and others show some peculiarities. Evidence of adaptation is obtained directly by the recording of nerve impulses, or indirectly by studying the progressive changes in absolute and differential thresholds.

Although the most common meaning of the term adaptation emphasizes the decrement in response or sensitivity, the adaptive process actually consists of two phases. The decrement in response occurs during the first phase; in the second phase, when the stimulation of the sensory system is terminated, the sensory system gradually returns to its former state of sensitivity. In the case of vision, for example, increasing the intensity of background light from a low to a high value produces a rise in threshold, while decreasing the intensity lowers the threshold. These two conditions are called, respectively, *light adaptation* and *dark adaptation*. For some modalities, however, there are no terms that have been conventionally used to distinguish between these two phases of adaptation. It might be helpful and less confusing to the beginning student if these two phases (or processes) were identified by two distinct terms. One investigator has proposed the term *adaptation* for the first process in which the sensory system is exposed to a constant stimulus and decreases in sensitivity, and *recovery* for the second process in which there is an absence of stimulation producing an increase in sensitivity (Stuiver, 1958). This terminology will be utilized in the present chapter.

We will turn now to a consideration of certain generalizations on sensory adaptation and recovery. In this presentation, a series of three general laws will be proposed and selected experimental evidence from different sensory systems will be provided to support these generalizations. The evidence is not intended to be exhaustive, but representative of some of the findings in the various sensory systems.

Temporal Relations and Stimulus Intensity in Adaptation and Recovery

Two of the most significant variables related to the phenomena of adaptation and recovery are *time* and *stimulus intensity*. Each of these enters into a particular generalization that specifies how the fundamental sensitivity of a given sensory system is modified, as the duration or intensity of stimulation is altered systematically under controlled conditions. In many studies, adaptation and recovery are measured as a function of time, with stimulus intensity as the parameter. Consequently, it will be appropriate to consider two of the three generalizations on adaptation and recovery more or less simultaneously in the present section; in many instances, experimental data from a single source will serve to support both generalizations.

The first generalization concerning the adaptive processes which we will consider is that *sensitivity decreases as a function of the duration of the adapting stimulus and increases in the absence of stimulation*. This indicates that under conditions of adaptation and recovery the sensitivity of a given sensory system will show marked changes with the passage of time. When the system is exposed to a constant stimulus, adaptation will lead to a rise in the particular absolute (adaptive) threshold. The longer the duration of the adapting stimulus, the greater the threshold and, hence, the less the sensitivity. When the system is no longer exposed to stimulation, recovery occurs and the absolute (recovery) threshold becomes smaller; hence, the longer the absence of stimulation, the lower the threshold and the more sensitive the system.

The specific form of the function which shows the changes in sensitivity, under adaptation or recovery as a function of time, will depend upon the particular sensory modality being considered. For some systems, once the adaptive or recovery process has started, it proceeds at a very rapid rate during the initial period and then gradually slows down as it approaches a state of equilibrium. In this case, the course of adaptation or recovery may best be described as a negatively accelerated function of time. For other systems, the rate of adaptation or recovery is constant, and the course of adaptation or recovery may be represented as a linear function of time. Both types of functions have been obtained experimentally.

The second generalization concerning adaptation and recovery is that *the time required to reach a constant level of sensitivity varies directly with the intensity of the adapting stimulus*. If a criterion value for adaptation or recovery is specified in relation to the absolute threshold, then the time required to reach this specified level will increase as the magnitude of stimulation is made larger. The nature of this functional relationship, however, may be linear or nonlinear depending upon the particular sensory system and, even within the same system, upon the particular stimulus.

Now we will consider some experimental studies in the various sensory systems that provide data supporting the generalizations on stimulus duration and intensity in relation to sensory adaptation and recovery.

Visual Processes.   Classic examples of curves for adaptation and recovery are found in vision. As we have already indicated, there are two aspects of the visual adaptive process related to changes in the level of luminance: specifically, light adaptation (retinal fatigue) and dark adaptation (recovery).

One method for measuring the effect of light adaptation is to stimulate a given area of the retina for a specified time interval with a light of known intensity; then, at the end of this interval, the observer is required to make a quick brightness match between the stimulating (adapting) light and a comparison light falling on some previously unstimulated portion of the retina. If the exposure (adapting) times are properly selected, the shape of the light adaptation function will be revealed for that particular level of adapting intensity.

Figure 9-5 shows that steady illumination of the *macula* of the human retina produces a loss in sensitivity, that is, the relative value of the comparison light which is required to yield a brightness match becomes a smaller and smaller percentage of the adapting light (Wallace, 1937). The retinal area stimulated by the adapting light loses a great deal of sensitivity in the first 30 sec; but, after one minute of stimulation, the adaptive process has reached a state of equilibrium. At this point and beyond, the intensity of the comparison light needs to be only 20 percent, approximately, of the standard (adapting) light to produce a brightness

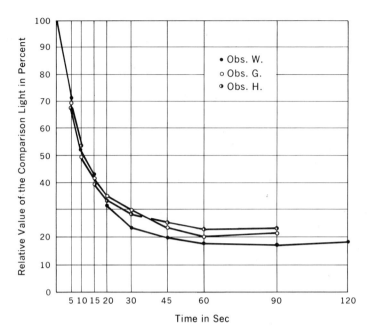

Figure 9-5. The course of light adaptation of the cones in the macula of the human retina. (From Wallace, *J. gen. Psychol.*, 1937.)

match. It may be seen that the general course of the loss in sensitivity as a function of time is described by a negatively accelerated, decreasing function with an asymptotic value being reached after approximately one minute of light exposure.

Similar results are obtained when the retina is stimulated with white light under conditions of *binocular matching*. In this experimental situation, the observer looks through a binocular eyepiece such that one eye sees half of a circular patch of light while the other eye sees the other half. One eye is then exposed to an adapting stimulus and the task of the observer is to match the two halves of the circular patch in terms of subjective brightness. Since the intensities of the two half-fields are always maintained well above the cone threshold, this procedure permits the study of light adaptation on cone vision and clearly demonstrates that the states of adaptation of the two eyes are independent.

If, for example, the right eye is exposed to a bright-adapting light, the changes in sensitivity of this eye may be measured by matching its half-field with that seen by the left eye (the left half-field). It has been found (Wright, 1939) that during exposure of the right eye, the intensity of the left half-field has to be continuously reduced to provide a brightness match, as shown in Figure 9-6.

From the moment of exposure, the right eye becomes rapidly less sensitive to light until a stable condition is reached after approximately 50 sec. From this point on, the intensity of light in the left eye needs to be only about ¹⁄₁₆ of the value originally required to achieve the binocular brightness match. It may be concluded, therefore, that the apparent brightness of the light as seen through the

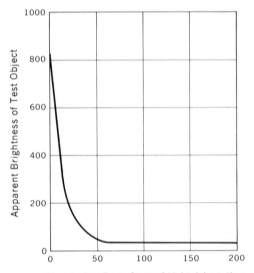

Figure 9-6.   Sensitivity of the human fovea under conditions of light adaptation. Binocular matching of brightness is determined under conditions in which one eye (right) is adapted to a bright light, while the other (left) is adapted to a light of lesser intensity. With continued exposure, the apparent brightness of the light as seen through the right eye becomes less and less, as indicated by the ordinate values at which a binocular brightness match is obtained. (From Wright, *Trans. Illum. Eng. Soc.* (London), 1939.)

right eye decreases with exposure time up to approximately one minute, and that sensitivity remains essentially constant beyond that point.

Now we will consider what happens to visual sensitivity when the eye is *dark adapted* or recovers, that is, the observer is allowed to remain in the dark or has his eyes covered with light-tight goggles fitted with opaque or special lenses. Under conditions of dark adaptation, the sensitivity of the human eye to a light stimulus is markedly increased; this increase is usually expressed in terms of the stimulus threshold. As dark adaptation (recovery) proceeds, the minimal intensity of the visual stimulus detectable on a given percentage of test trials becomes smaller and smaller until a fairly stable value is reached. Thus, as stated in the first generalization on temporal relations, recovery increases the sensitivity of the sensory system.

To control for differences among observers with respect to prior light adaptation, the experimenter ordinarily requires that each observer be exposed to an intense field of light for a specified period of time, for example, 3 to 5 min. The field is then extinguished and the observer's task is to report the presence of small "test flashes" of light that are delivered at various intervals following the extinction of the adapting field. It has been found that the duration of the light adaptation period, called the *pre-exposure* or *preadapting period,* affects the course of dark adaptation as measured by the intensity of the threshold "test flashes." As the pre-exposure period increases up to 4 min (for a standard white light of 447 milli-lamberts, mL), there is a rise in light adaptation that reduces the rate of the subsequent dark adaptation or recovery (Haig, 1941).

In the same study it was found that the time required to recover to a given level of sensitivity is shorter when the pre-exposure light is less intense. This is shown in Figure 9-7. For example, a threshold value of 6 log u uL is obtained after approximately 2.5 min in the dark for a pre-exposure light of 447 mL, but a period of approximately 6 min is required for 1150 mL and approximately 9 min for 2090 mL. Conversely, it may be stated that the level of dark adaptation (recov-

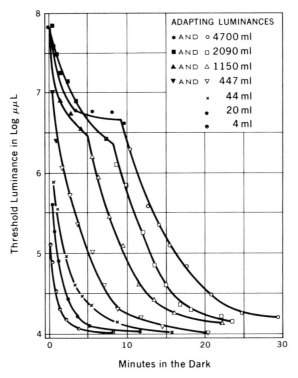

Minutes in the Dark

Figure 9-7. Dark adaptation curves for different luminances of white light presented during a 4-minute pre-exposure period. The test light was violet and the color could be identified at the threshold values indicated by the solid symbols; the color of the test light could not be recognized at the values indicated by the open symbols. For the three lowest luminances, the test light appeared colorless at threshold. The data are for one observer. (From Haig. Reprinted by permission of the Rockefeller University Press from *J. gen. Physiol.,* 1941, **24,** 735–751.)

ery) reached in a *fixed* amount of time is *inversely* related to the pre-exposure intensity.

The curve for 4700 mL in Figure 9-7 should be examined further; it contains the major features of normal dark adaptation when a light of short wavelength is used for establishing the absolute threshold after pre-exposure to a high level of luminance. As the time in the dark increases, there is a gradual lowering of the threshold (increase in sensitivity). The curve continues to decrease up to 30 min, beyond which smaller changes may be expected to occur for several hours. The curve also shows a point of discontinuity at approximately 8 min in the dark. The shorter segment of the curve up to 8 min represents the recovery of the cones in the test region of the retina. Cone recovery is essentially complete in about 10 min, with approximately a tenfold increase in sensitivity. The longer segment of the curve represents the recovery of the rods which increase in sensitivity by approximately 10,000 times in a 30-min period.

As might be expected, if the test field is restricted to the fovea which is rod-free, the curve of dark adaptation (recovery) will not show the rod segment; likewise, if the test field is shifted peripherally, the cone segment will be minimized and there will be an increase in the rate of recovery, together with a lower final value of threshold (Boynton, 1963). These findings are shown graphically in Figure 9-8 and support the generalization regarding the temporal course of recovery.

Some consideration must now be given to the physiological and photochemical bases that have been advanced to account for the processes of visual adaptation and recovery. As already noted, the duplex nature of the dark adaptation curve is attributed fundamentally to the presence of rods and cones in the retinal test area. In the initial minutes of dark adaptation, the cones are more sensitive than the rods and begin to recover very rapidly; after approximately 7 or 8 min, the rods take over and generate the second segment of the curve. This view is, of course, an oversimplification of the events that occur in the retina during the recovery process.

Further consideration must be given to the changes that involve the capacity of the eye to integrate photic energy (Weale, 1961). The evidence seems to indicate that the scotopic visual system exhibits greater summation than the photopic system, and that this difference is accentuated during the period of dark adaptation. In part, then, the decrease in threshold during dark adaptation is probably related to an increase in the *areal size of neural summation*.

A second factor involved in the course of dark adaptation is the *increase in sensitivity of the receptor elements*. For a visual response to occur, only a few quanta of light need to be distributed among several receptors and absorbed by the photochemical material (rhodopsin). As light impinges upon the rods, there is a bleaching of the rhodopsin and the amount of pigment available for absorbing additional quanta of light is reduced. Decomposition (bleaching) of rhodopsin occurs in the presence of light (light adaptation); regeneration (resynthesis) occurs in the absence of light (dark adaptation). Accordingly, when the concentration of rhodopsin is low, the threshold may be expected to be high; when the concentration is high, the threshold will be low.

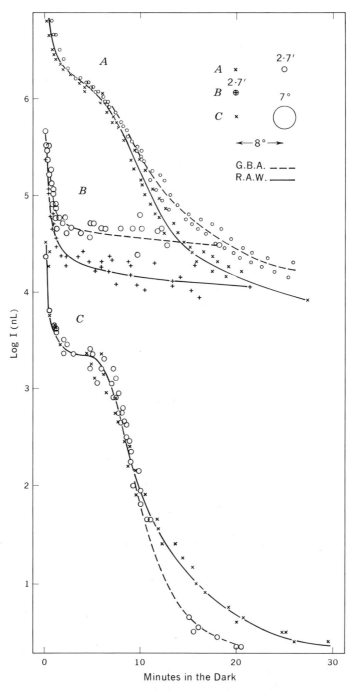

Figure 9-8. Dark-adaptation curves for two observers for different experimental conditions. The ordinate represents log luminance (in nanolamberts required for threshold visibility; the abscissa represents time in the dark following the extinction of the pre-exposure field. Curve A is for a small test field located to one side of the fixation point; Curve B, a small test field delivered at the fixation point (cone vision); Curve C, a large test field located to one side of the fixation point. (From Boynton, 1963).

At one time it was believed that the origin of the changes in the sensitivity of the eye during adaptation was directly due to the changes in the concentration of rhodopsin. However, it has been shown that exposing the eye to an amount of light calculated to bleach about 2 percent of the available rhodopsin raises the threshold by a factor of 100, not by 2 percent (Rushton and Cohen, 1954). Other investigators have also found that at moderate levels of illuminance, the amount of light adaptation is much greater than would seem to be appropriate for the small amount of light reaching the rods to produce bleaching of the rhodopsin (Baumgardt, 1949; Pirenne and Denton, 1952).

Rushton (1961a) has concluded that there is no one-to-one correspondence between the amount of rhodopsin available and the value of the dark-adapted threshold, that is, the relationship between these two variables is not linear. By studying a *rod monochromat* (a human observer deficient in cone vision), Rushton (1961b) showed that the *logarithm* of threshold intensity depended directly upon the amount of rhodopsin present and that this relationship could be expressed in the form of a linear function, as shown in Figure 9-9.

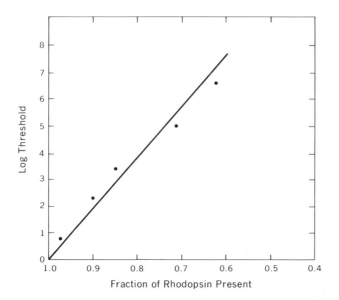

Figure 9-9. Relation between the logarithm of threshold intensity and the fraction of rhodopsin present in the retina of a
subject deficient in cone vision (photanope). (From Rushton, *J.
Physiol.*, 1961b.)

Rushton, Campbell, Hagins, and Brindley (1955) have found that human rhodopsin is more or less completely regenerated by 40 min following the end of an exposure which produces full bleaching, but human cone pigments are re-synthesized in about 8 min (Rushton, 1958). It is a remarkable finding that no matter how much rhodopsin needs to be regenerated after various conditions of light exposure, the rods first become more sensitive than the cones, that is, the rod-cone "break" in the dark-adaptation curve occurs, at the moment when 92 percent of the rhodopsin is regenerated (Rushton, 1961a). Thus, the rods are inoperative when they contain less than approximately 90 percent of their total amount of rhodopsin; or, stated in complementary terms, removing approximately 10 percent of the rhodopsin molecules will produce essentially complete blindness in the rods, which constitute 95 percent of the human retinal receptors.

The two factors of neural summation and retinal bleaching have been taken into account by Blakemore and Rushton (1962) in their explanation of changes in sensitivity during dark adaptation. They have postulated that during dark adaptation the background gradually fades, thereby changing the *differential sensitivity* of the whole neural "pool" to which the receptors are connected. (Since this change in sensitivity involves the "summation pools" of the rods previously stimulated, the effect is said to be a synaptic phenomenon.) The rods continually "signal" the state of regeneration of their photochemical pigment to the "pool" and in this way alter the "pool's" temporal and spatial organization. Thus, the effect of bleaching upon the "summation pool" depends upon the average amount of bleached rhodopsin in the rods connected to the "pool," but it is independent of the distribution of the bleached rhodopsin in the receptive fields. Simply stated, dark adaptation depends upon the average bleach, but not on its spatial distribution. Rushton (1965) has developed a feedback model of visual adaptation from these concepts which shows how a neural signal that is proportional to the average bleaching of rhodopsin can regulate the rod threshold; the model takes into account the liminal brightness due to both the external test light and the visual afterimage that results from bleaching.

The changes that occur in the cone pigments during dark adaptation have not been studied to any great extent. Part of the problem lies in the fact that the cones contain very little extractable visual pigment. A whole human retina would be expected to yield approximately 0.1 percent of cone pigment and 99.9 percent of rhodopsin (Rushton, 1962). However, Wald, Brown and Smith (1955) have extracted iodopsin (cone pigment) from the retina of the chicken, and have demonstrated that its absorption spectrum does not differ greatly from the photopic sensitivity curve, although the agreement is not nearly so close as that for the absorption of rhodopsin and scotopic sensitivity. By using a special technique (*reflection densitometry*) that involves so exposing the eye of the observer to a particular colored light that bleaching of the receptors is obtained, Rushton (1959) was able to demonstrate the presence of two cone pigments which he called "erythrolabe" (red-catching) and "chlorolabe" (green-catching), but he could not detect the blue pigment "cyanolabe" which is required for a trichromatic theory of color vision. The difficulty in identifying the blue-absorbing substance may be due to its occurrence in very minute quantities.

As in the case of rod adaptation, the cones show a decrease in sensitivity (*foveal light adaptation*) during exposure to light (see Figures 9-5 and 9-6) and recover their sensitivity in the absence of light. The cones, however, recover much more rapidly than rods, presumably due to the more rapid regeneration of the cone pigments. DuCroz and Rushton (1963) have obtained curves of dark adaptation for cones from which they have concluded that the blue and green mechanisms operate through "pools" that are independent of one another, as are red and green. This means, for example, that bleaching red cones changes their sensitivity in the "pool" but it does not affect the green cones. As in the dark adaptation of rods, the shift in differential sensitivity of cones is attributed to the fading of the background ("dark light") that affects the threshold in proportion to the amount of the specific pigment that is bleached.

Wright (1946) has used his binocular matching technique to study the course of recovery of the red, green, and blue mechanisms. In this situation, the observer was presented with a yellow patch in front of his right eye, while his left eye was presented with a patch composed of the three primaries (red, green, and blue). The proportions and intensities of the three primaries could then be adjusted by the observer whose task was to match the yellow patch in both hue and brightness. After the match was made, the right eye was exposed to an adapting white light for 3 min and then both eyes again viewed their respective patches. It was found that the previous match no longer was appropriate—the two patches appeared different as a result of adaptation. The matches were repeated every 30 sec and, by appropriately changing the color of the test patch, three separate curves were obtained showing the recoveries of the red, green, and blue mechanisms. It was found that (1) adaptation produced a general reduction in sensitivity to all wavelengths and that (2) there was a specific reduction in sensitivity to the adapting wavelength. Thus, when the eye is adapted to white light, the sensitivity to all wavelengths is proportionately depressed; when the adapting light is colored, there is a decrease in the sensitivity to this color so that a greater amount of it is required to reproduce a previous match. These conclusions hold for the binocular matching technique; however, in daily activities, when both eyes are equally adapted, color matches made under one condition of adaptation will hold under different conditions of adaptation (at least for moderate ranges of light intensity).

Auditory Processes. If the phenomena of light and dark adaptation in vision are considered as phenomena that produce temporary shifts in the absolute threshold, then similar phenomena are to be found in audition. Several terms have been used to describe these effects: (1) *adaptation* (or *short-duration auditory fatigue*) in which the threshold shift produced by relatively weak and brief stimuli is very transitory, and (2) *auditory fatigue* which arises from more stringent conditions of stimulation and is of longer duration. Both of these phenomena are characterized by a reversible threshold shift, provided the intensity and duration of stimulation are not excessive. Whether the two phenomena are different manifestations of the same reversible process, however, remains to be determined.

Harris and Rawnsley (1953) have summarized the evidence which indicates that adaptation, if not a separate phenomenon, must at least be considered as a special case of fatigue. Four criteria may be used to differentiate adaptation from fatigue: (1) In adaptation, the duration of stimulation does not have a cumulative effect on threshold up to 10.0 sec, while in fatigue the effects of duration are cumulative from 30 sec to 10 min. (2) The recovery curve for adaptation is a straight line, whereas the temporal course of recovery of threshold for fatigue is negatively accelerated. (3) In adaptation, the maximal threshold shift occurs at the stimulus frequency, but in fatigue the maximal effect may lie a half-octave higher. (4) The curves for other selected auditory phenomena (for example, *recruitment*, in which certain types of deafness show that the loudness of tones increases more rapidly than normal when stimulus intensity is increased) differ for adaptation and fatigue. For these reasons, it appears desirable to differentiate between the two phenomena until experimental evidence indicates that such a view is untenable.

In recent years more effort has been directed to the problem of auditory fatigue than to adaptation; research in this area is now generally identified with the topic of temporary threshold shift (*TTS*). *Temporary threshold shift* is defined as the difference in the threshold of audibility measured before and after an individual has been exposed to sounds with known physical characteristics. This shift is a transitory phenomenon in which the absolute threshold that has been elevated (decreased sensitivity) by exposure to intense sound returns to its pre-exposure level (increased sensitivity) in the absence of sound, usually within a matter of hours. To describe the amount of *TTS* produced by a particular exposure to sound, it has become common practice to specify the amount of threshold shift that is present 2 min after the end of exposure (TTS_2).

Studies conducted under controlled laboratory conditions have provided data showing the relation of sound parameters such as duration, intensity level, repetition rate, and acoustic spectrum to *TTS*. In one study (Ward, Glorig, and Sklar, 1958) the dependence of *TTS* upon two of these variables, stimulus intensity and duration, was investigated at 4000 cps. Thirteen young men with normal hearing were exposed to *broad-band noise* (that is, noise having equal energy in all octave bands from 75 to 10,000 cps) varying according to the experimental design from 88 db SPL to 106 db SPL and lasting for a cumulative period of 12, 24, 51, or 108 min. At each stimulus intensity, there were two types of exposure: one was continuous noise and the other was interrupted noise. The interrupted noise was presented with a given duty ("on-off") cycle for a particular testing condition; three different cycles were used in the experiment so that the interrupted noise was "on" 33, 50, or 67 percent of the time.

The results of the study at 4000 cps are shown in Figure 9-10 in which *TTS* in db is plotted as a function of exposure time in minutes, with the intensity level and "on-percentage" of the noise as parameters. All *TTS*'s were calculated in reference to median pre-exposure thresholds and show that *TTS* is a linear function of the logarithm of exposure time. Also, the rate of growth of *TTS* with the logarithm of time is approximately proportional to the fraction of time that the noise is "on," and the slope of the function increases with the sound pressure level of the fatiguing stimulus.

The relationships shown in Figure 9-10 may be expressed as:

$$TTS_2 = 1.06R \ (S - 85)\left(\log_{10} \frac{T}{1.7}\right), \tag{9-7}$$

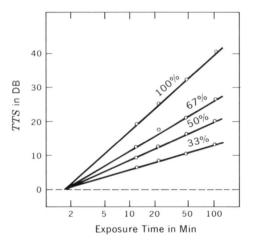

Figure 9–10. Temporary threshold shift *(TTS)* at 4000 cps as a function of exposure time for broad-band noise of 106 db sound-pressure level *(SPL)*. The parameter is the "on-percentage" of the noise. The open circles represent observed data and the straight lines were calculated from Equation 9-7. (From Ward et al., J. acoust. Soc. Amer., 1958.)

where TTS_2 is the temporary threshold shift in db 2 min after cessation of noise exposure, T is the duration of exposure in min, S is the sound pressure level of the noise in db, and R is the fraction of time that the noise is "on." This equation holds for $T > 75$ min, $85 < S < 110$ db, and all values of R, provided the noise bursts are 250 msec to 1 min in duration.

The recovery curves for this experiment are shown in Figure 9-11 in which TTS_2 may be seen to be a linear function of the logarithm of time following the cessation of stimulation. Also, the rate of recovery seems to be proportional to the amount of TTS which is present 2 min after termination of the fatiguing stimulus.

The equation for recovery of TTS at 4000 cps may be expressed as:

$$TTS_t = TTS_2 \left(1 - K \log_{10} \frac{t}{2} \right), \qquad (9\text{-}8)$$

where TTS_t is the TTS at t minutes after the termination of a 2-hr noise exposure, and K is a constant equal to 0.37 if there is complete recovery at 1000 min. This equation holds when t is 2 min or more and when TTS_2 is less than 50 db. It was also determined that similar relations for fatigue and recovery hold for 3000 and 6000 cps, but the slopes of the curves for 1000 and 2000 cps are markedly less. While the higher frequencies at and above 3000 cps are resistant to TTS for only about 2 min, 1000 cps shows no TTS up to approximately 15 min of noise exposure.

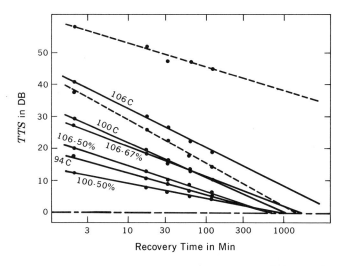

Figure 9–11. Recovery of temporary threshold shift *(TTS)* at 4000 cps following a 2-hour exposure to broad-band noise at 106 db sound-pressure level *(SPL)*. The parameter is the "on-percentage" of the noise. The upper dashed curve is for 4 ears with initial *TTS* greater than 50 db; the lower curve, for 22 ears with initial *TTS* less than 50 db. (From Ward et al., 1958.)

The classical relation predicted by the equation $It = C$ in vision does not hold for *TTS* in audition. For a constant *TTS* at 4000 cps, the tentative equation is given by:

$$\left(\log \frac{I}{I_0} \right) \left(\log \frac{T}{T_0} \right) = C, \tag{9-9}$$

where I is the SPL of the noise in db, I_0 is the intensity of noise ($= 85$ db SPL) which is required to produce *TTS* after an "indifference" (no effect) period of T_0 minutes, and T is the exposure time in minutes.

Although the present discussion has involved noise as the fatiguing stimulus, it should be pointed out that Hood (1950) found that the growth of *TTS* is also proportional to the logarithm of time when 2000 cps is used as the fatiguing stimulus; Epstein and Schubert (1957) and others have shown that the log-time function for recovery is similarly obtained after stimulation by pure tones.

The practical significance of *TTS* is that numerous data have suggested that *TTS* is approximately linearly related to the permanent threshold shift (hearing loss) induced by exposure to high levels of noise; furthermore, the regression line of the mean permanent shift after ten years of exposure on TTS_2 has a slope of one and an intercept of zero, at least to a first approximation. Thus, *"damage-risk criteria"* for noise exposures (that is, the maximal levels and durations of sounds with different spectra that can be tolerated by people without endangering their hearing) may be specified for a criterion *TTS*.

Such criteria have recently been proposed (Kryter, Ward, Miller, and Eldredge, 1966). The recommendations vary according to the specific characteristics of the noise environment, but are all derived from the same three basic postulates: (1) TTS_2 is a consistent measure of the effects of a single day's exposure to noise; (2) all exposures that produce a given TTS_2 are considered equally hazardous; and (3) there is a quantitative relation between TTS_2 and the permanent shift after ten years of exposure. While these postulates appear reasonable at present, it is quite likely they will need to be revised in the light of future evidence. In general, exposure to any sound environment producing a TTS_2 that approaches or exceeds 40 db is imminently capable of producing a permanent impairment in hearing sensitivity.

Given that the ear exhibits the phenomena of adaptation and fatigue, what portions of the auditory system are involved in producing these effects? Rawnsley and Harris (1952) have shown that the site of adaptation cannot be the middle ear since normal curves of recovery from adaptation were obtained for a patient whose ossicles had been removed (*ossiculectomy*). Lüscher and Zwislocki (1949) performed experiments which showed that the threshold of one ear was not raised by providing an adaptation tone to the other ear, thereby ruling out the central nervous system.

The evidence seems to indicate that adaptation is a peripheral process that occurs in the cochlea at the organ of Corti, but it is not known whether neural or nonneural structures are responsible for the phenomenon (Harris and Rawnsley, 1953). This conclusion was based upon a study in which it was shown that recruitment occurred in an ear already exhibiting adaptation due to a preceding tonal stimulus. The loudness of a brief tone in the adapted ear was adjusted to match the loudness of an identical tone simultaneously presented in the nonadapted ear. It was found that there was an accelerated growth of loudness (recruitment) in the adapted ear. Thus, since recruitment is a nonneural phenomenon probably confined to the hair cells of the organ of Corti, and recruitment was present in the ear exhibiting adaptation, it appears that adaptation is a function of the peripheral organ and not the auditory nervous system.

The basic mechanisms involved in auditory fatigue are most probably associated with the organ of Corti. Hirsh and Bilger (1955) have postulated two different processes associated with different phases of recovery from TTS produced by a tone of 1000 cps. The first process (identified as R-1) is operative for the first minute or two of recovery, after which the second process (R-2) comes into effect and determines the remainder of the course of recovery. Ward (1960), however, has provided data that indicate a third process (R-3) is necessary to account for the course of recovery from high values of TTS several hours after exposure. While the R-1 and R-2 processes are approximately linear functions of the logarithm of time, the R-3 process is simply linear in time, that is, the process reduces TTS at a constant rate in db per unit time. It has been speculated that the R-1 process is related to the excitability of auditory nerve fibers and that the R-2 process is related to the chemical properties of nerve cells; no attempt has been made to specify the locus of the R-3 process.

When the exposure to sound produces a permanent shift in threshold (a hearing loss), the damage may be in the conductive mechanism (tympanic membrane and ossicular chain) that transmits the vibratory energy across the middle ear to the cochlea. This often occurs when the sound is impulsive and of high intensity. Such damage does not ordinarily produce complete deafness but may elevate the threshold by as much as 50 or 60 db. Protection against such sounds is provided by the *aural reflex,* which can reduce the intensity of sound transmitted to the inner ear by as much as 15 db, approximately. The aural reflex involves the contraction of the tensor tympani and stapedius muscles of the middle ear in response to sounds of high intensity, with a resulting loss in the efficiency of sound transmission by the ossicular mechanism.

The usual form of hearing loss produced by noise involves the organ of Corti. Damage to the hair cells on the basilar membrane appears to progress in stages. The initial destruction resulting from noise involves the hair cells along the outer side of the organ of Corti; the hair cells along the inner side and other structures within the organ of Corti may then be destroyed progressively. It is usually found that the first or basal turn of the organ of Corti, which mediates hearing at approximately 4000 cps, is affected first, followed by a spreading of damage for frequencies in the speech range below this point. It is not until the latter stage is reached that the individual with such a hearing loss will detect any interference with his ability to hear or, more precisely, his ability to understand speech. Thus, the onset of noise-induced hearing loss is an insidious one, with no preliminary "danger signals" to alert the individual of the impending deafness. Unfortunately, the damaged structures do not regenerate and, once established, the destruction of the structures within the organ of Corti cannot be reversed by any known medical or surgical procedures.

Proprioceptive Processes. Matthews (1931) performed a series of experiments to investigate the general properties of the sensory end organ that is stimulated by stretching a muscle. Specifically, he studied a single muscle spindle imbedded in a "small muscle on the upper outer side of the middle toe of the frog." The whole muscle was freed from its neighbors and the top end was left attached to the bone; the bottom end was attached to a thread led over a pulley. This arrangement made it possible to load the tendon with weights or springs. Photographic recordings were made of the electrophysiological properties of the neural activity associated with the muscle spindle (proprioceptor) under different load conditions. It was found that *the rate of neural impulses* (frequency of impulses per sec) *decreased as a negatively accelerated function of time* after the load was hung on the thread attached to the tendon. As shown in Figure 9-12, the maximal rate of discharge with the preparation at 15°C is approximately 120 per sec as the load reaches its full value upon attachment (1/5 sec), decreasing to a rate of approximately 25 per sec after 14 sec. (If the temperature of the preparation is increased, there is a corresponding increase in the initial frequency of impulses, but the response declines much more rapidly and attains essentially the same asymptotic value.) As in vision, adaptation

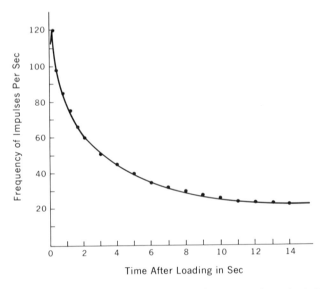

Figure 9–12. Decline in the frequency of response after a load of 2 grams was suspended from the tendon of a frog. (From Matthews, *J. Physiol.*, 1931.)

of the receptive elements produces a decrement in neural response which is directly related to the duration of stimulation.

Tactile and Pressure Processes. Adrian and Zotterman (1926) studied the afferent impulses generated in the plantar digital nerves of the cat when the pad of the toe in the hind foot was stimulated by light contact or by pressure. By means of a mechanical lever system it was possible to apply a gradually increasing or a steady pressure of any value from 25 to 1500 gm on the cat's pad. The apparatus also provided a means by which the pressure and the electrophysiological responses in the nerve could be recorded simultaneously.

The results of this study agree very closely with those obtained from the tension receptors in the frog's muscle. When a glass disc is brought lightly into contact with the pad, there is a high rate of impulses for about 0.1 to 0.2 sec, but within 0.5 sec the discharge has nearly completely ceased. This is in marked contrast to the tension receptors of the frog's muscle in which the frequency of discharge fell to half its maximal value in about 10 sec, given a constant stimulus. The maximal rate of discharge from the single tactile end organ, however, was about the same as that for the frog's tension receptor, approximately 150 per sec. Thus, it appears that pressure receptors (Pacinian corpuscles) adapt at a much faster rate than tension receptors (muscle spindles); in both cases, however, the *curves of adaptation are negatively accelerated functions of time following stimulation.*

In a more recent study, Loewenstein and Mendelson (1965) investigated the components of receptor adaptation in the Pacinian corpuscle of the cat. In the Pacinian corpuscle, the sensory nerve ending is surrounded by a lamellated, fluid-filled capsule. The process of mechanoelectric conversion of the stimulus energy takes place entirely in the nerve ending, but the capsule provides the coupling between the nerve ending and the external stimulus; consequently, the characteristics of the sensory response must depend upon the mechanical properties inherent in the coupling.

After most of the lamellated capsule of a Pacinian corpuscle had been removed by dissection, the nerve ending was activated directly by pulses of compression from a mechanical stimulus. It was found that the duration of the generated potential was continuously variable with stimulus duration, but that *the potential eventually decayed when a sustained mechanical stimulus was applied.* The potential of the decapsulated corpuscle lasted more than 70 sec, while that of the encapsulated corpuscle decayed to a value of zero in 6 sec. Two components in the adaptation of the Pacinian corpuscle were identified: (1) a mechanical component which serves as a mechanical filter which prevents the slow components of a stimulus from reaching the sensory endings of the nerve fibers, and (2) an electrochemical component which operates at the level of the neural impulse and prevents repetitive firing under conditions of constant stimulation.

Experimental evidence of adaptation to pressure in human observers has been obtained by Nafe and Wagoner (1941). Weights varying from 8.75 to 70.0 gm were placed carefully on the observer's leg just above the knee, and a sensitive recording system was used to measure the amount of compression of the underlying tissue as a function of time. It was found that after a weight was placed on the skin surface, it did not "sink" immediately, but moved downward very gradually. As long as a supraliminal rate of movement was maintained, pressure was felt; but, when the movement was negligible due to increased tissue resistance, pressure was no longer felt. At this point adaptation was complete. Removal of the weight produced a period of recovery and a rearousal of pressure responses.

Hensel and Boman (1960) also conducted a series of experiments to study the response of receptors to mechanical and thermal stimulation of the human skin. Seven observers were used and a selected branch of the radial nerve serving the area between the thumb and index finger was surgically exposed and dissected. Mechanical stimulation was provided by means of a perspex rod (1 mm dia) on a small calibrated springbalance that could be adjusted to various tensions. Simple hair receptors were stimulated by bending the hair with a preparation needle under a stereomicroscope. Thermal stimulation was provided by water-circulated thermodes (5, 10, and 18 mm dia) or by a small heat radiator. At the end of the experiments, the wound was sewed and after seven months, recovery of feeling was nearly complete.

Measurements made during the experiment indicated that the "thresholds for eliciting a simple impulse in a single mechanosensitive fiber were the same as those for arousing a subjective touch sensation" (p. 576), that is, approximately 0.5 gm. Receptors excited only by mechanical stimulation revealed that the *im-*

pulse frequency increased as a positively accelerated function of stimulus pressure; however, when a constant pressure of about 1 kg/sq cm was applied simultaneously with rapid cooling and rewarming of the receptive field, the *impulse frequency decreased as a negatively accelerated function of time.* It was also concluded that "those receptors in human skin which are excited by pressure as well as by cooling are similar to a group of nerve endings found in the cat's skin" (p. 576).

Zigler (1932) studied both pressure adaptation and recovery as a function of stimulus intensity. He used a set of five weights which had the same diameter (1 cm): 50, 100, 500, 1000, and 2000 mg. Measurements were made on the back of the hand, the forearm, forehead, and cheek. For the adaptation series, the observers reported when they no longer felt any pressure from the weights; for the recovery series, they reported the moment at which the aftereffects of removal of the weights first disappeared.

The results of the study are shown in Table 9-1. Part A of Table 9-1 presents the mean adaptation time for eight observers at four different bodily locations.

Table 9-1   Adaptation and Recovery of Cutaneous Pressure

| | Part A: Adaptation | | | |
| | | Bodily Location | | |
Stimulus (Mg)	Back of Hand	Forearm	Forehead	Cheek
50	2.4	2.3	5.1	5.7
100	3.8	3.3	6.2	6.4
500	6.0	4.9	10.0	11.6
1000	6.7	5.6	10.4	13.5
2000	9.5	7.8	16.0	19.4
	Part B: Recovery			
		Bodily Location		
Stimulus (Mg)	Back of Hand	Forearm	Forehead	Cheek
50	4.3	3.4	5.3	3.9
100	5.8	4.0	7.0	5.5
500	6.7	6.2	10.2	8.0
1000	9.3	8.6	10.7	10.0
2000	11.8	9.3	13.3	11.9

Source: M. J. Zigler. Pressure adaptation time; a function of intensity of extensity. *Amer. J. Psychol.,* 1932, **44**, 709–720.

Notice that the adaptation times are shorter for the hand and forearm than they are for the forehead and cheek, with intensity held constant. The major conclusion, however, is that *adaptation time increases as a direct function of stimulus intensity.* The heavier the weight, the longer the adaptation time.

Part B of Table 9-1 presents the mean recovery time for three of the eight observers measured at the same bodily locations. The data reveal that recovery time following the removal of the stimulus from the skin is approximately of the same magnitude as that for adaptation. This suggests that adaptation and recovery for cutaneous pressure may represent essentially reciprocal changes in the receptors. It may also be seen that *regardless of location the heavier the stimulus, the longer the recovery time.*

Gustatory Processes. Abrahams, Krakauer, and Dallenbach (1937) performed a study to determine the characteristics of adaptation to a strong salt (NaCl) solution of constant and unvarying intensity. Seven observers were used and a specially designed gustatory stimulator was constructed to permit a constant amount and strength of preheated solution (37°–39°C) to flow through the mouth of the observer. The solution was carried to the back of the mouth by an intake tube and from there it flowed forward along the sides and over the surface of the tongue to a drain-tube that opened beneath the tongue. The stimulus concentrations were set in 50 gm steps, that is, the molar concentrations ranged from 0.84 to 3.93. The criterion of adaptation was the disappearance of the taste of salt.

It was found that all observers reported *complete adaptation to all five salt solutions within 20 sec to 120 sec, depending upon the stimulus concentration.* As each solution was introduced into the mouth, maximal saltiness was experienced depending upon the strength of the particular solution; then the taste became less and less intense until it finally disappeared. *The course of adaptation was characterized typically by a gradual and continuous decline in the magnitude of the salty taste.* All stimulus solutions, except the weakest (0.84 mol), also aroused pain as well as taste. Like vision, taste may be completely adapted under proper conditions of general stimulation. To produce this effect, however, not only must constancy of stimulation be maintained, but slight movements of the tongue must be eliminated to avoid bringing previously sheltered taste receptors into contact with the salt solution.

In a subsequent study, Krakauer and Dallenbach (1937) extended their observations to the gustatory adaptation of sweet, sour, and bitter. The same apparatus was used as in the salt experiment and all solutions were heated to temperatures varying from 39°–41°C before passing down the intake tube. For sweet, five strengths of solution were made with sugar cane (24, 47, 95, 190, and 380 gm/1000 ccm of water); for sour, three strengths of solution were made with tartaric acid (0.33, 1.00, and 2.00 gm/1000 ccm of water); and for bitter, three strengths of solution were made with quinine hydrochloride (0.05, 0.15, and 0.30 gm/1000 ccm of water). These strengths ranged from a weak to a strong solution for the particular substances. Again, the criterion of adaptation was the disappearance of the specific taste under observation.

The results of this study also showed *complete adaptation within 75 sec to 325 sec, depending upon the particular stimulus and its intensity of concentration.* For every concentration of sweet, sour, and bitter, every observer reported the disappearance of the specific taste. From a maximal intensity dependent upon the particular stimulus concentration, *there was a gradual decline in taste until it finally disappeared.* Slight movements of the tongue, however, tended to destroy the level of adaptation at a

given moment, since new tissue relations were produced and previously unstimulated taste receptors were brought into play. It may be concluded from these two
studies that *salt, sweet, sour, and bitter are subject to complete adaptation under conditions
of constant and general stimulation.*

Olfactory Processes. The adaptation of the sense of smell is widely known. When
a person enters an environment in which a strong odorant is present, he will at first
detect the strong odor; but, for many substances, the odor will soon become weaker
and weaker and may disappear altogether within a few minutes. It follows, then,
that a legitimate problem for study is the determination of the adaptation time
required for the cessation of smell upon prolonged stimulation.

There are several difficulties in arriving at a solution to this problem. One of
these is that many odorous substances produce a "trigeminus sensation," that is,
they stimulate gustatory or thermal receptors or generate a stinging or burning
response via the trigeminal nerve. The activation of these extraneous neural elements tends to interfere with the olfactory judgments that are required of the
observer. A second difficulty is that there is no single answer to the question of
adaptation time. The adaptation time required for the cessation of an olfactory
response will depend upon the intensity of the adapting stimulus. Unless this
factor is controlled, different results will be obtained in the measurement of adaptation time.

Woodrow and Karpman (1917) took this second factor into account and varied
the concentration of the odorant in such a way that the stimulus was exactly defined in terms of temperature, vapor tension, and intensity. The apparatus permitted a steady stream of odorous vapor to enter the observer's nose while he was
breathing through his open mouth. Three odorants were used: propyl alcohol,
camphor, and naphthalene and, for each experimental condition, the observer
was required to report "now" just as soon as he could decide for the first time
that he was no longer detecting the particular odor. The results indicated that
*each of the odorous substances produced complete adaptation within 63 sec to 206 sec, depend-
ing upon the physical intensity of the given odorous vapor.*

In an extensive series of experiments, Stuiver (1958) investigated, among other
problems, the raising of the olfactory threshold during adaptation and the recovery of the sense of smell following a previous state of adaptation. These two
situations are analogous, respectively, to the problems of light and dark adaptation in vision. In the first set of experiments, the aim was to study the rise in
threshold while the observer was breathing in a current of odorous air in which
the odorant was maintained at a constant value of concentration. This was accomplished by using an injection apparatus with an independent control of the
stimulus duration, the rate of flow of the vaporous concentration, and the number
of odorous molecules. The stimulus was introduced into the nostril by means of
a tight-fitting nosepiece. After the observer's absolute threshold was determined,
the subject was adapted to a given concentration of the odorant, for example, 20
times or 100 times the concentration at threshold. The problem then was to determine the increase in the absolute threshold as a function of adaptation time.
The general procedure was to suddenly lower the concentration of the odorant

while the observer was being adapted to a given stimulus concentration and to have the observer state whether he smelled the test concentration. After this report, the original stimulus concentration was again supplied. If the observer detected the reduced (test) concentration of the odorant, the whole trial was repeated until no odor was perceived. The *adaptation time* was taken as the time required to produce a rise in the threshold concentration equal to the test concentration of the odorant. The same procedure was used for different concentrations of the odorous substance (d-octanol or meta-xylene).

Figure 9-13 shows the adaptation curves for seven different concentrations of the adapting stimulus (d-octanol). The increase in absolute threshold is plotted as

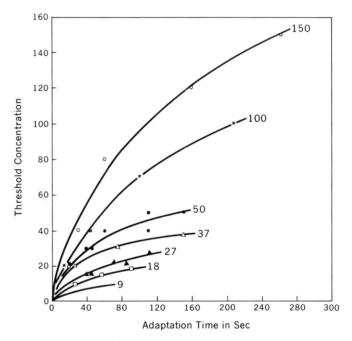

Figure 9-13. Increases in absolute thresholds for d-octanol as a function of adaptation to different intensities of odorous concentrations. The adapting intensity for each curve is indicated by a number which specifies the concentration as a multiple of the original (unadapted) threshold. (From Stuiver, 1958.)

a function of adaptation time in seconds with adapting concentration as the parameter. Regardless of the intensity of the adapting concentration, expressed as a multiple of the unadapted threshold concentration, there is *a negatively accelerated increase in the olfactory threshold as the adaptation time increases*. For example, when the sense organ adapts itself to a concentration 100 times the original threshold, there is an increase in threshold by a factor of approximately 40 after 40 sec of adaptation, but only a factor of 60 after 80 sec. Notice that each curve reaches an asymptotic value within approximately 2 to 5 min, indicating that complete adaptation for d-octanol occurs rather quickly. The shapes of the curves for meta-xylene are similar to those obtained for d-octanol.

The adaptation time (t) required for the cessation of smell may be expressed as:

$$t = b \sqrt{C - 1}, \tag{9-10}$$

where b is a constant and C is the concentration of the odorant used as the adapting stimulus. When the adapting stimulus has a concentration equal to the concentration at the absolute threshold, C equals one. For d-octanol, the constant b is approximately 20; for meta-xylene, approximately 30.

In the second set of experiments, Sruiver studied the capacity of the olfactory system to recover from the effects of adaptation to intensive stimulation. The general procedure was to determine the threshold concentration of the observer prior to adaptation and, then, to adapt the observer to a given stimulus intensity. The adapting exposure was terminated when the observer was no longer able to detect the particular odor under study. After cessation of the adaptation period, the observer breathed the pure air in the testing chamber in a normal manner. During this time the concentration of the odorant in the controlled air stream was adapted to a lower value. At periodic intervals, the observer took one breath in the airstream and indicated when he was able to detect the odor of the test concentration. The same procedure was repeated to obtain recovery data for successively lower concentrations of the stimulus. In this way the course of recovery was described in terms of the absolute threshold as a function of time, following the cessation of stimulation by the adapting odorant.

The results of this set of experiments showed that at the beginning of the recovery period, the *sensory system recovered at a very rapid rate but, after a few minutes, the rate was much slower.* The shape of the recovery curves was the same for various adaptation (exposure) times and adapting intensities. The data supporting these generalizations are presented in graphical form in Figure 9-14 for d-octanol and meta-xylene. The adapting intensities are given on the ordinate (logarithmic scale) and are equal to the threshold concentrations at the beginning of the recovery period; recovery time is shown on the abscissa; and the number at the right of each curve indicates the exposure time in seconds during which the adapting stimulus was presented. The curves show that, *after previous exposure, there is a decrease in threshold concentration as a function of time;* the initial portion of the curve shows rapid recovery while the latter portion shows recovery at a much slower rate. Recovery is essentially complete for d-octanol after approximately 800 sec; for meta-xylene, after approximately 1400 sec. However, full recovery of the olfactory system may require several hours.

Cheesman and Mayne (1953) devised a method for determining the absolute olfactory threshold for a test stimulus under conditions that produced adaptation to a masking odor. The procedure was to use the sniff-bottle technique to establish

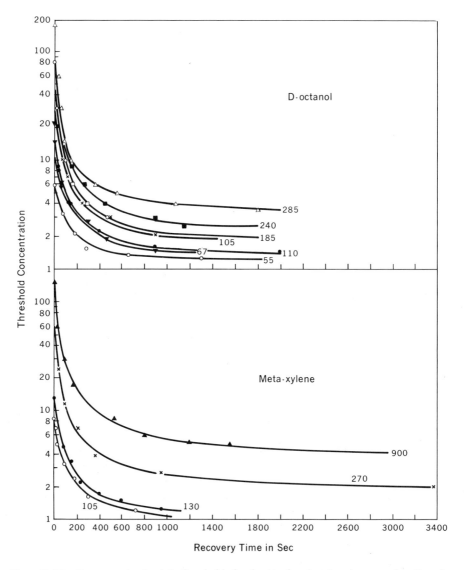

Figure 9-14. Decreases in absolute thresholds for d-octanol and meta-xylene as a function of exposure time and adapting intensity. The adapting intensities are equivalent to threshold concentrations at the beginning of the recovery period (on ordinate); the exposure time in seconds is shown at the right of each curve. (From Stuiver, 1958.)

the mean absolute olfactory threshold for the test stimulus for a group of observers and then to measure the change in sensitivity due to adaptation to a masking odor. Sometimes *homogeneous* pairs of stimuli were used, that is, the test stimulus and the masking stimulus were the same; at other times, *heterogeneous* pairs were used, that is, the test stimulus and the masking stimulus were different. The appropriate pairs of stimuli were selected from three substances: isopropanol, dioxan, and cyclopentanone. *For both homogeneous and heterogeneous pairs, linear functions were obtained when the logarithms of the threshold concentrations of the test stimuli were plotted against the logarithms of the concentrations of the masking stimuli.* The slopes of the linear functions for the homogeneous pairs were approximately equal (-0.7); but, for the heterogeneous pairs, the slopes varied from -0.2 (for example, test stimulus: isopropanol; masking stimulus: cyclopentanone) to -1.0 (test stimulus: dioxan; masking stimulus, isopropanol). It was suggested that the gradient of these functions might be used as an index of the degree of commonality of the odorous properties between the pair of substances. The smaller the slope of the function, the smaller the effect of the masking stimulus upon the test stimulus. The results of this study indicate that the course of adaptation is a linear function of the intensity of the masking stimulus.

Thermal Processes. The problem of adaptation to thermal stimuli has been studied more extensively than adaptation to other forms of stimulation for the cutaneous senses. In one study (Jenkins, 1937*a*) a technique was devised whereby the effects of adaptation could be investigated in a single cold spot, without the contaminating effects of tactual stimulation. The apparatus made it possible to surround a cold spot with a field 16 mm in diameter and to stimulate it with a thermal stimulus from a metal tip 1.25 mm in diameter. The temperature of the field and of the stimulator tip were independently variable. A cam arrangement permitted the stimulator rod to be moved downward so that its tip was even with the surface of the field. Thus, by maintaining the field disc just above the volar surface of the forearm, the skin was not disturbed and tactual stimulation was absent.

Six observers were tested, among other conditions, to determine the effects of continuous and constant stimulation on a single cold spot. Four temperatures were used: 10°, 15°, 20°, and 25°C. It was found that when the cold spot was stimulated continuously, the observers usually reported that the feeling of cold died out entirely in less than 4 sec. This occurred in 78 percent of the observations regardless of the particular temperature of the test stimulus. For 11 percent of the cases, the duration of the cold response was more than 6 sec. When cold "died out, there was nothing left," that is, cessation of the feeling of cold was not followed by pressure, as had been reported in earlier studies by some other investigators.

It was also found that continuous or intermittent stimulation at these low temperatures produced a long-lasting decrease in the sensitivity of the cold spots. Some cold spots "faded out" completely after a few applications of a threshold stimulus at 30 sec intervals. Normal sensitivity could, however, be rapidly restored by applying a stimulus of high temperature for one min. Such recovery tended to be unstable if the depression of threshold had been extreme; rest periods of 2–5 min also brought about recovery, but this was very likely to be unstable. The results of this study indicate that *punctiform stimulation of human cold spots produces complete thermal adaptation to a cold stimulus in a few seconds* and that *the application of high temperatures for approximately one minute produces rapid restoration of the unadapted thresh-old value.*

Glaser, Hall, and Whittow (1958) studied localized thermal adaptation for warming and cooling, by using large cutaneous areas and measuring certain physiological variables. Three observers immersed the same hand six times daily for 60 sec in water at 47°C and six times daily for 60 sec in water at 4°C. Prior to each series of immersions, the hand was kept in water at 31°C for 30 min; between identical immersions within each series, the hand was kept in water for 60 sec.

On the first day of the experiment, there was a rise in mean systolic blood pressure by 16 mm of mercury when the hand was immersed at 47°C, and by 32 mm at 4°C. For the same conditions, the mean diastolic blood pressure rose by 8 mm and 28 mm, respectively. *Within 9–15 days, the original reports of pain had diminished and the rise of blood pressure and heart rate had essentially disappeared,* both during hot and cold immersions. At the end of the experiment, the systolic blood pressure change was zero at 47°C and +3 mm at 4°C, and the diastolic pressure was −2 mm at 47°C and +6 mm at 4°C. Comparison of single immersions of the hand opposite that which was tested revealed no reportable differences between hands either prior to the series of immersions or at the end of the study. It did not appear that localized changes in the blood vessels or in the pain receptors could account for the observed adaptations; thus, it was hypothesized that simultaneous adaptation to localized warming and cooling might be mediated by the brain, rather than by the peripheral structures.

Pain.   For many years, certain biological views concerning the survival value of pain tended to propagate the classic notion that pain was incapable of adaptation. Even as late as 1909, Titchener wrote that "the pain sense does not appear to show the phenomenon of adaptation" (p. 154). The problem, however, was not that pain was incapable of adaptation, but that difficulties inherent in controlling the conditions of stimulation precluded satisfactory measurement of the phenomenon. As in the other sensory modalities, constant and steady stimulation must be maintained in order to produce adaptation; headaches, toothaches, and pains due to injuries seldom show adaptation since the physiological and stimulatory conditions at the site of the trauma involve rhythmic changes associated with activities of the circulatory system.

Straus and Uhlmann (1919) were the first to study the phenomenon of pain adaptation systematically. They used a mechanical needle (*algesimeter*) to stimulate the volar side of the forearm that rested in a plaster cast. Three intensities of stimulation, as measured on a pressure balance, were used with a constant rate of application: 3.0, 5.5, and 8.0 gm, respectively. By inhibiting the movement of the skin and arm, adaptation of pain was obtained with a high degree of regularity. Although there were large individual differences (by approximately a factor of 2), the results showed that *adaptation time for pain increases essentially as a linear function of the intensity of stimulation.* The mean adaptation time for two observers is shown in Figure 9-15.

Later, in the first of a series of three studies, Burns and Dallenbach (1933) also used a needle algesiometer to investigate the qualitative changes in the course of pain adaptation. They found that in every case pain was replaced by pressure before complete adaptation was secured. The typical course was described as "a gradual subsidence from a maximal pain through pressure to indifference"; but, was the pressure simply a residual effect from the particular mechanical stimulus?

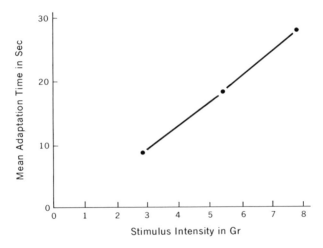

Figure 9-15. Adaptation time for pain as a function of stimulus intensity applied to the forearm. (From Strauss and Uhlmann, *Amer. J. Psychol.*, 1919.)

The question was answered by Stone and Dallenbach (1934). To avoid the arousal of pressure, radiant heat was used to elicit pain from the dorsal surface of the forearm. The stimulator was a pyrex glass tube that was heated by passing an electric current through a coil of resistance wire wrapped around the tube. For each trial, the stimulator was positioned by a rack and pinion gear at a point one mm above the skin surface; the oral reports of the observer were recorded and timed with a stopwatch. When the stimulus was applied, the first report was that of warmth; warmth became more intensive until heat and then increasing pain were reported. The maximal pain remained constant for a short time and then declined through heat and eventually warmth. An analogous situation was obtained in the third experiment (Edes and Dallenbach, 1936) when dry ice was used as the stimulus in the adaptation of pain aroused by cold.

The mean time required for the arousal of pain for five observers in the heat experiment varied from 40.3 to 41.7 sec. The criterion of adaptation was specified as the disappearance of pain for an interval of 20 sec. Under this criterion, complete adaptation occurred in 60 percent of the total trials for the five observers and adaptation for a period less than 20 sec occurred in 40 percent of the trials. The mean time from the first arousal of pain to complete adaptation varied considerably among observers, but in no case was it greater than approximately 5 min. Once complete adaptation had occurred, it required on the average approximately 0.5 min for the rearousal of pain. The stimulation times of the rearousals averaged approximately 18 sec shorter than the first arousals and were attributed to the "softening effect" of the first stimulations.

This series of experiments not only provides data on the adaptation of pain, but indicates that pain is a separate and distinct sensory modality. It stands apart from pressure, warmth, and cold and has its own receptor organs (free nerve endings). One of the classic views (Goldscheider) maintained that the cutaneous system for pressure was also responsible for pain. Thus, pressure and pain were said to differ only intensively from each other, with the consequence that the sufficient weakening of pain should change subjectively into pressure. The alternative view (von Frey) held that pain should adapt independently of the other cutaneous modalities, that is, the residual effects of adaptation in a given modality should reflect qualities characteristic of the appropriate stimulus for that modality. Pressure stimuli should leave an impression of pressure; heat should leave warmth; and cold, cold. Pain should adapt and disappear without changing into pressure. This was precisely the finding of Dallenbach and his co-workers.

Extent of Stimulation and the Rates of Adaptation and Recovery

The third generalization on the adaptive processes states that *there is a direct relation between the extent (areal size) of the stimulus and the duration of adaptation and recovery*. That is, as the area stimulated becomes larger, the adaptation or recovery time becomes longer. This relationship, of course, holds only for those sensory systems in which the stimulus has spatial properties; it does not, for example, apply to olfaction and audition. In general, the variable of areal size and its relation to adaptation and recovery has not been studied as extensively as duration or intensity. There are, nevertheless, a few studies which suggest that the duration of the adaptive processes becomes longer as the area stimulated becomes larger, other factors being held constant.

Visual Processes.   One study which supports this generalization is that of Hecht, Haig, and Wald (1935) in vision. Three observers were light-adapted for 2 min to 300 mL under conditions of monocular viewing. Threshold determinations were then made for areas of white light subtending diameters of 2, 3, 5, 10, and 20 degrees of visual angle. The observer's fixation point was at the center of the field where the test flashes were presented and his vision was through an artificial pupil 2.85 mm in diameter.

The results of this study for one observer are presented in Figure 9-16, which shows the thresholds of dark adaptation (recovery) as a function of time (min) in the dark. Two facts emerge from these functions: (1) *as the size of the fixated field increases, the recovery process requires a longer time and the recovery curves yield lower (more sensitive) threshold values;* and (2) *as the stimulus area increases, there is an earlier appearance of the rod portion of the recovery curve.* With centrally fixated fields of increasing size, the threshold seems to be determined by the sensitivity of the receptors at the

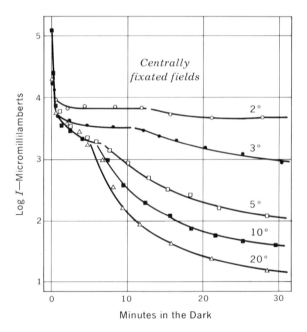

Figure 9-16. Dark adaptation (recovery) curves as a function of time in the dark, with centrally fixated fields subtending larger and larger angles at the observer's eye. (From Hecht *et al.* Reprinted by permission of The Rockefeller University Press from *J. gen. Physiol.*, 1935, **19**, 321–329.)

circumference of the field, and this changes as the area becomes larger, encompassing more and more rods from the peripheral regions.

Cutaneous Temperature.   Jenkins (1937 *b*) performed a study of adaptation with a series of small circular stimulators ranging from 1.25 to 10 mm in diameter. Four observers were tested on the forearm with the temperature of the stimulators at 10° and 44°C in different testing sessions. The results of the study showed that the *period of adaptation time increased with the size of the stimulator;* however, since the square root of area, diameter, and perimeter vary concomitantly, the relevant dimension of the stimulator can not be specified. There were no marked differences in the levels of adaptation time for warmth as compared with those for cold. Individual differences in adaptation time were quite large, but the range of magnitudes was about 20 to 120 sec or more for both cold and warm stimuli. The form of the function relating adaptation time to stimulus diameter is erratic for individual observers, but it appears to be roughly linear for stimuli at 10°C.

Cutaneous Pressure.   Adaptation to cutaneous pressure is a commonplace occurrence. We seldom feel the pressure of rings or eyeglasses unless we change the stimulus conditions by moving our fingers or eyebrows; even our clothes and shoes cease to be felt if we remain perfectly still.

For cutaneous pressure, adaptation time *decreases* as the area stimulated becomes larger. This is *contrary* to the generalization stated at the beginning of this section. The data are shown in Table 9-2 in which adaptation time (sec) is shown

Table 9-2   Adaptation Time in Seconds for Cutaneous Pressures of Different Sizes

Stimulus Diameter (mm)	Region Stimulated Forehead	Cheek
5	18.9	21.2
10	16.1	16.4
15	14.6	14.4
20	12.3	12.2
25	9.9	10.3

Source: M. J. Zigler. Pressure adaptation time; a function of intensity and extensity. *Amer. J. Psychol.,* 1932, **44,** 709–720.

as a function of the diameter of the stimulator. One set of values is for adaptation on the forehead, the other, on the cheek. Except for the smallest diameter, there are no differences in adaptation time between the forehead and cheek; both locations, however, show shorter adaptation times with the larger stimuli and negate the hypothesis that the period of adaptation is directly related to the areal size of the stimulus.

Comment

Although there are a number of available studies dealing with problems of sensory adaptation, the literature on recovery functions is considerably more restricted. For a complete understanding of the various sensory processes, these functions should be established. It is quite possible that the inherent problems of experimentation in this area have tended generally to restrict such studies, except for research in vision and audition. The sources of error in studying adaptation and recovery are numerous and critical—the stimulus situation must be completely controlled and maintained at a constant level if the desired functions are to be obtained. Despite these and other difficulties, the literature in this area provides a sufficient and adequate basis from which to generalize on adaptation and recovery. Three of these generalizations have been formulated in the present chapter and supporting evidence has been provided. The generalization on the relation of areal size of the stimulus and the rates of adaptation and recovery is the least well substantiated and requires additional research. The lawfulness of adaptation and recovery as sensory phenomena, however, cannot be disputed and any theory which purports to explain the functioning of a given sensory modality must be able to encompass these effects.

Afterimages

In addition to the processes of adaptation and recovery, there are certain other temporal effects that occur in the various sensory systems. The terms commonly used to designate these effects are *"afterimages"* or "after-sensations." Each of these terms refers to the persistence of sensory excitation, in a given system, that can be detected and reported by an observer following the removal of the adequate stimulus. Although afterimages occur in several modalities, the most readily observed are those that occur in vision.

Vision

The afterimages that occur in vision are of several kinds and depend upon the kind of stimulation which was originally present. With the termination of a given stimulus, one or more of these afterimages may occur. When the stimulus is a very intense flash of white light, a *flight of colors* may be "observed" in which there is a successive series of colors changing from purples, blues, yellows, greens, reds, and bluish-greens. Dark intervals are interspersed between the colors. The series may vary from observer to observer, but the number of changes and the total duration of the series will depend upon the intensity of the original flash (Berry and Imus, 1935). A complete explanation for the flight of colors is not yet available.

There are two other kinds of visual afterimages: *positive* and *negative afterimages.* When an observer looks at a patch of color for approximately 30 seconds, certain changes produced in the retina will persist for a short time. Since there is a lag in retinal activity, the original color will continue to be "seen" for a brief time after the stimulus is terminated. This is called a positive afterimage; the observer "sees" a patch of color similar in both brightness and hue to the original. Positive afterimages are difficult to detect without practice; they can best be observed after the dark-adapted eye has been exposed to a moderately intense stimulus of brief duration.

The negative afterimage "develops" quite promptly after the positive afterimage has faded. It builds up in a few seconds, but usually decays over a somewhat longer period. Every color of the negative afterimage appears as the complementary in hue to the original and is opposite in brightness. Green areas in the original stimulus appear red in the afterimage; whites appear black; and neutral gray remains the same. Negative afterimages are of longer duration than the positive and can be obtained under a wide range of conditions. A typical procedure is to have the observer stare steadily, without moving the eyes, at a small patch of color for approximately 30 seconds so that the eyes become light-adapted. Then the observer stares at a piece of gray paper (or neutral wall) until, after a few seconds, the negative afterimage "develops." If the eyes are blinked or moved, the negative afterimage may disappear temporarily. For this reason, in everyday situations we do not normally notice the persistent negative afterimages; however, these afterimages may influence our judgments of color and their effects must be controlled in laboratory studies.

While a totally acceptable explanation of afterimages has not been given, the effect appears to be related to the phenomenon of recovery from stimulation; furthermore, afterimages are assumed to involve processes that are chemical in nature due to the relatively long period of visual recovery. A simple explanation of negative afterimages is that the receptive elements or processes of the retina are adapted in direct proportion to the stimulation provided by the original patch. This means that different types of elements or processes are adapted to different degrees. When the stimulus is terminated and the observer is exposed to a uniform white light, the retinal processes are capable of responding only to the extent that they were not adapted. Thus, the receptors fire at different rates depending on their states of adaptation. This means, according to the Helmholtz theory of color perception, that the observer will "see" the complement of the original color. Such an explanation probably points in the proper direction, but we might expect that this is far too simple an explanation to account for the detailed effects of afterimages.

One other aspect of visual afterimages needs to be considered, that is, their apparent size. *Emmert's law* states that the judged size of the image is proportional to the distance from the eye to the surface on which the afterimage is projected. The afterimage looks larger when it is projected on a more distant surface. The reason for this is that the physiological process involved in the original adapting period has a fixed areal size on the retina. Thus, if a one-inch square of white paper on a black background were to be fixated at a distance of 10 inches, and the black afterimage observed on a white background *at the same distance,* the image would cover one square inch. If the projection surface were moved 50 inches away, the image would be five inches in diameter on the background. Since the physiological process has a fixed retinal size, the size of the image will vary directly with the distance of the projection surface. Once a negative afterimage has been developed, it may be made to appear larger or smaller simply by fixating alternately on a far or near projection surface.

Other Sensory Systems

Studies of afterimages in sensory systems other than vision have been very limited. For pressure, the afterimages are positive, that is, similar to those produced by the original stimulation. Eyeglasses may feel as though they are still being worn even after they have been removed for some time. The origin of the afterimages is probably related to the expansion of tissues which were previously compressed by the stimulus object.

Positive afterimages also occur for cold and warmth. When the original stimulus is held constant for a second or two, there is a direct relationship between the intensity of the afterimage reported for a spot and its duration. It may be that the afterimages are due to the relatively slow changes of the temperature receptors, such that there is continued stimulation at the receptors after the stimulus object is removed.

The afterimages produced by stimulation of the vestibular receptors have not been studied to any great extent. If a subject is rotated to the left and rotation is suddenly stopped, the perception of motion (among other effects) will be to the right. It is not clear, however, whether these are pure afterimages, or the result

of real stimulation. It is possible that, after the cupula is bent by the initial acceleration, it overshoots and bends the other way as it returns to its original position following the cessation of rotation. This would produce an effect opposite that
at the start of rotation. Similarly, afterimages in taste which persist after the
stimulus flow has been stopped have been shown to be due to continued excitation
of the receptors; in this case the "afterimages" are produced by the presence of
salt in the crevices of the tongue and cheeks, and in the spaces between the teeth.

In audition, the search for an afterimage has been unsuccessful. The most
nearly comparable situation to that in vision is found in tinnitus—the annoying
ringing in the ear that often occurs when the ear has been exposed to sounds of
high intensity. However, tinnitus often has a pathological origin and may last
for hours at a time. These conditions do not correspond to the usual characteristics
of afterimages, which suggests that the auditory effects are not strictly analogous
to those in vision.

In recent years, there has been relatively little interest in the study of afterimages, although it would appear that additional research in all sensory systems
could produce findings of substantial theoretical significance.

Chapter 10

SENSORY MALFUNCTIONS
AND ABNORMALITIES

Orientation

In the foregoing chapters our primary concern has been the study of the various sensory systems under normal conditions of stimulation and response. This is, of course, the usual approach of the experimental psychologist who attempts to establish laws describing the basic processes of these systems. Now, in this chapter, we deviate from the usual approach and extend our interest to sensory malfunctions and abnormalities. We will consider various forms of derangement of sensory mechanisms, as produced by accident, disease, or other conditions, and will be concerned with their functional effects as evidenced in behavior. From time to time other writers in psychology have presented fragmentary or isolated accounts of sensory disturbances; here, however, the intent is to present selected material on abnormal or pathological conditions in a systematic manner so that a more comprehensive understanding of the various sensory systems may be obtained.

This chapter will not transform the reader into a medical practitioner, any more than the earlier chapters will have converted him into a physicist or philosopher. It will, however, provide an opportunity to continue to explore the human sensory systems from a functional point of view. The presence of an abnormal or pathological condition in a given system will not ordinarily lead to a random state of affairs; the system may be expected to continue to function in certain predictable ways, provided the posited theory is substantially correct. Thus, the adequacy of a theory may in part be determined from the accuracy of its predictions under abnormal circumstances.

In this presentation, we will consider the extent to which the principles at work in the normal sensory systems are still in operation in a defective system. The effects of certain abnormalities and pathological conditions will be presented and interpreted in relation to particular theories of sensory behavior. This treatment of material should provide for a more unified concept of the functioning of sensory systems, from an understanding of the physical conditions of stimulation through normal modes of response to common malfunctions induced by accident, disease, environmental or hereditary factors. This provides for a somewhat broader perspective of experimental psychology than is usually offered in traditional textbooks.

The Visual System

Disturbances Involving the Oculomotor Muscles

In Chapter 4, it was indicated that there are two groups of muscles in each eye: the intrinsic and the extrinsic. The intrinsic muscles include the ciliary body and the iridal musculature; the extrinsic muscles consist of the two oblique and four recti which determine the position of the eye in relation to the skull. Thus, the action of the extrinsic muscles is to rotate the eye around a *center of rotation* which is located, theoretically, in the horizontal plane about 12 or 13 mm behind the cornea.

In every movement of the eye, each of the extrinsic muscles is involved to some degree, either in contraction or inhibition. For the normal eye, there are three types of motion: (1) rotation around the vertical axis so that the eye is turned from side to side; (2) rotation around the horizontal axis so that the eye is turned upwards or downwards; and (3) rotation around the centeroposterior axis so that a movement of *torsion* is created. *Intorsion* occurs when the upper pole of the cornea rotates nasally and *extorsion* occurs when it rotates temporally. In these movements, the muscles that contract together are called *synergists;* those that are inhibited, *antagonists.* Each movement of the eyeball is, therefore, called a *synkinesis.* Synkinesis may be *uniocular* or *binocular,* in which abduction of one eye is normally accompanied by adduction of the other, that is, *conjugate deviation.*

Strabismus. There are certain derangements, however, in which the visual axes assume a position with respect to each other that does not correspond to that required by the normal physiological conditions. *Strabismus,* or *squint,* is the generic term for such disturbances. In *paralytic* strabismus due to a neural lesion below the level of the midbrain, there is often paralysis of an ocular muscle and the eye loses its ability to turn in the direction of the normal action. If the defect is slight (*paresis*), the lack of mobility may be so small as to escape detection unless special tests are used. For those eye positions in which the affected muscle is not involved, the visual axes assume their normal relationships, that is, each eye fixates an object with its fovea (*binocular fixation*); otherwise, the eyes move in such a manner that the image fails to fall on the fovea of the deviating eye. In some cases, both eyes can fixate the same object only when both are exposed, but when either eye is covered, the covered eye deviates (*heterophoria*); the deviation may be temporally, nasally, upward or downward, while the uncovered eye continues to fixate the object.

Diplopia. The primary complaint of patients with paralysis of an extrinsic muscle is usually that they have "double vision," that is, they see double (*diplopia*). This occurs only over that part of the field of fixation toward which the affected muscle or muscles move the eye. *Binocular diplopia* is present when both eyes are functional, but only one deviates. The squinting eye produces a *false or apparent image* which is usually less distinct than that produced by the fixing eye (*true image*), since the properly fixing eye has the image falling upon the fovea centralis. The false image has an angular displacement which is equal to the angle of deviation of the eye. To lessen the diplopia and its associated annoying consequences, the individual usually holds his head so that his face is turned in the direction of the action of the paralyzed muscle, for example, the head is turned to the right when the right lateral rectus is paralyzed.

False projection also occurs in binocular diplopia. In this case, the object is projected or "seen" too far in the direction of action of the paralyzed muscle. When the right lateral rectus is paralyzed, the object is fixated too far to the right. In old paralysis, the individual may learn by experience to compensate for this false projection. When false projection occurs in conjunction with binocular diplopia, *vertigo* is produced; objects appear to move with increasing velocity in the direction in which the affected eye is moving. This leads to nausea and even vomiting. Over a long period of time, relief may be obtained as the individual learns to ignore the impressions from the affected eye.

Nystagmus. *Nystagmus* is the term for the condition in which the eyes exhibit rapid oscillatory movements, independent of the ordinary movements that occur normally. The oscillations are usually lateral, but may be vertical, rotatory, or a mixed combination of these. Nystagmus is nearly always bilateral, although the movements may be more marked in one eye than the other. In *latent nystagmus,* no oscillations occur when both eyes are open; however, when either eye is covered, nystagmus is elicited. Sometimes *nystagmoid jerks* occur in normal people, such as when they are fatigued. These jerks are larger rhythmic movements that are most noticeable at the extreme limits of ocular movement. Nystagmus of this type is not a true nystagmus.

Nystagmus may be of several different kinds, depending upon the conditions that produce it. It may be *congenital* or may be *acquired,* either during infancy or adulthood. Congenital and early infantile nystagmus occurs in congenitally malformed eyes, in albinism, and in eyes with opacities in the various ocular structures. These conditions lead to an inability to develop normal fixation and the eyes exhibit "searching movements." In adults, nystagmus may occur due to diseases of the midbrain, cerebellum and vestibular tracts, and of the semicircular canals. Disease of the inner ear (involving the semicircular canals) produces *labyrinthine nystagmus,* which can be simulated in normal adults by rotation in a specially designed chair, by syringing the ears, or by passing a galvanic current through the head. The nystagmic movement that occurs will depend upon the particular semicircular canal involved, but any pair of semicircular canals can be stimulated by placing the head in a suitable position. Ordinarily the nystagmus is rhythmic, with a rapid component in one direction and a slow component in the opposite direction; it is bilateral and horizontal, or rotatory. If one labyrinth is destroyed, rhythmic nystagmus occurs toward the opposite side; this ceases if the other labyrinth is also destroyed.

Errors of Refraction (Ametropia)

Visual Acuity.   From an optical point of view, the human eye may be regarded as a single system with a biconvex lens with one *optical center* (the nodal point, N) which lies in the posterior portion of the crystalline lens. With thin lenses, any light ray that passes through the optical center will not be refracted, that is, it will not deviate in its direction of propagation as it enters and leaves the lens. This is shown in Figure 10-1, as it applies to the formation of the image on the retina of the human eye.

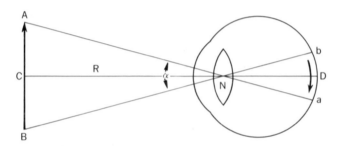

Figure 10-1.   Schematic representation of the formation of the retinal image in the normal human eye.

The optical axis (CD), extended backward to the retina, meets the retina almost exactly at the fovea centralis. Thus, parallel rays from a distant object will be brought to a focus at the fovea, provided the eye is normal and the object is located on the forward projection of the optical axis. Due to the action of the biconvex lens, however, the image at the fovea is optically inverted.

Since the nodal point (N) corresponds to the optical center of a convex lens, it is an easy matter to determine the size of the retinal image which any external object will produce. This may be shown with reference to Figure 10-1. In this figure, the line AB represents the length of some characteristic of a visual stimulus, such as the length of a line or the separation between two points. For the condition in which the optical axis (line of regard) bisects the line AB, the visual angle (α) is given by

$$\tan \frac{\alpha}{2} = \frac{L}{2R},\tag{10-1}$$

where α is the angle formed by ANB, L is the length of the line AB, and R is the distance from N to line AB along the optical axis. R is measured most practicably from the anterior surface of the cornea, but must be specified from the vertex of the angle in order to calculate the size of the retinal image. The length of the line ND is typically taken to be 17 mm.

For small visual angles where $\tan \alpha = \alpha$, approximately,

$$\alpha = \frac{L}{R}, \text{ in radians or} \tag{10-2}$$

$$\alpha = \frac{57.3L}{R}, \text{ in degrees.} \tag{10-3}$$

Equations 10-2 and 10-3 hold perfectly when line AB is curved so that all points on the line are equidistant from N. Otherwise, Equation 10-3 overestimates α by 1 percent at a value of 10 degrees (Graham, 1951).

The visual angle (ANB) subtended by the object at the nodal point is, geometrically, exactly equal to the angle aNb, which is subtended by the retinal image at the nodal point. Thus, the concept of visual angle may be used either to specify the size of a test object or its corresponding retinal image, or to indicate the ability of the eye to resolve fine detail in an external object, that is, *visual acuity*. Visual acuity is the reciprocal of the minimum visual angle expressed in minutes of arc; the larger the angle, the lower (poorer) the visual acuity and vice versa.

For the normal eye, the minimum visual angle that can be discriminated is usually specified as 1 min of arc. However, there are several experimental variables that will determine the exact value of the minimum visual angle. The kind of test used may affect the results, so that the minimum visual angle may vary from about 2.0 sec to 1 min of arc, or more. Also, the size of the minimum angle is inversely related to the level of retinal illuminance, ranging from about 10 min of arc for low levels to 0.5 min (30 sec) at high levels. The limit of visual acuity under ideal viewing conditions is about 0.5 sec of arc—this is approximately equivalent to seeing a wire, $\frac{1}{16}$ in. in diameter, at a distance of a half-mile.

Figure 10-2 shows visual acuity as a function of retinal illuminance for two kinds of target: the Landolt C (broken circle) and a grating (a field of contrasting dark and light stripes of equal width). Below approximately 30 trolands, the grating provides for higher visual acuities; above this point, the Landolt C provides for higher acuities. The greatest acuity possible with the grating is lower than with the Landolt C by about 30 percent. Although the shapes of the two curves are somewhat different, the data of both may be adequately described by a set of equations that are similar except for the constants that are used.

In the clinical setting, visual acuity is measured by the well-known Snellen Chart. This consists of nine horizontal rows of letters that diminish in size by known visual angles. On the chart, the rows are marked in feet, going from 200 feet for the top row (large E) to 10 feet for the last (smallest) row. The person being tested indicates whether he is seeing properly simply by reading aloud the names of the various letters in each row. This test, however, has serious limitations, one of which is a lack of control of the various factors that are known to affect visual acuity. For example, the level of illumination is usually not uniform over the

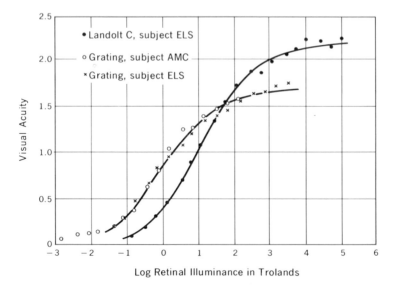

Figure 10-2. The variation of visual acuity as a function of retinal illuminance for two types of tasks: resolution of a grating and recognition of the orientation of a Landolt C test figure. (From Shlaer. Reprinted by permission of The Rockefeller University Press from *J. gen. Physiol.*, 1937, **21**, 165–188.)

entire area of the chart. Also, some letters are easier to identify than others due to their intrinsic shapes and the relative spacing of their structural elements. Consequently, the Snellen Chart is not used for laboratory purposes, but is useful in the clinical situation for detecting problems in visual acuity.

The Snellen Chart is ordinarily presented at a test distance of 20 feet. At this distance, a normal observer can see a separation between the portions of a letter target that subtend a visual angle of one minute of arc. If a patient sees at 20 feet what he is expected to see at 20 feet, he is classified as having a visual acuity of 20/20. If a patient requires a separation of 2 minutes at 20 feet, he is classified as 20/40, since a normal observer could detect the same separation at 40 feet. According to this system, the patient's visual acuity (v) is specified by the relation

$$v = D/d, \tag{10-4}$$

where D is the standard viewing distance of 20 feet and d is the distance at which the detectable separations of the letter target subtend a minimum angle of 1 min of arc.

Table 10-1 presents a summary of some common ratings on the Snellen Chart and their corresponding values in terms of visual acuity. The table also contains the loss of central vision in percent as rated by the American Medical Association (1955).

The Landolt C and the Snellen letters measure acuity in terms of a task of visual recognition. This task, however, is not the only type used in measuring

Table 10-1 Ratings on Snellen Chart, Corresponding Visual Acuity, and the Percent Loss of Central Vision

Snellen Chart	Visual Acuity (decimal system)	Minimum Visual Angle[a] (in min of arc)	Loss of Central Vision (percent)
20/10	2.0	0.5	None
20/20	1.0	1.0	None
20/25	0.8	1.25	5
20/32	0.6	1.6	10
20/40	0.5	2.0	15
20/50	0.4	2.5	25
20/64	0.3	3.3	35
20/100	0.2	5.0	50
20/200	0.1	10.0	80
20/400	0.05	20.0	90
20/800	0.025	40.0	95

Source: The Executive Committee of the Section on Ophthalmology, American Medical Association, Atlantic City, New Jersey, June, 1955. (See *AMA Arch. Industr. Hlth.,* 1955, **12,** 439–449, 527.)
[a] Visual angle of the constituent part of the Snellen letter. Multiply the visual angle of each constituent part by 5 to obtain the visual angle of the entire test character.

vision, although all types of tasks express visual acuity in terms of the reciprocal of visual angle. The differences in the types of tasks relate to the critical features of the stimulus situation that determine the observer's response. There are four basic types of tasks: (1) *detection,* (2) *recognition,* (3) *resolution,* and (4) *localization.* Some commonly used stimulus figures for each of these tasks are shown in Figure 10-3 (Riggs, 1965).

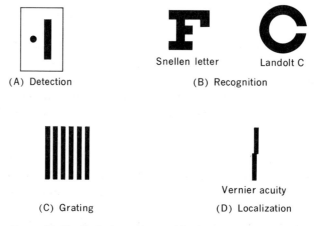

(A) Detection

Snellen letter   Landolt C

(B) Recognition

(C) Grating

Vernier acuity

(D) Localization

Figure 10-3. Typical targets used in the measurement of visual acuity in four different types of tasks: (A) detection, (B) recognition, (C) grating, and (D) localization. See text for details.

The task of *detection* requires the observer merely to report the presence or absence of the test object in the visual field. In the task of *recognition,* the observer must name the test letter or specify the location of a critical aspect of the test figure, such as the gap in the Landolt ring. The Snellen letters have lines and serifs that have a thickness equal to one-fifth the height or width of the whole letter; the Landolt ring has a gap and a thickness of line that are both equal to one-fifth of the outer diameter. Given the task of *resolution*, the observer must respond to the separations that are present between the elements of the pattern. In the acuity grating, the width of the dark and light lines are made equal. Although a single dark line is detectable with a minimum width of 0.5 sec of arc, the grating can only be resolved if the dark and light lines are each increased to at least 25 sec of arc under high levels of illuminance. The task of *localization* is exemplified by vernier acuity in which the observer must report the lateral displacement of one segment of a line divided at the middle. The significance of these four types of tasks for the experimental psychologist is that the visual acuity measured for a given observer will depend, in part, upon the particular task imposed.

One of the limiting factors in visual acuity has been assumed to be the fineness or coarseness of the discrete receptive elements in the retinal layer of the eye. This pattern of elements is called the *retinal mosaic*. In the classical view, it was proposed that in order for a test figure such as an acuity grating to be resolved, there must be a row of unstimulated cones between any two rows of cones stimulated by the figure. The dark and light lines had to fall on separate rows of cone receptors. This is shown schematically in Figure 10-4.

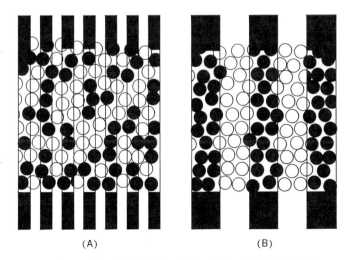

(A)   (B)

Figure 10-4.   The classical view of visual discrimination. (A) When the retina is stimulated with a very fine grating, the pattern of neural discharge is random and the grating is unresolved. (B) When the spacing between the bars is increased sufficiently, the grating pattern is "stamped" on that of the discharge and resolution occurs. (From Weale, 1960.)

The evidence on visual acuity now makes it clear that for some types of tasks, the separation between individual cones is not of primary significance (Riggs,

1965). The diameters of the finest cone receptors of the retina are approximately 24 to 27 sec of arc (O'Brien, 1951), but certain tasks of detection and localization yield minimum visual angles much smaller than this. An offset of 2 sec of arc is easily located in a task of vernier acuity (Berry, 1948). It appears that the fineness of the retinal mosaic is not the principal limiting factor for visual acuity, but that the limit is imposed by the diffraction of the light entering the eye via the pupil. Thus, even if the retinal mosaic were more compact, visual acuity would probably not be improved.

Accommodation.   The ability of the eye to discriminate detail is controlled to a large extent by the process of *accommodation*. Accommodation involves an adjustment of the lens of the eye so that the light rays entering the normal eye are brought to a focus on the retina. More precisely, this adjustment changes the *focal length* of the lens, that is, it changes the distance between the nodal point of the lens and the point of convergence on the optical axis at which incident light rays that are parallel to the axis are brought together.

Accommodation refers to the refractive state of the lens and depends upon its shape; it provides a fine degree of control over the formation of the image. The mechanism of accommodation changes the curvature of the anterior and posterior surfaces of the lens of the eye. At rest, the radius of curvature of the anterior surface is 10 mm; that of the posterior surface, 6 mm. In accommodation, the curvature of the posterior surface remains essentially constant, but the anterior surface changes so that in strong accommodation it is about 6 mm.

Physiologically, the lens capsule is attached to the ciliary body by means of suspensory ligaments and the change in the shape of the lens is brought about by the action of the ciliary muscle. When the ciliary muscle contracts, it pulls forward the posterior part of the ciliary body and the anterior part of the choroid; this produces a slackening of the suspensory ligament and the lens capsule. Since the lens is pliable, it tends to conform to the shape of its capsule. As the capsule slackens, the lens becomes thicker with the anterior surface bowed forward. The support of the vitreous tends to hold the posterior surface of the lens relatively fixed. Under this condition of *dynamic refraction,* the eye is capable of producing a considerably greater effect upon the convergence of incident rays than when it is in a condition of *static refraction,* that is, in a state of rest.

In accommodation, as shown in Figure 10-5, the lens becomes thicker when a person is looking at a near object; it becomes thinner for a far object. If the process of accommodation is functioning properly, the image of the object will be focused directly on the retina. The greatest distance from which the light rays from a target (object) can be properly focused on the retina is called the *far point of vision.* In the normal (*emmetropic*) eye, this distance is infinity. Likewise, there is a point that defines the nearest distance at which a target can be placed and still be seen clearly. This is called the *near point of vision.* The linear distance between the near point and far point is called the *range of accommodation.*

With advancing age, the near point recedes so that the range of accommodation becomes less and less. This is particularly marked after the age of 20 years. For example, at 10 years of age, the near point is approximately 7 cm from the normal

LENS ACCOMMODATION

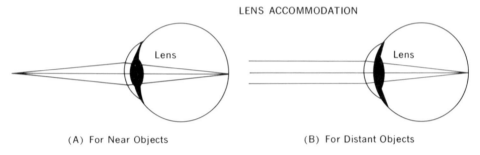

(A) For Near Objects   (B) For Distant Objects

Figure 10–5. Representation of the accommodation of the lens in the human eye. (A) The lens thickens to focus on nearby objects. (B) The lens flattens to focus on distant objects. In each case, the normal process of accommodation brings the image to a focus on the retina.

eye, while at 30 years it is 14 cm. In the aging process, the lens exhibits a continuous accumulation of insoluble proteins and a concentration of a yellow, unidentified pigment (Weale, 1960). Thus, aging produces both a hardening of the lens—which reduces the range of accommodation—and a decrease in the amount of light reaching the retina, particularly on the blue end of the spectrum. This physiological change in the power of the eye to accommodate as a function of age is called *presbyopia*. It follows, then, that "reading" glasses will be needed to see near objects sharply, even if the eye were originally emmetropic, that is, capable of focusing parallel rays exactly on the retina when at rest.

In some eyes, the distance between the lens and the retina is too large or too small for the images of distant objects to be focused clearly upon the retina. If the retina is too near the lens, the eye is said to be *hypermetropic* (farsighted). In this case, the parallel rays would not have come to a focus, given the eye at rest. If the retina is too far away from the lens, the eye is said to be *myopic* (nearsighted). In this condition, parallel rays have not only come to a focus but have started to diverge. Both of these disorders (hypermetropia and myopia) are *errors of refraction* (*axial ametropia*) and produce a blurred image upon the retina, thereby impairing vision.

The total refracting power of the normal (emmetropic) eye is about 60 diopters (D), with the cornea contributing 38 D and the mature lens 22 D. For ophthalmic purposes 1 diopter is taken as the refractive power of a lens with a focal length of 1 meter (or 100 cm). A lens with a focal length of half a meter will be twice as strong as one with a focal length of 1 meter; the refractive power of this lens would be 2 D. The dioptric power (D) is thus the reciprocal of the focal length (F, expressed in cm) multiplied by 100. Stated in the form of an equation,

$$D = 100\left(\frac{1}{F}\right). \tag{10-5}$$

Figure 10-6 is a diagrammatic representation of three refractive states of the eye: (a) emmetropic, (b) hypermetropic, and (c) myopic. In hypermetropia, if the rays are given the requisite amount of convergence before they enter the eye

REFRACTIVE STATES OF THE EYE

(A) Emmetropia (Normal Vision)

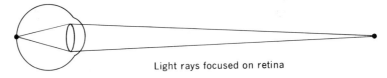

Light rays focused on retina

(B) Hypermetropia (Farsighted Vision)

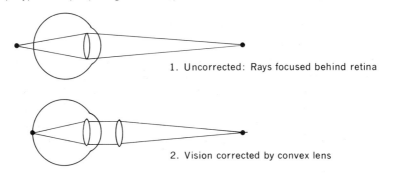

1. Uncorrected: Rays focused behind retina

2. Vision corrected by convex lens

(C) Myopia (Nearsighted Vision)

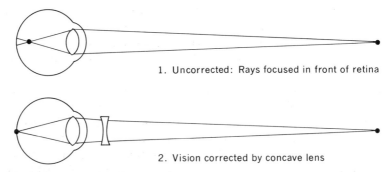

1. Uncorrected: Rays focused in front of retina

2. Vision corrected by concave lens

Figure 10-6. Representation of the three retractive states of the eye: (A) emmetropia (normal), (B) hypermetropia (farsighted), and (C) myopia (nearsighted). In hypermetropia and myopia, the use of glasses with properly prescribed lenses may correct these conditions by bringing the light rays to a focus on the retina.

by placing a convex lens in front of it, they will be brought to a focus upon the retina. Similarly in myopia, if we give the rays the requisite amount of divergence before they enter the eye, they will be brought to a focus upon the retina. This can be accomplished by placing a concave lens in front of the eye.

Correcting glasses not only focus the image on the retina but, depending on the distance from the cornea, may produce a change in the size of the retinal image. If the lens is more than 15 mm from the cornea, the retinal image in hypermetropia is larger and, in myopia, smaller than the emmetropic image. In hypermetropia, the enlarged image is advantageous but, in myopia, the decrease in size is disadvantageous. Consequently, in myopia, glasses ought to be made to fit as closely to the eyes as possible, with the optical center of the spectacle lens about 12–13 mm from the cornea. In all cases of ametropia, the prismatic effects of glasses can be eliminated by the use of plastic contact lenses; also, the field of clear vision is greatly increased. Contact lenses are, therefore, particularly valuable in high errors of refraction, as in myopia and *aphakia,* that is, in the absence of the crystalline lens of the eye.

Errors in refraction may arise from causes other than the axial shortening or lengthening of the eye. They may, for instance, be due to alterations in the curvatures of the refractive surfaces. This produces an error of refraction called *astigmatism.* In most cases, the corneal surface is flatter from side to side than it is from above downwards. *Regular astigmatism* refers to the condition in which the cornea has the direction of greatest and least curvature at right angles to one another. The correction for this condition is to use a cylindrical lens so that one set of rays will be affected more than the other. When parallel rays fall upon the lens in the direction of the axis of the cylinder, the lens will not affect the rays; in the direction at right angles to the axis, the rays will converge if the lens is plano-convex, or diverge, if the cylinder is plano-concave.

Deficiencies in Color Vision

Colorimetry. Colorimeters are instruments that are designed for the measurement of color, and *colorimetry* is the scientific method that employs colorimeters in the measurement and specification of color. In this approach, the emphasis is on obtaining the visual equivalence of a given sample from a synthesized stimulus. The physical specifications of the components of the synthesized stimulus are then used to provide scales for the psychophysical specification of the visually equivalent color.

Figure 10-7 shows a plan view of the Wright colorimeter (Wright, 1946). This instrument is basically a spectrometer, with one half of the light from source O_1, forming a spectrum (test beam) at S_1, and the other half forming a spectrum (matching beam) at S_2. During color-matching tests, the three prisms (R_3, R_4, R_5) at S_2 are centered at 460 mμ (blue), 650 mμ (red), and 530 mμ (green), respectively. By means of the lens and mirror system, the test and matching beams are brought to a focus at the exit pupil T. The intensity of the test beam is controlled by neutral density filters that can be inserted at W_1; the intensity of the components of the matching beam is remotely controlled by sliding neutral density filters at W_3, W_4, and W_5 in front of the three prisms (R_3, R_4, and R_5).

The observer is placed so that one of his pupils is at T and his head is steadied by a mouthpiece which carries his dental impression. The appearance of the photometric field as seen through T is a filled square of light; the lower half is illuminated by the test beam and the upper half, by a mixture of the three com-

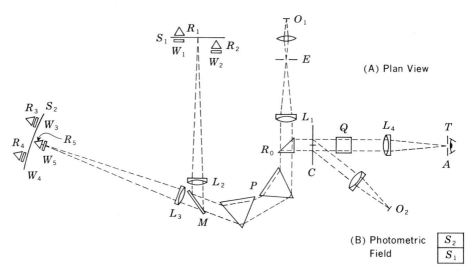

Figure 10–7. Schematic drawing of the Wright colorimeter: (A) plan of the instrument; (B) the appearance of the test field (S_1) and the matching field (S_2) as seen by an eye located at A. See text for further details. (From Wright, *J. Scient. Instrum.*, 1939. By permission of The Institute of Physics and The Physical Society.)

ponents of the matching beam. In color-matching, the task of the observer is to independently adjust the intensity of the lights of 460, 650, and 530 mμ so that the mixture matches this light of a given wavelength place at S_1. Although the mixture matches a monochromatic test light in hue, that is, it can match the dominant wavelength, it generally appears somewhat desaturated in comparison with the test light. Consequently, some white light would need to be added to the test light to achieve a perfect match. However, since a white light can be produced by a suitable mixture of the three matching lights, the desaturation of the test light is actually produced by adding a small amount of one of the matching stimuli to the test light.

Numerous studies in colorimetry have led to the important generalization that *any colored light can be matched by a suitable mixture of three chromatic lights, provided none of these three can be matched by a mixture of the other two.* The average results for the color mixture functions for different classes of observers are shown in Figure 10-8. The ordinate scale of coefficients is obtained by determining the amounts of the three matching components (red, R; green, G; blue, B) necessary to produce white and specifying these amounts as the units for the three respective components. If, for example, the three components mixed in the proportion R:G:B = 1:1:1 produce white, then, as read from Figure 10-8, the wavelength of 625 mμ is matched in hue by mixing the same three components in the proportion 0.92, 0.13, and 0, approximately.

Notice that in the figure most test lights can be matched by an appropriate mixture of the three components. In these instances, the amounts of the com-

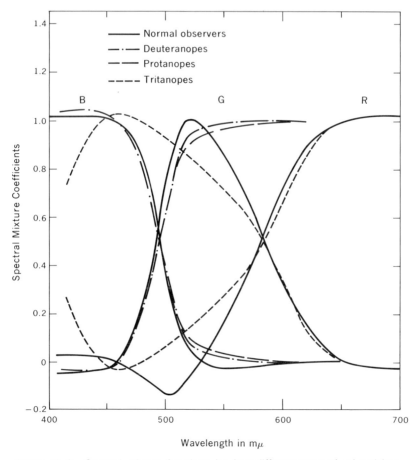

Figure 10–8. Spectral mixture functions for four different types of color vision: normal observers, deuteranopes, protanopes, and tritanopes. (From Weale, 1960.)

ponents are indicated by positive coefficients. However, as already indicated, some samples of light, for example, 500 mμ, cannot be matched with such a mixture of the three components, since the sample is more saturated than the mixture and has to be desaturated by adding a small amount of the complementary color. In this case, the amount of the complementary color that is mixed with the sample light is considered to be a negative quantity. This quantity is subtracted from the sum of the amounts of the two components that were used in the mixture to produce the color match. Thus, the algebraic total of the proportions of the three components necessary to yield a color match is equal to unity—as it is in all cases of three-color colorimetry.

The color-matching data for the normal observers shown in Figure 10-8 can be used to derive a *chromaticity diagram*, which is perhaps easier to understand than the original curves. The chromaticity diagram presented in Figure 10-9 is derived from the fact that the sum of the proportions of the three components required

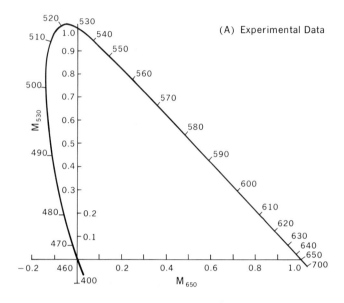

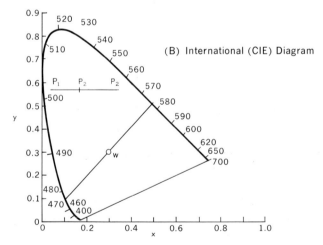

Figure 10-9. Chromaticity diagrams: (A) diagram derived from the experimental data for the normal observers shown in Figure 10-8; (B) the internationally standardized (CIE) diagram derived by an algebraic transformation from diagram (A). (From Weale, 1960; after Wright, 1946 and Judd, 1952.)

to produce a color match is equal to unity; thus, if two of the proportions are known, the third can be readily calculated. In other words, a plot of the proportion of green as a function of the proportion of red used to match light of any given wavelength will contain all of the information shown in Figure 10-8. Such a plot is presented in the chromaticity diagram of Figure 10-9A, which indicates the locus of the spectrum plotted in terms of the stimuli used in the color-matching measurements.

By means of a series of algebraic operations, the chromaticity diagram in Figure 10-9A can be transformed into that shown in Figure 10-9B. This is the chromaticity diagram that has been standardized by the International Commission on Illumination (CIE, 1931). Notice that it has the advantage of containing only positive values. The point W represents white light which is obtained by mixing equal proportions of the three standard stimuli: red, green, and blue.

How can the chromaticity diagram (Figure 10-9B be used? Since the diagram was derived from color-matching data, it can be used in four basic ways to indicate the appearance of colors. (1) If a color is matched such that the plotted point for the values of the two matching components (R, G) falls in the lower right-hand portion of the chromaticity diagram, the color looks reddish; in the lower left-hand portion it looks bluish; in the upper portion of the diagram, it looks greenish. The closer the point is to the spectral locus (perimeter) of the chromaticity diagram, the greater the saturation of the color; the closer the point is to W, the more desaturated it is. (2) If any straight line is drawn through the point W and is extended to intersect the plotted function, it will connect a pair of complementary colors. When these colors are mixed in the appropriate proportion, as determined by the linear segments on each side of W, they will produce white.

(3) Purple does not appear in the visible spectrum, but is produced by the mixture of red and blue, as shown by the straight line connecting the two extremes of the spectrum (400 μ to 700 mμ); this line provides the chromaticity coordinates of purples. (4) A straight line drawn between any two points on the chart will show all the possible color combinations that can be obtained by mixing the colors represented by the two points, for example, P_1 and P_2. The obtained color (P) will be located on this line and the distance of P between P_1 and P_2 will be inversely proportional to the amounts of color used in the mixture; the greater the amount of P_2, the smaller the distance between P and P_2. There are other uses for the chromaticity diagram, but the general point is that the color of any light or object can be specified in terms of this coordinate system.

The Young-Helmholtz Theory of Color Vision. The color mixture facts presented in the preceding section represent principles and laws that are completely independent of any theory of color vision. Theories of color vision attempt to explain the phenomena of color in terms of the retinal structure and function, neural action and interaction, and cerebral projection areas. Such theories, however, if they are to be taken seriously, must be able to provide an accurate explanation for the facts of color mixture and for the various forms of color blindness or color weakness found in human observers. The Young-Helmholtz theory is ordinarily associated with color mixture data and color deficiencies since it can provide a straightforward account of the observed phenomena in this area. The simplicity of this account does not, of course, "prove" that the theory is correct, nor does it eliminate more elaborate theories that exist and can also account for the same phenomena. Our presentation, however, will be restricted to the Young-Helmholtz theory; the reader may pursue the other theories, namely, the Hering theory, the Ladd-Franklin theory, and the Land theory, in other sources (Teevan and Birney, 1961).

The phenomena of color mixture and matching demonstrate conclusively that in cone vision the retina must respond in at least three different ways to different colors. Three components are sufficient to produce all the colors, including white; hence the name, *trichromatic theory*. Young, in 1802, suggested that color vision depended upon the presence of three sorts of receptors in the retina of the human eye; when the outputs from these receptors were integrated in appropriate proportions, all colors would be experienced. Some fifty years later Helmholtz revived this forgotten idea. He postulated a separate spectral sensitivity curve for each of the three receptors (designated as red, green, and blue); in time, this became known as the Young-Helmholtz theory of color vision. Three different kinds of receptors, each differently sensitive to different parts of the spectrum, were assumed. According to this theory, all colors that are perceived result from the blending of different amounts and proportions of the outputs from these receptors. This blending or integration controls not only the hue but also the brightness of the color. The spectral sensitivity curve for each type of cone is broad and each has a different peak, that is, it responds maximally to a particular region of the spectrum. Thus, given a narrow band of light, it will stimulate all three receptors, but one of these will respond more strongly than the others. When all three are stimulated equally, the resulting color is reported as white.

In recent years, the follow-up on the Young-Helmholtz theory has been the endeavor to isolate the sensitive substances of the retinal receptors and to determine their corresponding curves of spectral sensitivity (Marriott, 1962). The first method used in this approach was to extract the photolabile pigments from the excised retinas of both vertebrates and invertebrates. The extractions from over a hundred species have yielded spectral absorption curves that, in many cases, agree very satisfactorily with the scotopic curve of visual sensitivity. So far, however, the in vitro examination of visual pigments has not produced a very satisfactory correspondence either with photopic sensitivity or color vision, despite the fact that an almost certain cone pigment has been extracted from the retinae of squirrels (Dartnall and Tansley, 1963) and from the retinae of fowl (Wald, Brown, and Smith, 1955).

More satisfactory support for the Young-Helmholtz theory has been obtained from in situ examinations of visual pigments, although exact experimentation by this method provides greater difficulties (Crawford, 1965). The in situ procedure may be subdivided into in vivo and in mortuo. In general terms, in the in vivo condition the characteristics of the light emerging from the eye are compared with those of the light entering the eye. As the light traverses the eye, some of it will come into contact with the photolabile pigments contained in the retinal receptors. A measurable effect will be produced by the partial or complete bleaching of these pigments. The bleaching light can be experimentally varied in intensity, wavelength, and time of exposure; the effect is measured in terms of the wavelength and time at which absorption occurs. Using this approach, Rushton (1963) has discovered and named chlorolabe as the pigment in the retinal receptors that absorbs wavelengths in the green portion of the spectrum and erythrolabe as the red-absorbing pigment.

Although the presence of the blue-absorbing pigment, cyanolabe, has been suggested by the in situ approach, the in mortuo condition has provided strong evidence for red, green, and blue (Brown and Wald, 1964). In this condition, a single retinal receptor in an excised retina is illuminated with a specially designed microdensitometer and the difference spectra (before and after exposure to a flash of light) were determined by the bleaching technique. The maxima of the absorption curves were located at approximately 555 mμ (red), 525 mμ (green), and 450 mμ (blue). Thus, the results from studies of cone pigments, when coupled with the data on color-matching and mixing, lend considerable support to the Young-Helmholtz theory of color vision.

Normal and Anomalous Color Vision. The relevance of the preceding material on color-matching and color-mixing may now be shown with respect to normal and defective color vision. It has already been indicated (see Figure 10-8) that a normal observer can match the entire spectral gamut with any three chromatic stimuli, provided that none of these can be matched by a mixture of the other two. This classification of normal color vision, or nearly normal color vision, is called *trichromatism*.

Even in the normal observer, however, there are certain anomalies that can be detected under special circumstances. When, for example, the portion of the central fovea that is tested is reduced in area from 1°–2° to less than 30′ in diameter, there is a marked change in color vision. Wavelength discrimination becomes considerably poorer and only two colored lights are required to match any spectral stimulus. This condition is referred to as *small-field tritanopia*. Another anomaly occurs when color vision is tested in extrafoveal regions, even though the size of the test field is maintained at a diameter of one or two degrees. If adaptation to a high level of luminance is maintained in a small peripheral part of the retina, color vision is essentially monochromatic and is much poorer than when a large retinal area is light-adapted.

Table 10-2 presents a summary of the different types of color vision. The differences between the normal and abnormal observer may involve any or all of the fundamental attributes of color vision: hue, saturation, and brightness. The mildest form of defective color vision is *anomalous trichromatism* which occurs in 5 or 6 percent of all males. Although anomalous trichromats vary considerably in their symptoms, from nearly normal to those like dichromatism, they all require three chromatic stimuli for color-matching and they all see the hue circle in the same way as the normal, that is, with no true neutral or achromatic points or "breaks."

There are three kinds of anomalous trichromatism. (1) *Protanomaly* occurs in about 1 percent of the general population; it is considered as a red weakness since protanomalous observers require more than the normal amount of red to match a particular yellow. (2) *Deuteranomaly* occurs in about 5 percent of the general population and is the most common type of all chromatic defects; it is considered as a green weakness since deuteranomalous observers require more than the

Table 10-2   Classification of Types of Color Vision

Type	Name	Discriminations	Neutral Points (Mμ)	Peak of Visibility Curve (Mμ)
Trichromatism	Normal	Light-Dark Yellow-Blue Red-Green	None	555
Anomalous Trichromatism	Protanomaly	Light-Dark Yellow-Blue Red-Green weak	None	540
	Deuteranomaly	Light-Dark Yellow-Blue Red-Green weak	None	560
	Tritanomaly	Light-Dark Yellow-Blue weak Red-Green	None	560
Dichromatism	Protanopia	Light-Dark Yellow-Blue	493	540
	Deuteranopia	Light-Dark Yellow-Blue	497	560
	Tritanopia	Light-Dark Red-Green	572	560
	Tetartanopia	Light-Dark Red-Green	470 580	560
Monochromatism (Achromatopsia: Total Color Blindness)	Congenital	Light-Dark	All	510
	Acquired	Light-Dark	All	560

normal amount of green to match a particular yellow. (3) *Tritanomaly* is exceedingly rare; it is considered to be a blue weakness since tritanomalous observers require more than the normal amount of blue to match a cyan (bluish-green).

Dichromatism, sometimes referred to as "partial color blindness," is inherited as a sex-linked recessive characteristic; it occurs in about 70 times as many males as females and affects about 2 percent of the males of European origin. In dichromatism, only two chromatic stimuli—usually one from the long wavelength-end and one from the short wavelength-end of the spectrum—are required to match all colors that are perceived. All color matches made by a normal observer are acceptable, in general, to the dichromat, but the reverse does not hold. Whereas the normal observer can discriminate over 150 different hues, the dichromat can distinguish only two.

There are four subclasses of dichromatism. (1) *Protanopia* occurs in about 1 percent of the males; it is often called "red blindness" since nothing but blues, yellows, and grays are visible. There are two neutral points in the hue circle and a marked reduction in brightness compared with the normal. Protanopes have no visual experience, either chromatic or achromatic, beyond approximately 680 mμ, and the maximum of their luminosity function is at about 560 mμ. (2) *Deuteranopia* is a form of complete red-green blindness that occurs in over 1 percent of males and 0.01 percent of females. For the deuteranope, blue and yellow appear normally, but there are two neutral points located where the normal observer sees bluish-green and red-purple. Since the deuteranope sees as achromatic colors those stimuli that appear red and green to the normal observer, he tends to confuse reds, greens, and grays. (3) *Tritanopia* is a rare form of dichromatism. It is characterized by a weakness and reduction of brightness in the short wavelength-end of the spectrum; there are two neutral points, one at about 572 mμ and the other at a short wavelength. (4) *Tetartanopia* is an extremely rare disorder in which the observer cannot perceive blue and yellow. The luminosity curve is approximately normal and there are two neutral points in the spectrum at about 470 mμ and 580 mμ.

Total color blindness (*achromatopsia*) is extremely rare and is estimated to occur in only about 0.003 percent of the general population. As a single inherited recessive trait, it affects men and women about equally and is attributed to a complete lack of functioning of the retinal cone mechanism. Since the typical form of achromatopsia involves only pure rod vision, the photopic luminosity function resembles the scotopic curve of the normal observer. In this condition there is also reduced foveal acuity and the presence of nystagmoid eye movements. Achromatopsia sometimes occurs in atypical form and is associated with defects in the neural pathways or cortical centers, rather than in the retina itself.

Unlike the various forms of inherited color defects that are permanent, acquired total defects often occur that are more temporary and quite unstable. The incidence of these defects is unknown, but is probably not very high. The apparent factors leading to acquired color blindness include drug and toxic poisoning, such as lead, tobacco, and alcohol; diseases and infections of the visual tracts and the nervous system, including multiple sclerosis, brain injuries, and certain vitamin deficiencies.

Tests of Color Vision.   There are many daily activities and occupational job requirements in which abnormal color vision is either undesirable or unacceptable. In many situations, color vision is routinely tested. Consider, for examples, the problems associated with the identification of butterflies, color photography, paint mixing, graphic arts, piloting operations, fabric and wallpaper designing, costuming, flower arranging, chemical analysis, and color television productions. Techniques of measuring color vision serve an important practical function.

Some of the psychological criteria of color defects have already been mentioned. These include data on color confusions and mismatches, color-mixing data, and abnormal luminosity curves. Tests for color vision range all the way from lengthy laboratory measurements to rapid screening procedures such as the driver's license requirement of identifying a few familiar colors. There is a wide variety of tests and they can be classified according to whether the observer's response is obtained from sorting color samples, color matching, color naming, the arrangement of color samples in serial order, the perception or the reproduction of colored patterns.

The *Nagel anomaloscope* is a telescope that presents combinations of colors to determine the normality or abnormality of color vision. It is the only available test that can distinguish among all four of the more common color defects. The anomaloscope presents the observer with a circular field that is divided in half by a horizontal line. The upper half of the disk is filled with a variable mixture of lithium-red (671 mμ) and thallium-green (535 mμ) light; the lower half is filled with sodium yellow (589 mμ) of variable luminance. The observer can turn a screw to vary the upper half from red to yellowish-green and he can turn another screw to control the apparent brightness of the lower half.

The normal observer can find only one ratio in the red-green half that will match the yellow half, but the deuteranope or the protanope finds that the yellow can be matched by *any* ratio of the red-green, assuming that the luminances of the two halves have been adjusted to equality. The deuteranope is then differentiated from the protanope in terms of the luminances of yellow required to match pure green and pure red. For the deuteranope this requires about equal luminances of yellow, but the protanope requires far more luminance of the yellow to match the pure green than the pure red. Anomalous trichromats are also considerably more consistent in their settings of red-green since only one ratio produces a match; the dichromats do not repeat their settings unless by chance— any ratio will match the yellow if the luminance is suitable. The deuteranomalous and the protanomalous are differentiated in terms of the red-green ratio; the former need a great amount of green to match the yellow whereas the protanomalous need more red.

One of the most commonly used tests of color vision is that known as the American Optical (AO) Company Pseudoisochromatic Plates. A revised version of this test consists of 18 plates selected from the original 46 plates of the test. A pseudoisochromatic plate consists of a figure and a background, each of which is composed of many small dots that vary in terms of size, reflectance, and chromatic purity. The figure is either an Arabic number or some other identifiable pattern. The only controlled difference between the dots of the figure and those of the ground is in hue. The normal observer distinguishes the figure on the basis of this systematic difference in hue, but dichromats and anomalous trichromats have difficulty in perceiving the pattern. On the other hand, some plates have figures that can be perceived by the defective observer but not by the normal. The test must be administered under standardized conditions; if the observer fails on four or more charts, he is classified as color-defective. Unfortunately, this test fails to discriminate reliably between dichromats and anomalous trichromats; it is, nevertheless, an effective and valuable screening device. The Ishihara test is another commonly used test that utilizes the principle of pseudoisochromatic plates.

Some Diseases of the Eye
and Visual Tracts

Although there are many types of disorders, diseases, and injuries that can affect the visual system, we will be concerned with only a few—those that can affect the lens, the retina, and the visual tracts.

The Lens.   The lens is composed entirely of epithelium surrounded by a capsule; it is, therefore, incapable of becoming inflamed. There are, nevertheless, certain conditions that lead to a loss of transparency. Any opacity in the lens or its capsule that produces a loss of transparency is called a *cataract*. One common type of cataract is the *developmental cataract* in which the fibers of the lens are poorly developed and degenerative changes occur during life. Since the lens is formed in layers and this process continues until late adolescence, a developmental cataract has a tendency to affect the particular zone that was being formed when the process was disturbed. Several conditions may affect the normal development of the lens; these include maternal and infantile malnutrition, maternal infections by viruses such as rubella (German measles), and deficient oxygenation due to placental hemorrhages. Cataracts of this type tend to be nonprogressive and have little functional effect on vision unless they are large in size and are located in the center of the lens.

A second type of cataract is the *acquired cataract* that is due to the degeneration of the lens fibers already formed. The reasons for this degeneration are not fully understood, but they probably involve physical or chemical factors that upset the critical intracellular and extracellular equilibrium of water and electrolytes, or that disturb the colloid system within the fibers. One kind of acquired cataract is the *senile cataract,* a form seldom found in healthy persons under 50 years of age, but almost always found in some degree in persons over 70. It occurs equally in men and women and is usually bilateral, but there is a considerable genetic influence in its incidence. Another form of acquired cataract is due to radiant energy, particularly heat, ultraviolet light, X rays, the gamma rays of radium or neutrons, and ultrasonic radiation.

The symptoms of acquired cataract are entirely visual and one of the early complaints is that of seeing spots before the eye. These spots retain their relative position in the field of vision when the eye is moved in different positions. Sometimes objects are seen as double or triple and sometimes colored halos may be seen. Since the shorter wavelengths are absorbed, the reds may appear more prominently. When, in a senile cataract, nuclear sclerosis is prominent, there is an increase in refractivity that leads to the development of a progressive myopia. Thus, it is possible that a previously presbyopic person may be able to read again without the aid of his spectacles—this "improvement" in visual ability is commonly called "second sight." As senile opacification continues, there is a steady diminution of vision until only the perception of light is possible.

The treatment of cataract will depend upon the particular case under study. Once opacities have developed, however, there is no medical treatment by drugs that has been shown to have a significant effect in inducing the disappearance of the cataract. If the cataract is due to diabetes, control of this condition may result in a disappearance of the changes in the lens. In senile cataract, the degenerative process of opacification may cease spontaneously for a number of years. The most suitable operation for cataract up to about 30 years of age is *discission;* in this operation two small cuts are made in the lens at right angles to each other so that the soft lens matter may be absorbed or extracted by mechanical means. As an extreme measure in older persons, the lens may be surgically removed and the refractive error of aphakia may be corrected with glasses or, more preferably in the case of unilateral aphakia, with contact lenses. More recent techniques have attempted to employ a lens of acrylic plastic implanted within the capsule as a substitute for the cataractal lens.

The Retina. The primary affections of the retina are nearly always associated with some general disease and, consequently, the conditions are usually bilateral. A variety of symptoms may or may not be present, depending upon the individual case. Ordinarily there is a decrease in visual acuity and the field of vision may also be decreased. Photophobia may occur, brightness discrimination may be impaired, and discomfort may be experienced, although pain is invariably absent.

Of the many disorders that can affect the retina, we will consider only *detachment* of the retina and its treatment. In the normal condition, the two retinal layers— the retina proper and the pigmentary epithelium—lie in opposition. When the two layers become separated, the event is called retinal detachment or separation. From the clinical point of view, this condition may be subdivided into two classes. (1) *Simple* detachment is nearly always due to the formation of a hole in the retina that allows fluid from the vitreous to seep through and dislodge the retina from its normal position. (2) *Secondary* detachment is due to the retina being pushed away from its bed by an accumulation of fluid, such as blood, or by the action of mechanical forces. Although the clinical syndrome of a detached retina is characteristic, the appropriate diagnosis may in certain cases be extremely difficult.

The treatment of a simple detached retina is by operation. The objective of such an operation is to bring the torn parts of the retina into contact with an area of the choroid by diathermy, light coagulation, or some other technique. If the operation is successful, adherence of the two tissues results and the retinal hole is obliterated. Surgical treatment is effective in 80 or 90 percent of certain disorders. The prognosis in simple or secondary detachment of the retina is unfavorable if untreated. The detachment becomes total and cataracts may follow.

The Optic Nerve. The disorders of the optic nerve include disturbances of circulation, inflammations, and toxic amblyopias (that is, loss of vision due to harmful chemical agents). Toxic amblyopias include a number of conditions in which the optic nerve fibers are damaged by poisonous substances, such as tobacco, ethyl and methyl alcohol, lead, arsenic, quinine, and carbon disulphide. In some of these, the disease is primarily retinal and, in others, there is a direct effect upon the nerve fibers themselves.

Tobacco amblyopia results from the excessive use of tobacco, either from smoking or chewing; sometimes it results from the absorption of dust in tobacco factories. Smokers of cigars and strong tobacco mixtures are affected most, while cigarette smokers are less likely to be affected. The toxic agent is regarded as nicotine, but some of the more volatile products of tobacco may be involved, for example, collidine or lutidine. The symptoms of tobacco amblyopia include fogginess of vision, less marked in the evening and in dim light. Central vision is considerably reduced and near work or reading becomes difficult. Both eyes are affected, although one eye may be more affected than the other. The treatment consists of the abstinence or severe curtailment of the use of tobacco; recovery, however, may not be evident to a noticeable degree for a period of several months.

The amblyopias produced by substances other than tobacco are of a more serious type in which marked optic atrophy occurs. The treatment is the same as that for tobacco. In most amblyopias of this type, however, restoration of vision is seldom complete.

The Auditory System

The classification of hearing impairment is sometimes made in terms of the *amount* of functional hearing that is present and available for the ordinary purposes of daily living. According to this schema, the *deaf* are those in whom the sense of hearing is nonfunctional for the routine activities of life and the *hard-of-hearing* are those in whom the sense of hearing is defective but functional, with or without a hearing aid. From a strictly medical standpoint, however, the term *deafness* is used correctly to describe *any* loss in hearing, regardless of the amount or specificity of impairment. In this chapter, then, the latter approach will be adopted and the terms *deafness, hearing impairment,* and *hearing loss* will be used more or less synonymously.

In Chapter 4, the auditory processes were described in detail; it follows that anything that interferes with these processes may produce a hearing impairment. Thus, a more appropriate classification of hearing impairment must be in terms of the auditory structures involved. This establishes two fundamental kinds of deafness: *conductive deafness* and *neural deafness. Conductive deafness* refers to hearing problems produced by conditions in the outer ear, middle ear, or Eustachian tube which interfere with the passage of the acoustic waves to the inner ear. *Neural deafness,* sometimes called *perceptive deafness,* refers to hearing problems produced by damage to the neural structures of the inner ear or to the eighth cranial nerve. Sometimes the peripheral auditory structures and nerve fibers are normal, but a hearing impairment is, nevertheless, present. This type of deafness is called *central deafness* and is due to the malfunctioning of the neural pathways in the higher auditory centers, or to a psychological disorder. The distinctions between conductive, neural, and central deafness are important ones since the prognosis and treatment of the different types of deafness vary considerably.

Factors in Conductive Deafness

Occlusion of the External Auditory Canal. In the outer ear, the most common condition leading to a hearing loss is the presence of impacted wax (cerumen); the wax normally present in the ear may harden in the canal and prevent sound waves from reaching the tympanic membrane. Impacted wax may be present at any age, but it occurs most frequently in older individuals, that is, beyond about 50 years of age (Corso, 1963*e*). Normally the wax comes out essentially unnoticed in tiny pieces, but for some individuals with narrow or hairy canals, this may not happen. When the ear canal is completely blocked, the individual notices that his hearing is impaired. It is a simple procedure for a physician to remove the impacted wax by applying hot water to soften the wax so that it may be extracted. If the wax is not removed, it may injure the skin of the canal. Injury may also result if the individual attempts to remove the wax himself by inserting a matchstick or hairpin; often this simply compresses the wax and pushes it deeper into the canal. If the ears are kept clean, the average individual will not develop impacted wax.

External Otitis. *External otitis* is an infection involving fungi or various types of bacteria. It occurs in the external auditory canal when the cerumen, and the scales of old skin tissue mixed with it, become decomposed and diseased. It is present most frequently in hot, wet climates and has been a considerable problem with American troops stationed in the southern part of the United States and in tropical regions of the world. The primary symptom of external otitis is pain associated with the manipulation of the ear. The condition never produces a severe deafness and often produces no deafness whatsoever. Although the infection invades the tissue beneath the skin, surgical incision is not ordinarily performed since this may only serve to spread the infection; treatment, therefore, is usually in the form of medication, for example, sulphonamides or penicillin, or through the application of a fungicide such as cresatin.

Perforation of the Tympanic Membrane. Perforations of the tympanic membrane may occur in a variety of forms; such perforations, however, may be classified as *marginal* (when the perforations extend to the edge of the membrane) or *central* (when the perforations do not affect the edges of the membrane). Contrary to popular belief, a perforation of the tympanic membrane does not produce complete deafness; it is quite possible to have a fair-sized perforation in an otherwise normal membrane without the individual having a hearing loss of more than 5 or 10 db. The major problem is not that of the perforation directly, but of the infectious disease that may have originally produced the perforation. If a perforation is not closed, water and infections from the nasopharynx and nose may be spread into the middle-ear cavity when the nose is forcefully blown. Marginal perforations usually reflect more serious infections and are less amenable to closure than central perforations.

Perforations of the tympanic membrane may also occur due to accidents or mechanical injuries. A sudden rupture of the membrane may be produced by a loud explosion near the ear (acoustic trauma) or by a solid slap over the ear, particularly if the slap occurs underwater. Sometimes injuries result from hairpins or other objects pushed forcefully into the external auditory canal. Normal precautions should be taken, whenever possible, to eliminate these hazards.

Normally, a perforated tympanic membrane heals without additional medical attention; however, if the perforation is quite large or complications set in, an operation may be necessary. In this operation (*myringoplasty*), the surface epithelium of the membrane is removed and a patch of living tissue from the same person is applied. Skin tissue or a piece of vein may be used for this purpose. As the tissue grows into place, the perforation is repaired and normal hearing is essentially restored.

Otitis Media. The most frequent condition leading to conductive deafness is *otitis media;* this is an infection in the middle ear. Otitis media may be *acute* or it may be *chronic*. The *acute* condition is of short duration and usually develops from a cold·in the nose or throat. In this stage there is an accumulation of mucus within the middle ear; if this accumulation continues, it soon impairs the conduction of sound via the ossicular chain to the inner ear. As the pressure continues to increase within the middle ear, the tympanic membrane bulges outward toward the external canal and, if the pressure is great enough, it may occlude the blood supply to the central area of the tympanic membrane. This weakens the membrane and, as a result, it may rupture spontaneously, thereby draining the mucus from the middle ear. After the acute infection has been eliminated, the tympanic membrane normally heals with little or no hearing loss being present.

If the ear discharges mucus or pus for more than two or three months, the condition is called *chronic* otitis media. This is usually attributable to neglect or to inadequate treatment. In this case there may be a hearing loss that may eventually become permanent. This loss is due primarily to the scar tissue that forms in the middle ear during the healing of a perforation and adds a resistive mass to the ossicular chain. This increased resistance tends to impair the passage of sound to the inner ear. Varying amounts of hearing loss may result from chronic otitis media, but ordinarily it does not exceed 30 or 35 db.

The treatment of otitis media ordinarily involves medication, such as sulfa drugs or penicillin and, unless the infection is very mild, drainage is also provided. Drainage can easily be effected by a surgeon who makes a small incision in the posterior inferior portion of the tympanic membrane. The incision produces no loss of hearing and is preferred to the spontaneous rupture of the membrane that leads to more deafness and more mastoiditis requiring medical attention than the surgical incision. Sometimes, as a preventative measure, the adenoids are surgically removed to minimize blockage of the Eustachian tubes; blockage of a tube and the presence of a nasal infection are both predisposing factors in the infection of the Eustachian tube and, consequently, to otitis media. As an alternative approach, the mass of the adenoid tissue near the entrance to the Eustachian tube may be reduced by radium treatment or X-ray techniques. Of course, neither surgery nor radiation will restore hearing, but they will tend to reduce the recurrence of otitis media.

Otosclerosis.   A common disease in the white race that leads to chronic progressive deafness is *otosclerosis*. This disease is estimated to occur in about 12 percent of white women and in about 6 percent of white men. Otosclerosis is an unusual disease which most often produces a soft bony growth at the stapes in the region surrounding the oval window. It will be recalled that the stapes is part of the ossicular chain of the middle ear and that, in response to sound waves, the stapes normally moves toward and away from the oval window. In otosclerosis, the new growth of bone fixes the footplate of the stapes in the oval window and prevents its characteristic movement. When the stapes is firmly fixed, the passage of acoustic vibrations from the tympanic membrane is inhibited and there is a resulting loss of hearing of the conductive type.

Despite the high rate of incidence of otosclerosis, hearing impairment associated with this disease occurs in only about 10 percent of the cases; nevertheless, it has been estimated that over a million cases of hearing loss in the United States are attributable to this disease. Otosclerosis is a hereditary disease and fixation of the stapes has been detected as early as the seventh year; the hearing loss, however, has usually been first noticed at adolescence or in early adulthood. One of the early signs which accompanies the hearing loss is *tinnitus* ("ringing in the ears"). This sound is usually high-pitched and is more bothersome at night and in quiet surroundings; it may have different qualitative characteristics, but often seems like a bell ringing or a steam whistle.

An unusual feature of otosclerosis is that an individual so affected at first seems to hear better in a noisy place, such as in a factory or in an automobile. This is due to the fact that persons with normal hearing ordinarily increase the intensity of their voices to overcome the masking noise in the environment. Individuals with otosclerosis can also hear well over the telephone; however, as otosclerosis progresses, nerve deafness is added to the mechanical problem at the stapes so that the individual finds it increasingly difficult to understand speech, particularly when several persons are speaking simultaneously as at a party.

There are five primary diagnostic signs of otosclerosis: (1) there is a history of deafness in the family; (2) there have been no previous infections of the ear that might account for the hearing loss; (3) the tympanic membrane appears otologically normal; (4) there is a progressive loss of hearing; and (5) audiometric tests show that air conduction is impaired, with about equal losses for all frequencies, while bone conduction thresholds are essentially normal. As otosclerosis progresses, there is a spreading of the hearing loss to frequencies above 1000 cps by bone conduction, as well as by air conduction. Also, as we have already indicated, otosclerosis may be combined with some degree of nerve degeneration.

In cases of otosclerosis, several surgical procedures may be used to help restore hearing. Each of these procedures is extremely intricate due to the smallness of the aural structures of the middle ear. The actual size of the tympanic membrane and ossicles is shown in Figure 10-10.

Figure 10-10.   The actual size of the tympanic membrane and the ossicles of the human ear.

One of the oldest surgical procedures for otosclerosis is called *fenestration.* This is a somewhat complicated operation in which the middle ear is reached through an incision in the tympanic membrane, and the incus and most of the malleus are removed. A small opening (fenestra) is then made in the ampullated-end of the horizontal semicircular canal, exposing but not damaging the underlying membraneous semicircular canal. A flap of skin, previously separated from the bone of the posterior and superior walls of the external canal, but with its attachment to the tympanic membrane left intact, is then laid over the fenestra. For postoperative recovery, the cavity is packed and a surgical dressing is applied over the ear.

This operation provides a new path for sound conduction as shown in Figure 10-11. The sound waves can now travel across the middle ear and, via the fenestra,

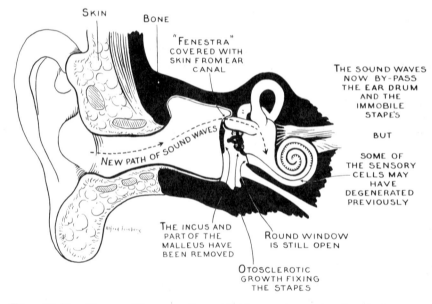

Figure 10–11.   Diagram of the new path provided for sound waves in a fenestration operation. (From Walsh, in Davis, *Hearing and deafness: a guide for laymen,* 1947.)

can move the fluid in the cochlea so that stimulation of the organ of Corti occurs in conjunction with the normal displacement of the round window. Fenestration operations often produce marked improvements in hearing, with lasting improvements recorded in over 70 percent of the operations performed by skilled surgeons. It has been estimated that if the fenestra remains open for about two years, it will probably remain open permanently.

Fenestration operations are a major undertaking for the patient in terms of postoperative care, and in some cases there is difficulty in obtaining complete healing. Persistent ear discharges may occur after the operation. Also, dizziness is often present when the head is moved and patients who have had a fenestration operation cannot swim or dive. The cold water entering the external canal would produce a temperature change in the horizontal semicircular canal and severe dizziness would result. For the same reason, cotton must be worn in the ear canal on cold, windy days. Furthermore, normal hearing can never be fully restored by this method and the operation is inappropriate for those patients with associated neural deafness.

In view of these difficulties, a new surgical procedure was introduced in 1953 which resulted in fewer unpleasant effects for the patient. This operation is referred to as *stapes mobilization*. In this procedure, the tympanic membrane is lifted and direct mechanical manipulation of the stapes is performed. It is possible by this manipulation to loosen the footplate of the stapes or to fracture the ossified connections so that almost normal movement of the stapes can occur. Unfortunately, the hearing improvement obtained by this method is temporary, lasting only a few months before the footplate again becomes fixed and the hearing impairment reappears.

In 1958, a more radical operation for dealing with the fixed stapes was attempted and later modified as the *plantinectomy operation* (Beales, 1965). In this modified procedure, the footplate of the stapes is removed but the two crura (prongs) of the stapes are preserved. The footplate is then replaced by a piece of vein from the back of the hand and the stapes is pivoted back into position so that the crura make contact with the vein. In contrast with the earlier technique in which the complete stapes was removed and replaced with a tiny piece of polythene tubing extending from the incus to the vein graft, the plantinectomy operation is completely physiological. Some regard this as the ultimate solution for deafness due to otosclerosis.

Factors in Neural (Perceptive) Deafness

Presbycusis. By far the most common factor responsible for perceptive deafness is *presbycusis,* that is, loss of hearing that occurs with advancing age. In this condition, there is a characteristic decrease in hearing sensitivity with increasing age due to the deterioration of hair cells in the cochlea and the degeneration of the acoustic nerve fibers. The sensory cells primarily affected are those in the part of the organ of Corti toward the base of the cochlea; when these degenerate, the nerve fibers connected to them atrophy and vanish. The result is that the hearing of frequencies associated with this part of the cochlea is impaired and hearing becomes poorer as the neural degeneration becomes more marked with advancing age.

The effects of presbycusis are shown in Figure 10-12 for men and in Figure 10-13 for women (Corso, 1963d). These data are for men and women who passed rigorous screening criteria to insure freedom from otological disorders and a life history of minimal exposure to high-intensity noise. Since these and other factors known to produce a loss of hearing were carefully controlled, it may be concluded that these curves provide typical threshold values for different age groups from which hearing loss as a function of age may be readily computed at each frequency.

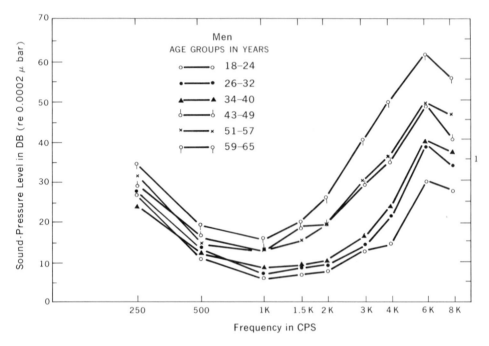

Figure 10–12. Mean threshold values for hearing as a function of frequency for men in six different age groups. (From Corso, *Arch. Environ. Hlth.*, March 1963.)

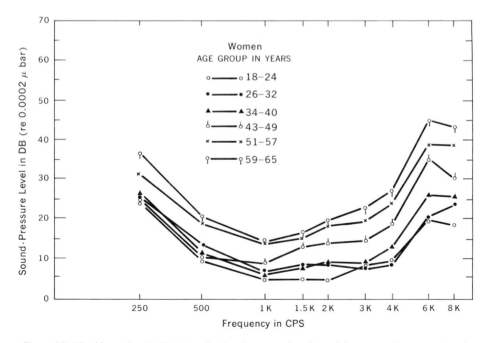

Figure 10–13. Mean threshold values for hearing as a function of frequency for women in six different age groups. (From Corso, *Arch. Environ. Hlth.*, March 1963.)

From the curves of Figures 10-12 and 10-13 it may be inferred that, for the men, differential effects in frequency start at about 32 years of age; for the women, at about 37 years of age. It also appears that the onset of the loss in sensitivity is more gradual for women than for men; however, once started, this loss proceeds at a faster average rate for women than for men. The average rate of deterioration in the hearing of women is fairly uniform, but for men it is discontinuous, with marked changes occurring in steps of about 15 years. For both men and women, the earliest detectable loss in sensitivity occurs at 4000 cps and above; with advancing age, these losses become more pronounced and the effects gradually spread into the lower frequencies, eventually reaching 250 cps. For comparable age groups, the hearing threshold for men and women are approximately the same at 1000 cps; however, for frequencies above this point, the women have better hearing than men while below this point, the hearing of women is generally poorer than that for men (Corso, 1963c).

One somewhat surprising fact is that not every older man or woman becomes hard of hearing with advancing age. Many people who are 80 or 90 years of age have been found to have almost perfect hearing, but most men and women show a significant loss. The factors associated with these individual differences in hearing have not yet been identified.

Noise Exposure. The perceptive type of hearing impairment resulting from prolonged exposure to high-intensity noise is commonly called *occupational* or *industrial deafness*. This type of deafness may be subdivided into two types: (1) *temporary* and (2) *permanent*. A detailed account of temporary hearing loss (temporary threshold shift, *TTS*) was presented in Chapter 9 as a form of sensory adaptation. The question here, however, relates to the *permanent* impairment of hearing produced by extended exposures to intense noise. (Glorig, Ward, and Nixon, 1961.)

> The line between temporary threshold shifts and permanent hearing losses is not easy to define. When threshold shifts are induced in the laboratory by means of short exposures, the subject's hearing usually returns to its pre-exposure threshold. In industry, where the exposure is repeated over and over again, some part of the "temporary" threshold shift may turn out to be irreversible or permanent hearing loss (American Standards Association, 1954, p. 9).

The problem of noise-induced hearing loss has become increasingly important in recent years for two main reasons: (1) the widespread use of jet aircraft, rocket engines, heavy machinery and equipment, motorboats and other devices that can generate high levels of noise, and (2) certain legal rulings that hold that industrial deafness is an occupational disease, thus entitling the affected worker to a schedule award under the Workmen's Compensation Law. The medicolegal aspects of noise-induced hearing loss encompass serious consequences that can no longer be ignored, either by industry or by the military services (Corso, 1963e).

Hundreds of scientific articles have been published on this subject and there is no longer any doubt that exposure to high-intensity noise may produce permanent hearing impairment. A typical set of data is shown in Figure 10-14 for airport inspectors. This figure compares the mean hearing level of airport workers,

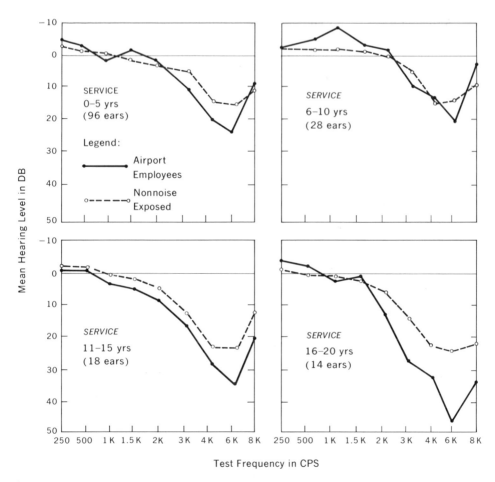

Figure 10–14. Comparison of mean hearing levels for airport inspectors and for non-noise exposed groups equated by age and sex; each graph provides a comparison for different lengths of service. (From Cohen, 1965.)

screened to eliminate those with otological disorders or a history of excessive noise exposure of a nonairport nature, with that of non-noise exposed groups of the same age and sex. Notice that, as the length of airport service is increased from 0–5 years to 16–20 years, the differences between the noise-exposed airport group and the non-noise exposed groups become more marked. Notice also that even the curves for the non-noise exposed groups show hearing losses from the baseline (0 db); these curves reflect losses due to aging (presbycusis). Furthermore, the general shape of the functions for the two groups is quite similar, with the greatest losses at the upper frequencies. This phenomenon often makes it difficult to distinguish which of these two conditions—aging or noise exposure—is the principal factor in producing an individual's deafness. The interaction effects of these two factors needs to be investigated.

Although it has been well-established that noise exposure may produce neural deafness, the question remains regarding the durations and levels of exposure that must be exceeded if hearing is to be impaired. Several sets of proposed damage-risk criteria have been reported in the literature for different kinds of noisy conditions. Figure 10-15 contains the maximum values per octave bands

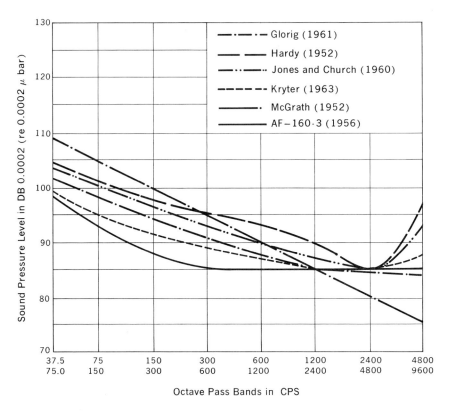

Figure 10-15. Proposed criteria for hearing conservation for daily exposures of 5 to 8 hours of steady-state noise. (From Cohen, 1965.)

for 5-8 hour daily exposures to continuous noise for a working lifetime, according to six different studies. To be on the conservative side in a practical situation in which this type of noise is present, the AF curve (United States Air Force) should be adopted; long-term exposures above the values indicated will most likely produce permanent deafness, such as that shown in Figure 10-14.

One of the major difficulties with occupational deafness is its insidious onset. The hearing of higher tones is lost first, so in the early stage there is no noticeable difficulty in understanding speech. As the deafness increases, the loss spreads to frequencies below 3000 cps and the ability to understand speech is reduced; the individual then realizes he is becoming hard of hearing. Tinnitus may also appear as an associated symptom. Ordinarily, the presence of pain or annoyance are reliable indicators of bodily injury; but, in industrial deafness, the absence of pain should not be construed to mean the absence of hearing loss. Pain is produced in the ear when noise levels are on the order of 110 db above 0.0002 microbar; however, as may be seen in Figure 10-15, noise-induced hearing loss can be produced at considerably lower noise levels. In all instances of this type of damage, bone conduction is also markedly reduced, indicating that the damage occurs in the hair cells of the cochlea. The unfortunate aspect of industrial deafness is that *no treatment is possible* that will *restore* lost hearing.

In those industries, governmental agencies, and other work situations in which there is high-intensity noise, the worker's hearing should be protected by an adequate hearing conservation program under medical supervision (Committee on the Conservation of Hearing of the American Academy of Ophthalmology and Otolaryngology, 1957). According to Beales (1965), "noise . . . has replaced nuclear fallout as the public's main scientific concern" (p. 178). Noise means more than minor annoyance; it means serious and permanent disability.

Ménière's Disease.   Another important factor in perceptive deafness is Ménière's disease. The pathology of this disease is the dilation of the endolymphatic system due to a rise in pressure of the enclosed fluid, but the reasons for this disturbance in endolymphatic circulation are still not fully understood. The increase in fluid produces dizziness, tinnitus, and a gradual loss of hearing in the affected ear. The symptoms are present in attacks and, between attacks, the hearing may even return to normal. During attacks, hearing is distorted and voices sound tinny, hollow, or fuzzy, and sometimes the same frequency may sound differently in the normal ear than it does in the affected ear (*diplacusis*). Usually the pitch is higher in the ear with Ménière's disease.

The type of deafness produced by Ménière's disease is perceptive, with a typical loss of hearing at the higher frequencies. In the early stages of the disease, hearing improvement is possible before irreversible changes occur in the cochlea. In the later stages, permanent hearing losses with severe tinnitus are common and occasionally both cochlear and vestibular functions are lost due to the pathological process.

The treatment for Ménière's disease may be divided into two categories: *medical* and *surgical*. In one of the earliest modern forms of medical treatment, the patient was forbidden to take sodium salt in any form in his diet, and foods rich in sodium, such as carrots, olives, spinach, cheese, and fish were eliminated. There was a strict adherence to a protein diet of low sodium content, accompanied by a diuretic such as ammonium chloride. Although this treatment is effective in a hospital where diets can be rigidly maintained, the results in controlling dizziness are not as favorable in outpatient treatment (Williams, 1952).

Another form of medication relates to the notion that a major factor responsible for hydrops of the labyrinth is hypoadrenocorticism. In 90 percent of a group of 75 patients, relief was obtained by the administration of whole adrenal cortical extract with other glandular therapy (Goldman, 1962).

The surgical procedures for Ménière's disease may be *conservative* or *radical,* depending on the objectives of the treatment. In the first group, the surgery is intended to stop the attacks of dizziness and to preserve or improve the hearing. One operation consists in relieving the pressure in the endolymphatic system by providing a shunt (a silicone rubber tube) so that the fluid can drain from the endolymphatic sac into the subarachnoid space of the brain (House, 1962). Another operation has consisted of partial sectioning of the eighth nerve, leaving enough fibers to preserve cochlear functioning. However, sectioning of the nerve does not seem to halt the progressive pathological changes in the inner ear and this operation is seldom used today to control Ménière's disease. Ultrasonic therapy (James *et al.*, 1960) has also been used with some success in destroying the functional activity of the vestibular apparatus without damage to the cochlea, although there is a definite risk of facial paralysis.

In the second group of surgical procedures, treatment is strictly destructive and is aimed at relieving the dizziness after the pathology has produced a complete loss of useful hearing in the given ear. Wright (1942) injected alcohol through the oval window into the labyrinth to destroy the cochlear elements, but this procedure was later abandoned since it often produced facial paralysis. More recently, *destructive labyrinthotomy* has been used in one or another form. Cawthorne (1957) has developed a procedure in which the stapes is temporarily removed from the oval window and the membranous labyrinth is then extracted with a hook. The entire operation is performed via the external auditory canal after the posterior part of the tympanic membrane has been elevated. After the membranous tissue has been removed, the stapes is replaced in the oval window. This procedure destroys both the labyrinthine and cochlear elements in the diseased ear and leaves the patient "stone deaf." There is some reluctance in using the destructive approach since, in some cases, the disease has also appeared in the other ear at a later time.

Infectious Diseases and Toxic Agents.   Perceptive deafness often occurs suddenly as a complication of infectious fevers, such as those usually associated with virus diseases. The most serious of these are measles, whooping cough, influenza and mumps, but acute deafness also occurs in rubella (German measles) and pneumonia. In mumps, only one ear is usually affected and the deafness is incomplete but recovery of hearing rarely occurs. The prognosis is equally bad for the other diseases and there is no known curative treatment.

Perceptive deafness may also result from toxic poisoning attributable to pharmacological substances. In these cases, the onset of deafness is usually gradual, but may develop within a few days of medication with streptomycin or its derivatives. Dihydrostreptomycin is exceedingly toxic to the cochlear system and should never be used. At least seven other antibiotics are known to be toxic to the labyrinth to a greater or lesser degree, for example, neomycin, framycetin, and polymyxin B. These should never be administered without audiometric control to insure that no impairment of hearing is occurring.

Factors in Central Deafness

Central deafness may be *physiological* in origin, based on definite anatomical abnormalities, or it may be *psychogenic* (psychological).

Physiological Conditions.   In man, the primary function of the auditory cortex is to mediate the recognition of electrical impulses that reach it from the lower centers. The most important electrical patterns are those associated with words. When the auditory cortex is diseased, word deafness occurs. Electrical stimulation of the brain shows that pure tones are interpreted in the extreme upper part of the temporal gyrus, at the edge of the Sylvian fissure, while the more outlying parts of the auditory cortex are involved in the representation of words or meaningful sounds. Whenever there are lesions in the superior temporal gyrus, word memory and word association are impaired (*aphasia*). Spoken words may be heard, but are not understood, and attempts to speak may result in the utterances of meaningless jargon.

Lesions which produce these effects may be found to occur in the brain due to the formation of tumors, arteriosclerosis, cerebral hemorrhage, multiple sclerosis, syphilis, brain abscess, or plugging of the cerebral blood vessels (thrombosis). Part of the disability associated with the deafness of senility may be attributed to degeneration of the auditory cortex, in addition to the atrophy of cochlear elements. Cortical lesions are also responsible for certain types of infantile deafness.
Psychogenic Conditions. *Psychogenic deafness* is present when there is no actual damage to the hearing mechanism and yet the individual does not fully utilize his residual hearing. Cases of partial or complete hysterical deafness are often seen among soldiers exposed to the stresses and rigors of combat. It is now recognized that hysterical deafness occurs in civilian life much more frequently than previously supposed. It is estimated that between 10 and 25 percent of all hearing losses have a significant degree of functional involvement (Sataloff, 1957). The miraculous cures of total deafness at shrines or other nonmedical agencies are undoubtedly cases of hysterical deafness. Hysterical reactions arising from the conversion of psychological problems into physical symptoms often occur in adolescent females.

Since the hysterical patient is usually uninformed regarding the manifestations of deafness, this type of deafness is relatively easy to detect. A number of diagnostic points differentiate hysterical from other deafness. In the hysteric, deafness is often complete and bilateral; the vestibular responses are normal; the voice remains unaltered; and lipreading is learned with remarkable rapidity. Since psychogenic deafness is an expression of an abnormal psychological state, the restoration of hearing does not present an unusually difficult problem and may be treated by any one of several psychotherapeutic techniques. Frustration, emotional conflict, and insecurity are among the most common etiological factors in producing functional deafness. Unless these problems are resolved, relapse will be almost inevitable.

Auditory Theory
and Hearing Aids

In the preceding discussion of different kinds of deafness, we have seen that the application of various medical and surgical treatments has depended upon a thorough understanding of the auditory process. The successful application of these treatments attests to the adequacy of our understanding of the mechanico-electrical events that occur in hearing. It is established that sound normally enters the ear via the external canal and that the acoustic energy is transmitted to the oval window by means of the ossicular chain of the middle ear. It is also established that the sounds may be conducted to the cochlea via the bones of the skull. The treatments described for the various causes of conductive deafness revealed how the normal sound pathways that were obstructed by physical agents or disease could be opened or circumvented to reestablish hearing. It was further indicated that, in conductive deafness, hearing by air conduction was impaired while hearing by bone conduction was normal.

In perceptive deafness, hearing is impaired for both air and bone conduction, particularly at the higher frequencies. Very often, both conductive and perceptive-type losses are present (*mixed deafness*). Representative threshold curves for these three types of deafness are shown in Figure 10-16.

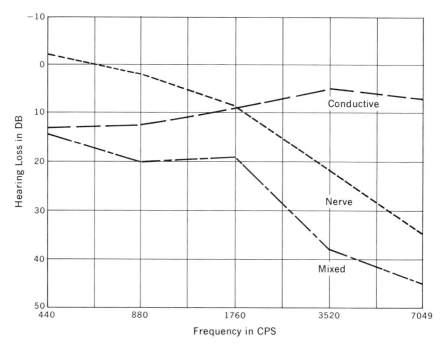

Figure 10–16. Representative curves for the threshold of hearing for three types of deafness: (A) conductive, (B) perceptive (nerve), and (C) mixed. (From Rosenblith *et al.*, 1953; after Webster *et al.*, *J. acoust. Soc. Amer.*, 1950.)

It is generally accepted that the frequencies which are poorly heard, or not heard at all, in perceptive deafness are those in which certain neural elements have been damaged or destroyed in the cochlea or auditory (VIIIth) nerve. The evidence for this conclusion comes in part from the correlation between hearing loss and cochlear defects. Crowe, Guild, and Polvogt (1934) obtained audiometric data on a large number of patients and, after their death, performed an analysis of their cochlear structures by means of a microscopical examination. Figure 10-17

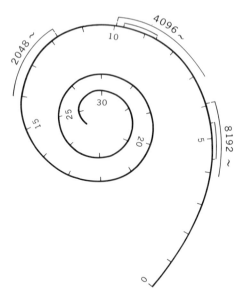

Figure 10–17.   Diagram of the localization of high-frequency tones on the basilar membrane as derived from pathological observations. The scale shows the distances in millimeters from the basal end of the basilar membrane at which different frequencies maximally stimulate the receptor cells. (From Crowe, Guild, and Polvogt, Bull. Johns Hopkins Hosp., 1934.)

shows the cochlear localization for different frequencies in terms of the distance in mm along the basilar membrane as measured from the oval window. The ability to hear 8192 cps, for example, depends upon the receptor elements located about 5 mm from the basal end of the cochlea. This does not mean, however, that every discriminable tone has its own *exact* locus in the cochlea and in the auditory nerve fibers; rather, there is a spreading of action over the receptor elements. Each tone produces its own peculiar pattern on the basilar membrane (Békésy, 1943). The high tones have patterns in which the major excitation is in the basal region, with little excitation in the apical region. The low tones have broader patterns in which all regions of the cochlea appear to be involved. To account for the high degree of specificity which is present in the perception of pitch, a secondary "sharpening" process has been postulated (Huggins and Licklider, 1951). This conception of a spatial representation of the frequency of a sound on the basilar membrane is the basis of the *place theory* of hearing.

The place theory of hearing, however, holds only for frequencies above the region of about 4000 cps. Experimental observations show that below this region, the *frequency principle* of hearing is applicable, that is, the periodicity of a sound is maintained in the responses of the sensory cells and, to some degree, in the action of the auditory nerve fibers. Thus, the frequency of impulses in the VIIIth nerve reproduces the frequency of the sound waves, from the lowest audible frequencies to the region of 4000 cps. This synchrony is also preserved in the processes of the acoustic nuclei of the medulla oblongata. When the frequency exceeds the limits of 4000 cps, the synchronous relations break down and asynchronism gradually develops.

The place and frequency principles are combined in the *volley theory* of hearing (Wever, 1949). The frequency principle alone is taken to hold up to about 400 cps; from 400 to about 4000 cps both frequency and place are taken to hold; above 4000 cps, frequency fails and place alone accounts for pitch. According to the volley theory, the cortical centers for hearing can utilize both the spatial and temporal dimensions of neural activity as a basis for pitch. Loudness, then, depends upon the number of nerves fibers that are active at a given moment and their individual rates of firing. These two factors combine to determine a composite rate which represents the total number of neural impulses carried in the nerve discharge to the brain per unit of time.

Now we will consider these aspects of auditory theory in relation to the use of hearing aids. Before recommending a hearing aid, it is necessary to determine whether the patient will be helped enough to justify the purchase of one. The audiogram is a useful guide for this purpose. In general, if the hearing loss in the better ear averages more than 30 db in the speech range, that is, 300 to 3000 cps approximately, the need for a hearing aid is indicated. At this level, the individual starts to have difficulty in hearing speech comfortably, unless the speaker keeps his voice at a high intensity level.

It should be clear that a hearing aid is essentially a miniature amplification system that increases the intensity of sounds when they are presented at the ear. The amplified sound may be presented either by means of a bone-conduction receiver placed on the mastoid bone behind the ear or by an air-conduction receiver inserted into the external canal. Since the faithfulness of reproduction of a good air-conduction receiver is generally better than that of a bone-conduction receiver, the large majority of the hard-of-hearing prefer the air-conduction receiver. Despite optimistic advertisements, a hearing aid is not a perfect instrument and does *not* provide complete compensation for hearing impairment. The hearing aid has no remedial effect on the user's actual hearing and some types of deafness benefit less from a hearing aid than others.

Since a hearing aid helps the individual to hear better by amplifying the sounds that enter the microphone, a hearing aid is of little benefit in presbycusis. This condition may be of two types (Schuknecht, 1955). The first type, called *epithelial atrophy*, is characterized by degenerative changes that begin at the basal end of the cochlear duct and proceed toward the apex. It affects, almost equally and simultaneously, the various structures in the cochlea, including the afferent and efferent nerve fibers. The second type, called *neural atrophy,* is characterized by degeneration of spiral ganglion cells beginning at the basal end of the cochlea, as well as neurons of the higher auditory pathways.

Typically, the patient with presbycusis is either intolerant of amplification or may be confused by multiple sounds; he also may have difficulty in understanding speech. *These symptoms may be present in any high-tone perceptive deafness,* including industrial deafness, deafness due to infectious diseases or drugs, and Ménière's disease, in addition to presbycusis. Hearing impairment of the perceptive or central type involves the inability to *discriminate* among speech sounds and does not depend solely on amplification. In this context, a hearing aid will improve hearing to the extent that there are remaining receptor elements and nerve fibers that are undamaged. Nevertheless, the use of a hearing aid, *supplemented by an appropriate program of intensive auditory training in the discrimination of sounds which comprise speech,* can be of great assistance.

Thus, a hearing aid does not cure an abnormal ear, nor does it alter the status of impaired hearing. It simply enables the user to make better use of the hearing that remains intact and keeps the listener in practice and attentive to sound. There are limits to the benefits that can be derived from a hearing aid. Since hearing aids provide *more energy* for sounds than is normally present, an individual with impaired hearing may be made to hear, provided there are intact structures in the cochlea and auditory nerve. Hearing aids are, therefore, of maximal benefit in cases of conductive deafness and mild perceptive deafness.

The Vestibular System

Symptoms and Effects of Vestibular Disorders

Symptoms of Labyrinthine Disease.   Oftentimes a person will complain of giddiness and his symptoms are difficult for him to describe accurately. He may feel lightheaded and dizzy. These symptoms may be produced by any physiological or pathological condition that interferes with the circulation of blood to the brain, but they may also signal the onset of a vestibular disorder. This is especially true if spells of vertigo (pallor, nausea, and vomiting) occur from time to time, with each spell more serious than the one before, as in Ménière's disease. Another possibility is that the patient may have one intense attack of vertigo which gradually subsides over a period of two or three weeks. This history suggests that the labyrinth has been invaded by infection and subsequently has been destroyed.

Furthermore, labyrinthine diseases are usually associated with changes in hearing. Signs of impending disorders include the total deafness of a "dead" labyrinth, the tinnitus and perceptive deafness of Ménière's disease, and lesions of the cochlea or cochlear nerve. The changes in hearing are clinically significant since they often aid in the correct diagnosis of a vestibular problem.

Effects of Labyrinthine Damage.   It will be recalled that the semicircular canals are activated by movements of the head. These movements result in the displacement of the endolymphatic fluid in the canals, moving the hair cells and generating a train of neural impulses that travel along the vestibular nerve to the vestibular nuclei in the medulla. From the medulla, the impulses are relayed so that some pass to the ocular centers and produce movements of the eyes; others pass to the anterior horn cells of the spinal cord and result in movements of the head, neck, and trunk. These movements are called the *kinetic labyrinthine reflexes* and preserve the individual's balance during movement and help him maintain an essentially steady field of vision. Thus, we would expect that any damage to or destruction of the labyrinths would produce effects that would be noticed in ocular or bodily movements.

Whenever one labyrinth is more active than the other, or whenever one labyrinth is damaged or diseased and the other is normal, certain signs and symptoms are present. These include: (1) vertigo, (2) falling to the side of the inactive labyrinth, (3) movement of the outstretched hand to the side of the inactive labyrinth, and (4) nystagmus to the side of the intact labyrinth, that is, slow movement of the eyes to the side of the lesion with the quick movement back to the healthy side. Such effects, however, are ordinarily not permanent in unilateral labyrinthine destruction, since compensation or, more appropriately, relearning gradually takes place. Vertigo and nystagmus disappear in a few weeks as the neural impulses arriving at the vestibular nuclei from the normal, but unopposed, side of the head are reinterpreted.

In some instances, as in cerebrospinal meningitis, both labyrinths may be destroyed by the bacterial invasion, but the patient can, after some weeks, control his bodily movement as in walking, running, climbing, and skiing. These movements, however, would be controlled primarily by the visual and kinesthetic systems. Consequently, if such a patient were to dive into deep water, he would undoubtedly drown. The kinesthetic system would be essentially useless against the uniform water pressure and the visual system would be ineffective due to blurring. Directional disorientation would occur and the patient would no longer know where to move to approach the surface of the water.

Clinical Tests
of Labyrinthine Function

There are several clinical tests that can be used to determine quantitatively whether one or both labyrinths are normally or abnormally excitable (Reading, 1966). Qualitative tests are also employed to assess the relative excitability of each labyrinth, but these will not be considered in this text.

Clinical Rotation Test.   The classical rotation test was devised by Barany to determine the duration and amplitude of nystagmus after the labyrinth was stimulated by spinning the patient in a rotating chair. This test is now seldom used since it often produces nausea and vomiting; also, it does not provide reliable differential information on each labyrinth, but on both taken together.

Quantitative Caloric Test.   In this test, the excitability of the labyrinth is evaluated by placing the patient on his back, with his head flexed 25° so that the horizontal canal is in the vertical position. The external meatus of the ear is then irrigated with *cold* water. This cools the tympanic membrane and the walls of the canal so that convection currents are produced in the endolymph of the external semicircular canal. The eyes move slowly down towards the irrigated ear and jerk rapidly back towards the *other* ear. If warm water is used, the nystagmus will be directed to the same side. If no nystagmus is produced, it indicates that there is a loss of function in the labyrinth of the ear being tested.

Positional Test. In the positional test, the patient lies on his back so that his head and neck project over the end of the examination couch. The examiner places a hand on each side of the patient's head and rapidly lowers it over the end of the couch so that the neck is hyper-extended. The head is turned first with one ear up, and then, if there is no nystagmus, with the other ear up. A positive finding is present if nystagmus occurs, with the rapid component directed toward the undermost ear. If the nystagmus persists throughout the period in which the head is held in position, the nystagmus indicates a lesion of the central nervous system.

A word of caution should be injected at this point. It is commonly found that not all patients who are suffering from labyrinthine vertigo show spontaneous nystagmus at the time of their physical examination. Conversely, not all patients who exhibit spontaneous nystagmus are suffering from labyrinthine disease. A differential diagnosis of labyrinthine dysfunction can only be determined from a series of extensive medical tests.

Labyrinthine Disorders and Their Treatment

Infective Disorders. Numerous diseases can occur that will affect the normal functioning of the labyrinth. (1) In *para-otitis,* there is a local infection of the bone surrounding the labyrinth that produces an abnormal excitability of the otherwise healthy structure. This occurs when the bone is eroded and exposes the membranous labyrinthine wall. The treatment involves a mastoidectomy in which the mastoid bone is hollowed out by scraping away the bony partitions forming the mastoid cells. When the opening is healed, the vertigo disappears. (2) In *purulant labyrinthitis,* there is a bacterial infection of the labyrinth and the patient experiences the symptoms of a unilateral destruction of the labyrinth. Two or three weeks later, he recovers his equilibrium and loses his nystagmus. The casual appearance is that there is no labyrinthine lesion at all. Unfortunately, it may be that the labyrinth is "dead" and the symptoms are hidden through the re-learning of bodily movements. If the disease is detected in its early stage, however, it may be treated with penicillin. (3) There are many other diseases that may result in infective labyrinthitis. These include cerebrospinal meningitis, mumps, and syphilis and are usually treated by medication.

Toxic Agents. In addition to the (endogenous) toxins from the foci of infection that may produce vestibular dysfunction, there are (exogenous) toxins that may have similar effects. Alcohol is the most commonly known of this group, but drugs such as quinine and salicylates may also result in impairment. Streptomycin is a severe offender of the vestibular tract and should not be prescribed for minor infections; for severe infections, it should be prescribed with extreme precautions in the course of treatment.

Other Factors in Labyrinthine Dysfunction. In closing this section on the vestibular system, a few additional factors should at least be mentioned. These include *vascular, neoplastic,* and *traumatic* conditions that may produce labyrinthine

dysfunction. In arthritic changes in the intervertebral joints of the cervical vertebrae, there may be a kinking of the vertebral artery; this temporarily cuts off the
blood supply to the vestibular centers and produces attacks of vertigo. No treatment is required for this condition but the patient should avoid excessive twisting
and backward bending of the head and neck. The neoplastic factors are associated
with fibrous or tumorous growths of the eighth nerve that appear within the
internal auditory meatus or intracranially. Such growths produce a progressive
destruction of all the functions of the inner ear. Traumatic disorders are due to
concussion of the inner ear or brain brought about by an accidental injury or
heavy explosion. Vertigo, with or without nystagmus, and permanent perceptive
deafness will be manifested depending upon the particular locus of the lesion or
fracture. The treatment for neoplastic conditions and traumatic damage usually
involves operative surgery.

The Olfactory and Gustatory Systems

Dysfunctions and Diseases of Olfaction

Anosmia.   *Anosmia* is the inability to smell any and all substances or, less·seriously,
the inability to smell a particular substance or group of substances. This inability
to smell renders food as tasteless, since the flavor of food is dependent upon the
normal activity of both the olfactory and gustatory systems. Anosmia results
whenever an obstruction or disease prevents a free current of air from passing
up the nasal passages, as in a deviated nasal system or suppurative (pus forming)
sinusitis. Some of these conditions can be remedied by surgery; others can be
treated by medication so that the ability to smell is restored with little difficulty.

Permanent anosmia may be produced by more serious conditions. If, for example, the floor of the anterior cranial fossa (the cribriform plate) is fractured,
there may be a leak of cerebrospinal fluid from the nose. Sometimes damage may
result from surgery in which the nasal system is involved or in which the fibers of
the olfactory nerve are severed.

While there are individuals with complete anosmia, such as might result from
a severe blow to the head or face, the theoretically more interesting cases are
those with partial anosmia. By studying these individuals, psychologists have,
for example, been able to discover the primary odors. Some of the mercaptans
are relatively specific in "smell blindness" such that their odors cannot be detected
in partial anosmia, whereas the odors of other substances can be distinguished.
Other factors that decrease olfactory sensitivity include smoking, nasal congestion
due to infection, pus, or water from swimming, and exposure to a general anesthetic, for example, ether. Some evidence indicates that certain olfactory thresholds for women are related to the level of estrogen in the body. About 50 to 60
percent of the adult males cannot detect the odor of exaltolide (Kalmus and Hubbard, 1960), while the threshold for post-adolescent females varies with the
menstrual cycle and is lowest at ovulation (Le Magnen, 1950).

Cacosmia.   Some diseases (for example, syphilis, atrophic rhinitis) produce a putrid odor that is perceptible to everyone but the patient. This is in contrast with suppurative sinusitis in which the patient notices a bad smell in his nose. Sometimes there is no organic problem; but, due to a psychological disorder, the patient complains of odors that have no objective existence.

Seasonal Hay Fever.   A fairly common aberration of the sense of smell involves the swelling of the olfactory mucosa which may be sufficient to block the normal passage of air. This condition, which produces a profuse flow of mucus from the nose, is called *vasomotor rhinitis;* the pathology is present in seasonal form in hay fever. Additional symptoms involve frequent sneezing and watering of the eyes. Typically, the passageways of the nose become blocked due to the sensitization of the patient's tissues to the pollens of grass, trees, garden flowers, weeds, and other plants. This occurs in spring and early summer. The symptoms can be alleviated if the patient remains in a darkened room, but they are accentuated when the patient goes out into bright sunshine.

Treatment for vasomotor rhinitis involves medication that will relieve the nasal obstruction during a hay fever attack. The nose may be sprayed, for example, with a 0.5 percent solution of ephedrine in normal saline. The effect of the drug is to produce vasoconstriction and, when the drug is taken in weak solution, there are no serious aftereffects. In the early hours of an attack, the symptoms may be controlled by the use of antihistaminic drugs. If the patient is willing to undergo a series of intradermal tests to determine which pollen produces the symptoms, yearly attacks may be reduced by the administration of a series of injections during February and March of the allergen responsible for the hay fever (Reading, 1966).

Acute Nasal Sinusitis.   It is often f und that, in response to any form of infection, there is a general engorgement in the mucosa of the sinuses in addition to that in the mucosa of the nose. This may occur, for example, when there is a heavy cold in the head and a cold that takes three or four weeks to clear up may be considered as a real case of sinusitis. The symptoms include the swelling of the nasal mucosa as a result of drainage of pus from the mouth of the infected sinuses. Pain may also be felt over the cheek and in the upper molar teeth, but is mainly present over the frontal sinus. The pain in the forehead is more pronounced about noon and gradually decreases throughout the day so that by evening it is essentially absent.

The treatment for acute nasal sinusitis is by medication and not by operative surgery. The objective of the treatment is to combat the infection by antibiotic therapy and to have the sinuses reestablish their normal drainage in order to remove all pus. The patient is confined to his bed, or at least remains indoors, and periodically applies 0.5 percent ephedrine sulphate in normal saline into his nose according to a prescribed procedure. Ordinarily this will relieve the acute inflammation; if it does not, more complicated procedures of medication are attempted. Surgery is indicated only when there is real danger that the infection will become chronic.

There are, of course, numerous other dysfunctions and diseases of the nose which can occur, but we have discussed only the more prevalent ones.

Dysfunctions of the Gustatory System

Ageusia. *Ageusia* is the medical term for the loss of the sense of taste. Although there are wide individual differences in taste sensitivity, there is no evidence to indicate that "taste blindness" can occur for all stimuli associated with a particular quality. The theoretical reasons for this are not clear. It could be that there are specific neural connections between or among the taste systems, so that the systems function together or fail together. Also, there is the possibility that if a single taste quality were lost, it might not be noticed due to the contribution of odor stimuli in the flavor of food.

There are, nevertheless, some synthetic substances, for example, phenylthio-carbomide (PTC), that can be tasted by a large number of people, but not by others. The taste thresholds for PTC fall into a bimodal distribution. Thus, the data reveal that there are not simply two classes of individuals—tasters and non-tasters—but that the ability to smell PTC is on a continuum with the majority of the people at the high and low ends of the threshold scale. It is estimated that approximately 30 percent of the people are nontasters; for the rest, PTC tastes *bitter* (Harris and Kalmus, 1949). The inability to taste PTC, however, is specific and does not extend to bitter substances that are unrelated to PTC. Geneticists, as well as psychologists, are interested in this problem since the taste deficiency for PTC seems to follow the Mendelian laws of inheritance.

Other Factors Leading to Loss of Taste. It is frequently found that changes and loss of taste and smell occur after trauma, such as gunshot wounds, operative surgery, and X-ray irradiation. Fortunately, if no gross lesions persist anatomically, these changes are usually reversible. Slow degenerative changes in the ability to taste and smell occur in the process of aging, but similar changes may also occur as a consequence of a chronic local infection or as the result of some treatment.

An example of the recovery of sensitivity for various gustatory stimuli is shown in Figure 10-18. The data are for a 56-year-old man with neck cancer who was irradiated on the left side of the oral cavity and oropharynx from a cobalt source supplemented with super voltage X rays. The treatment extended over a period of approximately one and a half months. The salivary glands and the conducting nerves received heavy doses of radiation, while the taste buds of the tongue received very little. Consequently, the losses in tasting ability following irradiation were due to impaired nerve conduction, rather than to damaged taste receptors. With the exception of hydrochloric acid (HCL), the sensitivity to all substances decreased very markedly. The lowering of the curves in Figure 10-18 show that there was a recovery of sensitivity over a two-month period.

As a result of disease or surgery, lesions may be produced in the Vth cranial nerve. These lesions may produce a permanent loss in taste sensitivity or a reduction in the intensity of taste. In a large majority of cases, taste is lost on the front of the tongue immediately after the lesion occurs, but recovery occurs from a matter of minutes up to weeks, months, or years.

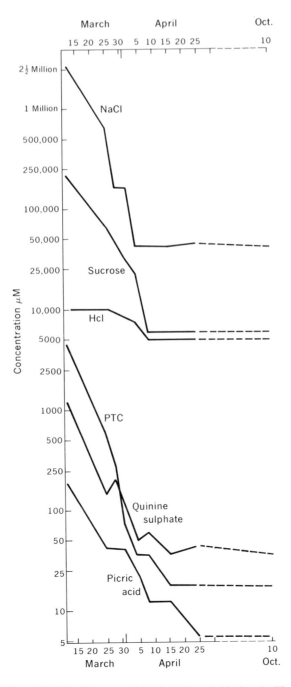

Figure 10–18. Recovery of the taste thresholds for six different substances following cobalt irradiation of the oropharynx. (From Farnsworth and Kalmus, *J. Laryngol. Otol.,* 1959.)

Unlike visual or auditory phenomena, abnormal taste experiences in the form of gustatory hallucinations (*parageusia*) are rather rare occurrences in psychotic behavior patterns.

Pain

Theories of Pain and Their Implications

Some Theoretical Aspects of Pain.   The scientific controversy on the physiology of pain, which began near the turn of the century, continues relatively unabated in the current literature. Two theories have been most prominent: (1) the *specificity* theory, which maintains that pain is a specific modality with its own peripheral receptors and central pathways (Sweet, 1959); and (2) the *pattern* theory, which states that the nerve-impulse pattern for pain is generated either by the intense stimulations of non-specific peripheral receptors (Sinclair, 1955) or by the summation of neural impulses in central mechanisms (Livingston, 1943).

More recently, a new theory of pain has been proposed; it is consistent with the physiological evidence on peripheral specialization and spinal mechanisms and it incorporates the evidence on the central control of afferent inputs, as well as on central summation. This theory is called the *gate control* theory of pain (Melzack and Wall, 1965).

A schematic representation of the gate control theory is shown in Figure 10-19. According to this theory, stimulation of the skin produces nerve impulses that are transmitted to three spinal cord systems: (1) the large (L) and small (s) fibers

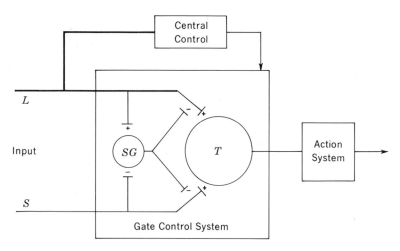

Figure 10-19. Schematic diagram of the gate control theory of pain. See text for details. (From Melzack and Wall, *Science,* copyright November 1965 by the American Association for the Advancement of Science, **150,** 971–979.)

that project toward the brain, (2) the cells of the substantia gelatinosa (SG) in the dorsal horn of the spinal cord, and (3) the first central transmission (T) cells in the dorsal horn. The large (L) diameter fibers and the small (S) diameter fibers project to the substantia gelatinosa (SG) and to the first central transmission (T) cells. The substantia gelatinosa functions as a gate control system whose inhibitory effect on the afferent fiber terminals is increased by activity in L fibers and decreased by activity in S fibers. The excitatory effect of the arriving neural impulses is, therefore, dependent upon the total number of active fibers and the relative balance of activity in large and small fibers. The T cells provide for the temporal and spatial summation of the arriving impulses. When this summation reaches or exceeds a critical level, there is a firing or a discharge of the T cells; this in turn activates the neural mechanisms of the action system responsible for the perception of pain and the reflexive pain response. This entire process is further influenced by central variables, for example, attention, emotions, and memories of prior experience, which provide feedback that is mediated through descending efferent fibers and acts upon the sensory input to the gate control system.

The particular way in which the central activities are triggered into action has not yet been resolved. However, there is sufficient experimental evidence to suggest that one or both of two known systems could be utilized. These are (1) the medial lemniscus system of the dorsal column and (2) the dorsolateral path which originates in the dorsal horn and, after relays in the lateral cervical nucleus, projects to the brain stem and thalamus.

Theoretical Implications for the Relief of Pain.   According to the specificity theory, the free nerve endings are pain receptors which are distributed in a mosaic pattern in the body tissues. When these receptors are adequately stimulated, they generate neural impulses that are carried to the pain center in the thalamus by large (A-delta) and small (C) fibers in peripheral nerves and by the lateral spinothalamic tract in the spinal cord. It would seem, therefore, that if appropriate surgical lesions of the peripheral and central nervous system were made, certain pathological pain states would be eliminated. The clinical evidence indicates, however, that this is not the case. Surgical lesions have been unsuccessful in permanently abolishing pain, although the lesions have been made at various levels as shown in Figure 10-20. Even after a surgical lesion has been made, pain can often be elicited by providing stimulation below the level of the lesion and it may even be more severe than before the operation (Livingston, 1943). Lesions such as those shown in Figure 10-20 may be made in the treatment of the pathological states of *causalgia* (a severe burning pain which may result from a partial lesion of a peripheral nerve), *phantom-limb pain* (which may occur after a limb has been amputated), and *peripheral neuralgias* (which may result from infections or degenerative diseases of peripheral nerves).

The gate control theory has different implications for the treatment of pain. It follows from the theory that the control of pain should be achieved by decreasing the input of the small neural fibers and increasing that of the large fibers. This is consistent with the findings of Livingston (1948), who effectively cured causalgia by bathing the painful limb in gently moving water and then massaging it. Both

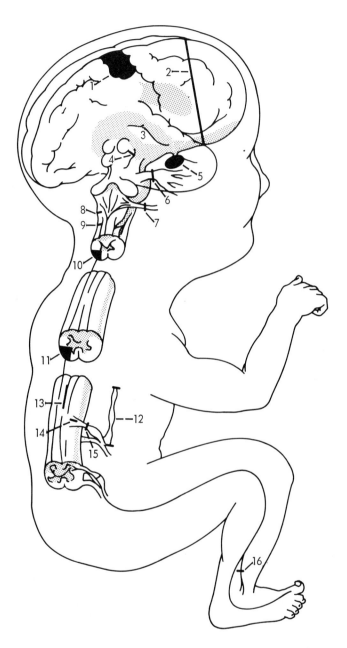

Figure 10–20. Illustration showing the various surgical procedures designed to alleviate pain: (1) gyrectomy; (2) prefrontal lobotomy; (3) thalamotomy; (4) mesencephalic tractotomy; (5) hypophysectomy; (6) fifth-nerve rhizotomy; (7) ninth-nerve neurectomy; (8) medullary tractotomy; (9) trigeminal tractotomy; (10) cervical chordotomy; (11) thoracic chordotomy; (12) sympathectomy; (13) myelotomy; (14) Lissauer tractotomy; (15) posterior rhizotomy; (16) neurectomy. (From MacCarty and Drake, 1956, in Melzack and Wall, *Science*, copyright November 1965 by the American Association for the Advancement of Science, **150**, 971–979.)

of these actions serve to increase the input in the large, rapidly-conducting nerve fibers. A second approach suggested by the theory for the relief of pain involves the substantia gelatinosa. Since the resistance of the substantia gelatinosa to nerve-cell stains indicates that its chemistry may differ from that of other neural tissue, future attempts to control pain may be directed to the discovery of drugs affecting the excitation or inhibition of activity in the substantia gelatinosa (Melzack and Wall, 1965).

Factors Which Reduce Pain

Analgesics.   An *analgesic* is a chemical substance which is administered to reduce pain; it is usually assumed that analgesic drugs act at the site to which the ascending neural impulses from painful stimuli are projected—the hypothalamic nuclei (Smith, 1960). The more commonly-known analgesics are aspirin, morphine, and codeine. It is an interesting experimental finding that morphine and other opiates give "pain relief" without necessarily changing the pain threshold. While some investigators have reported that these drugs elevate the threshold, others have found that the pain threshold may be raised, may be lowered, or may remain unchanged. Apparently, the effect of opiates in "pain relief" is simply part of a more generalized state in which the patient is provided with "freedom from anxiety." The evidence also indicates that opiates give "pain relief" without altering the patient's "awareness of pain"; thus, it may be concluded that opiates serve as effective analgesic agents by reducing "anxiety" and increasing the tolerance for pain (Barber, 1959).

Analgesic agents are routinely used in the treatment of headaches but it should be recognized that, at the medical level, headache therapy falls into two categories: (1) *symptomatic,* or treatment of the individual attack of headache, and (2) *prophylactic,* designed to prevent or reduce the frequency and severity of recurrent headaches. Also, the particular treatment employed will depend upon the particular type of headache that is present. In *tension* headache, produced by sustained contraction of the skeletal muscles about the head and neck, the use of nonaddicting analgesics alone is seldom efficient in symptomatic treatment; however, a combination of an analgesic and a sedative gave effective relief in 71 percent of 1500 patients. *Migraine* or *vascular* headache is another common disorder. In this condition there is vasodilation of the arteries and the cranial vessels have both an altered sensitivity and an increased amplitude of pulsation. The symptomatic effects of migraine headache are effectively controlled by ergotamine tartrate, which constricts the smooth muscles of the blood vessels and produces a decrease in the amplitude of pulsation. Patients with hypertension may also complain of severe headache. The degree of *hypertension* headache does not correlate with the blood pressure level; the headache may be present when the blood pressure is low as well as when it is high. It is believed that the pain is produced by variations in the contractile state of the cranial arteries and that the elevated blood pressure is only an accessory factor. The treatment of this condition is aimed at the management of the general state of hypertension and may include rest, sodium restriction, specific antihypertensive drugs, and psychotherapy (Friedman, 1960).

Hypnosis.   *Hypnosis* is another method that has been used both in the laboratory and in the clinic to relieve pain. A typical set of clinical observations dealing with the surgical use of hypnosis has been reported by Kroger (1957). In one case, a 20-year-old female showed no indication of pain and was "fully aware" of the entire surgical procedure in which a large tumor was removed from the right breast without preoperative or operative medication. In another case, a patient underwent a Caesarian section and hysterectomy with only hypnotic "anesthesia"; she conversed with everyone in the operating room and watched the birth of her baby, showing no discomfort when forceps were used for the delivery or when the uterus was removed. The literature contains a fairly large number of reports in which hypnosis has been successfully used to minimize the pain and suffering during normal childbirth, terminal cancer, fatal burns, tumor operations, and other painful states (Barber, 1958).

It may be generally concluded from these clinical observations that for *some* patients, hypnotic treatment may be as effective as opiates in reducing the pain syndrome in pathological conditions and in alleviating or eliminating the discomfort that is usually present in surgery. However, these observations do *not* establish the necessary and sufficient conditions for hypnotic "anesthesia." The evidence does suggest, nevertheless, that the patient must be able to be "deeply hypnotized" and must have complete confidence in both the hypnotist and the effectiveness of the hypnotic procedures. These factors point toward the subjective or psychological aspects of pain, indicating that, as in the case of morphine, a treatment will reduce pain if the patient is relieved of the "anxiety" about his personal welfare.

Audio Analgesia.   A recently discovered phenomenon is that of *audio analgesia* (Gardner and Licklider, 1959). This is a procedure in which acoustic stimulation is used to minimize pain and unpleasantness, with special application to dentistry and dental operations. In this situation, the patient wears earphones and is provided with a control box by means of which the intensity and quality of acoustic stimulation can be altered. There are two control knobs: one for music; the other, for "white" noise. At the beginning of the session, the patient selects a stereophonic tape recording he wishes to hear and sets the intensity at a comfortable listening level. As the dentist starts his work or as the discomfort sets in, the patient raises the intensity of the music. Then, as soon as there is any indication of pain, the patient turns the knob controlling the noise. The sound pressure level of the noise may be set as high as 116 db above 0.0002 dyne/sq cm (microbar).

The clinical efficacy of this procedure in "drowning out" or suppressing pain in the great majority of dental cases is no longer in doubt (Licklider, 1961). In more than 1000 cases treated by one dentist, audio analgesia was completely effective with 65 percent of the patients; it was effective enough with another 25 percent so that no other analgesic was required and this procedure was preferred on later visits. In more than 5000 patients treated by ten other dentists, similar results were obtained in operations involving drilling, grinding, and extraction. Although there are wide differences in the use of the acoustic controls by the patients, audio analgesia is more effective when the noise is turned up *before* pain develops than it is after pain is clearly present.

Licklider (1961) has developed a mathematical (computer) model to clarify the understanding of audio analgesia. It involves a "hearing" channel and a "pain" channel, each with positive and negative feedback circuits to itself and to the opposite channel. Changes in the electrical parameters associated with the feedback circuits, through amplification, biasing, and smoothing operations, produce changes in the dynamic characteristics of the model. With appropriately-set values, the characteristics of the model reflect many of the behavioral aspects of audio analgesia. It is significant to note that, as with the treatment of pain by opiates and by hypnosis, the effectiveness of audio analgesia increases with the "relaxed" state of the patient and decreases with "tension."

Congenital Indifference to Pain

Any valid theory of pain must be able to account not only for the "normal" responses to noxious stimuli and for the modification of these responses by psychological or medical procedures, but also for the absence of painful responsiveness, as in congenital indifference to pain. At present, there is no adequate explanation of the latter phenomenon; we mention it only to indicate the wide range of behaviors that have been manifested with respect to pain. Three case reports have recently been published (Magee, Schneider, and Rosenzweig, 1961) all of which showed: (1) the absence of a demonstrable lesion involving the neurosensory pathways; (2) normal thresholds for various forms of stimuli and normal tendon reflexes; and (3) defective reactions to strong noxious stimuli. Each patient indicated he had learned to avoid stimuli that would prove injurious and none had experienced frequent severe injuries, as commonly reported in the literature. There was no inability to perceive noxious stimuli, only a failure to appreciate the unpleasantness or painfulness of such stimuli. All three showed similar personality characteristics, for example, they referred to others as "sissies"; they insisted on independence and strength; they had feelings of invincibility; but the question remains whether the indifference to pain is determined by, or is the determinant of, the personality structure.

IV

General Theories
in Contemporary
Experimental Psychology

Chapter 11

THEORIES
OF SENSORY
DISCRIMINATION

Orientation

Contemporary psychology accepts the view than man lives in an environment consisting of physical and social objects and events. These objects and events generate or redirect various forms of energy, such as heat, light, and sound, which comprise the reservoir of potential stimuli for initiating perceptual responses and sequences of behavioral activities. Before these perceptions and actions can occur, however, certain variables in the energy pattern must be "registered" by an appropriate sensory system. Man's ability to adjust to his environment depends, in part, upon his ability to discriminate among the various energy states (stimuli) that surround him.

In sensory psychology, man's ability to discriminate may be considered from two points of view: (1) the ability to perceive the presence or absence of a given stimulus under specified conditions, and (2) the ability to detect a change in a given stimulus whenever one or more of its dimensions is increased or decreased. Technically, as we have seen, these two aspects of discrimination are stated in terms of the absolute threshold and the differential threshold, respectively.

In Chapter 8, substantive material was presented on absolute and differential thresholds for the various sensory modalities. This material, however, was presented primarily from a factual point of view, with relatively little attention directed toward the underlying theories that have been proposed to account for these findings. It is not enough to know that if we perform a certain set of computations on a distribution of experimental scores, we will obtain a numerical value for the absolute or differential threshold for that particular combination of conditions. Implicit in the computations we perform is an underlying theory or rationale of discrimination. Given a different theory, a different set of operations would be performed. This is the problem we wish to consider in this chapter, that is, to account *theoretically* for the behavior observed in experimental determinations of absolute and differential sensitivity.

Three major theories of sensory discrimination will be presented in detail in Chapter 11, together with some of the related experimental findings. These are: (1) the classical theory of sensory discrimination, (2) the neural quantum theory of sensory discrimination, and (3) the theory of signal detection. In each case, the theory will be described in sufficient detail to permit the student to understand the fundamental propositions involved in the theory and to see the relationship between the theory and its predictions. Throughout the chapter material will be introduced showing the adequacy or inadequacy of the particular theory in predicting experimental results. It should be indicated, however, that this presentation is not intended to provide "final answers" on the relative merits of the various theories, but is aimed at providing the student with information on alternative approaches that have been proposed to account for the findings obtained in various experiments on sensory discrimination. We are dealing, then, with different psychophysical theories.

The Classical Theory of Sensory Discrimination

The Psychometric Function and the Phi-gamma Hypothesis

The *classical theory of sensory discrimination* which originated with Fechner (1860) may be introduced through a consideration of the differential threshold, or difference limen. As noted in Chapter 7, this threshold is defined as the smallest stimulus difference that can be detected by an observer in a specified proportion of the trials in which it is presented. Since the method of constant stimulus differences with two categories of judgment was described in detail in Chapter 7, only a brief sketch of the method of determining the difference threshold will be presented here.

At the beginning of an experiment on discrimination, several values of the variable stimulus to be employed are carefully selected. These stimuli, some greater and some less than the standard stimulus in physical magnitude, are presented to the observer a large number of times in an irregular order, or in a prearranged order unknown to the observer. On each trial, the variable is preceded or followed by the standard or, depending on the nature of the stimuli, the two may be presented together. The observer then makes a judgment of "greater" or "less" with reference either to the standard or to the variable, according to a prearranged plan. In the calculation of the differential threshold, the proportion of each type of judgment ("greater" or "less") is determined for each value of the variable stimulus used in the experiment. The results can then be presented graphically in the form of a *psychometric function* as shown in Figure 11-1.

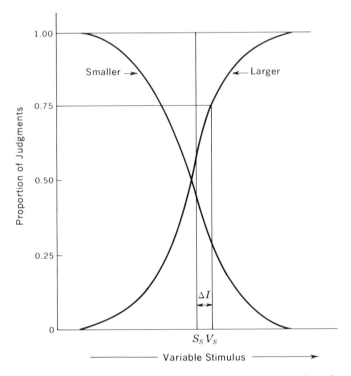

Figure 11-1. The psychometric function for two categories of judgment ("larger" and "smaller") as predicted by the classical theory of sensory discrimination. The standard stimulus is denoted by S_S and a given variable (comparison) stimulus is denoted by V_S; the difference in physical magnitude between the two which is detected 75 percent of the time is shown as ΔI (the upper differential threshold). (From Corso, 1950.)

The psychometric function shows the proportion of times that each variable (comparison) stimulus is judged to be in a given category (for example, "larger" or "smaller") when compared with the standard stimulus. From the experimental data, a psychometric function is obtained for each judgment category. In Figure 11-1, the two functions are idealized (theoretical) curves unlike those in Figure 7-2 in which the data points were simply connected with straight lines. Also shown in Figure 11-1 is the upper differential threshold (ΔI) which indicates the magnitude of the difference between the variable stimulus (V_s) and the standard stimulus (S_s) which is detected 75 percent of the time. This is the increment that must be added to the standard stimulus in order for the observer to make the correct discrimination in three-fourths of his attempts.

The point to be stressed in considering Figure 11-1 is that an actual experiment does not produce either of the curves exactly as shown, but it does provide empirical (data) points through which each of these curves can be drawn. For a given set of data, a particular curve may be obtained either by using a free hand approximation or by assuming that a certain type of function is adequate for describing the specific relationship contained in the data. In the latter case, the best-fitting curve can be determined by any one of several curve-fitting procedures, such as the *method of least squares*. This method generates the constants for a mathematical function such that the sum of the squares of the deviations (differences) between the obtained data points and their corresponding predictions on the fitted curve (line) will be a minimum. According to the *principle of least squares,* the function which yields the smallest value for the sum of squares of the deviations is the line of best fit.

Now, if all that were involved in this type of experiment was the fitting of a particular function to a set of data points, the situation would not be particularly interesting to the experimenter. In effect, fitting a function to the data points has provided the experimenter with an empirical equation. This equation is descriptive of the relationship between the variables involved (in this case, stimulus magnitude and the proportion of judgments in a given category); it provides a basis for making predictions of the value of one variable (the proportion of judgments), given the value of the other variable (the magnitude of the comparison stimulus).

However, if the experimenter begins with a particular theory from which a specific equation can be derived, the situation now takes on a "new look." In this case, the experimenter is not just computing an empirical equation for a set of data points; rather he is using the data points to test the adequacy of his theory as exemplified in the logically derived equation. Specifically, if the theory is appropriate, the data points can be fitted by the particular equation which embodies the essential features of the theory. There is a logical justification for using the particular equation that is being experimentally verified. The problem of curve fitting, then, reduces to two main considerations: (1) the choice of the type of mathematical function to be used in describing the relationship between the variables, and (2) the evaluation of the degree to which the function selected fits the experimental data. We will now consider the choice of the mathematical expression that was adopted in classical psychology to represent the psychometric function.

Jastrow (1888), in his critique of psychophysical methods, was among the first to speculate on the nature of sensory discrimination. He asserted that

> sensation and stimulation each forms a continuum [and that judgments of stimuli as in the constant methods were often in error due to] lapses of attention, slight fatigues, and all the other numerous psychological fluctuations that go to make us now better and now worse judging agencies than our average selves . . . These fluctuations . . . are of such a nature as to be frequently and to the same degree in favor of our judging powers as antagonistic to them . . . And the law that regulates the probabilities of the deviations by various degrees from the average . . . is the law expressed by the "probability curve," which pictures the effect of a very large (strictly infinite) number of small causes no one of which has of itself any decided influence (pp. 284–285).

We have indicated, then, two major elements of the classical theory: (1) the assumption of the existence of two continua, one *physical* (implied by "stimulation") and the other *psychological* (denoted by "sensation"), and (2) the assertion that an infinitely large number of factors operates on a chance basis according to the normal law of error to affect psychophysical judgments.

In considering the question of why, in a given psychophysical method, the same stimulus was not accompanied by the same sensation, Cattell (1893) endorsed Jastrow's position.

> The natural answer is that conditions do not remain the same. In the first place the stimulus itself cannot be kept exactly the same . . . We have, therefore, a variable stimulus which in part accounts for the variation in sensation. In the second place the nervous mechanism is constantly changing . . . These latter changes (brain centres) [are associated with] a more or less regular rhythm in attention, and very numerous irregularities due to fatigue, interest, inhibition, etc. These sources of variation . . . are . . . so numerous and to a certain extent so independent, that they justify roughly the assumptions of mathematicians [that an error is composed of a very large number of comparatively small and independent errors], and the results of experiments show that the errors are in a general way distributed as required by the theory of probability (p. 287).

Somewhat later, Urban (1910) provided a further clarification of the classical position by noting that the concept of the probability of a judgment was basic to the analysis of psychophysical methods of measurement. "Experience shows that if a standard stimulus of given intensity is compared under constant conditions with stimuli of varying intensities, the probabilities of the different judgments vary in a certain way with the intensity of the comparison stimulus" (p. 229). Urban then proceeded to indicate that the "mathematical expression which gives the probability of judgment (smaller, equal, or greater) as a function of the comparison stimulus is called the *psychometric function* of that judgment." He cautioned that there was no special difficulty in devising mathematical expressions which could serve as hypotheses about the psychometric function; the question, however, was to decide "which one of a certain group of functions is best suited to represent a given experimental material."

Urban doubted that an expression could be found that fitted all data equally well; nevertheless, he endorsed the *phi-gamma (ϕγ) hypothesis* which was derived from "the notion of a threshold which is subjected to chance variations, the frequency of which is a function of their size" (p. 250). The ϕγ hypothesis is fundamentally the classical theory of sensory discrimination. It predicts the general form of the psychometric function and stipulates that "the series of frequencies increases continuously, although not at a constant rate" (Urban, 1907). The requirement of a continuous but *nonlinear* rate of change in the psychometric function is one of the major differences between the classical position and the theory of the neural quantum which will be considered in the next section of this chapter.

It should be clear from the preceding paragraph that the choice of a mathematical formula to represent a psychometric function is essentially a statement of a hypothesis about the psychometric function. The classical theory of sensory discrimination maintains that the data of a psychometric function can be most adequately represented by the phi function of gamma (ϕγ function). This is equivalent to stating that the psychometric function may be described by the integral of the normal probability distribution. According to the classical theory, the curve which best fits a graphical plot showing the relationship of the probability of a certain judgment (p) to the value of the stimulus (S) is a normal ogive. This is the *phi-gamma hypothesis;* it assumes that the normal *cumulative* distribution accurately describes p as a function of S, as shown in Figure 11-1.

Boring (1917) presented a detailed account of the classical view of the psychometric function and indicated how the function could be generated in terms of neural activity. He proposed that the stimulated sensory organs and the brain are at a given moment "variously disposed for impression." These variations toward a particular impression, for example, a judgment of "two" in an experiment on the two-point threshold, occur independently of the value of the stimulus; they result from the interaction of a large number of different factors that operate by chance whenever the stimulus is applied and work "for or against the impression 'two'." In other words, a judgment of a given category ("two") will occur for a given stimulus whenever the level of chance disposition which is required for that judgment occurs, or is exceeded. The factors ("coins") which determine the disposition toward a given category are independent of each other and are favorable (positive) or unfavorable (negative) in chance combinations. Whenever the stimulus is weak, more factors must be favorable for a given judgment ("two") to occur than when the stimulus is stronger.

There are, then, two functions to be considered, one which shows the cumulative frequency of occurrence of the various "grades of chance disposition," that is, the various combinations of positive and negative factors, while the other shows the frequencies (or proportions) of a given judgment as a function of the magnitude of the stimulus. The first of these is the normal ogive, and the second, the psychometric function. Under the assumption that the frequency of occurrence of the judgment ("two") corresponds exactly to the frequency of the disposition ("two") as determined by chance factors, the two curves will be expected to be identical.

Boring (1917) illustrated his position with a chart of the psychometric function for the two-point limen as shown in Figure 11-2. To simplify his exposition, only six chance factors were assumed to be operative in the experiment on the two-point limen. For example, with a stimulus (separation) of 8 mm, all six factors must be favorable simultaneously to produce a judgment of "two." At 9 mm, at least five must be favorable; at 10 mm, at least four, and so on, as presented on the abscissa of Figure 11-2. If 64 trials are given for each stimulus, we can determine from the binomial distribution that the theoretical probability of a judgment of "two" at 8 mm is 1/64 at 9 mm, 1/64 plus 6/64, at 10 mm, 1/64 plus 6/64 plus 15/64, and so on. In Figure 11-2, the various classes of outcomes (dispositions) are depicted in the histogram (bar graph) with a favorable factor indicated by "X" and an unfavorable factor by "O." For example, given six factors presented 64 times, there will be fifteen times in which a combination of four favorable and two unfavorable factors will occur. The cumulative proportions (probabilities) for the various "dispositions" at each stimulus are, respectively, 0.016, 0.109, 0.344, 0.656, 0.891, and 0.984. Thus, the ogive represents both the cumulative distribution of the normally distributed combination of chance factors and the expected distribution of "two" judgments for the particular set of stimulus magnitudes. To

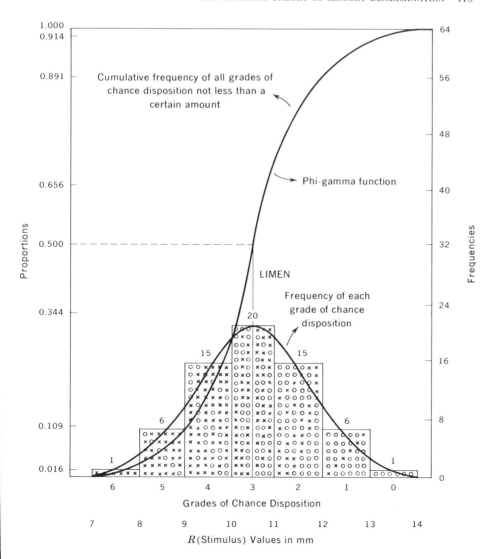

Figure 11–2. Graphical representation of the classical theory of sensory discrimination, showing that the phi-gamma function is equivalent to the integral of the normal probability curve. The histogram shows the theoretical frequency of occurrence of the various classes of outcomes in which six independent factors, each of which may be favorable (x) or unfavorable (o), are assumed to be operating in each of 64 trials. For smaller stimulus values, a greater number of favorable elements must be present for a correct judgment to occur than for larger values of the stimulus. (From Corso, 1950; after Boring, *Amer. J. Psychol.*, 1917.)

differentiate between the two curves, the cumulative chance curve is called the normal ogive and the psychometric function is called the phi-gamma function. Classically, the stimulus value corresponding to the 50 percent point on the phi-gamma function was taken as the stimulus (absolute) limen; this, as noted in Figure 11-2, is also the maximal point of the noncumulative chance distribution.

We will now describe the $\phi\,\gamma$ function mathematically and show its relation to the normal probability distribution. The normal distribution function is often expressed as

$$y = \frac{1}{\delta\sqrt{2\pi}}\, e^{-x^2/2\delta^2}\ ,$$

(11-1)

where y represents the ordinate values of the noncumulative curve, δ is the standard deviation of the distribution of measures, x is the deviation of a measure from the mean of the distribution, e is a constant of 2.718, and π equals 3.1416.

If we now let $h = \dfrac{1}{\delta\sqrt{2}}$ and substitute h in Equation 11-1, we obtain

$$y = \frac{h}{\sqrt{\pi}}\, e^{-h^2x^2}\ .$$

(11-2)

The phi function of gamma is derived directly from Equation 11-2 by integration. That is:

$$P = \int_{-\infty}^{x} \frac{h}{\sqrt{\pi}}\, e^{-h^2x^2}\, dx,$$

(11-3)

where the integration is performed from $-\infty$ to a given value of x, and P represents the proportion of area under the curve within these limits on the abscissa.

Let $\gamma = hx$, giving $d\gamma/dx = h$ and $dx = d\gamma/h$, and substitute in Equation 11-3 to obtain:

$$P = \int_{-\infty}^{x} \frac{1}{\sqrt{\pi}}\, e^{-\gamma^2}\, d\gamma$$

(11-4)

Equation 11-4 is the phi function of gamma.

The interpretation of the phi function of gamma may be described quite readily in terms of a typical psychophysical method—the method of constant stimulus differences as presented in Chapter 7. In Equation 11-4, P represents the proportion of judgments in a certain category; $\gamma^2 = h^2x^2 = (X-M)^2/2\sigma^2$, and $\gamma = 0.7071\, x/\sigma$, so that γ is the distance of a given stimulus from the mean (stimulus limen) expressed in terms of h. It is this quantity, h, which measures the "precision" of the curve represented in Equation 11-4; more specifically, h is related to the slope of the cumulative curve. The larger the value of h, the steeper the rise of the ogive (cumulative) curve.

The relationship of h and x to the ogive curve is shown graphically in Figure 11-3. Here, the proportion of judgments is plotted as a function of the magnitude of stimulus values. It should be noted that these functions are similar to the "higher" curve of Figure 7-2. As the value of h increases, the slope of the ogive becomes greater. This means, for example, that given two observers and a particular set of stimulus values, the observer whose judgments generate the steeper psychometric function has the greater differential sensitivity. By referring to Figure 7-2, it may be seen that the greater the slope of the psychometric function, the smaller the value of the interval of uncertainty (IU) and the smaller the mean DL ($= IU/2$). For purposes of later discussion, is should also be observed that the middle segment of each phi-gamma function in Figure 11-3 is essentially linear.

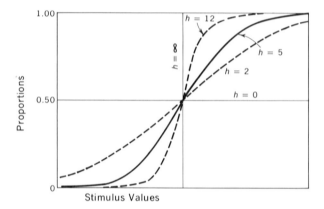

Figure 11-3. Changes in the phi function of gamma for different values of h. (From Guilford, *Psychometric methods*, copyright © 1936, 1954, McGraw-Hill Book Company. Used by permission.)

An explanation of the mathematical technique of fitting psychophysical data to the phi-gamma function lies outside the scope of this book, but a treatment of this topic may be found in Guilford (1936, 1954). The general procedure is to start with the series of stimulus values and their corresponding proportions of judgment (p). From prepared tables, γ values are obtained for every value of p. Then, using $\gamma = hx$ and knowing that $x = (X-M)$, we compute a value of h for each value of x. The value of h which will give the best-fitting phi-gamma function is then obtained by the method of least squares. An additional refinement in the procedure is to use weighting factors (Müller-Urban weights) for the proportions involved in fixing the value of h, but this procedure is not too often warranted due to the usually limited number of observations and the small effect the procedure has upon the computed values of h and the mean of the psycho-metric function. Finally, it may be theoretically significant to know how well the phi-gamma function actually fits the obtained proportions. This is accomplished by performing a test of goodness of fit involving chi-square (χ^2) and plotting, if desired, the obtained best-fitting curve to show graphically how closely the curve fits the data. The degree to which the curve fits the data is taken as an indication of the adequacy of the theory from which the mathematical function was derived.

The major elements of the classical theory of sensory discrimination may now be summarized. The theory is based on the assumption of two psychophysical continua: (1) a *physical continuum*, which represents a series of objects or physical phenomena that differ only in the magnitude of some given property, for example, the energy of a sound wave, the wavelength of visible light, or the volume of a cube; and (2) a *psychological continuum*, which referred classically to "sensations" and formed a subjective series parallel to the physical series, for example, the loudness of tones, the hue of chromatic colors, or the perceived size of a cube. While the physical continuum was considered to extend from zero to infinity, the corresponding psychological continuum, as described in Chapter 2, was considerably more limited and paralleled the physical continuum only over a relatively small portion of the total range available. The task of classical psychophysics was to determine the functional relations between the physical and psychological continua. It was assumed that the events on the psychological continuum were directly represented in the judgments of the observer.

In addition to the assumption of two psychophysical continua, the classical formulation maintained that (3) a judgment (discriminatory response) for a given stimulus depended not only upon the designated *magnitude of the stimulus,* but also upon the *random (independent) influences of a large number of uncontrolled factors* whose effects combined according to the normal law of error (chance probability). Whenever the stimulus was presented, these factors intervened to aid or to hinder the judgment. It was asserted that a plot of the proportion of judgments in a given category as a function of stimulus magnitude (the psychometric function) was best described by the phi function of gamma (a normal ogive). Given the psychometric function and a specified criterion of response, the value of the stimulus, or stimulus increment, could be determined to establish the absolute or differential threshold. While these values were considered to be fixed at a particular moment, the classical view held that they were subject to increases or decreases through random influences in the course of the experimental trials. Thus, *sensitivity* (the inverse value of the absolute or differential threshold) was considered to be a variable, not a constant. Other equations have been proposed for the psychometric function (for example, the phi-log-gamma hypothesis of Thurstone, 1928, and the logistic function of Berkson, 1944) and other explanations have been offered for the occurrence of the normal ogive in psychophysical experiments (see Fullerton and Cattell, 1892; and Thurstone, 1927), but the phi-gamma function and the concept of random errors have been most widely accepted as a statement of the classical theory.

Examples of Classical
Psychometric Functions

Some typical psychophysical data will now be presented to illustrate the general form of the psychometric function according to the classical theory of sensory discrimination.

A traditional psychophysical experiment is that of weight lifting. Brown (1910) used a standard of 100 gm and a variable which ranged from 18 gm below to 18 gm above the standard in 1-gm steps. There were also two additional steps of 0.5 gm, one on each side of the standard. The judgments were obtained by the method of constant stimulus differences, with 700 trials at each value of the variable stimulus. The cumulative proportions of "heavier" judgments are shown in Figure 11-4. The curve connects the obtained data points and no smoothing of

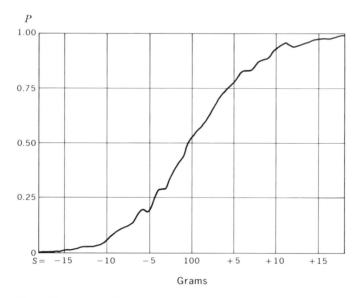

Figure 11–4.   Cumulative proportion of "heavier" judgments in a two-category experiment on weight-lifting. The standard was 100 grams and the variable stimuli were symmetrically spaced on each side of the standard from −18 to +18 grams in 1-gram steps, except for two additional stimuli which were 0.5 gram above and below the standard. The data were collected by the method of constant stimulus difference, with 700 judgments per stimulus. (From Woodworth, 1938; after Warner Brown, 1910.)

the function has been performed. The function is ogival in form and satisfies the requirements inherent in the classical phi function of gamma. Large differences between the variable and the standard are detected more often than smaller differences; as the difference increases, the frequency (proportion) of correct judgments increases according to the integral of the normal probability curve. Large positive differences (heavy variable stimuli) are not always correctly detected, and sometimes light variable stimuli are judged to be heavier than the standard. Nevertheless, as the magnitude of the variable stimulus increases by small steps from 82 to 118 gm, there is a cumulative ogival increase in the proportion of correct judgments.

    In a study on hearing, Corso (1951) obtained data for frequency and intensity discrimination. The observers were selected on the basis of the Seashore Measures of Musical Talent and were given a one-hour practice session on each of two days, providing more than 500 judgments. The data on frequency discrimination obtained in the test session for one observer are presented in Figure 11-5. Judgments were made following the method of constant stimulus differences, with the standard tone set at a frequency of 1000 cps and the intensity set at 20 db above the observer's absolute threshold, that is, 20 db SL (sensation level). Six fre-

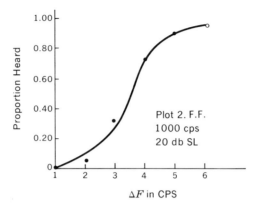

Figure 11-5. The phi-gamma function of the classical theory of sensory discrimination fitted by visual inspection to a set of data on frequency discrimination. (From Corso, *Amer. J. Psychol.,* 1951.)

quency increments (ΔF) were used (1, 2, 3, 4, 5, and 6 cps) and the observer was instructed to press a response key each time he heard an increase in the pitch of the tone. The frequency increments were presented at 3-sec intervals and lasted 0.3 sec; the increments were presented in random order but in blocks of 25 consecutive trials each. There were 200 judgments made at each increment value. The ogive shown in Figure 11-5 was fitted to the data points by visual inspection simply to illustrate for purposes of the present discussion the general form of the psychometric function. The high degree of similarity between the obtained function and the theoretical curve of Figure 11-2 is quite apparent.

In the part of the study dealing with intensity discrimination, the selection, training, and testing of observers followed the same plan as that for frequency discrimination. The data for one observer at 1000 cps, 40 db SL, are shown in Figure 11-6. Again, for this presentation, the ogive was fitted by visual inspection; the sigmoidal (S shaped) form of the curve corresponds to that predicted by the classical theory of sensory discrimination.

Stuiver (1958) obtained a set of psychometric functions for the smelling of different odors. He was interested in determining the number of molecules of certain odorous substances required to excite one human olfactory cell and the number required to produce a reportable sensation. Assuming that about 2 percent of the molecules of an odorous substance are absorbed by the olfactory epithelium and that these are uniformly distributed over all sensory cells, it was estimated that approximately 6 molecules (not less than one nor more than 8) are required to excite a single olfactory cell. From the psychometric functions shown in Figure 11-7 it was estimated that at least 40 molecules are required to produce

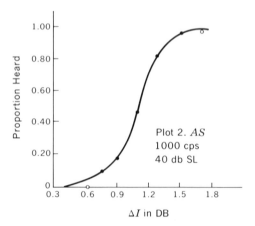

Figure 11-6. The phi-gamma function of the classical theory of sensory discrimination fitted by visual inspection to a set of data on intensity discrimination. (From Corso, *Amer. J. Psychol.*, 1951.)

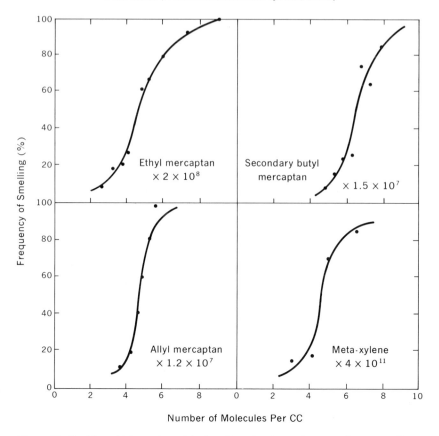

Figure 11-7. Sigmoidal psychometric functions for four odorous substances. (From Stuiver, 1958.)

a threshold sensation that can be reported by the observer. Notice that while all four functions in Figure 11-7 are ogival in form, they vary in slope (steepness). This indicates that changes in the concentration of certain substances (for example, allyl mercaptan) are much more readily detected than similar changes in another substance (for example, ethyl mercaptan).

A set of data obtained by Bouman and Walraven (1957) reveal that in vision, given a particular wavelength, there are two psychometric functions, one for the perception of color and the other for the perception of light without color. As we indicated in Chapter 8, there is an achromatic zone, that is, given a particular wavelength at a particular intensity, an observer may be able to detect the presence of a test flash of light—but the flash appears to be colorless. At a greater intensity, the test flash is not only detectable but appears to be colored according to its particular wavelength. Bouman and Walraven found that when short-duration flashes were presented briefly at the fovea, the absorption of two quanta of light at 580 mμ produced a colorless sensation, but when three quanta were absorbed, the flash appeared to be green. The two psychometric functions (judgments with and without hue as a function of stimulus intensity) are presented in Figure 11-8 for a wavelength of 580 mμ. Both functions are ogival in form as

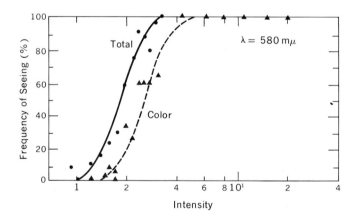

Figure 11-8. Classical psychometric functions for judgments of a foveal light flash (580 mu) which was perceived as colorless (left curve) and colored (right curve). (From Bouman and Walraven, *J. opt. Soc. Amer.*, 1957.)

predicted by the classical theory of sensory discrimination, but the hue curve is displaced to the right. This indicates that for a given probability of response (for example, 50 percent), greater intensity is needed to produce a judgment involving color than one which simply indicates the occurrence of a (colorless) flash of light.

These are a few examples of the many psychophysical experiments in which the sigmoidal psychometric function has been obtained, thereby supporting the classical theory of sensory discrimination. The form of this curve, the phi-gamma function, is attributed to the observer's discriminatory ability and to the intervention of random fluctuations which influence the observer's judgments in accordance with the laws of chance (normal probability distribution). The classical view thus asserts that the frequency of psychophysical judgments and, hence, the underlying sensory excitation or sensation, increases in a smooth and continuous manner as the value of the corresponding physical stimulus is increased continuously along some specified dimension.

However, what if the effects of random fluctuation could be eliminated or reduced during the experimental trials? What would be the form of the psychometric function? Would it still be sigmoidal, or would it assume some other shape? Since the specific form of the function is assumed to indicate the "internal workings" of the discriminatory mechanism, any departure of the psychometric function from the classical ogive would suggest a new hypothesis about the nature of sensory discrimination. Some investigators have obtained rectilinear rather than sigmoidal psychometric functions and have proposed an alternative to the classical theory of sensory discrimination. This alternative is the *neural quantum theory of sensory discrimination* to which we will now turn.

The Neural Quantum Theory of Sensory Discrimination

Historical Background of the Theory

The controversy of the classical theory versus the neural quantum theory (sometimes called the sensory continuity-noncontinuity issue, Corso, 1963*a*) had its origins in early psychophysics. While some classical psychophysicists (Fechner and Lotze) argued for the noncontinuity position which included the concept of threshold, others (Delboeuf, Pierce, Jastrow, and Müller) insisted that the sensory continuum consisted of a continuous series of intermediate degrees of sensation and that there was "no threshold in any true sense," that is, the sensory continuum represented a continuous function with no discontinuities as implied by the absolute and differential thresholds. The question is whether the changes on the psychological continuum occur in a smooth and continuous manner as the value of the physical stimulus is increased continuously along a specified dimension, or whether there is an abrupt step-like change from no sensation to sensation or from sensation to a difference in sensation.

The classical notion of threshold, as held by Fechner (1860), was that the brain in its waking state was physiologically active; consequently, in order for an incoming stimulus to be detected, it had to generate neurological excitations which were sufficiently larger than those residually present as the result of the spontaneous activity of the brain. A liminal stimulus, or a liminal stimulus difference, was one which "lifted the sensation or sensory difference over the threshold of consciousness." Herbart (1824) adopted this "barrier" concept of threshold in developing his elaborate system of "mental mathematics" and Titchener (1905) placed the locus of the "barrier" not in the brain but at the sensory organ. For

Titchener, the application of a stimulus produced a corresponding change in sensation only if the "frictional resistance" which characterized the given sensory organ was overcome. Once the "nervous machine" was started and adequate stimulation was maintained, sensation was said to follow the changes in stimulation in a continuous manner.

Licklider (1951) proposed a similar idea but maintained that the stimulus threshold owed its existence to the effect of a small barrier "between successive stages in the neural processes" of the given sensory modality. He specifically asserted that "if the Difference Limen is more than a statistical artifact, the neural mechanism must function in a stepwise or quantal manner" (p. 1001). Troland (1930) had also pointed to the tendency to use quantal concepts in dealing with the processes of the human nervous system. He maintained that "the all-or-none principle, as applied to nerve activity, forces us to think of the latter in terms of fixed units of influence" (p. 37). Thus, the issue becomes clearer. Given sensory mechanisms which are composed of discrete neural elements that function according to the all-or-none law of physiology, how can a continuous change in environmental energy give rise to an apparently continuous change in sensory experience?

One solution to the problem is to show experimentally that with appropriate techniques discrete steps can be obtained in studies of sensory discrimination, thereby suggesting that the fundamental nature of the discriminal process is noncontinuous. Békésy (1930) obtained such evidence in a study dealing with the differential threshold in hearing. He presented the observer with a standard tone of 0.3 sec duration and followed this *immediately* with a comparison tone of the same duration, but of variable intensity. The task of the observer was to report whether he heard a difference in loudness between the two tones. The results of this study are presented in Figure 11-9 in which the percentage of judgments of differences is plotted as a function of $\Delta I/I$. Since the obtained functions were rectilinear, it was proposed that the findings were indicative of the quantal nature of differential sensitivity to intensity.

Why had the psychometric function *not* been of the classical ogival form, as might have been expected? Apparently the experimental procedure used by Békésy minimized the variability associated with factors outside the specific part of the sensory nervous system involved in making the required psychophysical judgment. This *"extrinsic variability"* would include such factors as shifts in attention, changes in the criteria of judgment, variations in the observer's motivation, and so on. With the elimination or minimization of this source of variability, the "true" mechanism of sensory discrimination was assumed to be revealed; apparently it was no longer masked by extraneous factors in the experimental situation which tended to produce variability and errors in judgment.

In a subsequent study, Békésy (1936) obtained further evidence on the quantal nature of sensory functions. The study was designed to determine the absolute threshold (*MAP*) for pure tones from about 2 to 50 cps. This was accomplished by starting at 2 cps and alternately increasing frequency and decreasing intensity until the upper frequency limit (about 50 cps) was reached. The task of the observer was to report whenever he heard the tone. Each time the intensity of the

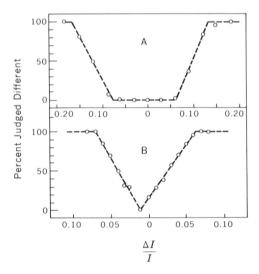

Figure 11-9. Distributions of "different" judgments for two tones which varied in intensity by a
given amount, ΔI. Plot A is for less practiced observers; Plot B is for well practiced observers. (From
Stevens and Davis, *Hearing: its psychology and
physiology*, 1938; after Békésy, 1930.)

tone was reduced so that the observer no longer heard it, the frequency of the
tone was then increased (holding intensity constant) until the observer again
reported he heard the tone. At this frequency, the intensity was once more reduced
to a value below threshold and then, once again, the frequency was increased
until the tone became audible. When the audibility curve was plotted, step-like
discontinuities were found to occur at fairly regular intervals between 4 cps and
50 cps, with the most prominent step located at 18 cps.

The quantal interpretation of these results, however, has been questioned by
Corso (1961). In the first of two experiments, he indicated that there were certain
critical features of methodology that would have forced the audibility function
to display step-like discontinuities, regardless of the quantal or nonquantal characteristics of the discriminatory process. He then proceeded to replicate Békésy's
experiment, but with an addition in procedure—the threshold function was obtained not only in an ascending sequence (that is, from lower to higher frequencies)
but also in a descending sequence (from higher to lower frequencies). The results
of the study showed that there was excellent agreement with Békésy's data regarding the *frequency location* of the "quantal" steps; there was also excellent agreement
between the ascending and descending functions, although the location of the
steps tended to be lower in frequency in the descending sequence.

Figure 11-10 shows the similarity of ascending data for one observer in Corso's
study with that of the observer in Békésy's study. Although both curves show
discontinuities ("steps"), these are purported to be experimentally induced arti-

facts, in Corso's view, and result primarily from the testing procedure and from the method of treating the data.

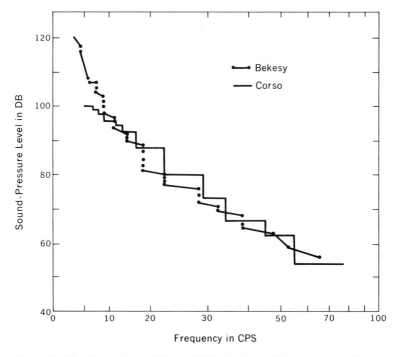

Figure 11–10. Comparison of the audibility function obtained for one observer in each of two studies on quantal discrimination. (To equate for differences in auditory sensitivity, the function from Békésy's study has been displaced downward by 12 db.) (From Corso, *Amer. J. Psychol.,* 1961.)

Given the same testing method, but with *repeated* judgments at each testing point, the step-like discontinuities in the function may be analyzed in a different manner and the continuous classical function can be obtained. This is shown in Figure 11-11. Notice the set of hypothetical values that is connected by a step-like function similar to that in Figure 11-10. Each point represents many judgments, and, accordingly, each horizontal segment of each step and each vertical segment of each step may be considered to yield a particular psychometric function. For example, the vertical segment at 30 cps can be replotted separately to show the cumulative proportion of judgments as a function of sound pressure level. From this function, the absolute threshold (50 percent) can be determined, as represented in Figure 11-11 by an open square. It should be noted that this value is exactly the same whether the psychometric function is considered to be linear or ogival. When these values have been computed for each segment of each step, a *continuous* line can be drawn through these points and will correspond to the traditional threshold function, thereby eliminating the step-like discontinuities.

In the second experiment of this series, Corso modified the testing procedure to take into account the methodological limitations identified in the first experi-

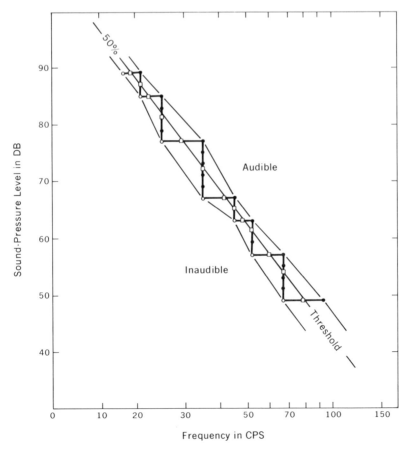

Figure 11–11. Theoretical derivation of the classical audibility function (50% threshold) from a hypothetical set of quantal steps. The open square in each segment of each step corresponds to the assumed absolute threshold for a particular psychometric function. (From Corso, *Amer. J. Psychol.*, 1961.)

ment. Ten observers were tested and their audibility data were fitted with both linear and ogival psychometric functions. These functions were in turn used to predict the physical values corresponding to the "90 percent response points" and further calculations were then performed. The results indicated that both the quantal and phi-gamma hypotheses were equally acceptable in predicting the 90 percent audibility function for pure tones. Thus, support of one theory to the exclusion of the other was not obtained.

The Neural Quantum Theory and Derived Predictions

The theory of the neural quantum was first made explicit by Stevens, Morgan, and Volkmann (1941) within the context of auditory discrimination. A detailed treatment of the theory was later presented by Corso (1956), who reexamined the theory in terms of the experimental evidence that had been accumulated up to that time. Unlike the classical theory of sensory discrimination which states that the proper form of the psychometric function is a normal ogive, the neural quantum theory asserts that the relationship between the proportion of judgments and corresponding stimulus values is best represented by a *linear* function. This implies that sensory discrimination is fundamentally a discontinuous process which is characterized by finite, discrete (quantal) steps. The theory is intended to be consistent with the all-or-none principle of physiology since it is generally believed that discriminatory judgments are mediated by the activities of underlying neural structures.

The theory of the neural quantum is derived from the basic assumption that these neural structures or processes are divided into functionally distinct units or quanta. As used within the framework of this theory, the term "quantum" (or the plural, "quanta") does not have a physical connotation; it does not refer to energy units in contemporary physics, nor to the use of these physical units in visual or auditory theory. In the psychological theory of the neural quantum, the term refers specifically to a *functionally* distinct unit in the neural mechanisms which are involved in sensory discrimination. When used in this way, the term "quantum" implies a perceptual unit, not a physical unit.

The fundamental concepts involved in the neural quantum theory are represented schematically in Figure 11-12 for the condition of intensity discrimination. Figure 11-12 shows two assumed continua: (1) a physical continuum with stimuli located on an arbitrary scale of intensity, and (2) a psychological (sensory) continuum with hypothesized discrete neural units, or quanta. Changes on the stimulus continuum are associated with corresponding changes on the sensory continuum. On the stimulus continuum, the magnitude of the standard which completely excites a given number of neural units, and which may or may not leave some "residual excitation" (p), is denoted by the symbol S; ΔSq is the magnitude of the stimulus increment which will always excite one quantum more than the number of units completely excited by S; and ΔS is the amount of energy (magnitude of the stimulus increment) which is required to activate a neural unit that has been "partially" excited.

Now we will consider a hypothetical experiment in intensity discrimination. Suppose that a certain stimulus (S) has been presented and that the intensity of this stimulus was sufficient to excite a fixed number of quanta, *leaving no "residual" excitation* (p). If it is assumed that the neural units are stable and of constant size, the presentation of stimulus increments (ΔS) which are added to S (in accordance with specified procedures) will not excite an additional quantal unit until ΔS has increased to the size of ΔSq.

On the assumption that the observer has adopted a "one-quantum" criterion of discrimination (which, as we will show, is quite unlikely), this incremental value when added to S will produce a just noticeable difference (jnd) in loudness. Obviously, any value of ΔS greater than this particular value will also be sufficient to produce a difference in loudness. Thus, assuming only the existence of neural

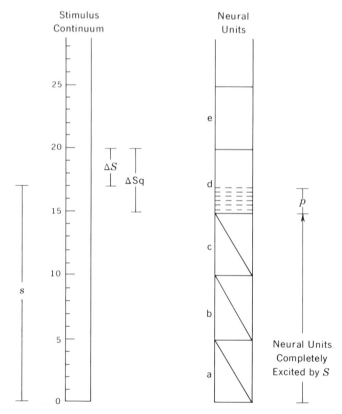

Figure 11–12. A schematic representation of the basic concepts involved in the theory of the neural quantum. (From Corso, *Psychol. Bull.*, 1956.)

quanta and a judgment criterion of one quantum, the resulting psychometric function would be a perpendicular straight line as shown in Figure 11-13. Given a series of progressively larger stimulus increments, 0 percent response would be obtained up to a certain point; beyond this, 100 percent response would be obtained, that is, each time a stimulus increment was presented that exceeded the critical value, the observer would be able to detect a difference between the standard stimulus and the standard stimulus plus the increment.

Functions of the type shown in Figure 11-13, however, are not obtained in experiments on sensory discrimination. This indicates the need for an additional assumption. This assumption states that the overall sensitivity of the observer does not remain fixed at a constant level, but exhibits momentary and random fluctuations which may exceed the magnitude of a single quantum. Given these fluctuations in sensitivity, the size of the stimulus which is required to activate a fixed number of neural units will vary from moment to moment; conversely, a stimulus of certain size will activate a different number of neural units from moment to moment.

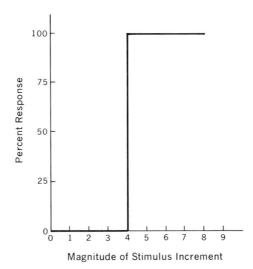

Figure 11-13. The form of the psychometric function as predicted from the single assumption of the existence of neural quanta. (From Corso, *Psychol. Bull.,* 1956.)

Recall, however, that the variation in the number of activated units is assumed to be quantal; consequently, all of the available energy in a particular stimulus will not necessarily be utilized in a given presentation to the observer. If this occurs, the stimulus will completely excite a certain number of quanta, but an additional quantum will be "partially" excited by the small amount of residual (unused) energy in the stimulus. Although the residual energy is incapable of activating an additional quantum by itself, it becomes available under certain testing conditions for summation with the succeeding stimulus increment. If the residual energy combined with the energy of the succeeding stimulus increment is sufficient to stimulate an additional quantum, a discriminatory response will be produced, in a situation in which the observer has adopted a one-quantum criterion of judgment.

The concepts of the neural quantum theory which have been developed up to this point will now be summarized by a series of simple equations. At any given moment, the size of the stimulus increment (ΔS) which is required to activate one quantum, in addition to the total number excited by the standard stimulus (S), will depend upon the amount of residual (surplus) energy in the standard stimulus or the degree of corresponding "partial" excitation (p). Since ΔSq is the size of the increment which will always excite one additional quantum, this relation is given by:

$$\Delta S = \Delta Sq - p. \tag{11-5}$$

According to Equation 11-5, ΔS will completely activate the additional quantum needed for discrimination whenever $\Delta S \geq \Delta Sq - p$. Consequently, as the magnitude of ΔS increases from some small value, there would be an expected increase in the number of discriminatory responses. The specific manner in which the responses would increase as a function ΔS would depend upon the relative frequency of occurrence of the different residual values (p). If it is assumed that the sensitivity of the observer fluctuates due to the influence of a large number of unknown, independent factors, two things will occur: (1) the residuals (surpluses) in stimulus energy will occur over the same range of neural units as stimulated during the course of random fluctuations in sensitivity, and (2) the distribution of surpluses over this range will approximate a normal curve.

These effects are represented graphically in Figure 11-14 which shows a normal

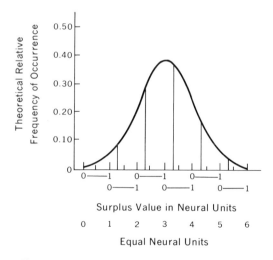

Figure 11-14. Chance distribution of surplus values of energy assumed to result from random fluctuations in organismic sensitivity. (From Corso, *Psychol. Bull.*, 1956.)

distribution of surplus values. The abscissa represents the range over which the observer fluctuates in sensitivity; this range has been divided arbitrarily into six equal neural units. Also, each of these units has been further subdivided arbitrarily into ten equal values of surplus. Thus, a surplus of a given magnitude may be found to occur in each neural unit. The ordinate of Figure 11-14 represents the relative frequency of occurrence of the various surplus values in the several neural units; for illustrative purposes, a vertical line has been drawn at a surplus value of 0.3 of a neural unit. Notice that while the surplus value is constant (0.3), the relative frequency of occurrence of this value is not the same for the six neural units. For instance, for the fourth neural unit, the ordinate has a value of approximately 0.37; but, for the second neural unit, the value is approximately 0.08.

The significance of Figure 11-14 is that it provides the basis for determining the probability function of the surplus values that will be used in making certain specific predictions about the psychometric function. The probability function is obtained by summating the relative frequency of occurrence of all possible values of surplus, from zero to neural unit size, over the range of neural units excited by random fluctuations in sensitivity. This is demonstrated graphically in Figure 11-15.

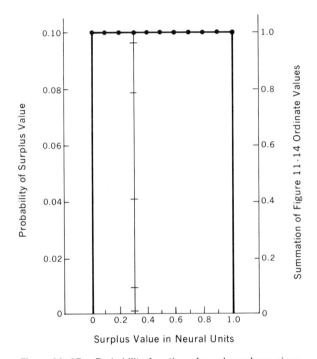

Figure 11-15.   Probability function of surplus values; given a standard stimulus, any value of surplus is as likely as any other. (From Corso, *Psychol. Bull.,* 1956.)

In this figure, the rectangular distribution was obtained by summating, over the six neural units of Figure 11-14, the relative frequencies of occurrence of the ten individual surplus values. The segmented vertical line in Figure 11-15 shows the graphical summation for the surplus value equal to 0.3 of a neural unit. Each segment of this line, starting at the bottom, corresponds in length to the appropriate ordinate shown in Figure 11-14, starting at the left end of the abscissa. There is a segment in the vertical line for each of the six quantal units. The same procedure was used to obtain the summation value for each of the nine remaining surplus values. Since the resulting form of the obtained distribution is essentially rectangular, and the neural unit is divided into equal parts, the probability of occurrence of each surplus value is the same for all surpluses. Consequently, given a standard stimulus, any value of surplus is as likely to occur as any other.

On the basis of the rectangular function in Figure 11-15, it is now possible to predict the form of the psychometric function. It has already been pointed out that the number of responses to a stimulus increment will increase as a function of the size of the increment; the greater the increment, the greater will be the number of responses. Since it has been shown that the probability function of surplus values is rectangular, this means that for a given increase in the size of the increment, the proportion of surpluses that can be augmented to neural unit size, or greater, is always the same. Thus, this produces a constant rate of increase in the number of responses as the size of the increment is increased; stated in terms of a mathematical function, this indicates that the relationship between increment size and the percentage (or proportion) of responses is linear.

Given Equation 11-5 ($\Delta S = \Delta Sq - p$) which indicates that an additional quantum will be activated whenever the amount of energy in an increment is sufficient to augment the surplus energy to a neural unit amount, and given fluctuations of p between $0 \leq p \leq \Delta Sq$, with any value of p as likely to occur as any other, the proportion of times (f_1) that an increment will activate one additional neural unit is given by:

$$f_1 = \Delta S / \Delta Sq. \tag{11-6}$$

There are two features of Equation 11-6 which should be noted: (1) given a one-quantum criterion of judgment, the proportion of responses increases as a linear function of the size of the increment, and (2) this proportion may vary between zero and one.

Equation 11-6 holds, however, only for those experimental situations in which the excitation of a *single* additional quantum is sufficient for producing a discriminatory response. The evidence of Békésy (1930), Miller and Garner (1944), and Blackwell (1953), does not support the assumption of a one-quantum criterion of judgment. Usually *two* additional quantal units must be excited before a response occurs.

The need for a two-quanta criterion is attributed to the fluctuations in sensitivity that may occur during the presentation of the standard stimulus. Since the observer's fluctuation in sensitivity may produce surplus values of neural unit size, the observer is unable to distinguish between this excitation and that resulting from an adequate stimulus increment. In order to distinguish between the two effects, the observer adopts a certainty criterion of two quanta; in this way, the combined effect of increment and surplus must excite two quanta before he responds. This effect is perceptually different from that produced by the surplus alone, which can excite only one additional quantum. It follows that, in the *two*-quanta case, the proportion of times a given increment will produce a discriminatory response (f_2) may be expressed as:

$$f_2 = \Delta S / \Delta Sq - 1. \tag{11-7}$$

As in Equation 11-6, the proportion of responses (f_2) increases as a linear function of ΔS and may vary from zero to one.

Equation 11-7 may be rewritten in terms of the percentage of discriminatory responses (P) that an observer should be able to make as a function of the size of the stimulus increment. In this form,

$$P = 100\left[\left(\frac{\Delta S}{\Delta Sq}\right) - 1\right],\tag{11-8}$$

and P may vary between 0 percent and 100 percent.

From Equation 11-8 it may be seen that stimulus increments smaller than the size of one quantum can never stimulate two additional quanta since the value of surplus (p) cannot exceed one unit. In this instance, no discriminatory response will occur as the combined effect of increment and surplus will be less than two quanta. However, a response will occur whenever the increments are of quantal size or larger; also, the percentage of responses will increase in the same linear manner as described for the one-quantum criterion.

The psychometric function predicted by the theory of the neural quantum may now be presented graphically. Figure 11-16 shows the rectilinear relationship

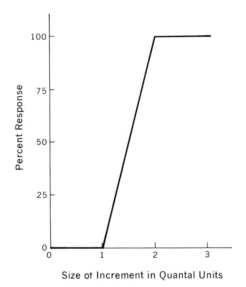

Figure 11-16. The rectilinear form of the psycho-metric function predicted by the theory of the neu-ral quantum. (From Corso, *Psychol. Bull.*, 1956.)

which is predicted to obtain between the percentage of responses and the size of stimulus increments expressed in quantal units. Under a two-quanta criterion of judgment, 100 percent response will occur at the smallest incremental value which can always excite two additional quanta. This value is independent of the surplus and so its magnitude will be twice that of the largest increment to which a response never occurs. The latter increment, that is, the largest increment which "just never" elicits a response, is taken as a measure of one quantal unit; the smallest increment which "just always" yields 100 percent response is taken as two quantal units. Since it is assumed that the neural units are equal in size, a two-to-one ratio may be expected between the stimulus increment at which the psychometric function reaches 100 percent and the value at which it first departs from 0 percent, provided the observer has adopted a two-quanta criterion of judgment.

If the underlying assumptions of the neural quantum theory are satisfied, and if appropriate experimental methods are employed, a typical psychometric function would be expected to show three essential characteristics. (1) There will be a linear relationship between the magnitude of stimulus increments and the cumulative percentage of responses (judgments) from 0 percent to 100 percent. (2) There will be a two-to-one ratio between the value of the stimulus increment eliciting 100 percent response (a two-quantum increment) and that eliciting 0 percent response (a one-quantum increment). (3) The slope of the psychometric function will be inversely proportional to the intercept of the function on the x-axis, that is, the size of stimulus increment at which the function departs from 0 percent.

To illustrate the third prediction, consider two quantal psychometric functions, one of which departs from 0 percent at a size of stimulus increment equal to one on an arbitrary scale, and the other departs at an increment of 2 on the same scale. The first function will reach 100 percent at an increment of 2, while the second will reach 100 percent at an increment of 4. Thus, the slope of the first function is $100/1$, while that of the second function is $100/2$, or $50/1$, which is only half as large as that for the first function. The second function intercepted the x-axis at an incremental value that was twice as large as that of the first function, but the slope of the second function was only half as great.

The three predicted characteristics of the psychometric function should hold for any quantal experiment on differential sensitivity, whether it involves loudness, pitch, brightness, or any other psychological dimension. If these predictions are not met by the experimental data, the adequacy of the theory or of the experimental procedure is open to question. One of the commendable features of the neural quantum theory is that it does provide specific deductions which can be subjected to experimental verification. The significance of this characteristic of a scientific theory has been covered in detail in Chapter 5.

Requirements of the Quantal Method

Proponents of the theory of the neural quantum method assert that the demonstration of quantal units in sensory discrimination requires very rigorous experimental controls. It is argued that unless certain precautions are taken, the relatively large fluctuations in overall organismic sensitivity that occur from moment to moment will tend to obscure the "true" character of the discriminatory process. Stevens, Morgan, and Volkmann (1941) have stated that "we must add ΔI instantaneously, and remove it before the organism is able to change in sensitivity by more than a negligible amount" (p. 319). This may be accomplished by (1) allowing no time interval between the presentation of the standard stimulus and the variable stimulus and by (2) presenting the variable stimulus for only a very brief period of time. If these conditions are not satisfied, the random shifts in overall sensitivity will be expected to generate a nonrectilinear psychometric function.

Several other precautions should also be observed. (1) The observer should be well-trained and the experimental situation should be such that the observer can focus his attention on the experimental task and maintain a stabilized criterion of judgment. (2) If possible, all judgments should be made in a single testing session so as to avoid the need for averaging results that are affected by temporal variability. (3) Some observers may need a "warning" signal, such as a dim light, to alert them at the proper moments in the test trials, thereby reducing the fatigue induced by sustained attention. (4) The testing system must be free from extraneous cues, such as transient noise between the presentation of the standard stimulus and the variable, if the observer's responses are to be interpreted in a meaningful way.

Some investigators have objected to the severe restrictions imposed in the quantal method. Blackwell (1953) reported: "Essentially, the quantum theorists have so restricted the allowable conditions of measurement and the analysis of data that it is difficult to obtain an unambiguous evaluation of the theory" (p. 398). The primary objections involve three points. (1) Unlike the usual approach to psychophysical problems where one or more methods may be appropriate for the collection of data, the applicability of the quantum theory may be tested by only one method—the quantal method, with its rigorous requirements and the use of the observer's "phenomenal report." (2) The quantal method also requires that in the process of data collection, the stimulus increments must be presented in blocks of presentations of the same magnitude. Blackwell (1953), Koester and Schoenfeld (1947), and Osgood (1953) contend that this procedure provides the observer with the opportunity to respond in an invalid manner since he soon learns that all increments in a given series are of the same magnitude, thereby enabling him to "adjust and cut-and-fit" his judgments throughout a series. (3) Finally, the restriction that only data collected in a single experimental session may be used to test the quantal predictions makes it practically impossible to reach any conclusion with a high degree of confidence, since at least 40 presentations must be made in each testing session at each of 10 stimulus increments, if the normal ogive is to fail to fit the data when, in fact, the data may actually conform to the predictions of the quantum theory (Blackwell, 1953).

Some Experimental Tests
of the Neural Quantum Theory

Although the predictions of the neural quantum theory are very specific, it is extremely difficult to evaluate these predictions on the basis of experimental evidence due, in part, to the severe restrictions imposed by the quantal method. Also, as shown in Figure 11-17, the differences between the two psychometric functions —rectilinear and ogival—are not so marked as might be expected. Given a set of

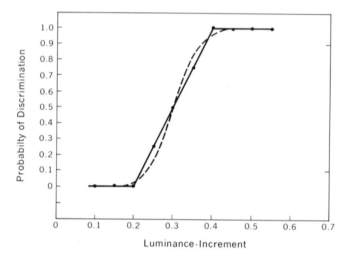

Figure 11–17. Psychometric functions predicted by the classical theory of sensory discrimination (the normal ogive) and the theory of the neural quantum (the rectilinear curve) based on a two-quanta criterion of judgment. (From Blackwell, *Amer. J. Psychol.,* 1953.)

data, the question is which of the two functions provides the better fit to the experimental points. The usual procedure is to determine the best-fitting sigmoidal and rectilinear functions by the method of least squares and then to perform a chi-square test of goodness of fit. The results of this analysis will reveal whether or not the specific hypothesis being tested should be rejected.

When the best-fitting linear function has been determined for a particular set of experimental data, values of the stimulus increment corresponding to the 100 percent and 0 percent points of response may be obtained algebraically or graphically. As indicated in the discussion of the quantal predictions, the ratio of these two values should yield an integral value equal to two, under a two-quanta criterion. Regardless of the criterion adopted by the observer, the quantal index (QI) is defined in the general case as:

$$QI = \frac{\Delta S}{\Delta S_1 - \Delta S_0},$$

(11-9)

where ΔS_1 is the size of the smallest stimulus increment at which 100 percent discrimination occurs and ΔS_0 is the largest stimulus increment at which 0 percent discrimination occurs. The quantal index and the rectilinearity of the psychometric function are the two criteria on which the adequacy of the neural quantum theory has been primarily tested.

Stevens and Volkmann (1940*b*) and Stevens, Morgan, and Volkmann (1941) have obtained data supporting the neural quantum theory. In the latter experiment, a continuous tone of 1000 cps was presented to an observer via an earphone at 54 db SL and every 3 sec a frequency increment lasting 0.3 sec was added to the base tone (1000 cps); the task of the observer was to press a key when there seemed to be a change in pitch. The increments, all of which were less than 10 cps, were presented in a series of 25 trials with the same-sized increment occurring on each trial of the series. Each of six observers made a total of 100 judgments at each of eight to ten increments. In the treatment of data, linear functions were fitted to the experimental values by the method of least squares and, according to the results of chi square tests, these functions showed better fits than corresponding phi-gamma functions.

Figure 11-18 shows the results for six observers. Although certain criticisms have been made of the treatment of data (Flynn, 1943; Lewis and Burke, 1949), it

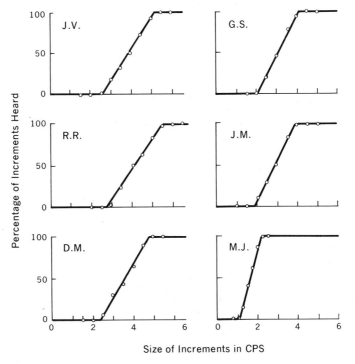

Figure 11-18. Rectilinear psychometric functions in frequency discrimination for six different observers. The standard stimulus was a continuous 1000 cps tone; every 3 sec an increment of a given size was added for 0.3 sec. Approximately 100 judgments were made at each value of increment. The neural quantum unit is specified in terms of the stimulus increment at which the intercept of the psychometric function is zero percent. (From Stevens *et al., Amer. J. Psychol.,* 1941.)

appears that the experimental points may be adequately represented by a linear function. Also, in most cases the value of QI is approximately two as predicted by the theory. The inverse relation of slope to *x*-intercept is the third prediction that seems to be confirmed. Observer G.S. has a neural quantum of 2 cps (intercept at 0 percent) and observer M.J., a quantum of 1 cps; as predicted, the slope of the function for observer G.S. is less than that for observer M.J.

After performing additional statistical tests, Stevens, Morgan, and Volkmann concluded that the quantal hypothesis was supported and the classical hypothesis was quite unacceptable. Lewis and Burke (1949), however, recomputed the chi square values for the phi-gamma functions of the six observers, taking into account extreme proportions of responses and other statistical factors, and found that the phi-gamma hypothesis could not be rejected, that is, the observed deviations of the experimental values from the theoretical ogive could have been due to random (chance) factors. Although 14 of the 15 psychometric functions obtained in this study were fitted by linear functions that provided a "good" or better fit, nine of the phi-gamma functions fitted the data just as well. In view of this and in view of the fact that the quantal index for the 15 sets of data ranged from 1.89 to 2.34 (compared with the predicted value of 2.0), Corso (1956) has contended that both the quantal and phi-gamma hypotheses remain tenable within the findings of this study.

Flynn (1943) used three trained observers to obtain quantal data on frequency discrimination at 1000 cps, 55 db SL. The tone lasted 1.25 min per block of 25 trials and periodically varied in frequency for 0.30 sec. Each increment was usually presented 50 or 100 times. Thirty sets of data were obtained in the study and, for each, the best-fitting normal ogive and the best-fitting straight line were computed by the method of least squares. On the basis of chi square tests of goodness of fit, 16 sets of data were found to fit neither a straight line nor a normal ogive. Ten sets of data were found to fit a straight line better than a normal ogive and four sets of data were fitted better by a normal ogive. Flynn concluded that the results of the study supported the quantum theory, but Corso (1956) pointed out that, in addition to certain statistical limitations, the predicted two-to-one relation (QI) did not hold in those cases where linear functions were obtained. Since both predictions (linearity and $QI = 2$) were not met, the results were interpreted as failing to support the quantal hypothesis.

Corso (1951) performed an experiment to test the hypothesis that data obtained in the auditory discrimination of frequency and intensity satisfied the conditions predicted by the neural quantum theory. The experimental procedures for intensity discrimination were the same as those of Stevens and Volkmann (1940b), and for frequency discrimination, the same as those for Stevens, Morgan, and Volkmann (1941). The 20 observers were carefully screened from a larger population and were given two separate practice sessions in which each observer made a total of 425 to 1225 judgments under conditions identical to those of the subsequent test trials. In the test trials for both intensity and frequency discrimination, at least six values of stimulus increment were presented, with approximately 200 judgments being made at each increment value.

Figure 11-19 shows four representative *nonlinear* psychometric functions obtained in this study, two for frequency discrimination and two for intensity discrimination. Figure 11-20 shows four representative *linear* psychometric functions, two for frequency discrimination and two for intensity discrimination. In all, 70 sets of data were obtained and fitted with a linear function by the method of least squares. The goodness of fit of each function was tested by chi square. It was found

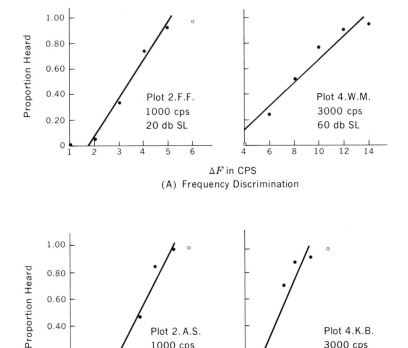

Figure 11-19. Representative nonlinear psychometric functions obtained by the quantal method: (A) frequency discrimination; (B) intensity discrimination. (From Corso, *Amer. J. Psychol.*, 1951.)

that the linear hypothesis was acceptable in only nine cases of the 70, seven of these were in frequency discrimination and two in intensity discrimination. Furthermore, the prediction of $QI = 2$ was satisfied in only one of the nine cases in which the hypothesis of linearity was retained. It was concluded, therefore, that the experimental results failed to satisfy the predictions of the neural quantum theory.

The theory of the neural quantum has been extended beyond audition to include the problem of sensory discrimination in other modalities. Jerome (1942) used an Elsberg olfactometer to obtain psychometric functions with stimulus pressure as the independent variable. The task of the observer was to judge whether or not the odor of citral was present when the stimulus was delivered. There were ten presentations of the stimulus from each of two bottles (control and citral) at each of seven to nine different pressure values. Thirteen sets of data were obtained and fitted with a linear function by the method of averages. Although no tests of goodness of fit were performed, the hypothesis of linearity seemed to be met, but

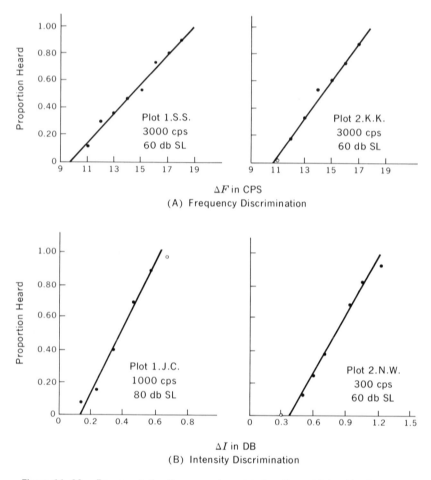

Figure 11-20. Representative linear psychometric functions obtained by the quantal method: (A) frequency discrimination; (B) intensity discrimination. (From Corso, *Amer. J. Psychol.*, 1951.)

the integral relation of the quantal index was not satisfied. It was concluded that the existence of a differential olfactory quantum had not been demonstrated.

DeCillis (1944) followed the general quantal method in attempting to determine the nature of the psychometric function for stimulus movement over a cutaneous area. A fine column of air at a pressure of 35 lb/sq in. was presented at a point on the skin for 0.10 sec, then the air column was moved across the skin at a rate of 143 mm/sec to another location where it remained stationary for at least 0.10 sec. After the air column was turned off, the needle controlling the stimulus was returned to its original starting position for the next trial. A given amplitude of movement was presented for a series of 20 trials, but the amplitude was varied from series to series. The task of the observer was to report whenever he perceived the movement of the air column.

For three observers, 35 sets of data were selected and fitted with straight lines by the method of least squares. Chi square tests of goodness of fit indicated that in twenty cases the linear hypothesis was substantiated. However, in these twenty cases, the integral relation ($QI = 2$) did not hold. Since extensive data were not collected at those points on the psychometric function where maximal differences between the quantal and phi-gamma hypotheses might have been expected, it has been suggested that the "... empirical points would probably not have deviated from a straight line, whether or not the 'true' function were ogival or linear" (Corso, 1956, p. 387).

In a study on visual discrimination, Blackwell (1953) obtained psychometric functions for four observers using normal binocular viewing and natural pupils at a luminance of 4.71 ft-lamberts. The stimulus was a circular luminance increment which subtended 18.5′ located 7° to the right of the fixation spot. This increment was presented for a duration of 0.06 sec once every 12.25 sec. Each psychometric function was based on 14 to 18 increment values, with 20 judgments at each value. The results showed that the data for two observers could not be used to evaluate the quantal hypothesis, but the data for the other two observers were fitted adequately in most cases by a two- or three-quanta linear function. Figure 11-21

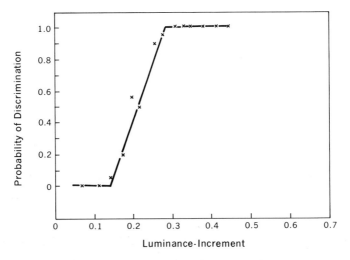

Figure 11-21. A rectilinear psychometric function based on a two quanta criterion in an experiment on the discrimination of luminance. (From Blackwell, *Amer. J. Psychol.*, 1953.)

shows a psychometric function "selected from among 18 sets of data as the most adequately fitted by the quantal curve based upon a two-quanta criterion" (p. 404).

Blackwell, however, considers his findings as lending spurious support to the quantum theory. There are two reasons for his position: (1) as the criterion of judgment increases from two to three quanta, the 50 percent threshold decreases rather than increases as predicted by the quantum theory, and (2) there was evidence that *response channelization* occurred, that is, there tended to be an increasing frequency of "yes" or "no" responses toward the end of a block of stimuli depending upon the predominant response in that series. Blackwell concluded that the "experimental data provide no satisfactory evidence at all in support of the neural quantum theory" (p. 408). Koester and Schoenfeld (1947) arrived at the same conclusion after performing an experiment in which they compared quantal and nonquantal procedures in frequency discrimination.

Miller and Garner (1944) performed a study to investigate some of the factors that could be present in a psychophysical experiment and that might obscure the quantal nature of the discriminatory process. Data were obtained on intensity discrimination for a 1000 cps tone at 40 db SL by using a modified quantal method. Rather than presenting the same-sized increment for 25 consecutive trials, these investigators varied the increment at random from trial to trial and did not stop the series after 25 trials. The object of this was to prevent the observer from establishing a fixed two-quanta criterion of judgment.

Two psychometric functions were obtained and were fitted by a series of three straight lines as shown in Figure 11-22. The three lines were fitted to the empirical values lying between successive quantal points as determined from the results of a previously administered standard (quantal) method. Miller and Garner contend that (1) the "three-line" technique of curve-fitting is appropriate in general for those cases in which the observer has shifted his criterion of judgment and it does not depend upon intensity discrimination or the random method of presenting increments, and (2) the combining of data either from different experimental conditions or from different observers tends to yield ogival functions in accordance with the phi-gamma hypothesis. This study tends to support the quantum theory and is one of the few in which an attempt has been made to isolate some of the factors responsible for nonquantal findings.

Neisser (1957) also attempted to determine the nature of the difficulties which have been encountered in studies designed to confirm the predictions of the quantal hypothesis; in particular, he was concerned with the question of response interdependence as proposed by Blackwell. Fifty-two psychometric functions were obtained in intensity discrimination at 1000 cps for four observers. It was found that "the majority of these functions do not have the rectilinear shape predicted by the quantal hypothesis, nor any other specific shape. A few roughly rectilinear functions and a few ogives occur . . ." (p. 516). Linear functions were *not* obtained even though "each S(ubject) received extensive practice with the quantal method (at least eight full sessions) . . ." (p. 515). This is considerably more practice than was given by Stevens, Morgan, and Volkmann (1941) to their six observers who practiced only for an hour or two before the test data were collected. Also, as Blackwell contended, "the results indicate that successive responses in the quantal method are not independent; a strong perseverative tendency is present" (p. 527).

Predominantly on the basis that the mean intercept ratio (QI) of the 52 psychometric functions was 2.15, Neisser concluded that "the data are . . . predominantly

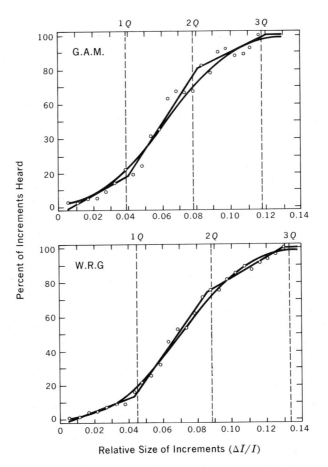

Figure 11-22. Psychometric functions for intensity discrimination at 1000 cps, 40 db sensation level. The data
points have been fitted by a series of three straight lines.
(From Miller and Garner, *Amer. J. Psychol.,* 1944.)

favorable to the quantal hypothesis" (p. 527). It should be noted, however, that
the first quartile of the distribution of these values was 1.85 and the third quartile,
2.40. In view of this spread of values and the marked lack of linear psychometric
functions, the results of this study do not seem to warrant this conclusion.

A Summary Statement

It appears that on the basis of the existing data, it cannot be determined whether
the theory of the neural quantum provides, in general, a better explanation of
sensory discrimination than the classical theory. After a critical review of the
literature, Corso (1956) concluded that "unequivocal support of the neural quantum theory is, for the most part, lacking" (p. 391). The tenability of the quantal
hypothesis as opposed to the phi-gamma hypothesis is extremely difficult to eval-

uate due to: (1) the severe restrictions in methodology and (2) the statistical limitations in the treatment of data. In addition, since it is held that "noises" of any kind will disturb the quantal function, observers must be competent, highly motivated, and performing at a level such that all sources of variability are eliminated, or at least minimized. It remains for the proponents of the quantum theory to specify the procedures whereby this requirement may be met in order that experimental findings may be replicated.

Corso (1967) has also noted that the primary emphasis of the quantum theory has been on problems of differential sensitivity, with relatively little regard for measurements related to the absolute threshold. As pointed out in a preceding paragraph, "steps" in the audibility function at low frequencies, which had earlier been described as representing neural or quantal processes, were shown to be accounted for in terms of experimental methodology. "The problem of obtaining quantal data in experiments on absolute thresholds remains a real and significant challenge for the quantum theorists" (Corso, 1963, p. 363). In terms of generality, therefore, the classical theory of sensory discrimination is perhaps to be preferred since it can explain both absolute and differential thresholds; furthermore, a considerable body of data is available in the various sensory modalities which tends to agree with the classical predictions regarding these types of problems.

There are two other developments, however, which detract from the neural quantum theory. (1) Barlow (1961) has presented an alternative hypothesis to account for the rectilinear psychometric functions which are sometimes obtained in experiments on sensory discrimination. The hypothesis asserts that thresholds are decision processes that are automatically adjusted to yield false positive responses at a low constant rate. Assuming there is some kind of "noise" or random disturbance, the threshold is so adjusted that the disturbance rarely produces false positive responses. From this concept, the slope of the psychometric function is predicted to be equal to 1/threshold or, considering different false positive rates and departures from a normal distribution of responses, the slope will be inversely proportional to the threshold value. In general, this alternative theory can account for the three predictions derived from the neural quantum theory, and Barlow asserts that "the apparently rectilinear functions are approximations to, or distortions of, ogival functions" (p. 787).

(2) While the derivation of neural quantum theory implicitly involves the all-or-none principle of nerve activity, it is now recognized that this principle is confined to the axon process of a neuron (Bishop, 1956). At both ends of the nerve cell there are graded responses that vary in accordance with the strength of a given stimulus. It may be, therefore, that the nerve activity underlying sensory discrimination does not reflect a simple all-or-none mechanism, but the resultant combination of a large number of graded responses; although these responses are delivered via the axons as successive discrete impulses, they are reconverted into graded responses within the branching terminals of each neuron. Presumably the processes of neural analysis and synthesis occur at the presynaptic and postsynaptic regions of the nerve cell, with the all-or-none impulse merely serving to transport the graded responses, as necessary, within the central nervous system.

The Theory of Signal Detection

Introduction

The theory of signal detection provides still another approach to problems of sensory discrimination. One of the major innovations of the theory is that it deals with problems of psychophysics but does not contain any systematic reference to the threshold concept. It does, however, provide a method which permits the separation of the *observer's sensitivity* from his *criterion of response;* by appropriate treatment of the data collected in a discrimination experiment, it is possible to obtain two measures that describe these characteristics of the observer.

Another unique feature of the theory of signal detection is that noise is introduced as part of the experimental requirement, unlike the neural quantum theory in which all "noise" must be eliminated or reduced to a minimal level. In this case, noise is always present and the task of the observer is to decide whether or not a given signal was present during a specified time interval. The derivation of the theory of signal detection requires only two assumptions regarding sensory discrimination: (1) it varies continuously due to the noise that is always present in the sensory system, and (2) it is a unidimensional variable in terms of its effects on the observer's decisions.

The Signal Detection Experiment

The basic problem in a signal detection experiment involves the observation (detection) of signals (stimuli) that are weak relative to the background against which they are presented. Detection, therefore, is a function of two factors: (1) signal intensity and (2) background intensity, excluding certain organismic variables. The modality of detection is not particularly significant and the theory of signal detection may be considered a general theory of sensory discrimination.

In the simplest type of experiment, a series of trials is presented in which either noise alone (N) or signal plus noise (SN) occurs; all trials are of the same duration. The observer attends to the events that occur during each trial and reaches a decision based on his observation; he reports whether the trial consisted of noise alone or signal plus noise. Noise is always present and the signal may or may not occur. The signal is usually presented at different values of intensity according to a predetermined experimental plan; the observer knows that if the signal is presented, it will be one that has been selected from a specified ensemble of signals.

Four possible events may occur in a given observation interval: the signal may or may not be present in the noise background and, for each of these alternatives, the observer may respond that the signal has or has not occurred. In reaching his decision, the observer must consider two factors: (1) the actual sensory (stimulus) input and (2) the decision function to be maximized. The particular decision function to be maximized will depend upon the definition of an optimum strategy. Some common definitions include the maximization of the percentage of correct responses, the reduction in uncertainty as to whether a signal was or was not present, and the total expected value of the decisions. For a given situation, the decision function to be maximized may be specified if the a priori probabilities of the various possible signal inputs are known; also, if all the physical parameters of the signals and noise in the channel are known, an *"ideal observer"* may be defined. In effect, the ideal observer is simply a mathematical expression which specifies the maximal performance that may be obtained in a particular situation. This permits a comparison of the performance of the ideal observer with that of a human observer; from this comparison it is possible to gain some understanding of the manner in which the human observer is reaching his decisions.

In many signal detection experiments, the expected value of the decisions is the function that is maximized. The usual procedure is to pay the observer at a certain basic rate per hour and to have the observer make hundreds of judgments. Every time the observer makes a correct decision, he is paid a small amount, for example, a tenth of a cent; every time he makes an error he loses the same amount. Since the basic rate of pay is on the order of one dollar per hour, the game may proceed for quite some time; also the experimenter may make the outcome favorable to the observer by appropriately selecting the signals for the various trials. Consequently, the expected value of the decisions becomes the function to be optimized. The object of the experiment (game) is to study the changes in the observer's decisions that are brought about by changing either the a priori probabilities of the signals or altering the values (gains) or costs (losses) of the decision, that is, the *pay-off matrix.*

The Theory of Signal Detection

The theory of signal detection is fundamentally a combination of two sub-theories: (1) decision theory and (2) the theory of the ideal observer. We will examine each of these in turn.

Decision Theory.   The elements of decision theory provide the basis for analyzing the experimental situation in which the observer reports whether or not he detected a given signal (stimulus). The decisions made by the observer will be affected by several factors which we have already described, depending upon the particular nature of the experiment: the a priori probabilities of the signal and of the signal plus noise, the values of correct decisions and costs of incorrect decisions, and the physical parameters of the signal. The observer uses information about these factors to create a dichotomy between those signals he reports he detects and those he doesn't detect. The dichotomy is determined by a criterion that can be adjusted by the observer. Through an appropriate analysis of the data, a quantitative estimate of this criterion can be obtained.

Now we will examine the elements of decision theory in detail. There are four main concepts: *observation, likelihood ratio, decision rule,* and *criterion.* To make the exposition more specific, we will assume a detection experiment in hearing. Note, however, that the theory extends in generality to the detection of signals in any sensory modality and that the fundamental concepts are drawn from the theory of statistical inference.

In the experiment, the task of the observer is to reach a decision indicating whether in a given interval only noise occurred or whether a predesignated signal (tone) occurred in the presence of the noise; the decision of the observer is based on his *observation* (x) of the events that occurred during the fixed interval. The observation refers to the sensory datum of the observer and comprises the basis for his decision. It is assumed that the observation represents a continuous variable and may be unidimensional or multidimensional. For example, the observation may involve only the amplitude of a signal, but could involve the frequency and waveform in addition to the amplitude. (Some may find it helpful to consider the observation as a measure of neural activity, that is, the number of neural impulses arriving at a given cortical locus within a specified period of time, but this is not necessary for the development of the theory.) The observation may arise either from noise alone or from signal plus noise, with specific probabilities.

The distributions associated with these two conditions are usually designated as $f_{SN}(x)$, which represents the probability density function of x given the occurrence of signal plus noise and $f_N(x)$, which represents the probability density function of x given the occurrence of noise alone. These functions of x, or some monotonic transformation of these functions, are assumed to be normal with equal (unit) variance (Peterson, Birdsall, and Fox, 1954).

The assumptions of the theory are shown graphically in Figure 11-23 for a signal of a given amplitude. The two distributions are shown with the observation continuum (x) as the abscissa. The $f_{SN}(x)$ function is placed to the right since the observations will tend to be of greater magnitude when the signal is present, thereby providing a mean value which will be greater than that for the noise distribution alone. The amount of separation of the two means will depend upon the amplitude of the signal; the greater the amplitude of the signal, the greater will be the separation between the means of the two distributions.

Now, given an observation (x), the problem becomes one of deciding whether the observation is an instance drawn from the noise (N) distribution or the signal plus noise (SN) distribution. For every observation, there is some probability density that it resulted from noise alone $[f_N(x)]$ and, similarly, some probability density that it was due to signal plus noise $[f_{SN}(x)]$. By referring to Figure 11-23, it

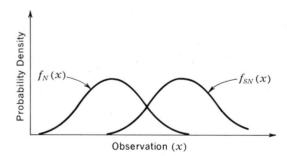

Figure 11–23. The probability density functions of noise and signal plus noise assumed by the theory of signal detection. (From Swets *et al.*, *Psychol. Rev.*, 1961.)

may be seen that any x value has associated with it a probability density from each of the two distributions. This makes it possible to define a new quantity, the *likelihood ratio*. Each value of x is identified with or characterized by a particular likelihood ratio, $l(x)$, which is defined as:

$$l(x) = \frac{f_{SN}(x)}{f_N(x)}. \tag{11-10}$$

The likelihood ratio, $l(x)$, expresses the likelihood (probability density) that the response of the sensory system (x) arose from SN (signal plus noise) relative to the likelihood that it arose from N. Notice that while the numerator and denominator of the likelihood ratio are the probabilities of an observation under two different hypotheses, the likelihood ratio is a *number*, not a probability. The number is a function of whatever variables were involved in the observation, but $l(x)$ is itself only a *single* variable. We may say, then, that the *decision axis* becomes the likelihood ratio and the axis is continuous and unidimensional. Now, how does the observer use the likelihood ratio in making his decisions?

According to decision theory, the observer operates in terms of a *decision rule*. The decision rule is a formal statement that indicates the basis on which the observer should make his decision about a particular event. In terms of signal detection theory, the rule can be stated as follows: Choose SN if $l(x) \geq 1$. This statement defines the decision rule and specifies the choice to be made by selecting or designating a particular number, the number "one." This number is called the *likelihood ratio criterion*, or simply the criterion. Should the criterion always be set at one? Definitely not. If, for example, we know before we make any observations that N is nine times as likely to occur as SN, the odds are 9 to 1 in favor of N. So we should choose SN only if $l(x) \geq 9$. The point of this example is to indicate that the specific value set for the likelihood ratio criterion should be an appropriate criterion for a certain set of circumstances.

We have seen, then, that the observer accomplishes his task by acting as though he computes the likelihood ratio associated with each sensory input and compares it with some number, β. Whenever $l(x) \geq \beta$, he reports that a signal was present; otherwise, he reports noise alone was present. The particular value of β should be set so as to provide an optimal criterion and the optimal criterion will depend upon the particular circumstances of a given experiment. Although in general a decision procedure is intended to achieve any one of several possible objectives, it is a remarkable fact that a decision criterion based on likelihood ratio (or some monotonic transformation of this ratio) is optimal for all these objectives, for example, maximizing the percentage of correct decisions, maximizing the expected value of decisions, minimizing risk, and estimating the a posteriori probabilities (Green, 1960).

We will examine the concept of β still further. β is defined as a critical value of $l(x)$, which equals $f_{SN}(x)/f_N(x)$; β is an exact value of $l(x)$ and specifies the optimum operating level for a particular set of circumstances. This means that the decision criterion contains all observations with a likelihood ratio greater than

β, and contains none of those with a likelihood ratio less than β. Thus, β represents a boundary condition for optimal performance. In a given experiment, however, an observer adopts a certain criterion which may or may not be optimal; his criterion may be too lax or too strict for the conditions imposed in the study. It follows, therefore, that in a signal detection experiment two levels may be determined: (1) the optimal criterion (β) and (2) the actual criterion established by the observer.

Now refer to Figure 11-23. It may be seen that the value of $l(x)$ is given by the ratio of the ordinate value of $f_{SN}(x)$ to the ordinate value of $f_N(x)$, measured at some cutoff value of the observation (x_c) specified along the x-axis. If the a priori probabilities of noise and signal plus noise are equal, that is, if in a given interval one is as likely to occur as the other, the likelihood ratio criterion should be set so that $\beta = 1$ and the optimal value of x_c will correspond to the point where the two functions cross, that is, $f_{SN}(x) = f_N(x)$. The optimal criterion or likelihood ratio (β) is equal to $P(N)/P(SN)$, where $P(N)$ is the a priori probability of noise alone and $P(SN)$ is a priori probability of signal plus noise. Having established some criterion level, the observer should reach his decisions in accordance with the appropriate cutoff value (x_c). If in a given interval, the experimental observation equals or exceeds x_c, the observer should report that a signal has occurred; if the observation has a value less than x_c, he should report that noise alone has occurred.

The decision in each instance will have one of four possible outcomes, since the observer may give a positive or negative report in a given interval and he may in each case be right or wrong. The decision outcome may be: (1) a *"hit,"* that is, SN has occurred and, with the observation greater than x_c, the observer has reported the presence of a signal; (2) a *"miss"*—the same situation as in (1), but the observer has reported that only noise has occurred; (3) a *correct rejection*—noise alone has occurred and, with the observation less than x_c, the observer reports that no signal was presented; and (4) a *"false alarm"*—the same situation as in (3), but the observer reports the presence of a signal. The four outcomes stated in terms of probabilities are summarized in Table 11-1. Notice that the four outcomes are interdependent; given the probabilities for any two cells, the probabilities of the two remaining cells are fixed since there is a complementary relationship among the cells. For example, if the observer attempts to increase the probability of a hit, he will say "yes" more frequently, thereby increasing the number of false alarms and decreasing the number of correct rejections and misses. The probability of total "yes" and "no" responses must equal 1.00.

Now we will consider how these concepts may be used to describe the observer's capacity to detect a signal in the presence of noise. We will do this by referring again to the likelihood ratio. Recall that the ratio is a number computed from two probabilities $[f_{SN}(x)/f_N(x)]$. If we change the number, we change both probabilities. A graphical plot showing how the probabilities change as the cut-off criterion is allowed to vary from negative infinity to positive infinity is called an *ROC (Receiver Operating Characteristic)* curve. The upper curve of Figure 11-24 is

Table 11–1   The Four Possible Outcomes of a Decision in a Signal Detection Experiment

| | | Event in the Observation Interval | |
		Noise (N)	Signal Plus Noise (SN)
Report of the Observer	Yes (*y*)	False Alarm $P_N(y)$*	Hit $P_{SN}(y)$
	No (*n*)	Correct Rejection $P_N(n)$	Miss $P_{SN}(n)$

*$P_N(y)$ is read as the probability of reporting a signal, given only noise in the observation interval. In this notation, the subscript in each cell indicates the event that occurred in the observation interval and the symbol in parentheses denotes the nature of the observer's response ("yes" or "no").

a typical ROC curve and indicates the best possible performance in a two-alternative decision task.

The two probabilities which are plotted [$P_{SN}(y)$ and $P_N(y)$] are generated by

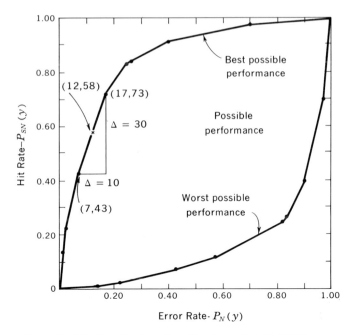

Figure 11–24.   The Receiver Operating Characteristic (ROC) curve for the best possible performance (upper curve) and the worst possible performance (lower curve) in a particular experimental situation. The area bounded by the two curves represents the performance which is attainable in this task using any decision procedure. The hit rate $P_{SN}(y)$, is plotted on the ordinate; the error rate $P_N(y)$, is plotted on the abscissa. (After Green, *J. acoust. Soc. Amer.*, 1960.)

adjusting the decision criterion in accordance with the shift in the cutoff value of the observation (x_c) along the x-axis of Figure 11-23; observe that two given probability values would completely specify the stimulus-response matrix of Table 11-1. If the cutoff value is set at the left end of the x-axis in Figure 11-23, the values of these two probabilities would equal 1.0 and would produce a point in the upper right-hand corner of Figure 11-24; if the criterion is set at the far right of the x-axis, the probability of hits and false alarms would equal zero and would produce a point in the lower left-hand corner. As the criterion is moved between these limits, the probabilities will change and yield the ROC curve. If a decision rule is adopted that is the exact opposite of that used in generating the ROC curve, the lower curve will be generated. This curve shows the worst possible performance in a given decision task. These two curves bound the limits of performance that may be observed when the observer uses *any* decision rule in such a task. If, for instance, the observer decides to flip an unbiased coin for each observation interval saying "yes" each time a head appears and "no" when a tail appears, his performance in the long run would yield a hit and error rate of 0.5 (a point in the center of the graph).

There are several aspects of the ROC curve that should be clearly understood. (1) The slope of the ROC curve is based on the optimum decision axis (likelihood ratio); if the curve does not show a monotonically decreasing slope, it implies that an incorrect decision rule is being used. (2) the degree to which the ROC curve differs from the diagonal line indicates the degree to which the best possible performance differs from chance performance. If two events are easily discriminated, the ROC curve will leave the origins with a steep slope and will deviate from the chance (diagonal) line by a considerable amount. If, however, two events are difficult to discriminate, the likelihood ratios will be near unity and the ROC curve will lie close to the diagonal. As shown in Figure 11-25, the particular ROC curve indicating the best possible performance will depend upon the value of d', where d' is defined as the difference between the means of the two density functions expressed in terms of their standard deviation. Stated mathematically,

$$d' = \frac{M_{f_{SN}}(x) - M_{f_N}(x)}{\delta_{f_N}(x)} . \tag{11-11}$$

As the value of d' becomes smaller, the ROC curve becomes flatter and approaches a diagonal line extending from the lower left-hand corner to the upper right-hand corner of Figure 11-25. (3) In a given experiment, the observer's data provide a pair of proportions that are estimates of $P_{SN}(y)$ and $P_N(y)$; these proportions yield one point on the observer's ROC curve. The slope of the curve at this point indicates the observer's value of the likelihood ratio at which he has established his criterion of judgment. This makes it possible to compare the observer's criterion with the optimal criterion (β) for that situation.

The Theory of the Ideal Observer.   Although the explanation of decision theory did not intentionally contain any reference to the ideal observer, the concept was inherent in the discussion of likelihood ratio and the ROC curve. An *ideal observer* is

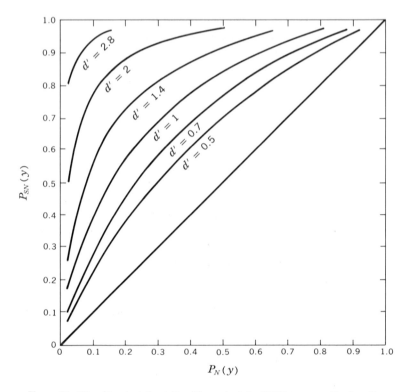

Figure 11–25. Receiver Operating Characteristic (ROC) curves with d' as the parameter. The probability of a "yes" response when noise alone is present, $P_N(y)$, is plotted on the abscissa; and the probability of a "yes" response when signal plus noise is presented, $P_{SN}(y)$, is plotted on the ordinate. (From Swets et al., *Psychol. Rev.*, 1961.)

a function that relates an observation to the probability of that observation. Thus, the ideal observer is defined for a given problem when the likelihood ratio is specified. The ideal observer employs the optimal criterion (β) and thereby minimizes the total error in an experiment. Consequently, the ROC curve describes the performance of the ideal observer and d' specifies the sensitivity of this mathematical entity.

Given the two experimentally derived quantities $P_{SN}(y)$ and $P_N(y)$, it is possible to use a table of areas under the normal curve to compute the value of d'. The quantity $P_{SN}(y)$ yields the distance of the criterion from the mean of $f_{SN}(x)$ in x/σ units; in the same way the quantity $P_N(y)$ yields the distance of the criterion from the mean of $f_N(x)$ in x/σ units. If the criterion lies between the two means, the two absolute values of x/σ are added (without regard to sign) to give d'; if the criterion does not lie between the two means, the smaller absolute value of x/σ is subtracted from the larger (again ignoring signs) to give d'. However, if the value of $P_{SN}(y)$ and $P_N(y)$ are known from a "yes-no" type of experiment in signal detectability, the value of d' need not be computed but may be read directly from published tables (Swets, 1964).

The empirical value of d' may be considered to be a measure of the observer's sensory capability, a measure of the effective strength of the signal, or an index of detectability. The observer's *efficiency* (η) may now be defined. It is the square of the ratio of the detectability index for the human observer divided by the index for the ideal observer (Tanner and Birdsall, 1958). That is,

$$\eta = \left(\frac{d' \text{ observed}}{d' \text{ ideal}}\right)^2 \tag{11-12}$$

As we might expect, the real observer in an experimental situation does not perform as well as the ideal observer in detecting the signals presented in an observation interval. Swets (1961) has pointed out three possible reasons for the kinds of discrepancies that occur, that is, the human observer's psychometric function has a higher mean value on the physical continuum and possesses a greater slope than that of the ideal observer.

The first of these three possibilities is that the ideal decision process is noiseless while that of the real observer may be noisy. If, for example, the response criterion of the real observer tends to fluctuate, the resulting point on the ROC curve will fall below that of the ideal observer. Second, there may be internal noise in the human sensory system such that this noise might be added to the experimentally controlled noise, thereby tending to mask the test signal to even a greater degree. Third, the human observer may display a "faulty memory" for the critical characteristics of the test signal. The third possibility is the preferred one, since an analysis of the theory in these terms will account for both the rightward shift of the psychometric function and its greater slope.

The theory of the ideal observer extends considerably beyond the basic concepts that have been presented in this section; see, for example, Sorkin (1962) who has applied the theory in situations in which the observer must specify whether two signals that have been presented are the same or different.

Some Experiments on the Theory of Signal Detection

Now that we have considered some of the basic concepts of the theory of signal detection, we will consider a few experimental studies in which various aspects of the theory have been tested.

One of the earliest studies was that of Tanner and Swets (1953). In one part of this study, the observers were required to respond with a "yes" or "no" for each observation interval. The stimulus was a 30-min circular patch of light with a duration of 0.01 sec which was flashed on a uniform background of 10 ft-lamberts. There were five values of the signal, four greater than the background level and one equal to it. Two a priori values of probability of presentation were used: $P(SN) = 0.80$, and $P(SN) = 0.40$. Before each experimental session, the observers were told what the a priori value would be.

The task of the observer was to maximize the expected value of the experiment.[*] Prior to each session, the observer was informed of the pay-off matrix that set the values of correct detections and correct rejections, and fixed the fines for incorrect detections and rejections. The observer was paid in cash following each session in accordance with the pay-off matrices. In a single session, the observer could win as much as $2.00 in addition to his hourly rate of pay.

According to the theory of signal detection, given (1) the characteristics of the noise and of the signal, (2) the a priori probability of the existence of the signal, and (3) the weightings of the two correct judgments and the two incorrect judgments, an optimum criterion of judgment (β) can be determined. A change in any one of these variables, or in any combination of these variables, will change the value of the optimum criterion. In the present experiment the a priori probabilities and the a priori values were changed so that β ranged from 0.25 to 3.00. It was expected, therefore, that these changes would be reflected in the proportion of the observer's judgments for both $P_N(y)$ and $P_{SN}(y)$. In addition, these changes should correspond to the relationship indicated by the particular d' curve for that particular value of signal intensity.

When the $P_{SN}(y)$ and $P_N(y)$ values for each signal intensity were plotted for the several observers of this study, the data points provided a satisfactory fit to the predicted ROC curves, as required by the theory. It was concluded that the mathematical model of signal detection was appropriate for analyzing problems of visual detection and that the observer did use a nearly optimum criterion in making his judgments on the presence or absence of the signal during the observation interval.

Tanner, Swets, and Green (1956) performed an experiment to determine the shape of the ROC for a task in psychoacoustics. The signal was a 1000-cps tone presented for 0.10 sec against a background of white noise. In each observation interval, either SN or N alone occurred; each interval was marked by the presence of a signal light. The task of the observer was to respond by pressing one button to signify "yes" when the signal was present, and another button to signify "no" when it was absent. The noise and signal levels were held constant during the experiment but the a priori probability of the signal was varied at five levels: 0.1, 0.3, 0.5, 0.7, and 0.9. The observer was informed about the particular a priori probability for a given session; 300 judgments were made at each level of probability. The observer was instructed to maximize the expected value of his decisions, that

---

*To maximize the expected value of the experiment, the observer should accept the hypothesis of signal plus noise, that is, respond by saying "yes" at the end of the observation interval, whenever:

$$l(x) = \frac{P(N)\,[V_{N.n} + K_{N.y}]}{P(SN)\,[V_{S.N.y} + K_{SN.n}]}, \tag{11-13}$$

where $P(N)$ is the a priori probability of noise alone, $P(SN)$ is the a priori probability of signal plus noise, $V_{N.n}$ is the value or gain of a correct rejection, $V_{SN.y}$ is the value of a correct decision (a hit), $K_{N.y}$ is the cost of a false alarm, and $K_{SN.n}$ is the cost of a miss. The values and costs are fixed in a pay-off matrix before the experiment is started, for example, $V_{N.n} = +0.2$ of a cent, $V_{SN.y} = +0.1$, $K_{N.y} = -0.2$, and $K_{SN.n} = -0.1$. The a priori probabilities, $P(N)$ and $P(SN)$, are also established by the experimenter as part of the design of the study.

is, to earn as much money as possible during each session. For each correct judgment, the observer was given a fraction of a cent; for each incorrect judgment, he lost the same amount. After each judgment, the observer was told immediately whether or not the signal had actually occurred.

The results of the study for one observer are shown in Figure 11-26. $P_{SN}(y)$ is the probability of responding "yes" when signal plus noise was presented, and

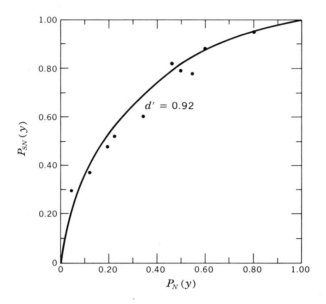

Figure 11-26. A typical ROC curve for an experiment in auditory detection. The observer's sensitivity (d') was computed to be 0.92 for this particular experiment. (From Tanner *et al.*, 1956, in Swets, 1964.)

$P_N(y)$ is the probability of responding "yes" when noise alone was presented. As is customary, the ROC curve is obtained by plotting $P_{SN}(y)$ as a function of $P_N(y)$. It is seen that the general trend of the data conform to the ROC curve predicted by the theory of signal detection. This indicates that the observer was able to vary his criterion, depending upon the a priori probability of the signal. However, while there was good agreement between the optimal criterion and the obtained criterion, the observers in general tended to depart systematically from the optimum value by maintaining a criterion which was too conservative or too strict.

Eijkman and Vendrik (1963) have applied the theory of signal detection to the experimental determination of the absolute threshold for the skin senses of touch and warmth. It will be recalled that according to the classical theory of sensory discrimination, the threshold is specified in terms of a fixed level of the stimulus (or of the corresponding neural activity) which divides the physical continuum into two parts: those stimuli above the threshold that elicit a response and those stimuli below the threshold that do not. Then, in order to explain the ogival shape of the psychometric function, it is assumed that there are a large number of extraneous variables that affect the judgments in a random manner such that there are fluctuations in the threshold level. Little, if any, consideration is given to the neural activity ("noise") in the sensory channel which is unrelated to the occurrence of the stimulus.

Unlike the classical theory, the theory of signal detection assumes that additive (internal) noise exists and that every level of input noise or signal plus noise can be detected. In the "yes-no" type of experiment, the observer adopts a criterion (decision level) that is adjustable and forms the basis for making a decision about the presence or absence of a signal. The observer adjusts the criterion to achieve optimum detection in the presence of purposely added noise. It is assumed that the neural activity existing in a particular sensory system is generated, in part, by the physical stimulus and, in part, by the spontaneous activity of neural elements. It is the total magnitude of the neural activity in the observation interval that mediates the detection of the signal. The purpose of the present study was to investigate the properties of internal noise as related to the detection process.

Only one of the three experiments performed by Eijkman and Vendrik will be considered in detail. This involved warmth, touch, and electrical stimulation of the skin on the inner side of the forearm. The warmth stimuli were administered by infrared irradiation of constant intensity which produced a linear increase in the temperature of the skin surface during the exposure interval (0.38 sec or 1.2 sec). The touch stimuli were deformations of the skin that increased linearly for 0.16 sec or were pulse-shaped with a duration of 70 msec. The electrical stimuli were also pulse-shaped and lasted 2 msec. The occurrence of a given observation interval was indicated by means of a sound or flash of light, and one of five stimuli of different amplitude was presented randomly to the observer. No costs or values were assigned for a correct response, a false alarm, or a missed signal.

The results for the three types of stimulation are shown in Figure 11-27 for one observer. In each case, the probability of correct response is plotted on the ordinate which has a Gaussian (normal) probability scale. For warmth, the experimental points lie approximately on a straight line, thus indicating that the distribution of probabilities is essentially Gaussian. For touch, and especially for electrical stimulation, there is a departure from the normal distribution.

These results, when interpreted in conjunction with those of the two other experiments in this series, indicate that, in sensory discrimination, internal neural noise exists that is indistinguishable from the neural activity produced by the signal. Furthermore, if it is assumed that the internal neural activity is normally distributed, then it follows that for warmth the neural activity is proportional to signal strength. For touch and electrical stimulation, however, this relationship is nonlinear. These findings are consistent with the theory of signal detection and, from an analysis of the false positive responses in this study, it was concluded that the decision model can account for the experimental data better than the classical threshold model.

One of the extensions of the theory of signal detection has been in the area of time discrimination (Creelman, 1962). In one of a series of experiments, Creelman

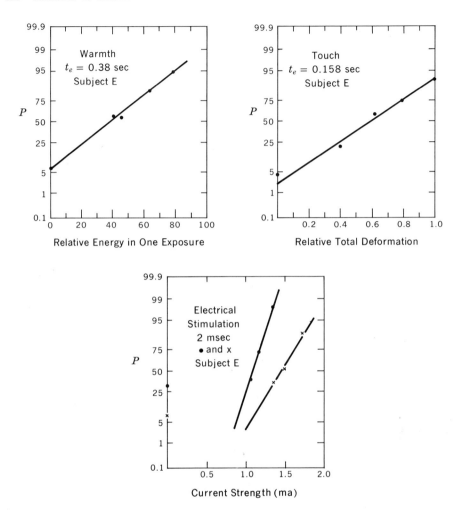

Figure 11–27. Percentage of positive ("yes") responses as a function of signal strength for warmth, touch, and electrical stimulation of the skin. The data are for one observer and are plotted on probability paper. (From Eijkman and Vendrik, *Biophys. J.*, 1963, **3**, 65–78. Reprinted by permission of The Rockefeller University Press.)

presented his observers with a signal of 1000 cps in a continuous background of white noise. The signal intensity was held constant at 0.084 v and was presented at five different durations ranging from 0.02 to 0.32 sec. The task of the observer was to detect an increment in duration of 0.01 sec, that is, to detect whenever each of the standard intervals was increased by 0.01 sec during an experimental trial. Several hundred trials were run on each value of time interval before another value from the set of five was randomly selected for the next block of trials. A warning light preceded each trial and a pair of lights was used to designate the beginning of the standard duration (T) and the comparison duration ($T + \Delta T$).

It was found that the detectability of the duration increment decreased in nearly a linear manner when d' was plotted as a function of the standard time (T) on log-log axes. The slope of the functions for four observer was somewhere between -1.0 and -0.5. From these and other results that were obtained, Creelman developed a general quantitative theory of duration discrimination based upon decision processes. The theory has practical implications related to the temporal discrimination of signals used in psychophysical experiments and, more generally, to the detection of temporal cues which provide linguistic meaning in speech perception.

Advantages of the Theory of Signal Detection

Although only a few studies related to the theory of signal detection were reviewed in the preceding section, numerous other studies are available which reveal that the theory is sufficiently general in scope to account for the detectability of signals in various modalities (Carterette and Cole, 1962; Eijkman and Vendrick, 1963). Furthermore, the psychological functions that can be treated within the framework of the theory extend beyond detection and involve such processes as the recognition of signals selected from various numbers of alternatives (Tanner, 1956), the masking of signals by the introduction of extraneous stimuli (Tanner, 1958), the intelligibility of speech signals (Clarke, 1960), and the memory for the wave form of a signal (Egan, Greenberg, and Schulman, 1961). It appears, therefore, that a considerable area of research in sensory processes is potentially capable of being integrated within the unifying concepts of statistical decision theory.

The theory of signal detection has two specific advantages over the conventional psychophysical approach to problems dealing with organismic sensitivity. While the approach of classical psychophysics does provide a measure of sensitivity specified in terms of the reciprocal of the absolute or differential threshold, it has no technique by means of which the measure of sensitivity can be separated from the stringency of the criterion adopted by the observer in making his judgments. If the observer adopts a low-certainty criterion which produces a high rate of false-positive responses (that is, the observer says "yes" most of the time when weak stimuli are presented), he will generate data indicating a low threshold (high sensitivity). If he adopts a high-certainty criterion and seldom says "yes" when weak stimuli are presented, he will have a high threshold (low sensitivity). Although a correction for guessing may be introduced in analyzing such data, the traditional approach does not separate the two factors of criterion level and sensitivity. The theory of signal detection, however, provides an analytical approach by means of which a quantitative measure of the cutoff criterion and an index of detectability (sensitivity) can be obtained. Furthermore, the measure of detectability (d') has been found to be essentially invariant under a wide variety of psychophysical procedures (Green, 1960).

The second advantage of the theory of signal detection is that it provides the ideal observer as a basis for comparison. The ideal observer provides a measure of the best possible performance under the conditions imposed in a particular experiment on detection and, accordingly, permits an evaluative comparison of the effectiveness of the human observer. By plotting the ROC curves for the ideal and real observer, a graphical comparison of the behavior of the two may be readily obtained, or this relationship may be specified quantitatively in terms of the index of efficiency (η).

It should be clear that the theory of signal detection is unlike both the classical theory of sensory discrimination and the theory of the neural quantum in that it does not postulate the existence of a sensory threshold. It does, however, permit the concept of a response threshold (Corso, 1963a). The conflict between "some version" of the threshold model and the statistical decision model has led to a considerable experimental effort to resolve the fundamental issues; however, while some of the results are particularly damaging to certain threshold positions, there are other variants of threshold theories that fit the data as well as the theory of signal detection. Also, some aspects of the theory that have not been discussed in this section are lacking in strong experimental support. Nevertheless, the future of the theory of signal detection seems promising due to the quantitative manner in which the theory can encompass a wide range of behavioral phenomena involving sensory and perceptual processes. It may be that the theory will serve to fulfill Urban's (1930) prophesy of a "psychophysics which does not start from the threshold hypothesis."

Chapter 12

INFORMATION
THEORY

Introduction

In Chapter 5 we discussed the various meanings of the term "model" and stressed that, in one sense, the term referred to a symbolic or language system with formal (logical) properties. In some instances, however, the symbols within such a formal system have been interpreted, that is, have been transferred from the abstract system to the world of observable events, and have become physicalistically meaningful. By an appropriate set of rules, abstract terms have been translated into operational terms; in effect, the model has become a theory and the scientist may view the phenomena encompassed by the theory in accordance with the particular relations that obtained in the formal system. Since the model has been interpreted, specific hypotheses may be derived and appropriate empirical tests may be applied to determine the adequacy of the hypotheses.

In attempting to explain man's behavior, psychologists have not only generated their own particular theories but have searched in related disciplines for models that might be applied fruitfully in a behavioral context. One ready-made model was uncovered in the physical communication sciences—*communication theory,* or less accurately, *information theory.* Information theory provides a formal system for considering certain relations among symbolic events which can be described in probabilistic terms. By assigning specific empirical meaning to the terms in information theory, different behavioral models can be generated. For example, man may be considered as a simple device for transmitting information; in a more complicated example, he may be considered as a component in a system that requires him to collect information, filter it, store it, evaluate it, and apply given rules to it—that is, man as a decision maker. Engineering psychologists and others have exhibited considerable ingenuity in taking those models that have been useful in the physical (engineering) sciences and testing them in behavioral settings. Sometimes these attempts have been pointless or laboriously contrived, but in other instances they have led to a more adequate formulation of certain psychological problems or have provided a new and powerful tool of statistical analysis.

The purpose of this chapter is to provide the student with an understanding of some of the basic concepts in information theory and to review some of the studies in which information theory has been used in attempting to understand man's behavior and his limitations under certain circumstances. It is not our purpose to generate a general behavioral model based on the fundamental concepts of information theory; accordingly, some may consider the title of this chapter a misnomer or, at best, misleading. The title is not intended to imply that there is only *one* single model or theory which may be successful in predicting human behavior, nor is it intended that the contents of this chapter will provide a unified argument for the acceptance or rejection of a given mathematical model. The chapter will, however, provide the student with a comprehensive summary of some informational methods that have been useful and productive in psychological research. It will be seen that some "old" problems in psychology can be formulated and resolved within the context of information theory and that new concepts based on informational variables may be meaningfully related to behavior.

One additional point remains to be made. Information theory has not provided an "instant" solution to all problems in psychology and it will not in the future, but the flexible and intelligent use of information theory should produce advances in our understanding of man's behavior in many psychological areas. The basic unit of informational measurement (the *bit,* a contraction of *binary digit*) has universal applicability and may be used wherever categories or classes of objects or events can be distinguished. Information functions can be applied appropriately to all scales of measurement, whether the scales are nominal, ordinal, interval, or ratio (see Chapter 5); information theory is a *quantitative* theory. It measures the effect of operations which lead to a particular selection or choice from a range of possibilities or, in different words, it evaluates an event against the entire class of events that could have happened. In S-R theory we emphasize stimuli that have occurred, past or present; in information theory, we extend this view to consider what might have happened but did not.

The material in this chapter must, of necessity, involve some mathematical concepts, but the purpose is not to present a rigorous, mathematical treatment of communication theory. Instead, formal expressions will be introduced only as they are required to understand certain behavioral phenomena. This should provide the student with a sufficient number of basic concepts in information theory so that the experimental literature may be read with understanding and with a critical attitude; however, if the student wishes to pass beyond a working knowledge of information theory and into its more advanced research phases, he must possess some mastery of mathematics, especially probability theory and the calculus.

The General Concept
of a Communication System

In recent years the system concept has been given increasing attention both from a technological and theoretical point of view. Within engineering and engineering psychology the emphasis has been on the application of systematic and orderly procedures intended to provide the most effective design, development, and evaluation of a particular system. These considerations, however, lie beyond the planned purpose of this chapter; our aim at this point is to understand the concept of a system as it relates to information theory.

In general terms, a *system* may be defined as a group of components designed to fulfill a given set of objectives through their collective action. A military example of a system would be a combination of components, men and machines, whose mission might be to provide early radar warning of an impending air attack by some aggressor. In industry the purpose of the system might be the production of some commodity, such as a bottle of carbonated beverage. In any setting, if the purpose of the system were to pass information from one location to another, then the system would be designated as a *communication system*.

While the specific components differ from one type of communication system to another, certain functions must be performed if the transmission of information is to occur. These functions, five in all, have been abstracted and are shown in Figure 12-1.

In every communication system there must be a *source* of information and a *destination* for the information that is generated by the source; the source and the

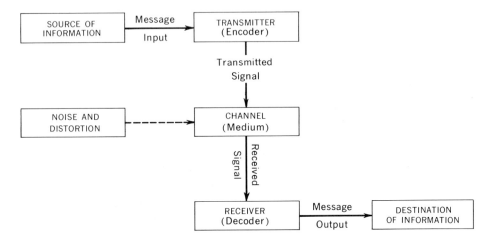

Figure 12–1. The five components of a general communication system: source, transmitter, channel, receiver, and destination. While the signal is passing through the channel, noise may be added or the signal may be distorted.

destination must be separated in space or time. The link in the system that bridges the source and the destination is called the communication *channel;* it is the medium which carries the information after it has been *coded* in some form suitable for transmission by that medium. The component that acts upon the original message from the source and, by its operation, makes the encoded message suitable for sending via the channel is the *transmitter.* The input to the transmitter is the *message* and the output of the transmitter is the *signal,* which passes via the channel to the next component of the system. While passing through the channel, the signal may be *distorted* or may become imbedded in a background of added *noise.* The output of the channel is the *received signal;* this then enters the *receiver,* which operates on the received signal and converts the transmitted information into its original form. The decoding operation of the receiver is essentially the inverse of the encoding operation performed by the transmitter. The message, in its original form, arrives at the *destination;* this is the final component of the system and consists of the object or person to whom the message was directed. These five components—source, transmitter, channel, receiver, and destination— are the fundamental units in the general concept of a communication system.

One of the most common communication systems is the vocal communication system. In this system, as in most communication systems, the source of the information is a person. Depending upon the occasion he may have much, little, or no information to pass on to others. If he does have information to transmit as in a classroom lecture, he may use his transmitter—his speech mechanism—to operate upon his information and change it into an orderly pattern of acoustic waves. These waves or transmitted signals are carried in usual circumstances through the air medium as the communication channel. The channel connects the talker's voice mechanism with the destination—the listener's ears. The ears serve as receivers and operate upon the sound waves to convert them into neural impulses which are projected to the temporal lobes of the brain. The nervous system of the listener, then, comprises the destination of the information.

In this example, let us say that the operation of the transmitter is to encode the information in spoken symbols of the French language. If the listener knows the code, that is, the system of symbols comprising the French language, the message will be decoded and understood. Stated in communication terms, we would say that the source and the destination are matched components and will function to transfer information effectively, unless certain disorders are present or interfering disturbances disrupt the process. In both instances, the possibility of error is introduced. The errors may occur in the encoding process or in the decoding process, or even while the signals are being transmitted over the channel. At the encoding end of the system, consider the mistakes that are often made by the beginning student as he attempts to communicate in a foreign language. At the decoding end, consider the same beginning student as he attempts to translate a passage of text; or, more generally, think of the extreme decoding problems that are faced daily by the millions of individuals with hearing disorders.

It is common practice to designate all the sources of error in a communication system under a specific name, *noise.* In a noisy communication system, the possibility for the occurrence of errors is high; in a system with a low noise level, the possibility for errors is markedly reduced. Conceptually, the presence of noise in a generalized communication system is treated as a second source, feeding signals into a channel already in use. The noise source has the property that neither the source nor the destination can predict in detail the messages or information that will be generated by it. Noise, in and of itself, is not necessarily a detriment in a system. It becomes a detriment only when it produces a *significant* interference in the reception of messages transmitted by the primary source of information. If there is no significant increase in the number of errors produced as a message passes through the system, the noise source may be disregarded and the system may be considered to be noise free or noiseless. In passing through the system, a message may be altered (and errors introduced) by *distortion*. The difference between noise and distortion is that noise involves statistical and unpredictable disturbances, whereas distortion applies some fixed operation to the signal. This means that the noise effects cannot always be eliminated from the system; on the other hand, the effects of distortion can be removed by applying an operation which is the inverse, or partial inverse, of the operation responsible for the distortion. In practice a communication system may be affected by a wide range of disturbances, from noise to distortion. The seriousness of the disturbance is dependent upon the degree to which it disrupts the passage of information through the system and introduces errors in the transmitted or received messages.

The Mathematical Meaning of Information

The word "information" as used in the scientific context of information theory or communication theory has a very precise meaning; however, like many other terms that have been absorbed into the scientist's vocabulary from the layman's vocabulary, there is some relation between the meaning of the word as it appears in the two contexts. In the nontechnical meaning, information refers to knowledge that is acquired in any manner; it applies to "facts" gathered from reading newspapers and books, by observing the world and its events, by listening to the neighbor's gossip, and in general by "keeping our eyes and ears open." Information is something we acquire from people, objects, and events—we learn something we didn't know before. Now, while we have gained some information, this does not mean that the information is necessarily valid or correct. The conversations carried on over the backyard fence contain much information, but the information may be inaccurate or may even be based upon rumor. In many instances, the layman is not concerned with the accuracy or inaccuracy of the information and does little, if anything, to establish the facts in the situation under consideration; but, in those cases in which he is faced with making a choice or reaching a decision in a given matter, the layman may seek additional information. The specific kind of information and the amount of information he requires before making a choice will depend upon the particular situation in which the information is to be used. The more complex the decision, that is, the greater the possible number of choices or courses of action, the greater the amount of information needed to arrive at a decision.

To crystallize these concepts, we will consider the following example. Two men (Mr. A and Mr. B) meet on a street corner. Mr. A tells Mr. B that "Today is Saturday." This statement gives Mr. B no information, assuming he already knows it is Saturday. Mr. A goes on to explain that today is the day of the "big horse race." Again, this gives Mr. B no information since he is already on his way to the racetrack. Then Mr. A whispers, "Topper will win in the third." Now Mr. B has gained some information—he didn't know this before the statement was made by Mr. A. Mr. B has received some information, but he has no way of knowing whether the information is correct, or incorrect. The information could be useful, particularly if he is planning on placing a bet in that race—so Mr. B might seek more information by asking a few direct questions. If only two horses were running in that race, Mr. B's choice would be relatively simple; with seven horses running—and each one a potential winner—Mr. B's problem is much more complicated. Before reaching a decision he will try to obtain all the information he possibly can, consulting not only Mr. A but all available published reports to determine the present condition of the horse and rider and to become familiar with their past performances. Later, at the racetrack, Mr. B ponders a "sure thing" before the third race. If Topper were the only horse running in the third, Mr. B would have no uncertainty about the winner of the race; consequently, if the "race" were actually run and Topper crossed the finish line, Mr. B would have gained no information from the outcome. However, when seven horses actually leave the starting gate in the third race, only one of these will come in first (barring the rare occurrence of a tie). Since Mr. B had some a priori uncertainty about the winner, he will get some information as the horses cross the finish line—and, most likely, the information will elicit an unpleasant reaction!

Now we have the basic elements that are needed to develop the technical meaning of information. Any act of communication will provide information insofar as it reduces the uncertainty in the situation under consideration. Whenever there is some a priori uncertainty, the transmittal of appropriate information will reduce this uncertainty. Uncertainty is based upon lack of knowledge about the given situation; information provides for the reduction of this uncertainty. The *amount* of information is determined by the amount by which the uncertainty is reduced. Thus, *uncertainty and information are quantitatively equal in a given situation.*

If the amount of uncertainty that exists can be specified before a given communicative act occurs, then it is possible to compute the amount of information that is given by that particular act. As in the example of the horserace, the uncertainty about the outcome of any act is related quantitatively to the number of possible outcomes that exist in that situation. Accordingly, an effective definition of information must consider not only the outcome that *did occur,* but also the complete set of outcomes that *might have occurred.* When a particular act does occur, it is a unique and specific event and completely reduces the uncertainty that had been present—we know the winner of the horserace; we have obtained exactly the same amount of information as there was uncertainty prior to the occurrence of the act.

We have already indicated that if our prior knowledge in a situation reduces the set of possible outcomes to a single event, then there is no choice to be made, and no information can be transmitted. The minimum condition under which information can be transmitted is that in which a choice or selection must be made between two alternatives. *The maximum uncertainty will exist when the two alternatives have the same probability of occurrence,* as in the tossing of a coin; this means that the maximum information is given by a choice between two equally likely alternatives. This choice is taken to represent one unit of information. By definition, *whenever a choice is made between two alternatives which on an a priori basis are equally likely, it is specified that the choice has transmitted one unit of information.* This unit is called the *bit*—a contraction of the words "binary digit." One unit of information is necessary to make a binary decision. Do not confuse the technical meaning of a *bit* of information with the layman's use of the same term, meaning generally, a small amount of something.

Now that the unit has been defined, it is necessary to consider how many of these units are transmitted when there are more than two equally likely alternatives. Consider that a choice is made from a finite set or ensemble of alternatives characterized by an arbitrary a priori probability distribution. If several choices are made from this ensemble, how many units of information are transmitted? In answering this question, there are certain correlations that we would like to have satisfied. The first is that if *two independent* choices are made from an ensemble of equally likely alternatives, then the total amount of information transmitted should equal *two* bits—since one choice from equally likely alternatives transmits one unit of information. This is the condition of *additivity: the total amount of information transmitted by successive and statistically independent choices from an ensemble of equally likely alternatives is the sum of the amounts transmitted by each of the selections.*

Another example will be used to show how the condition of additivity and the bit may be used. Suppose that we have an ensemble of eight geometric figures as follows:

and that each figure or element in the ensemble is equally likely to be selected. Now, when a particular element is selected from this ensemble, how many units of information are transmitted? The answer is three bits. To arrive at this solution, assume that I am thinking of a particular figure and that you are to determine my selection as quickly as possible. To each question you ask, I will reply only with "yes" or "no." You might start out in any one of several different ways, but suppose you ask, "Is it before the diamond?" My answer is "Yes." Then, "Is it before the circle?" My answer is again "Yes." "Is it before the square?" My answer is "No." Then you know that the figure I have selected is the square.

Notice that you have asked only three binary questions to arrive at the particular figure; notice also that each binary question you asked divided the ensemble in half and, therefore, on the basis of my reply, you were able to eliminate immediately half of the figures involved in each question. The strategy you used was the best one possible; no other method would *on the average* produce the selected figure with so few questions. With a greater number of elements in the ensemble, the superiority of this method would be even more marked. For an ensemble of sixty-four figures, only six appropriate (binary) questions are needed to arrive at the selected element.

We are now ready to summarize these basic concepts into a formal mathematical expression. Table 12–1 indicates the number of binary questions (H) that are required to select a particular element from an ensemble with equal

Table 12–1   Uncertainty (H) as a Function of the Size of the Ensemble with an Equally Likely Distribution

Size of Ensemble		Uncertainty	
No. of Elements (n)	No. of Elements (2^H)	No. of Binary Questions (H)	Units of Information (bits)
1	2^0	0	0
2	2^1	1	1
4	2^2	2	2
8	2^3	3	3
16	2^4	4	4
32	2^5	5	5
64	2^6	6	6

probabilities of occurrence for all elements in the ensemble; H is given for ensembles of various size (n) ranging from 1 to 64. In Table 12–1 it may be seen that each time the size of the ensemble doubles in terms of the number of elements (n), the number of questions required for the selection of a particular element increases by one. For any given ensemble, the isolation of an element requires as many binary questions or steps as are needed in the expression 2^H to yield a value corresponding to the total number of elements in the ensemble. Mathematically stated,

$$n = 2^H, \tag{12-1}$$

where n is the number of elements in an ensemble with an equally likely distribution, and H is the number of binary questions, choices, or decisions that are required to select a given element from the ensemble.

In Table 12–1 it may also be seen that the condition of additivity is satisfied. Each successive binary question (event or occurrence) adds the same amount of uncertainty, that is, it makes available the same amount of information, so that the amount of information (last column, Table 12–1) increases in an arithmetic progression. Thus, the second condition required for the quantitative measure of information is satisfied: the amount of information is monotonically related to the number of possible outcomes (n) in the ensemble. As the number of outcomes or elements in the ensemble increases in a geometric progression, the amount of information or the uncertainty of the ensemble increases in an arithmetic progression. This means that whenever the number of possible outcomes is doubled, the uncertainty is increased by one bit; halving the number of possible outcomes decreases the uncertainty by one bit.

Equation 12-1 may be rewritten in logarithmic form. By definition of the logarithm, when $n = 2^H$ then:

$$H = \log_2 n, \tag{12-2}$$

where H and n have the same meaning as in Equation 12-1. Equation 12-2 tells us that the uncertainty of the ensemble (H) is equal to the logarithm to the base 2 of the number of possible outcomes in an ensemble with an equally likely distribution of elements.

The use of logarithms to the base 2 follows from the decision to work only with binary questions. This decision is of course an arbitrary one, but, once this decision is made, logarithms to the base 2 are required. The binary questions and the logarithmic base of 2 are mutually necessary, but as a *pair* of conditions they are completely arbitrary.

Nevertheless, it is possible to change from one system of logarithms to another without altering the basic concept of information measurement as we have described it. Accordingly, the common system of logarithms to the base 10 may be used. It may be seen that in the generalized expression for uncertainty (U), as given in Equation 12-3, multiplying by the appropriate constant c will not change the numbers in the bit system. The general equation for uncertainty is:

$$U = c \log k, \tag{12-3}$$

where U is the measure of uncertainty, k is the number of elements or possible outcomes in the ensemble, and c is the constant of proportionality. Equation 12-2 is obtained from Equation 12-3 by taking logarithms to the base 2 and defining the unit of measurement in this system so that the proportionality constant is equal to 1. When the common system of logarithms (base 10) is used, c is not equal to 1 but has a value of 3.3219. Equation 12-3 may then be rewritten as:

$$H = 3.3219 \log_{10} n, \tag{12-3a}$$

where H and n have the same meanings as in Equation 12-2.

In computing the uncertainty or the amount of information in a given ensemble, the same answer will be obtained regardless of the particular logarithmic system used in Equation 12-3, provided the appropriate value has been assigned to the constant of proportionality. No matter which logarithmic system is used in computing the amount of uncertainty or information, the logarithmic measure will satisfy the condition of additivity; as the members of the original number series are obtained by multiplication, those in the corresponding logarithmic series are obtained by addition. The necessity of this condition will become apparent later on in this chapter when uncertainties are computed as the product of a number of separate possible outcomes.

The definition of information as given in Equation 12-2 applies *only* to those situations in which all of the outcomes or elements of an ensemble are equally likely; however, in most real situations this condition is not satisfied—the alternatives are *not* equally likely. For example, the letters of the alphabet and the various words in the English language do not occur equally often in writing or in speech. It is not likely that in a typical nine-inning game a baseball will be hit into right field as often as it is into left field. Of the eighty-eight keys on a piano keyboard, some have a greater probability of being played than others in the performance of a given selection, and the probabilities will change from selection to selection. If the measure of information is to be useful in general, it must be applicable not only to those situations in which the outcomes or events of an ensemble are equally likely, but also to those situations where the alternatives are *not* equally likely.

The development of the specific equation for computing the amount of information in the case of an ensemble with unequal probabilities will be based upon an example. Consider again the baseball game. Assume that we have kept records of all the baseball games played in the American League over a three-year period. We have divided the outfield into three parts—left field, center field, and right field—and our records show the total number of times a baseball was hit into each section of the outfield. From these records we can easily determine the *proportion* of times the baseball was hit into each location; each proportion represents the probability (p) associated with the hitting of a baseball into that particular section of the outfield.[1] Assume that these probabilities are 0.500, 0.375, and 0.125 for left field, center field, and right field, respectively. We have a series of three possible outcomes with differing probabilities each time a baseball is hit into the outfield. The question is: What is the *average uncertainty* (uncertainty in the long run) about where a baseball will go when hit into the outfield in an American League game?

Recall that in the situation with equal probabilities, $H = \log n$ (Equation 12-2).[2] Now let $p(x_2)$ represent the probability of occurrence of any *one* outcome (event or element) from the ensemble of n outcomes with an equally likely dis-

---

[1] Throughout this chapter, the symbol p will be used as a general symbol for probability. No distinction will be made between a true probability which is known on an a priori basis and a proportion which is calculated from a sample of observations. While there is a distinction between these two notions of probability, this distinction has no practical significance and does not alter the development to be presented in this chapter.

[2] Standard practice in information theory involves logarithms to the base 2. Since this system will be used in this chapter, the subscript 2 denoting the base of the logarithms will be omitted.

tribution.[3] This probability will be the reciprocal of the number of different outcomes that can occur. So we have

$$H(x) = \log \left[1/p(x) \right]$$

$$H(x) = -\log p(x), \qquad (12\text{-}4)$$

where x is a single variable which can take any value (x_i), from $i = 1$ to k. When
all the outcomes of x are equally likely, $H(x)$ is the uncertainty of any given outcome; it is also the average uncertainty of all the outcomes, that is, the complete
ensemble.

When, however, the alternatives are not equally likely, the uncertainty associated with each of the separate outcomes must be specified differently from the
average uncertainty of the complete ensemble. The uncertainty associated with
each of the separate outcomes is given by $-\log p$; the average uncertainty of the
ensemble is simply the weighted average of the separate uncertainties. These concepts are summarized in Table 12-2 for the example of the baseballs hit into the
outfield.

Table 12–2   Summary of Computations for the Average Uncertainty of an Ensemble
with Unequal Probabilities of the Various Outcomes

Outcome	No. of Recorded Hits to Outfield [a]	p [b]	$-\log p$	$-p \log p$ [c]
Left Field	2000	0.500	1.00	0.500
Center Field	1500	0.375	1.42	0.531
Right Field	500	0.125	3.00	0.375
Total	4000	1.000		$-\Sigma\, p \log p = 1.406$ bits

[a] Fictitious data.
[b] The value of p is the relative frequency of occurrence of a given outcome, for example, for left field $p = 2000/4000 = 0.500$.
[c] Values p and $p \log p$ may be obtained from Newman (1951) or Senders (1958).

In Table 12-2, the first column indicates each of the three possible outcomes
when the baseball is hit into the outfield. The second column gives the number of
times the ball was hit to each of the three sections of the field in three years, and
the third column shows each number converted into the corresponding relative
frequency of occurrence. The fourth column gives the $-\log p$ value for each outcome. These values are the uncertainties associated with each of the separate
outcomes. For example, when the ball is hit to right field, the associated information is 3.00 bits, since on the average this will happen only ⅛ of the time, that is,

[3] To simplify the notation that would otherwise become burdensome, the subscript i will be
omitted from this point on, unless absolutely necessary to avoid confusion. Thus, x will denote a
general variable in the ensemble and $p(x)$ will indicate the probability of a particular value of that
variable, (x_i).

only once in 8 hits to the outfield. Column five gives the $-p \log p$ values for each outcome.

The long-term average uncertainty is simply the average of the separate uncertainties, with each uncertainty weighted by its probability of occurrence. The sum of the weighted uncertainties is obtained by totaling the fifth column; the average (mean) uncertainty of the ensemble of outcomes is obtained by dividing by the sum of the weights. Since the sum of the weights is equal to 1.000, there is no need to perform the division. The average uncertainty, then, is the weighted average of the various uncertainties and may be obtained by adding the values in the fifth column of Table 12-2. For example, the average uncertainty is 1.406 bits.

In mathematical terms, the average uncertainty (H) associated with an ensemble of discrete events with unequal probabilities of occurrence is given by

$$H(x) = \sum_{i=1}^{n} \left\{ [-\log p(x)] \cdot p(x) \right\},$$

which may be rewritten in the more convenient form

$$H(x) = -\Sigma\, p(x) \log p(x). \tag{12-5}$$

Equation 12-5 may also be used to compute the average uncertainty of an ensemble with an equally likely distribution. The reader should be aware that in calculating the average uncertainty in either case by means of Equation 12-5, it is not necessary to determine the $-\log p$ values as in Table 12-2. For a given problem, merely look up the obtained proportions in a $\log_2$ table, copy out the corresponding values of $-p(x) \log p(x)$, and summate to determine the average uncertainty. Whether Equation 12-5 or Equation 12-2 is used to calculate the average uncertainty for an equally likely distribution is simply a matter of convenience. Equation 12-2 is a special case of the more general formula as given in Equation 12-5. When the events of an ensemble are equally likely we can write

$$p(a) = p(b) = \ldots p(x) = 1/n.$$

Thus, we can substitute $1/n$ for $p(x)$ in Equation 12-5 and the result is

$$H = -\Sigma\, (1/n \log 1/n).$$

Since all of the terms to be summated are equal and there are n terms, we obtain the formula given in Equation 12-2 by

$$H = n\, [-(1/n \log 1/n)]$$

$$= -\log 1/n$$

$$H = \log n.$$

At this point it might be helpful to summarize some of the characteristics of H which have been considered in this section. There are five major points.

1. A value of H can be computed for any discrete probability distribution by solving Equation 12-5.
2. As the size of the ensemble increases, the value of H increases, provided all the possible outcomes are equally probable.
3. When all the possible outcomes are equally probable, then for an ensemble of a given size, the value of H is maximum.
4. When there is only one possible outcome, the value of H is at a minimum; in this case, the value of H is zero.
5. The unit of uncertainty has additive properties, that is, the uncertainty of a whole ensemble is the weighted sum of the uncertainties of the subensembles.

Some Additional Concepts in Information Theory

Now that we have considered the basic concept of the amount of information in a discrete distribution, we will define some additional concepts and develop their meaning by example. The uncertainty measure (H) gives the actual uncertainty or unpredictability of a distribution. If we are to draw conclusions or make decisions under certain circumstances, the value of H may be all that we need; however, there may be instances in which we are interested in knowing the actual uncertainty in relation to the uncertainty that would exist if all the members of an ensemble were divided equally among the various alternatives. This measure is called the *relative uncertainty* (H_{rel}) and is defined as:

$$H_{rel} = \frac{\text{Actual Uncertainty}}{\text{Maximum Uncertainty}} = \frac{-\Sigma\, p(x)\, \log p(x)}{\log n}. \qquad (12\text{-}6)$$

As we have already indicated, if the members of the distribution are equally likely, that is, are divided equally among all the possible alternatives, then the actual uncertainty will equal H_{max} and H_{rel} will equal 1. If all the members fall into one category of the ensemble, then H_{max} is zero and, hence, H_{rel} will also be zero. Thus, H_{rel} can range between these limits, from 0 to 1.

In the previous example of the baseball outfield, the actual uncertainty was 1.406 bits of information. The maximum possible uncertainty would occur under the condition that the ball be hit an equal number of times to each of the three outfield positions. This would yield

$$H_{max} = \log 3 = -.333 \log .333 - .333 \log .333 - .333 \log .333 = 1.5849 \text{ bits}.$$

We will now consider these two values (actual uncertainty and maximum uncertainty) in terms of our example. If the baseball were hit equally often and in any order to the three outfield positions, the ensemble (the three outfield positions) could convey 1.5849 bits of information on the average or per position; however, the baseball is hit more frequently to some positions than to others. Thus, when the actual (average) uncertainty is computed, the result is only 1.406 bits of information per position. This means that in our hypothetical example we could convey just as much information per position with a playing field that has only 2.69 positions that are used equally often, as we can with the three outfield positions that are not used equally often. Therefore, the relative uncertainty is

$$H_{rel} = \frac{1.4060}{1.5849} = 0.88, \text{ or } 88 \text{ percent.}$$

The complementary quantity of relative uncertainty is called *redundancy* (R) and is defined as

$$R = \frac{\text{Maximum Uncertainty} - \text{Actual Uncertainty}}{\text{Maximum Uncertainty}} = 1 - H_{rel}. \quad (12\text{-}7)$$

Redundancy is the difference between the maximum uncertainty and the actual uncertainty expressed as a fraction of the maximum uncertainty, or as shown in Equation 12-7, it is equal to 1 minus the relative uncertainty. The redundancy of our baseball example, then, is (1–0.88) which yields 0.12 or 12 percent. This indicates the saving in the average number of binary questions required to identify the outcome of a given ensemble of events when optimal questioning is used and the statistical frequency of the possible outcomes is known; in different terms, it measures the unutilized possibilities to transmit information. This example of the baseball playing field is, of course, trivial, although it does embody the main concepts developed to this point.

So far we have been concerned with a source or ensemble of outcomes (events) in which the various possible outcomes are independent. The probability of the occurrence of one outcome has no effect upon, or is not affected by, the outcome of any other event in the ensemble; we have been dealing with a probability distribution of a single variable and have only considered whether the independent probabilities (summing to 1.00) were equal or unequal. In relation to Figure 12-1, we have been concerned primarily with the schematic block labeled "Source of Information," in which the source contained only a single variable.

Now we will consider the probability distribution defined in terms of *two* variables (Miller, 1953). Examples of a *bivariate distribution* include a distribution of stimuli and related responses, a distribution of two parameters of a visual stimulus such as brightness and areal size, a distribution of two parameters of a motor response such as latency and magnitude, or a distribution of stimuli or responses occurring in a series such that the successive members of the series may be paired in some predetermined manner. The essential point of the bivariate case is that we must consider *two* sources of uncertainty and these sources may be independent or nonindependent (correlated).

Consider Figure 12-2. Part A of the figure illustrates the case of two independent variables and Part B, two correlated variables. In Part A, it is shown graphically and algebraically that the amount of information $H(x)$ associated with two independent sources is the sum of the information of the constituent sources, Source Y

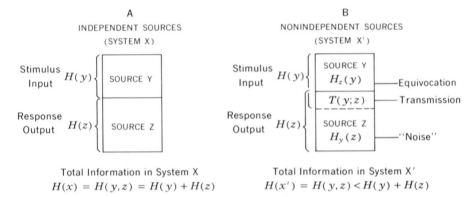

Figure 12–2. Schematic representation of the different quantities of information in a communication system. Part A, independent sources of information and Part B, nonindependent or related sources of information. As applied in a psychological setting, one source may be considered as the stimulus input to the subject and the other, the response output.

and Source Z. If Y and Z are not statistically independent as in Part B, then $H(x')$ $< H(y) + H(z)$. This is intuitively reasonable; some of the information in Source Y gives information about Source Z and so that segment of information in Source Z provides no new information.

In Part B of Figure 12-2, the two nonindependent sources of information or uncertainty may be considered in terms of a typical psychological situation. Assume that the system represents a human subject in an experimental situation. We have a series of stimuli (as in a reaction time experiment) and a series of responses; these are linked by the information channel, which is the subject. Designate the uncertainty of the stimuli H (in) and that of the responses H (out); in Figure 12-2 these are shown as the uncertainties of Source Y and Source Z, respectively. The two uncertainties in Part B, Figure 12-2, are related and are composed of the following parts:

$H(y)$ or $H(\text{in})$ is the uncertainty of stimulus input.

$H(z)$ or $H(\text{out})$ is the uncertainty of response output.

$H_z(y)$ or $H_{\text{out}}(\text{in})$ is the information which is in the input but is not contained in the output and is lost in the communication system. This term may be regarded as the uncertainty associated with the stimulus when the response is known and is called "equivocation."

$H_y(z)$ or $H_{\text{in}}(\text{out})$ is the information which is in the output but was not in the input. This term may be regarded as the uncertainty associated with the response when the stimulus is known and is called "*noise*" or "*ambiguity*" generated in the system itself.

$T(y; z)$ or $T(\text{in}; \text{out})$ is the information common to both input and output and is therefore called "*transmission*."

$H(y, z)$ or $H(\text{in, out})$ is the total amount of information in the system or the average uncertainty of all the possible states within the system and is the sum of $H_{\text{out}}(\text{in})$, $T(\text{in; out})$, and $H_{\text{in}}(\text{out})$.

By referring to the geometry of Figure 12-2, it may be seen that numerous relationships hold between the various uncertainties. Some examples are given without formal mathematical proofs:

1. The input uncertainty consists of two parts: the part which is transmitted and the part which is lost:

$$H(y) = T(y;z) + H_z(y). \tag{12-8}$$

2. Stimulus equivocation is the difference between the input uncertainty and the information transmitted:

$$H_z(y) = H(y) - T(y;z). \tag{12-9}$$

3. The output of the system is the sum of transmission and noise:

$$H(z) = T(y;z) + \text{H}_y(z). \tag{12-10}$$

4. The total information in the system is the sum of the input uncertainty and noise:

$$H(y,z) = H(y) + H_y(z). \tag{12-11}$$

5. The total information in the system is in the output except for the information which is lost:

$$H(y,z) = H(z) - H_z(y). \tag{12-12}$$

6. The total information in the system is the sum of equivocation, transmission, and noise:

$$H(y,z) = H_z(y) + T(y;z) + H_y(z). \tag{12-13}$$

7. The information transmitted is the sum of the input and output uncertainties minus the total information in the system:

$$T(y;z) = H(y) + H(z) - H(y,z). \tag{12-14}$$

These are the primary ideas of information theory. For our purposes only one further concept remains to be defined, channel capacity. *Channel capacity* is the upper limit in the amount of information which can be transmitted in a system. Channel capacity is often symbolized by C. With increases in the input information in a system, there are increases in the amount of information that is transmitted; however, there is a point beyond which transmission no longer increases. As $H(y)$ increases, $T(y;z)$ approaches an upper limit (C), which is the channel capacity of the system. From Figure 12-2 it may be seen that the ability of a communication system to transmit information cannot exceed the input or stimulus uncertainty in a given situation.

Figure 12-3 shows the amount of transmitted information as a function of stimulus uncertainty in a hypothetical discrimination task with a human subject. When the input information is less than the channel capacity, the subject may discriminate perfectly and the transmitted information would equal the input information, thereby producing the diagonal line in Figure 12-3. Then, as the

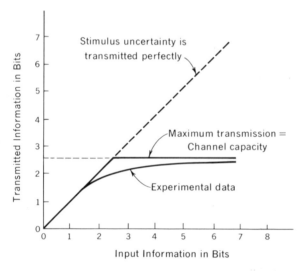

Figure 12-3. A hypothetical curve for a human subject on a discrimination task. The channel capacity of the subject is defined as the maximum amount of information which can be transmitted under the conditions of the experiment. With a channel capacity of 2.58 bits, this subject can discriminate perfectly among six equally likely alternatives. (After Miller, *Amer. Psychol.*, 1953.)

input information approaches the channel capacity, discrimination will not be perfect and the transmitted information would be less than the input information, producing a departure from the diagonal. Finally, when the stimulus information exceeds the channel capacity, the experimental points (transmission values) will yield an approximately horizontal line which denotes the channel capacity.

Information Measures and Perceptual Discrimination (Univariate Uncertainty)

Reaction Time

Now that we have considered some of the fundamental concepts in information theory, it will be profitable to review some experimental studies in which these concepts have been applied. For historical reasons, we will start by considering some studies on reaction time.

Within the framework of information theory, the choice reaction time experiment can be considered as a model of a communication system. The transmitter is represented by the display (usually visual or auditory) which contains alternative stimuli or signals; these stimuli or signals may also be considered to be encoded messages. The channel over which the signals are transmitted is taken to be the air space between the display and the subject. The subject acts as the receiver in that the signals impinge upon receptor mechanisms and are "detected," that is, they initiate afferent neural activity in an appropriate sensory system. The patterns of excitation are projected to corresponding cortical areas where the signals are decoded into messages that establish a course of action in relation to the perceived input. Outgoing impulses from the cortical mechanism activate appropriate effectors (usually muscles in the hands, feet, or vocal organ) which produce the designated response, that is, the "information" arrives at its destination.

The traditional experiments in reaction time were concerned with the general problem of the time required for the occurrence of the various "steps" in the chain of events within the subject, but the question remains unanswered except for approximations derived from estimates of the duration of the receptor and effector processes. More recently, interest in this problem has centered around the effects of an increase in the number of alternative stimuli on the magnitude of choice reaction time.

One of the significant findings in this area was reported by Hick (1952) who proposed that in making choice reactions the subject gains "information," in the technical sense of the term, at a constant rate. In these experiments, a display of ten small lights was arranged in an "irregular circle" and the subject was required to press one of ten telegraph keys on which his fingers rested. For choices less than ten, some of the lights were omitted. The stimuli were presented in a random order and the frequencies of occurrence of the stimuli were balanced so that the ensemble comprised an equally likely distribution. The stimulus for a given trial was presented 5 sec after the completion of the previous response.

The data for one of Hick's experiments are shown in Figure 12-4 and represent more than 2400 choice reaction times. If the number of possible signals is taken as n and reaction time is plotted as a function of $\log (n+1)$, the observed reaction times lie on a straight line passing through the origin. The relationship between choice reaction time (CRT) and the number of equally likely lights (n) can be written as:

$$CRT = k \log (n+1), \tag{12-15}$$

where k is a constant. Notice that when $n = 1$, $\log_2 (n+1) = 1$ so that k may be taken as a measure of simple reaction time. The empirical value of k was found to be approximately 0.63.

The quantity $(n+1)$ rather than n is used in Equation 12-15 since the subject must not only decide which key to press, but must first decide that a signal has occurred and the time is appropriate for a response to be made. The subject, in this view, must deal with 0, 1, 2, 3, ... n possible states and one extra alternative (that is, one alternative more than n) must be contained in the basic equation. If the total number of equally probable alternatives from which the subject has to choose is designated by N, then Equation 12-15 may be rewritten as

$$CRT = k \log N, \tag{12-16}$$

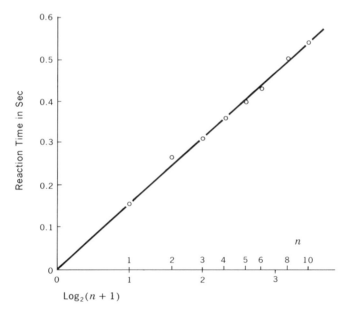

Figure 12–4.   Choice reaction time as a function of the number of equally probable stimuli. (From Hick, *Quart. J. exp. Psychol.*, 1952.)

where N includes the equivalent of one equally likely alternative associated with the "no signal" condition. This formulation is called *Hick's Law;* the law states that *choice reaction time is a linear function of stimulus uncertainty.*

This conclusion has been verified in a number of subsequent experiments (Archer, 1954; Crossman, 1953; Gregg, 1954); one of these will be described here (Hyman, 1953). Hyman presented his subjects ($N = 4$) with a square matrix of 36 lights, but used only 8 of these in three different experimental conditions. Each light was given a code name (single syllable) and when it was turned on, the subject responded with the code name he had learned for that light. This response activated a voice key, which in turn operated the stopping mechanism of an electric timer.

In one experimental condition, the stimulus had to be chosen from a number of equally probable alternatives, ranging from one through eight and presented in random order; in the second condition, the number of alternatives ranged from two to eight, with different probabilities of occurrence; and in the third condition, two to eight alternatives occurred equally often, but the probability of occurrence of a given alternative depended upon the alternative immediately preceding. These three conditions can be summarized by indicating that the average amount of information accompanying a single stimulus was varied by: (1) changing the number of equally probable alternatives from which a choice could be made (the stimulus uncertainty ranged from 0.00 to 3.00); (2) by changing the probability of occurrence of given choices (the stimulus uncertainty ranged from 0.47 to 2.75); and (3) by varying the sequential dependencies between successive choices of alternatives (the stimulus uncertainty ranged from 0.72 to 2.81).

The results of this study confirm Hick's finding that there is a linear relation between stimulus uncertainty and choice reaction time; furthermore, at least between 0.00 and 3.00 bits, it makes no difference which of the three methods is used to obtain a given stimulus uncertainty.

Crossman (1953) found, as did Hyman, that *unequal probabilities lower the average reaction time*. In this experiment, the subjects were required to sort ordinary playing cards into piles according to different sets of instructions. In one case, for example, the subjects sorted the pack of cards into two piles—red and black; in another, they put the plain cards into one pile and the picture cards in the other. Each of these tasks, of course, has just two categories of response, but in the first task each category of response occurs equally often (1 bit/card), while in the second task the probability of a picture card is 12/52 and that of a plain card is 40/52 (or 0.78 bit/card). The latter task (unequal probabilities) yields the lower average reaction time.

Leonard (1958) obtained similar results. Two series of stimuli were used, each containing 50 stimuli. In the balanced series, there were ten random presentations from each of five light sources (2.3 bits/stimulus); in the biased series, one light occurred 34 times and the other four lights occurred four times each (1.5 bits/stimulus) in an irregular order. The subject was required to press a telegraph key which corresponded spatially to the bulb that was lit. The results indicated that for the balanced series the mean time per response was 0.485 sec with 4.1 percent errors; for the biased series, 0.419 sec per response with 3.2 percent errors. Thus, *the biased series gave faster reaction times and fewer errors*.

In a series of three experiments that involved naming numbers and pointing to lights, the relative stimulus frequencies of the lights were varied in nine choice tasks (Fitts, Peterson, and Wolpe, 1963). These investigators found the same consistent result—that the differences in choice reaction time are linearly related to stimulus uncertainty, but their analysis of the data went further. The results revealed that, *as redundancy increased (less stimulus uncertainty), average reaction time to the frequent stimulus component decreased whereas the reaction time to the less frequent components increased*.

All these experiments show that *choice reaction time increases uniformly with stimulus uncertainty;* the greater the amount of information transmitted, the greater the choice reaction time. The empirical data suggest that the human subject in a choice reaction-time experiment responds as if he were complying with Hick's Law. Hyman (1953) obtained a median increase in reaction time of approximately 0.176 sec per bit of stimulus uncertainty in a situation using four highly practiced subjects who responded vocally to light stimuli; Brainard, Irby, Fitts, and Alluisi (1962) found an increase in reaction time of 0.178 sec per bit in a similar S-R situation with 12 naive subjects; Hick (1952) had one subject who showed an increase of almost 0.11 sec per bit for finger responses to lights with as many as ten alternatives. The differences in the slopes of the reaction time functions, however, are not always as great as these. For example, Fitts and

Switzer (1962) found that the maximum difference in voice reaction time for two versus eight numerals was only 0.03 sec, or 0.015 sec per bit of stimulus uncertainty; also, differences in reaction time were small comparing three versus twenty-six letters of the English alphabet. It appears that if there is a highly compatible S-R relationship and sufficient practice time is allowed, then minimal variation in verbal reaction time will occur as the number of alternatives (in the set from which the signal is drawn) is increased from at least two to eight (Davis, Moray, and Treisman, 1961).

In Equation 12-15 the slope of the linear function which relates choice reaction time and stimulus uncertainty is given by the constant k, and the reciprocal of k provides a measure of the rate at which information is transmitted (in bits/sec). Although $1/k$ varies from experiment to experiment depending upon the specific characteristics of the independent and dependent variables, the fraction is of importance in psychology since it reveals man's maximum rate of information transmission. The fact that $1/k$ has not been constant under various experimental conditions indicates that an important variable in the study of information transmission is the relationship of signal to response, that is, a coding problem (Brainard, *et al.*, 1962). Unfortunately, information theory does not provide a general solution to the problem of devising an optimal code. If the relationship of signal to response is simple and "natural" or one which has been well-practiced by the subject, the slope will be small; if, however, the relationship is difficult, "unnatural," or unpracticed, the slope will be large. It appears, therefore, that *man's maximum rate of information transmission is not a constant, but depends upon the circumstances which characterize a particular situation*. This is shown by the experimental studies that have been cited in this section, as well as others. Nevertheless, the relationship expressed in Hick's Law is significant both theoretically and practically, as in the case of engineering psychology where optimal relationships between displays and controls on various types of equipment must be determined (Krulee, 1954). Alternative formulations have been proposed for Hick's Law, but the evidence currently available seems in general to favor the formulation given in Equation 12-14 (Welford, 1960).

Recognition in Perceptual Tasks

In this section we will consider some recognition studies in which informational concepts have been used, or could have been used, in the basic experimental design or in reporting the major findings. The recognition experiment, as contrasted with a learning experiment, involves a controlled situation in which the subject's behavior is not a function of his *familiarity* with the stimulus complex, but of the *discriminal difficulty* of the complex. This is accomplished by providing the subject with a list of all possible stimuli to be presented in an experiment, or by having the subject thoroughly memorize the list of all possible stimuli before the criterion task is performed. Of course, another approach would be to use stimuli with which the subject is already thoroughly familiar before participating in the experiment, such as the use of the English alphabet (Fitts and Switzer, 1962). Each of these three methods is aimed at the elimination of learning effects when the primary objective of an experiment is to investigate some aspect of perceptual recognition; in this case, and within the context of information theory, we are interested in the relationship between performance on a perceptual recognition task and the number of alternatives available in the stimulus situation.

One of the earliest studies in which the influence of the number of alternatives on perceptual recognition was demonstrated was that of Miller, Heise, and Lichten (1951). In this study, the subject was presented with a list containing 2, 4, 8, 16, 32, or 256 monosyllabic words, corresponding to 1, 2, 3, 4, 5, or 8 bits of information. The subject studied the list carefully while he listened to a talker read one of the words from the given list; then he checked the item he heard. The spoken words were presented one at a time in different levels of masking noise and the subject always knew the list from which the test word was taken.

The results for part of this study are shown in Figure 12-5. The percentage of words correctly heard is plotted as a function of the size of the vocabulary list

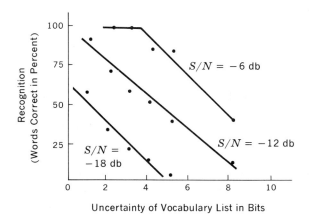

Uncertainty of Vocabulary List in Bits

Figure 12–5. Recognition of auditory monosyllables presented in noise as a function of the number of words in the test vocabulary. Each curve is for a different signal-to-noise (S/N) ratio as shown. (From Miller et al., *J. exp. Psychol.*, 1951; adapted from Garner, 1962.)

expressed in bits per word, with signal-to-noise ratio as the parameter. The marked negative slope of the three linear functions indicates clearly that the size of the list has a significant effect on the accuracy of perceptual recognition. For small word lists, the accuracy is quite high, but as the size of the list increases there is a linear decline in the percentage of words correctly identified. Also, the higher the signal-to-noise (S/N) ratio, that is, the stronger the signal with the noise, the greater the accuracy of word recognition, as might be expected. Notice, however, that when the S/N ratio is high (for example, -6 db), stimulus uncertainty has little effect for short word lists. This indicates that *when perceptual recognition is easily performed, the variable of stimulus uncertainty does not seriously affect the accuracy of judgments until the uncertainty is quite high,* for example, more than 5 bits.

Miller (1957) confirmed the finding of Miller, Heise, and Lichten in an experiment using 16 nonsense dissyllables as the stimulus words. The dissyllables in the test vocabulary were constructed by permutating four consonants around two vowels; four nonsense passages were then constructed to represent, respectively, 1, 2, 3, and 4 bits per item. These passages were presented at four different S/N values ranging from $+8$ db to -13 db. After familiarization training in which they learned the dissyllables, the subjects were instructed to write down the nonsense items as they heard them in the test trials, guessing when uncertain; during the test trials the subjects were provided with a card stating an appropriate organizational rule concerning the nonsense passage.

The results of this experiment are shown, in part, in Figure 12-6. The perception of the nonsense dissyllables (correct recognition in percent) is shown as a

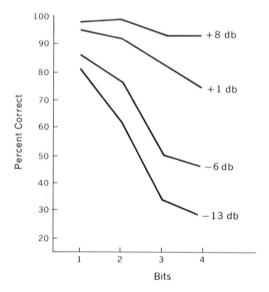

Figure 12–6.   Perception of nonsense dissyllables as a function of the average rate of input information in bits per item, with S/N ratio as the parameter. (From I. Miller, *J. exp. Psychol.,* 1957.)

function of the average rate of input information in bits per item; S/N ratio is the parameter. It is seen that as the average rate of input information is increased, there is a decrease in the percentage of items correctly identified, especially for the low S/N ratios. When perceptual recognition is easy (S/N ratio $= +8$ db), an increase in stimulus uncertainty has very little effect. The greatest overall decrease in recognition (53.0 percent) occurs between the 1-bit and 4-bit rates at a S/N ratio of -13 db. These findings firmly establish the principle that *test uncertainty affects the accuracy of perceptual recognition and that the amount of this effect is a function of the amount of noise present,* that is, the S/N ratio which determines the level of difficulty in auditory perceptual discrimination.

The results of the Miller study are in substantial agreement with the study by Sumby and Pollack (1954) performed several years earlier. While this study was concerned with the amount of information associated with the class of possible messages from the source (vocabulary size varied from 8 to 56 words), the contribution of visual factors to speech intelligibility was also studied. As might be expected, the percent words correct under noise-free conditions or high S/N ratios did not differ appreciably under the two listening situations: auditory presentation of the test words with and without visual observation of the speaker's facial movements; but, when the speech signal was low relative to the noise, for example, -30 db, the differences between the test scores for the two listening situations ranged from 40 percent for the 256-word vocabulary to 80 percent for the 8-word vocabulary. In other words, *there is a visual contribution to speech intelligibility and this contribution becomes more important as the S/N ratio decreases.* Figure 12-7 presents a graphical summary of these findings.

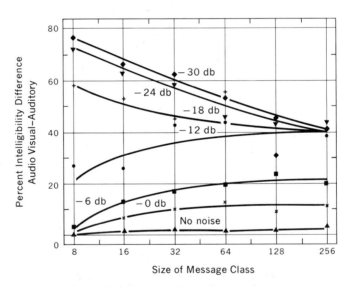

Figure 12-7. The difference between percent words correct under two listening conditions: auditory presentation alone and auditory presentation with visual observation of the speaker's facial movements, as a function of the size of the test vocabulary. The parameter on the curves in the S/N ratio. (From Sumby and Pollack, *J. acoust. Soc. Amer.,* 1954.)

Other studies bearing on the problem of perceptual recognition could be cited, but a sufficient number has been presented to establish the general principle that *when the subject knows the possible stimuli that can be presented to him and knows, also, that he can respond in as many ways as there are stimuli, then the subject's performance is a function of the uncertainty of the set of stimuli. The greater the stimulus uncertainty, the poorer the discriminatory performance.* Now we might pose a new question. What if the number of possible responses permitted the subject is reduced, that is, made less than the number of possible stimuli? What will be the effect of the uncertainty of a set of stimuli if the uncertainty of the responses is less than that of the stimuli? The answer to this question will reveal whether the critical factor in perceptual recognition is the restriction of stimuli or the restriction of concomitant responses.

Among others, Pollack (1959) has provided data on this question. In an extended series of experiments, he first determined that *the accuracy of auditory message reception in noise is essentially independent of the size of the set of possible messages, provided the size of the set of available responses is less than that of the set of messages.* This was determined by varying the size of the two sets independently, with the response uncertainty always equal to or less than the stimulus uncertainty. For example, the subject might listen to one of eight possible words and be required to select his response from among four available response alternatives. While the results showed that response uncertainty is the prime determinant of message reception, it was necessary to perform another experiment to distinguish between *response uncertainty* (the size of the set of admissable response alternatives) and *response differentiation* (the size of the set of relevant response categories that must be discriminated).

Given two to sixty-four possible messages that could be sent, the subject was required to state whether the word he heard was present in one or another of two word lists (Set A or Set B); on each trial, each word list contained half of the possible words that could be sent. For each test word, the response uncertainty was constant since only two equally likely alternatives were admissable (Set A or Set B); however, to make the correct decision the subject had to discriminate among the possible alternative words listed in Set A and Set B. Stated more simply, the subject had to discriminate correctly among a given number of words, discard the selected alternative from Set A or Set B, and report only one of two response categories. The results of this study showed that the size of the message set produced a marked effect on percent words correct. This was interpreted to mean that *the size of the set of response categories that had to be differentiated was the critical variable in establishing the accuracy of word recognition,* since the number of response categories used was always two. It is not response uncertainty per se that determines message reception, but the size of the set of required differentiable response categories that is the significant factor in perceptual recognition.

In a slightly different context, Michon (1964) has performed an experiment on the span of visual perception as affected by the temporal structure of letter groups. The procedure was to present by means of film projection groups of 12 letters, either as a whole for 1.5 sec, or in two successive units of 6 letters each for 0.75 sec, or in three successive units of 4 letters each (0.5 sec/unit), or in four successive units of 2 letters each (0.25 sec/unit). Thus, the experiment varied the temporal structure of the groups, holding the total exposure time constant at 1.5 sec and the total number of letters constant at 12. In addition, the letter groups were generated in zero-, first-, and second-order approximations of the

Dutch language.[5] The task of the subjects was to reproduce the 12 letters that were shown on the screen, paying attention to place and order.

The results of this study are presented, in part, in Figure 12-8. The number

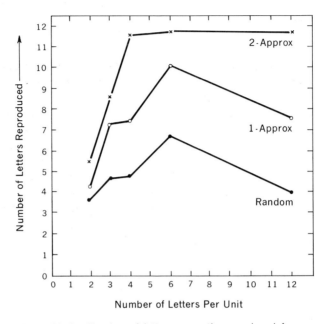

Figure 12-8. Number of letters correctly reproduced from a total of twelve as a function of subgrouping, with approximation-order to the Dutch language as the parameter. (From Michon, 1964.)

of letters reproduced is shown as a function of the number of letters per unit, with the order of approximation as the parameter. It is seen that the three orders of approximation result in significant differences in reproduction, with second-order approximation providing the greatest accuracy. (The average reproduction for the 12 letters was 4.74, 7.31, and 9.82 for the zero-, first-, and second-order approximations, respectively.) For the higher-order approximations the longer units (3 × 4, 2 × 6, and 1 × 12 letters) are reproduced more accurately. In general, the optimal reproduction is obtained when the 12 letters were shown in two groups of 6 letters each. This shows that, for reproduction, "temporal structuring will be advantageous when the complete message exceeds the amount of information that can be extracted from a simultaneous presentation (that is, span of perception) without filling out the span of memory" (p. 239).

[5] Zero-order approximation to Dutch consists of a completely random selection of characters from the Dutch alphabet; first-order approximation involves an independent selection of individual letters, but each letter has the same probability as it does in the Dutch language; second-order approximation involves digrams (two letters) in which the probability with which each letter follows the one that has just occurred is the same as in Dutch.

Verbal Learning and Remembering

So far we have considered some of the concepts of information theory in relation to experiments on reaction time and perceptual recognition; now we will consider the theory in terms of problems related to the learning process. We realize, of course, that the use of informational concepts requires that the number of stimulus categories or response categories must be known, as well as the probabilities of each of these categories. The informational concepts cannot be applied meaningfully when there is an indefinite or unknown number of alternatives in the behavioral situation. If, for example, we measure learning by a multiple-choice question with four alternative responses, we can compute the amount of information in the answer, but this is impossible if we use an essay-type question. Consequently, many of the experiments in the vast literature on learning cannot be considered from the vantage point of information theory; nevertheless, a few studies will be reviewed to show that in certain instances the informational concepts can be meaningfully applied and may even be useful theoretically.

It is now common knowledge that the rate of learning a list of nonsense syllables or words is a function of the length of the list (total number of items) to be learned. For example, it takes 0.13 min to learn a list of eight nonsense syllables to a criterion of one errorless recall, but 3.67 min to learn a list of sixteen nonsense syllables and 6 min for thirty-two syllables (Lyon, 1914). It has been estimated that for nonsense syllables the time per item increases as the square root of the number of items in the task (Thurstone, 1930). At first glance it might appear that, given the number of items in the list of words to be learned, information theory could be applied to evaluate the significance of the amount of information as an experimental variable, but the problem is not so simple. There is a complete confounding of the number of *different* items to be learned and the total amount of learning involved in the task situation, that is, the *total number* of items in the list. While the length of the list is an important factor in verbal learning, stimulus uncertainty (and, hence, response uncertainty) must also be considered. This has been shown by Adelson, Muckler, and Williams (1955).

These investigators required their subjects to learn lists of alphabetic letters; the lists always contained fifteen items, but a different number of letter alternatives was used in each list. Three basic conditions were involved in the construction of the lists: (1) random lists, in which two, four, six, and fifteen letters were arranged independently and appeared with equal probability; (2) unbalanced frequencies lists, in which two, four, and six different letters were arranged independently but were not equally probable; and (3) sequential dependencies lists, in which two, four, and six letters were used with equal probabilities, but the probability of one letter following another was not equal among the letters used. Each subject learned one of ten lists presented auditorily. He was informed of the length of the list and the number of different words from which the list was constructed. The criterion was one errorless anticipation of the entire list.

The results of this study indicate that the number of trials to learn a list of words is related linearly to the number of alternative symbols in the list. (The greater the number of alternatives, the greater the a priori uncertainty and the greater the number of trials required to learn the list.) For example, random lists with two alternatives are learned faster than lists with four, six, or fifteen alternatives. Also, a restriction on the probabilities of the alternative words in a list leads to easier learning, for example, the unbalanced frequency list with four alternatives was learned easier than the random list with four alternatives. Finally, the learning performance on the sequential dependencies list was similar to that on the other two kinds of lists. This indicates that *average uncertainty is an important parameter in learning and it makes little difference how the change in uncertainty is effected.* The mean number of trials to criterion performance for the three kinds of lists is shown in Figure 12-9 as a function of the stimulus uncertainty in the lists.

This study has indicated that information measures can serve as a useful index of the learning difficulty of verbal material. *The greater the number of alternatives*

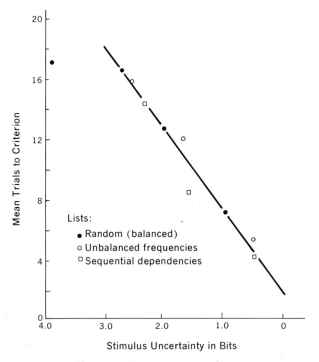

Figure 12-9. Mean criterion trials to learn a list of 15 letters as a function of the uncertainty in three kinds of lists. All lists contained 2, 4, 6, or 15 different letters. For the random lists, the letters occurred equally often; for the unbalanced frequencies lists, the letters occurred with different probabilities; and for the sequential-dependencies lists, the letters followed one another with different probabilities. (From Adelson et. al., in Quastler, *Information theory in psychology,* Glencoe, Ill.: Free Press, 1955.)

in the stimulus set and the more uniform their probability distribution, the greater the learning difficulty. The relationship of learning difficulty to stimulus uncertainty, however, need not be considered to be linear, although such a function is shown in Figure 12-9. A change in the learning criterion, the length of the list to be learned, the kind of stimulus material in the list, or the method of presentation of the learning task might well alter the obtained relationship. The main point is that stimulus uncertainty affects performance in a verbal learning situation and that concepts in information theory are useful in analyzing some of the significant variables in learning experiments.

Informational concepts are also applicable to studies on retention. This was demonstrated by Aborn and Rubenstein (1952). In this experiment the investigators developed an artificial language in which passages could easily be generated with controllable amounts of average uncertainty. There were sixteen readily pronounceable nonsense syllables of three letters each; the sixteen syllables were arranged into four groups such that the four syllables within each group started with the same letter, but the beginning letter varied from group to group.

The sixteen syllables were used to construct six passages of 30 to 32 syllables in length. The passages differed in the amount of average uncertainty, which ranged from 1 to 4 bits per syllable. In the first passage the sixteen syllables were presented randomly and equally often so that the average uncertainty was 4 bits/syllable. In the construction of the five remaining lists, sequential dependencies were introduced between successive syllables so that the average uncertainty ranged from 1.5 bits/syllable to 3 bits/syllable.

The procedure required the subjects to study a sheet of paper containing the whole language (sixteen syllables divided into four classes) for a three-day period. After that, each subject was given a sheet containing the organizational pattern of the passage on which he was to be tested and was allowed a 10-min period to study it. At the end of the study period the subject was shown, in turn, each of the six passages for a 3 min period and was required to memorize each passage. Following the 3 min memorization period, the subject recorded as much of the test passage as he could recall. There were two measures of performance: (a) the number of syllables correctly recalled, and (b) the amount of information recalled (that is, the product of the number of syllables correctly recalled and their average information content).

The results from one group of subjects in this experiment are shown in Figure 12-10. The dashed curve in Figure 12-10 shows that more syllables are correctly recalled from a verbal passage with a lower average amount of information than from a passage with a higher average amount, for example, more syllables are recalled from Passage 6 (32 bits) than from Passage 1 (120 bits) with the mean scores being, respectively, about 16.8 and 6.9. Notice that while Passage 1 has approximately four times as much information as Passage 6, the number of syllables recalled on Passage 1 is less than half that of Passage 6. In terms of the amount of information recalled, it is seen that recall is not constant for all passages. For passages 1–4 (120 to 64 bits/passage, or 4 to 2 bits/syllable), the amount

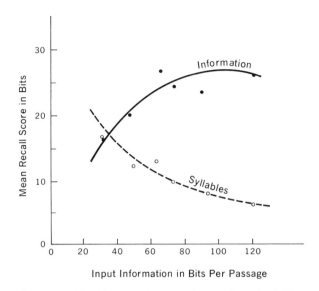

Figure 12-10. Mean recall scores for number of syllables correct and for information as a function of the informational content of the passages to be learned. (From Aborn and Rubenstein, *J. exp. Psychol.*, 1952.)

of information recalled was substantially constant but for passages 5 and 6 (48 to 32 bits/passage, or 1.5 to 1 bit/syllable), considerably less information was recalled. Thus, although an increasingly greater number of syllables was correctly recalled for passages 5 and 6, the total amount of information contained in the syllables was smaller than in the less organized passages (1–4). Rubenstein and Aborn (1954) repeated this experiment with some changes in procedure (increased study time) and obtained similar results with respect to the number of syllables recalled, but the amount of information recalled was found to increase rather than to remain essentially constant for the higher informational inputs. In both of these studies there is an indication that *the amount of information lost (forgotten) is related linearly to the average amount of information in the input.*

The final study to be mentioned in this section is that of Davis, Sutherland, and Judd (1961). These investigators were concerned with the psychological mechanisms involved in recognition and recall and tested the hypothesis that the same amount of information is transmitted in recall as in recognition. The reader may remember that when retention is measured by these two techniques, more correct responses are given in recognition than in recall, but these investigators held that this difference may have been due to the fact that in recall there is usually a greater number of alternatives from which to choose than in recognition. The stimuli used in the learning task were four lists of two-digit numbers and four lists of two-letter words selected from a pool of 90 two-digit numbers and 90 two-letter words, respectively. No number or syllable appeared in more than one list. The subjects were presented one number list and one letter list by means of a memory drum on each of four days. Each symbol was exposed for

1.5 sec and each list was presented only once. In the retention tests, each subject served under four conditions; he was required to recall as many numbers or letters as he could from each learning list and to mark on a given list all numbers or letters he thought had appeared in the original learning series. In the latter (recognition) task, the original items were imbedded in lists of numbers or letters with 30, 60, and 90 entries. For each subject, the performance scores were transformed into a measure of the amount of information transmitted under each of the four conditions.

The results of this study are presented in Table 12-3. The data show that in

Table 12-3   Average Information Transmitted per S under Recognition and Recall

Cond.	Letters				Numbers		
	Average I score in bits	Significance of difference between means	ρ		Average I score in bits	Significance of difference between means	ρ
Recog. 30	6.2 ⎫	< 0.02	0.32		5.0 ⎫	< 0.05	0.11
Recog. 60	9.9 ⎭ ⎫		0.10		9.0 ⎭ ⎫		0.21
Recog. 90	11.9 ⎫ ⎭	ns	0.35		6.6 ⎫ ⎭	ns	0.33
Recall	11.5 ⎭	ns			11.1 ⎭	< 0.01	

Source: R. Davis, N. S. Sutherland, and B. R. Judd. Information content in recognition and recall. *J. exp. Psychol.,* 1961, **61,** 422–429. By permission of the American Psychological Association.

the recognition conditions there is an increase in the amount of information transmitted, as the number of alternatives from which the selection was made increased for both letters and numbers. Also, it is seen that at least as much information was transmitted in the recall method as in recognition, thereby confirming the hypothesis that *recognition is superior to recall only because recognition usually involves a selection from fewer possible alternatives.*

The finding that information transmission tends to increase as the number of alternatives from which the selection is made increases is consistent with other data in memory experiments. Miller (1956) reported that, in immediate memory, information transmission increases as the size of the vocabulary from which the selection is made is increased. The results from these and other experiments in learning and retention demonstrate that information theory can be applied successfully to psychological problems, provided the basic conditions for the computation of the informational values are satisfied.

Information Transmission and Channel Capacity (Bivariate Uncertainty)

In the preceding part of this chapter we were concerned with univariate uncertainty, that is, the uncertainty associated with the probabilities of a given dimension or a given ensemble of events. The probability distribution was defined in terms of a single variable, or a simple method of classification, and the primary informational measure involved was the average amount of information contained in a given experimental situation. Now we will consider a probability distribution in terms of two variables; this is the case of bivariate uncertainty, which was presented in some detail earlier in this chapter in the section dealing with the more advanced concepts of information theory.

A Computational Example
on Information Transmission

Our major concern in this section will be the problem of information transmission that was presented diagrammatically in Figure 12-2. For the most part we will consider *contingent uncertainty* as a measure of information transmission, given a joint probability distribution involving a set of stimuli and responses. Although Equations 12-8 through 12-14 show some of the basic relations which hold in the bivariate situation, no indication was given at that time of the basic computational procedures which are required to compute the various terms in the equations. By referring to these equations, it may be seen that with some rearrangement of terms the amount of information transmitted, that is, $T(y;z)$ or *contingent uncertainty,* may be computed from several different formulas, such as Equations 12-8, 12-10, and 12-14. Regardless of the formula used, the answer will be the same, except for rounding errors that may be introduced. We will provide one problem and its solution using the relationship shown in Equation 12-10; detailed examples of two other approaches that could be used for solving the problem may be found in Garner and Hake (1951).

Starting with Equation 12-10, we have

$$H(z) = T(y;z) + H_y(z).$$

Rearranging terms, we obtain

$$T(y;z) = H(z) - H_y(z), \tag{12-17}$$

where $H_y(z)$ is called a *conditional uncertainty* and is the average uncertainty in the variable z when the variable y is held constant. This is obtained by solving the equation:

$$H_y(z) = -\sum_y p(y) \sum_z p_y(z) \log p_y(z). \tag{12-18}$$

Although Equation 12-17 may seem formidable, the solution is quite easily obtained, as shown following Table 12-5; Table 12-5 contains the computations for the term $H(z)$.

Assume an experimental situation in which five lines of different length are presented to a subject one at a time and are exposed for a fixed duration. Each line is presented 20 times in random order so that, in all, there is a total of one

hundred trials. The task of the subject is to identify each line as he sees it by assigning a number from 1 to 5, according to a prearranged code. For example, if the
lengths of the lines are 11, 12, 13, 14, and 15 centimeters, the lines might be assigned the numbers 1, 2, 3, 4, and 5, respectively. During the experiment, the
experimenter records the responses (numbers) given to each of the five lines.

In the analysis of data, the experimenter summarizes the judgments of his subject as in Table 12-4. The entries in Table 12-4 show the total number of times
each stimulus was identified by a particular response.

Table 12–4   Joint Occurrence of Stimuli and Responses for One Subject in a Hypothetical Visual Experiment

Response Number	Stimuli (Lines) 1	2	3	4	5	Total
1	13	3				16
2	5	11	4	2	1	23
3	2	6	10	7	1	26
4			6	10	6	22
5				1	12	13
TOTAL	20	20	20	20	20	100

Next we need to convert *each cell frequency* in Table 12-4 into a *conditional probability* by using the relationship

$$p_s(R) = \frac{n(RS)}{n(S)},$$

where R refers to responses and S to stimuli, and $p_s(R)$ is the conditional probability
of R, given S; $n(RS)$ is the number of outcomes that belong simultaneously to class
S and to class R; and $n(S)$ is the number of outcomes in class S alone. For example,
the conditional probability of Response 1, given Stimulus 1, is equal to $13/20 = 0.65$.

To solve Equation 12-17 we also need to determine $H(z)$ which depends upon
the *absolute probability* of each response. This is obtained from

$$p(R) = \frac{n(R)}{N},$$

where the probability of a given response (R) is given by $p(R)$; $n(R)$ is the frequency
of that response; and N refers to the total number of responses. For example, the
probability of Response 1 is equal to $16/100 = 0.16$.

The cells of Table 12-5 show the data of Table 12-4 converted into *conditional*
probabilities; the marginal totals for the response categories in Table 12-4 are
shown as *absolute probabilities* in the column $p(R)$.

We may now proceed to solve Equation 12-17. The value for $H(z)$ has already

Table 12-5   Conditional Probabilities for the Hypothetical Data of Table 12-4

Response Number	Stimuli (Lines) 1	2	3	4	5	p(R)	−p(R) log p(R)
1	0.65	0.15				0.16	0.4230
2	0.25	0.55	0.20	0.10	0.05	0.23	0.4877
3	0.10	0.30	0.50	0.35	0.05	0.26	0.5053
4		0.30	0.50	0.50	0.30	0.22	0.4806
5				0.05	0.60	0.13	0.3826
						1.00	$H(z) =$ 2.2792 bits

been calculated in Table 12-5 and is 2.2792 bits. Before calculating the value of $H_y(z)$ we may simplify Equation 12-18 by noting that each stimulus was presented equally often (20 times) so that $p(y)$ is a constant. This permits us to write:

$$H_y(z) = -\frac{1}{S} \sum_y \sum_z p_y(z) \log p_y(z), \qquad (12\text{-}19)$$

where S is the number of alternative stimuli in the ensemble (5).

Substituting the appropriate values in Equation 12-19, we obtain

$$H_y(z) = -\frac{1}{5} (0.65 \log 0.65 + 0.15 \log 0.15 + \ldots + 0.05 \log 0.05 + 0.60 \log 0.60)$$

$$= \frac{1}{5}(0.4040 + 0.4105 + \ldots + 0.2161 + 0.4422) = \frac{1}{5}(7.1016)$$

$$= 1.4203 \text{ bits.}$$

Returning to Equation 12-17 and substituting,

$$T(y;z) = H(z) - H_y(z)$$
$$= 2.2792 - 1.4203$$
$$= 0.8589 \text{ bit.}$$

Our answer, $T(y;z) = 0.8589$ bit, indicates the *contingent uncertainty* in the particular experimental situation we described earlier; in other words, it indicates the amount of information transmitted by the system under study.

In recent years many studies have been performed in psychology in which the contingent uncertainty has been computed, particularly in the areas of sensory psychology and engineering psychology. The model in this case is usually one of considering a set of stimuli as the input to a human subject, the set of responses as the output, and the nervous system as the communication system. As in our example, the contingent uncertainty is computed from the two-dimensional matrix, in which stimuli comprise one variable and responses, the other; thus the information transmitted may be considered a measure of the human subject's ability to discriminate among stimuli. In the example given, discrimination was poor with less than 1 bit transmitted; this is less than the amount of information that would be transmitted if two lines were discriminated perfectly. For a given system and a given set of circumstances, the maximum amount of information transmitted is taken as the channel capacity of the system. Since the amount of information transmitted cannot exceed the uncertainty in the set of stimuli, channel capacity can be established only by running tests that exceed the transmission characteristics of the system under study. If stimulus uncertainty is provided which is less than channel capacity, perfect transmission would result, given ideal conditions. When the stimulus uncertainty exceeds the subject's ability to transmit the information (exceeds his discriminatory ability), the amount of information transmitted remains constant regardless of how great the stimulus uncertainty becomes. (See Figure 12-3.)

Before proceeding to a review of a number of studies dealing with information transmission, an additional comment must be made concerning contingent uncertainty. Specifically, the computation of the measure does not require that either variable (input or output) be metric; if either or both variables are metric, this does not invalidate the analysis. This is one of the properties of the contingent uncertainty which has made it so extremely useful. Other properties relate to concepts in correlational analysis and in analysis of variance, but these lie outside the scope of the present treatment (Garner, 1962).

Absolute Judgments in Unidimensional Discrimination Tasks

The problem of information transmission for various sensory continua under a wide variety of conditions has been studied quite extensively in psychology. Several reviews of selected studies are now available, for example, Alluisi (1957), Attneave (1959a), Broadbent (1958), Corso (1967), Garner (1962) and Miller (1956). For this reason, an exhaustive review of the literature in this section is neither feasible nor desirable; instead, a limited number of studies will be presented to establish some of the fundamental principles of information transmission and to demonstrate the range of problems that has been investigated within the framework of information theory.

In an early study, Hake and Garner (1951) studied information transmission in a situation which required the subject to make judgments of the position of a pointer on a line. There were four different numbers of possible pointer positions (5, 10, 20, and 50) within a single interpolation interval on the scale; also, under one set of instructions the subjects restricted their responses to values given by the discrete positions on the scale and, under another set of instructions, they were permitted to use 101 different responses (zero to 100) regardless of the number of stimulus categories. There were two main findings in this experiment. (1) *The amount of information transmitted was least for the 5 pointer positions (approximately 2.3 bits) and remained essentially constant for the 10, 20, and 50 pointer positions (approximately*

3.2 bits or about 9 points along a line), regardless of the instructional set. This established the validity of the concept of channel capacity for human subjects in a perceptual discrimination task. (2) *The two different response conditions (instructional sets) gave the same result in terms of information transmission,* but the unlimited response condition yielded greater errors. This indicated that contingent uncertainty is a stable measure, easily interpretable, and not affected by the magnitude of errors. These properties make contingent uncertainty a useful measure in dealing with discriminatory ability in perceptual tasks.

In the field of hearing, information transmission has been determined for the single auditory dimensions of pitch and loudness. Pollack (1952) found that on the average human subjects could transmit *a maximum of only 2.3 bits,* given a set of eight alternative tones ranging in frequency from 100 cps to as high as 8000 cps. This is equivalent to perfect discrimination for five categories of frequency and seems rather small for a human subject with normal hearing, particularly when these results are contrasted with data which show that at moderate loudness levels there are approximately 1800 just noticeable differences in pitch for pure tones between 20 and 20,000 cps. These findings, however, are not discrepant. There are two different judgments (or, perhaps, two different processes) involved: one involves an absolute identification of frequency while the other involves a relative judgment in frequency discrimination. There is no reason to expect that the same results would be obtained in the two situations.

The results of this study further establish the appropriateness of the concept of channel capacity as applied to perceptual discrimination, since increasing the number of frequencies beyond five had no effect upon the amount of information transmitted. Furthermore, as shown in Figure 12-11, it made little difference

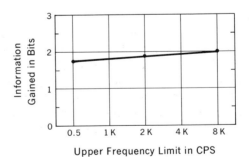

Figure 12-11. Information transmission as a function of the frequency range covered by the stimulus categories. The lower frequency limit was always fixed at 100 cps. (From Pollack, *J. acoust. Soc. Amer.,* 1952.)

whether the frequency range covered by the eight alternative tones extended from 100 to 500 cps or from 100 to 8000 cps, or whether the frequencies of the alternatives were evenly spaced in pitch over this range. This study not only adds to our knowledge of auditory discrimination, but is an excellent example in which the empirical findings with respect to a problem do not conform to what our "common sense" answer would have been.

Pollack (1953) later tried different techniques to improve information transmission in the frequency dimension, but none of the techniques produced appreciable changes in the subject's ability to discriminate among the test tones. Hartman (1954), however, found that several weeks of *practice* could lead to improvement, provided there was a sufficiently large separation in frequency among the alternative stimuli.

In a study dealing with absolute judgments of loudness, Garner (1953) used a 1000 cps tone and presented the subject with 4, 5, 6, 7, 10, or 20 stimuli covering the intensity range from 15 to 110 db (re 10^{-16} watts/sq cm). The information transmission, averaged for several subjects, was found to be approximately 2.1 bits, that is, between four and five tones, and may be interpreted as supporting the earlier results on frequency discrimination. These and other studies in audition clearly demonstrate that *there is a maximal level of performance in perceptual discrimination which can be stated quantitatively and that the equivalent number of categories which can be perfectly discriminted by a human subject is quite small.*

Studies in vision using information measures are somewhat fewer than in audition, but some experiments involving hue, brightness, and areal size have been reported. Halsey and Chapanis (1951) presented various numbers of categories of single spectral hues (7 mμ bandwidth) to two or four subjects; holding intensity constant at 2.8 candles/sq meter, they found that a selected series of twelve such hues could be discriminated with 96 percent accuracy. In a later study, Chapanis and Halsey (1956) estimated the information transmission in hue discrimination to be about 3.6 bits, or the equivalent of about twelve different categories. Munsell hues at maximal saturation yielded approximately the same value of information transmission (3.5 bits) for a set of twenty-five stimuli (Conover, 1959).

As part of a larger study, Eriksen and Hake (1955) also used Munsell papers to determine the accuracy of discrimination of hue, brightness, and areal size. For the hue and brightness series, ⅞ in. squares of Munsell papers were used, while the stimuli for the size series were cut from dark gray paper and varied from ⅛ in. sq to 2⅞ in. sq. There were twenty sizes of squares, twenty hues ranging from red through orange, yellow, green, blue, and red-purple, and seventeen brightness values ranging from 1 through 9 in the Munsell system. For all the series, the test patches were mounted in the center of a 3-in. square of white cardboard. Each of six subjects made 100 judgments to each stimulus in the three series, with as many response categories permitted as there were stimuli per series. The results indicated that the best information transmission was 3.08 bits for hue (a value slightly less than that obtained in later studies by other investigators who used practiced subjects); for size, the information transmission was 2.84 bits; and for brightness, 2.34 bits. This indicates that *the maximum number of stimuli which could be selected from the three dimensions of hue, size, and brightness to satisfy the criterion of perfect discriminability under conditions of absolute discrimination is eight, seven, and five, respectively.* The number for brightness (five) is essentially the same as that for the pitch and loudness dimensions. This suggests that the three psychological characteristics of pitch, loudness, and brightness are unidimensional, or at least involve judgments based upon psychological processes that are approximately similar in complexity.

Studies on information transmission in the other sensory modalities are practically nonexistent. Only a few scattered reports have appeared in the psychological literature. One study was performed on the channel capacity for concentrations of salt and sucrose (Beebe-Center, Rogers, and O'Connell, 1955). There were 3, 5, 9, and 17 different concentrations of salt solutions, ranging from 0.3 to 34.7 gm NaCl per 100 cc tap water, in equal subjective steps. The maximal amount of information transmitted was approximately 1.7 bits, or slightly less than *four discriminable concentrations*. For sucrose, a maximum of 1.69 bits of information transmission was obtained. This indicates that *in terms of absolute judgments the taste sense (for salt and for sucrose) is relatively poorer in discrimination than vision or hearing.*

The ability of the human subject to transmit information about odor intensity was studied by Engen and Pfaffmann (1959). Four odorants were used (amyl acetate, n-heptanal, n-heptane, and phenylethyl alcohol) and were prepared in a geometric dilution series of five steps (100, 50, 25, 12.5, and 6.5 percent) with Mallinkrodt's Benzyl Benzoate (USP XIII, 387 control TSN-1) as the diluent. After the subject was given a practice period in which he learned to identify the rank order of the intensities of a given substance by sniffing the contents of full test tubes arranged in order of dilution, each of the five stimuli was presented singly in a random sequence and the subject was required to identify its rank order among the five stimuli. Fifty judgments were made for each stimulus value by each of five subjects (except for n-heptanal, N = 4) who were informed of the correct rank order immediately after each judgment. The results of this study indicate that the information transmission for the four sets of odorants was slightly more than 1.5 bits, or about *three levels of intensity*. Small but reliable improvements in discrimination were obtained by increasing the intensity level of the stimulus series and by increasing the size of the step between stimuli; increasing the number of alternative stimuli beyond five had no effect. Data on three new subjects indicated that with practice information transmission could be increased to approximately 1.9 bits, or about *four* levels of intensity. The practice effects are shown in Figure 12-12.

Some data are also available for cutaneous sensitivity (Geldard, 1961). Although the findings in the cutaneous modality have not been obtained directly from research stemming from information theory, the investigation of the possibilities of cutaneous communication has provided data that are relevant to the present topic. The primary dimensions of mechanical vibration that may be used for a cutaneous language are location of stimulation, intensity of stimulation, and duration of stimulation. (Frequency of stimulation is a fourth possible dimension, but its interaction with intensity creates problems which indicate that it may be best to ignore this dimension in a practical system.) It has been determined that a good observer can discriminate perfectly among *seven vibrators* spaced on the ventral rib cage (2.8 bits), *three intensities* of stimulation between 50 and 400 microns of "trip-hammer action" of the vibrators (about 1.6 bits), and approxi-

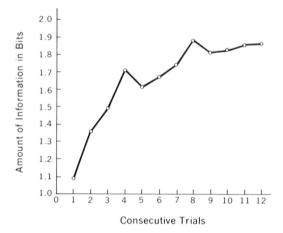

Figure 12–12. The amount of information transmitted in 12 consecutive trials in which absolute judgments were made of odor intensity. (From Engen and
Pfaffmann, *J. exp. Psychol.,* 1959.)

mately *five durations* of stimulation between 0.1 sec and 2.0 sec (about 2.3 bits).
(The reader may be interested to know that after 65 hours of training on a three-
dimensional cutaneous system, a subject can receive sentences, transmitted at the
rate of 38 five-letter words per min, with 90 percent accuracy. If the same inter-
word and intraword spacing is used as in the international Morse code, a maximal
transmission rate of 67 words per minute is theoretically possible—a speed more
than three times that of proficient Morse code.)

The channel capacities calculated in the studies which have been cited in this
chapter vary from 1.5 bits for odor intensity to approximately 3.25 bits per signal
for points-on-a-line. This range is equivalent to perfect identification of about
three to ten different stimuli of a given class. Several factors may account for this
variation in channel capacity for absolute judgments on a single stimulus continuum. These have already been pointed out, but a summary at this point may be
useful. First, there are intersubject differences between experiments which may be
accentuated by differing amounts of practice *Subjects selected randomly from a given
population may vary in the amount of information transmitted for a given dimension by a
factor of 2,* approximately (Alluisi, 1957). Second, the range of stimulus values
used in the various experiments differs from dimension to dimension. In general,
*the greater the range of stimulus values, the greater the amount of information transmitted
in bits per stimulus.* Third, the number of permissible response categories in relation
to the number of stimulus categories was not held constant throughout all experiments. *When the number of response categories is equal to or greater than the number of
stimulus categories, the amount of information transmitted is greater than when the response
categories are fewer than the stimulus categories.* Fourth, the method of spacing stimuli
along the stimulus continuum was not consistent from experiment to experiment.

The use of nonoptimal spacing between stimulus categories tends to reduce the amount of information transmitted (Garner, 1953).

Although these four possibilities may account for some of the observed differences in information transmission, it may well be that some stimulus dimensions are more efficiently handled than others when discrimination is required on an absolute basis. Thus, the obtained differences in information transmission may represent fundamental differences in psychological processes, rather than experimental artifacts. Whether we consider the range in information transmission from three or four to ten categories to be "remarkably narrow" (Miller, 1956, p. 86), there is little question that the concept of channel capacity is a valid one for describing the behavior of human subjects in discrimination tasks. The evidence points to a limitation in the information-handling capacity of man, even with unidimensional variables, but the source of the limitation is not clear. It may be a function of learning, or it may reveal some peculiarities in the design of the human nervous system (including the brain). Nevertheless, *man's ability to make absolute judgments is limited; the capacity for making unidimensional judgments is relatively small; and the differences in capacity among sensory attributes varies by a factor of about two-and-a-half to one.*

Absolute Judgments in Multidimensional Discrimination Tasks

However, the perceptive student may ask, "If my channel capacity is so small, how do you account for my ability to recognize over a hundred popular tunes, or recognize two thousand other students, or identify four hundred different food dishes?" Certainly our experience has shown that we must discriminate among more than ten different objects or events in the course of our daily lives. How is this accomplished?

The answer would seem to be in the number of dimensions that are involved in a given situation. To test this hypothesis, we would need to ascertain that stimuli can be more accurately discriminated if they differ on several dimensions than if they differ on only one or, stated slightly differently, we would expect more information to be transmitted in a given modality when stimuli are manipulated in two or three dimensions than when one dimension is involved. Furthermore, if channel capacity is increased when a subject must respond to two dimensions of a stimulus, such as hue and brightness, does the subject transmit all of the information he transmitted when he judged each dimension separately, that is, does the information transmission for the two dimensions tested together equal the sum of the information transmission for the two dimensions tested separately?

The evidence indicates that this is not so. Pollack (1953) in a two-dimensional test varied the frequency and intensity of a series of tones. The frequency was varied in five equal logarithmic steps between 125 and 7000 cps; the intensity was varied in five equal loudness steps between loudness levels of 20 and 90 db. This provided a total of twenty-five stimulus tones. The information transmission for the simultaneous pitch and loudness judgments was 3.1 bits. When these same stimuli were presented in a unidimensional situation, the information transmission for pitch was 1.8 bits and for loudness, 1.7 bits. Observe that the sum of the uni-dimensional tasks presented alone is 3.5 bits, and exceeds the information trans-mission in the two-dimensional situation (3.1 bits). However, when the two-dimensional unique responses were analyzed into separate components of fre-quency and intensity, the information transmission per dimensions was less: 1.6 bits for frequency and 1.3 bits for intensity, with a total of 2.9 bits. This indicates that *when two dimensions are used, there is an increase in information transmission over one dimension, but at a decrease in the amount of information transmitted per dimension.* These results are summarized in Figure 12-13.

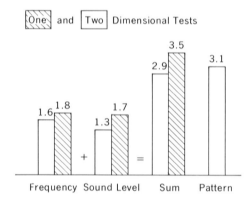

Figure 12-13. Comparison of information trans-mission in one-dimensional and two-dimensional tasks in auditory discrimination. (From Sumby and Pollack, *J. acoust. Soc. Amer.,* 1954.)

Conclusions similar to those in audition were obtained in the visual experiment previously mentioned (Eriksen and Hake, 1955). In addition to the initial series of judgments involving the single dimensions of hue, brightness, and size, there was a second series of judgments on stimuli which varied in two dimensions: size-hue, size-brightness, and hue-brightness. The information transmitted for the two-dimensional stimuli was, respectively, 3.55, 2.98, and 3.76 bits. Since the informa-tion transmission for the single dimensions of hue, brightness, and size was 3.08, 2.34, and 2.84 bits, respectively, it is seen that the information transmission in the two-dimensional situation is more than that for either of the components taken singly, but less than that of the two components when summed. In a third series of judgments, all three variables were manipulated simultaneously. The infor-mation transmission was 4.11 bits, or nearly perfect transmission of twenty stimuli. Table 12-6 contains the transmission results of the three series of judgments and shows the equivalent number of absolutely discriminable stimuli under each set of conditions.

The data on taste (Beebe-Center, Rogers, and O'Connell, 1955) also support

Table 12-6   Information Transmission for Visual Stimuli Varying in One, Two, or Three Dimensions

Stimulus Dimensions	Information Transmission (Bits)	Equivalent No. of Absolutely Discriminable Stimuli
Size	2.84	7.19
Hue	3.08	8.45
Brightness	2.34	5.06
Size-Hue	3.55	11.90
Size-Brightness	2.98	7.89
Hue-Brightness	3.76	13.55
Size-Hue-Brightness	4.11	17.28

Source: C. W. Eriksen and H. W. Hake. Multidimensional stimulus difference and accuracy of discrimination. *J. exp. Pyschol.,* 1955, **50,** 153–160. By permission of the American Psychological Association.

the generalization that the *total information transmission for a two-dimensional judgment is substantially higher than that obtained for either stimulus dimension judged alone, but the total is not so large as the sum of the information transmission for each dimension used separately.* For sixteen compound solutions (four concentrations of salt and four of sucrose combined in all possible ways), the total information transmission was 2.25 bits. This is less than the sum of the dimensions tested alone (1.70 bits for salt and 1.69 bits for sucrose), which is equal to 3.39. The two contingent uncertainties for salt and sucrose computed from the matrix of multidimensional judgments were 1.14 and 1.00 bits, respectively; thus, while the multidimensional situation produces greater information transmission, less information is transmitted per dimension than in the unidimensional situation.

This is also shown by the data of Klemmer and Frick (1953) who had subjects judge the position of a dot in a square. This is a two-dimensional situation, as the horizontal and vertical components must be identified. Since the channel capacity for judging points on a line is approximately 3.25 bits (Hake and Garner, 1951), the position of the dot in a square would seem to depend upon two such successive judgments and the channel capacity would be expected to be 6.5 bits. The obtained information transmission was approximately 4.4 bits of uncertainty, considerably less than the sum of the vertical and horizontal line estimations.

The same finding was obtained by Hawkes (1962) who studied the number of possible absolute identifications of electrical cutaneous stimuli varying in both stridence (subjective tactual intensity) and duration. Maximum transmission was obtained with combinations of four stridence levels and four durations in which experienced subjects attained a channel capacity of 2.97 bits. This is slightly less than the sum of 1.58 bits for four stimulus durations and 1.52 bits for four stridence levels obtained in an earlier single dimensional study—the sum equals 3.10 bits.

Some experiments have been performed in which more than two dimensions of stimulus situation were varied; the visual experiment of Eriksen and Hake (1955) has already been described. Engen and Pfaffmann (1960) studied olfactory discrimination by having subjects identify the qualities of odorants which varied in kind, intensity, and number of stimulus categories. With as many as thirty-six alternative stimuli, maximal information transmission did not exceed 4.03 bits; this value was obtained when twenty-four different odorants were used.

In one auditory study (Pollack and Ficks, 1954) as many as eight simultaneous dimensions characterized the stimulus situation: alternating noise and tone. The dimensions included the frequency of the tone, the frequency range of the noise, the intensity of the tone, the intensity of the noise, the duration of the tonal signal, the rate of interruption, the percentage of time the tone was presented rather than noise, and the apparent direction of the sound source. Each of these variables had two values, but in one experimental condition six of the eight dimensions were used with two, three, or five steps per dimension. Excluding the poorest condition of discrimination that involved the six dichotomous dimensions, the total information transmission for all of the conditions was nearly the same at approximately 7.0 bits, or about 128 absolutely discriminable auditory signals. The results of this experiment, when considered with the findings of a later study (Sumby, Chambliss, and Pollack, 1958), indicate that *maximum information transmission will be obtained when many stimulus variables are used, but with no more than three alternatives for a given dimension, rather than when few variables are used with many alternatives.*

These studies with multidimensional stimuli begin to approach to a limited degree the complexities of discrimination that are met in daily life. In the linguistic analysis of human speech sounds, for example, it is estimated that there are about eight or ten dimensions (*distinctive features*) that distinguish one phoneme from another. These features are usually binary, for example, oral and nasal consonants, or tertiary, for example, front, back, and middle phonemes. Five of these features were studied by forming sixteen different nonsense syllables in which each of sixteen consonants was placed before the vowel *a* (as in *father*) (Miller and Nicely, 1955). The features were voicing, nasality, affriction (degree of closure of the articulators), duration, and place of articulation. All features had two alternatives, except place of articulation, which had three (front, back, middle). In one part of this study, the nonsense syllables were presented under several different signal-to-noise ratios which ranged from -18 to $+12$ db. It was found that each of the features had a different value of maximum information transmission and that these values were attained at different S/N ratios, for example, voicing gave the greatest transmission with approximately 0.95 bit at 0 db S/N, while nasality reached a maximal value of about 0.53 bit at $+6$ db S/N. The total information transmission for the entire response matrix was 3.55 bits at $+12$ db S/N, which is *less than the sum of the contingent uncertainties* computed directly for the several dimensions (4.21 bits). Nevertheless, the information transmission is approximately equivalent to perfect discrimination among twelve stimulus categories from a possible maximum of sixteen. Numerous other studies have been done in the area of speech transmission, but this example should serve to illustrate that the concepts of information theory can be applied directly to problems of voice communication.

Rate of Information Transmission

Up to this point we have considered the concept of channel capacity in terms of the information transmitted per signal. However, it is possible to compute a related measure, the average information transmitted per second, if the signals or events are presented at a known and constant rate. This may be stated in equation form,

$$R_{IT} = nH(S), \tag{12-20}$$

where R_{IT} is the rate of information transmission, n is the number of stimuli presented per unit time, and $H(S)$ is the uncertainty per stimulus presented.

While mathematically the two terms in Equation 12-20 can vary in a reciprocal manner to maintain a constant value of R_{IT}, the experimental evidence indicates that human subjects do not function in this manner. There are limitations imposed by the time variable which produce high rates of information transmission only when there are few stimuli per unit of time, with relatively large amounts of stimulus uncertainty per presentation. According to Hyman's data (1953), it is unlikely that similarly high rates can be obtained using many stimuli per unit time with relatively small amounts of stimulus uncertainty per presentation. The concept of channel capacity, therefore, does not appear to be of general significance in relation to the rate of information transmission in human subjects.

Among others, Klemmer and Muller (1953) have shown directly that *time and stimulus uncertainty are not interchangeable* in Equation 12-20. These investigators required that their subjects press keys in response to flashing lights, both the presentation rate and stimulus uncertainty of which were systematically altered. The results indicated that, regardless of the presentation rate, the maximum value of R_{IT} was obtained when the stimulus uncertainty per presentation was at its maximum. Also, no matter what the amount of stimulus uncertainty, the optimum rate of stimulus presentation was found to be two or three stimuli per second.

A specific example of a study on the rate of information transmission in human subjects is that of Alluisi and Muller (1958). In one experiment, the subjects were shown the ten numbers, 0 to 9, and were required to respond in one series of trials by saying the number, and in another series by pressing one of ten numbered keys. The results indicated that when the subjects reported verbally, there were no errors up to the maximum signal input: 6 bits per second. For the manual response, the maximum R_{IT} was only slightly more than 3 bits per second. The results of this study, combined with the findings of others, reveal that *the kind of stimulus, the kind of response, and the specific relationships between stimuli and responses impose a limit on channel capacity.* The coding efficiency of a system has been studied extensively under the heading of *S-R compatibility* (Alluisi and Martin, 1958; Deininger and Fitts, 1955; Fitts and Deininger, 1954; Fitts and Seeger, 1953). The main finding has been that *S-R compatibility is a function of practice and that there is a direct relationship between S-R compatibility and the rate of information transmission.* Thus, while information variables such as stimulus uncertainty affect information transmission, these are not the only variables that are significant in determining the levels of human performance.

Some calculations have been made which provide us with theoretical estimates of the informational capacity of the major sensory systems. In audition, the estimates have been made by computing the number of discriminable tones per second and, after setting forth some highly tentative assumptions, applying the basic equations of information theory. *The maximum capacity for the human ear is calculated to be 8000 bits/sec for random sound and 10,000 bits/sec for loud sounds* (Jacobson, 1951). Spoken English is estimated maximally as roughly 50 bits/sec, given a 150,000 word vocabulary and a speaking rate of 300 words/min; musical listening gives a maximum transmission rate of 70 bits/sec, as a crude approximation. From this, it is seen that *the brain can process less than one percent of the information that our ears can pass.* With about 29,000 ganglion cells per ear and a maximum capacity of 10,000 bits/sec, the average rate of information transfer over a single nerve fiber is about 0.3 bit/sec.

In vision, the channel capacity is estimated as 1000 bits/sec for each nerve fiber, or 100 bits/100 msec. With an order of magnitude of one million channels in the optic nerve, this would yield a maximum of 100 million bits of information every 100 msec (Singer, 1959). Even if this figure were reduced by a factor of one hundred to account for nonindependence of nerve fibers, this would still be a tremendous amount of information. Any figure with even one million bits of information cannot be interpreted by the brain in a 100-msec period. Given a newspaper full of words, the rate of information absorption is only five or six words/sec (Pierce and Karlin, 1957). It may be concluded, therefore, that in vision and audition *the receptor systems are capable of transmitting data at rates enormously greater than those which the brain is capable of processing.*

Additional Applications of Information Theory in Psychology

There are numerous other areas in psychology in which the concepts of information theory have been applied, but the limitations of space and the complexity of the material preclude their inclusion in this textbook. It might serve a useful purpose, however, if some of the general, more typical areas were at least mentioned in this section in order to direct the interested student into the more advanced literature.

The advent of information theory has provided a "new look" to the classic problems of *visual and auditory form perception* (Alluisi, 1960; Attneave, 1954; Attneave and Arnoult, 1956; Corso, 1957). Miller and Frick (1949) and Frick and Miller (1951) have shown that information theory can be applied to the *operant conditioning* of a rat in a Skinner box. Experiments on *concept formation* are basically experiments involving discriminatory behavior and, accordingly, can be handled within the framework of information theory (Garner, 1962; Lordahl, 1961; Simon and Kotovsky, 1963). While it is not immediately obvious, decision making and information transmission are in essence similar activities, and uncertainty measures may be used in the analysis of *decision behavior* (Irwin and Smith, 1957; Lewis and Kanareff, 1959; Quastler, 1956). Information theory has also been applied to decision processes in *group situations,* particularly those involving different communication networks (Edwards, 1961; Shaw, 1961; Shaw, Rothschild, and Strickland, 1957). Finally, information theory has been utilized in analyzing problems in *clinical behavior* (Miller, 1960; Shands, 1959), in *multiple prediction* (Bendig, 1959), in *engineering psychology* (Krulee, 1954), in *motivation* (Welford, 1962), and in *attention* (Broadbent, 1962).

It should also be clear that the contents of this chapter have been restricted to one aspect of information theory, namely, as it applies to a noiseless or noisy communication system with a *discrete* source of messages that are independent or nonindependent. Information theory also applies to the transmission of *continuous* signals, that is, to signals that are not temporally ordered selections from a finite set of possible elements; in this case, the source makes selections from a *continuum* of elements. While there are applications of the continuous theory in the behavioral sciences, the applications to date have been of minor importance and, therefore, have not been considered; nevertheless, the student should realize that the continuous theory is available for the solution of certain classes of problems.

A Closing Comment

Although information theory has tremendous utility, it should always be applied with caution to problems in psychology. For example, there is a serious limitation in the use of information theory in problems involving operant or classical conditioning: *the concepts of uncertainty analysis may be applied legitimately only to stationary sequences,* that is, sequences in which the statistical parameters do not change with time. At best, this condition is only approximated in a learning experiment. Also, *as the length of dependencies increases in the response sequence, it becomes increasingly difficult to obtain adequate samples* from which to estimate the probabilities required in the computational equations. Another problem arises in using transmitted information as a measure of channel capacity; this measure of efficiency is related inversely to the number of errors that are made. However, *the measure disregards available information about the subject's performance since it does not consider either the direction or size of errors* made by the subject in a particular experimental situation. Despite these limitations, information theory has provided a vigorous impetus to certain kinds of psychological research, particularly in the areas of perception and psycho-physics. It provides a new way of analyzing the relations between stimuli and responses and has generated new views on classical problems. Information theory provides a powerful methodological approach to the solution of a wide variety of psychological problems and, as such, is a theory with which contemporary psychologists and students should be thoroughly familiar.

Chapter 13

ADAPTATION-LEVEL THEORY

Orientation

In considering the physical aspects of the environment in Chapter 2, stress was placed on the fundamental dimensions of physics and their quantitative measurement. The use of these dimensions in various behavioral situations was also emphasized. In Chapter 7, psychophysical judgments were considered and later, in Chapters 8 and 11, the relationships obtaining between physical and psychological dimensions were discussed. In Chapter 9, attention was directed to the problem of sensory adaptation within a given modality. Now we turn to a consideration of adaptation-level theory which embodies many of the concepts contained in these earlier chapters.

For the most part, the psychological problems described in this volume have been studied through the dimensional approach. Loudness has been related to the sound pressure of sound waves; hue has been related to electromagnetic wavelength; saltiness has been related to the concentration of saline solutions. We have differentiated continually between both physical and psychological variables. Many behavioral phenomena have been measured in appropriate physical units and, provided the distinction is maintained between the two classes of variables (physical and psychological), there should be little or no terminological confusion in considering these types of problems.

In Chapter 12, we studied information theory and the manner in which psychophysical judgments were made in terms of identifying specific objects and events on the basis of *absolute* judgments of given stimulus dimensions. However, just as we saw in Chapter 2 that concepts of relativity have entered into physics, concepts of *behavioral relativity* may be found in contemporary psychology within the framework of *adaptation-level theory* (Helson, 1947). In the physical theory of relativity, measurements of mass, space, and time are relative to the speed of light; in adaptation-level theory, behavior is relative to the present state of the organism. Fechnerian psychophysics initiated the concept that judgments of stimulus differences are dependent upon the magnitude of the standard against which judgments are made, that is, the differential threshold, but this relativistic notion considered only one aspect of the behavioral situation—the standard stimulus. Furthermore, classical psychophysics considered the judgments to be derived from a fixed zero point for all stimulus magnitudes presented in a given sensory modality, that is, the absolute threshold. Adaptation-level theory provides for a *changing* zero point from which the measurements of behavior are made; it provides an explicit statement of the frame of reference to which the behavioral phenomena are relative.

In this chapter, then, we will study adaptation-level theory and consider some of the related data. We will extend our discussion of the factors involved in behavior beyond the quantities that characterize the stimulus and we will include those quantities that specify the state of the organism. This apparent change in emphasis, however, does not invalidate the S-R approach that was presented in the earlier chapters; it simply adds another class of variables which must be considered in the prediction of behavior. Accordingly, this approach should permit a closer approximation between theory and empirical data and, since it involves a greater number of variables, it should be capable of encompassing a broader range of behavioral phenomena; nor does adaptation-level theory reject the presuppositions of science which were presented in Chapter 1. Behavior is still viewed as lawful, ordered, and predictable, with regularities postulated between S and R variables; these regularities, however, are founded upon factors that prevail in the organism as well as in the situation and that produce changes in the organism's level of psychological adaptation. As the adaptation or adjustment level is changed, corresponding changes may be observed (measured) in psychophysical judgments, psychometric ratings, perception, cognition, attitudes, and other behavioral phenomena. This chapter will consider adaptation-level theory as it applies to some of the main areas in psychology and will present the principles of the theory as unifying concepts across such substantively diverse fields as sensory processes, perception, learning, and personality.

The Concept of Behavioral Adaptation

The classical concept of adaptation has its roots in two disciplines: biology and physiology. In biology, the general meaning of adaptation relates to the adjustment of a particular species to the environmental conditions under which it must live if it is to continue to survive. In physiology, adaptation has the meaning presented in Chapter 9, that is, it relates to a change in the magnitude of a sensory or motor response as a consequence of prolonged stimulation or uninterrupted responding by some bodily part. In both instances there is a modification by which the organism or species is adjusted to meet the conditions that are present in the environment at that time. One special class of biological adaptation has been called "*homeostasis*," referring to the continuous physiological processes in animals through which bodily equilibrium is maintained. Homeostasis enables animals to react against external (environmental) conditions and internal (environmental) processes; it produces a state of equilibrium in the living body with respect to certain functions and to the chemical compositions of tissues and fluids, for example, temperature, heart rate, blood pressure, water content, and blood sugar. Homeostatic processes tend to compensate for changes in the body brought about by changes in the external and internal environment; they negate the disturbing forces in the environment and thereby maintain the bodily functions at normal levels.

Although the concept of homeostasis has been extended to higher levels of activity, such as intellectual behavior (Dempsey, 1951), the emphasis in homeostasis differs from that in *behavioral adaptation*. The major difference is that homeostasis tends to maintain relatively fixed levels of bodily activity around optimal values, for example, blood temperature at 98.6°F, whereas behavioral adaptation avoids fixed constants and stresses *changing* levels of adjustment to internal and external factors. In addition, the concept of behavioral adaptation is defined in *quantitative, operational* terms. All responses of the organism are then referable to this neutral point or *point of psychological equilibrium;* adaptation-level theory asserts that this state of equilibrium is the reference point from which behavior is measured and predicted. Behavioral adaptation or adjustment occurs not with respect to a fixed value of stimulation, as in homeostasis, but to a range of stimuli such that those stimuli above and below this critical region tend to be accentuated, while those within the critical region tend to be de-emphasized. In this way, behavioral adaptation is a *dynamic* process which neutralizes certain stimulus conditions, but which, unlike homeostasis, tends to enhance the effectiveness of other stimuli lying outside this range.

This is one of the postulates of adaptation-level theory, that is, that *all behavior is centered around the adaptation level* or the region of psychological equilibrium of the organism. It is also proposed that *for each state of adaptation there is a corresponding level of behavioral activity* and, conversely, *for each level of behavioral activity there is a corresponding state of adaptation*. These activities involve essentially all of man's organs of adjustment: receptors, effectors, and connectors, including the neural and humoral systems, and are said to mediate such diverse behaviors as sensory and perceptual responses, emotional and attitudinal responses, learning, problem-solving, interpersonal relations, and personality disorders. Since the kinds of behaviors encompassed by adaptation-level theory are so grossly different, it follows that the equilibrium level is not necessarily defined in the same manner from situation to situation. For example, in sensory problems, the level might be given in terms of threshold values or point of subjective equality (*PSE*), whereas in attitude measurement it might be given in terms of the number of individuals responding in a given way. Nevertheless, in every instance the adaptation level is specified precisely and defined by a particular set of operations. This does not lessen the usefulness or validity of the concept, but permits its application in a wider behavioral context, just as the concept of electricity may be stated in terms of its thermic effects, the sedimentation in an electrolytic solution, or by the deviation of a magnetic needle. In both cases (adaptation and electricity) a single term is used since, as a matter of fact, the alternative effects have been found to be consistent with each other.

If the concept of adaptation level or equilibrium level is accepted, this is tantamount to asserting the *bipolarity of behavior*. In simpler terms, the dynamics of adjustment result in behavioral responses that are *accepting, rejecting*, or *indifferent* to a given situation, object, or event. Stimuli at or near the adaptation level (AL) evoke neutral responses, stimuli above AL produce responses of one kind (red, pleasant, accept) and stimuli below AL produce an opposite type of response (blue-green, unpleasant, reject). Thus, every response of the organism may be considered as reflecting a positive, negative, or neutral adjustment of the organism. This response tendency (approach-avoidance behavior) is commonly expressed in technical terms associated with sensory processes, cognition, emotion and other behaviors, for example, references to experiences ranging from pleasant to unpleasant, tall to short, black to white, beautiful to ugly, loud to soft, and so on. Whenever objects or events are ordered on such continua, there is always a neutral or transitional region corresponding to the AL of the organism. If, for example, tones are ordered in terms of loudness, some are soft, some are loud, and some are *medium* or moderately loud. The entire range of judgments on this dimension (and many others) is bipolar, with the judgments forming a graded series of responses beginning at one end of the scale, passing through the neutral zone, to the opposite end of the scale.

The Quantitative Theory
of Adaptation Level

The fundamental proposition of AL theory may be stated simply:

> . . . an individual's attitudes, values, ways of structuring his experiences, judgments of physical, aesthetic, and symbolic objects, intellectual and emotional behavior, learning, and interpersonal relations all represent modes of adaptation to environmental and organismic forces. These forces do not act willy-nilly upon the organism from without, nor do they erupt spontaneously from within. Stimuli impinge upon organisms already adapted to what has gone before, and internal states depend upon previously existing internal conditions as well as external inciters to action. Furthermore, stimuli do not act singly even if they are in different sense modalities. Even the simplest sensory experiences are more or less complex, containing focal, contextual, and organic components. The pooled effect of these three classes of stimuli determines the adjustment or adaptation level underlying all forms of behavior (Helson, 1964a, p. 37).

Taking this statement we will now translate its basic meaning into the quantitative theory of adaptation level. We begin with the proposition that AL is determined by the pooled effect of three classes of stimuli, part of which relate to conditions in the external environment and part to the internal states of the organism. The two classes of stimuli in the external environment are designated as *focal* and *background*. The *focal stimuli* are those stimuli to which the organism is directly responding and which are in the "immediate focus of attention." The *background stimuli* are all other stimuli that are present in the behavioral situation and that provide the background or context within which the focal stimuli are operative. The effects of focal stimuli may be markedly altered by the particular characteristics of the background. The third class of stimuli, those relating to the internal state of the organism, are called *residual stimuli*. These are all the determinants of behavior which are ordinarily not under experimental control but which characterize the specific organism and include the effects of past experience, underlying organic and physiological states, and constitutional factors. These internal stimuli interact with the external stimuli to produce a *pooled* effect, which establishes a given level of activity in a particular behavioral setting, that is, it defines AL.

In mathematical terms, the level of behavioral adaptation (A) is defined as a weighted product of the three classes of stimuli: focal (X), background (Y), and residual (R) (Helson, 1959). Specifically,

$$A = \overline{X^h}\; Y^i\; R^j \tag{13-1}$$

or, rewritten in logarithmic form,

$$\log A = h \log \overline{X} + i \log Y + j \log R, \tag{13-2}$$

where A is the adaptation level, $\overline{X}$ is the geometric mean of the focal stimuli, Y is the background stimulus or, where there is no uniform background, Y is the geometric mean of several contextual stimuli, and R is the residual stimulus.

The relative contributions of the three classes of stimuli to adaptation level are given by weighting coefficients: h, i, and j in Equations 13-1 and 13-2. The values of the coefficients may be normalized by letting $h + i + j = 1.00$. The larger the coefficient, the greater the relative contribution of the given class of stimuli in determining the level of adaptation or equilibrium. Also, it may be seen that the weighting factors may be greater for background and residual stimuli than for the primary (focal) stimuli. Although the values of AL derived from Equations 13-1 and 13-2 have closely approximated the values obtained in a variety of experimental situations (for example, judgments of lifted weights, sound intensity, time intervals), it is sometimes necessary for certain conditions of stimulation to expand the equations by including additional terms or by modifying the weighting coefficients. The actual separation of stimuli into the three classes (focal, background, and residual) will depend upon the nature of the particular experimental situation; the focal and background stimuli are experimentally controlled and all other sources of variance are subsumed under the classification of residual stimuli.

Adaptation level has most often been defined as the weighted logarithmic mean, as given in Equation 13-2. There are several reasons for this (Helson, 1964a). First, the values predicted by the weighted logarithmic mean are in closer agreement with experimentally obtained values of AL than those provided by any other a priori value under a variety of conditions. Second, the logarithmic mean, unlike the arithmetic mean or median, is affected by the range of stimuli and the size of the step interval between stimuli when the stimulus values form a symmetrical distribution. Third, as larger and larger values of stimuli are added in the experimental setup, the logarithmic mean does not increase as rapidly as the arithmetic mean; this more adequately represents the gradual shift in AL which occurs with the addition of extreme stimuli. In general, the logarithmic mean tends to exhibit the same characteristics that have been found to occur in AL under a wide variety of experimental conditions. Nevertheless, other definitions of AL have been found to be appropriate for certain situations; Behar and Bevan (1961) used the power mean and Parducci, Calfee, Marshall, and Davidson (1960) used the median. Both of these are compatible with AL theory and all three formulations (logarithmic mean, power mean, and median) define AL as the pooling of all stimuli, present and past, that affect behavior.

The consequences of the weighted mean definition of behavioral adaptation have been succinctly summarized by Helson (1964a, pp. 62–63). These are:

1. In every situation confronting the organism there is established an adaptation level that is a weighted mean of focal, background, and residual stimuli.
2. Adaptation level represents the zero of function, and, since it is always associated with positive values of stimulation, stimuli *below* as well as *above* level exert positive effects on behavior.
3. Responses to stimulation are manifestations of positive or negative gradients from level.
4. Intensity of response is a function of distance from, or ratio of stimulation to, prevailing level; the greater the magnitude of the ratio or distance, the steeper is the excitation gradient and the greater is the response.
5. With positive gradients of excitation responses are of one kind, e.g., blue-green, pleasant, approach; with negative gradients they are of the opposite kind, e.g., red, unpleasant, avoid; and with zero gradients responses are neutral, indifferent, or absent, e.g., gray, affectively neutral, no response. Behavior is therefore basically bipolar in nature.
6. Level of output tends to match the level of input stimulation, i.e., the adaptation level is a weighted mean of input stimulation unless inner (residual) factors are very strong.
7. Organisms are space-time averaging mechanisms in which all dimensions of objects and events contribute differentially to the formation of levels. Among the more obvious and important weighting factors are area, intensity, frequency, nearness, recency, order of stimulation, and affective quality. Less obvious but often important in fixing levels are task, instructions, self-instructions, organic states, cognitive systems, and genetic factors.
8. Group behavior can be conceived as the resultant of pooled individual behaviors and hence as functions of individual modes of adjustment. Just as individual levels are established with respect to prevailing conditions, so group levels, conceived as weighted means of individual levels, are established with respect to situations involving interpersonal interactions.
9. Cognitive acts, sensorimotor responses, skills, and learning are differentially affected by focal, background, and residual stimuli and hence are functions of prevailing level no less than perception and judgment. Similar considerations apply to affective and emotional behavior.

Now that we have developed the basic concepts of the theory of adaptation level and have presented the implications of the quantitative definition of AL, we will proceed with a review of some of the experiments performed within this theoretical framework. These experiments will serve to illustrate the mathematical treatment of AL data and to establish the adequacy of the underlying theoretical formulation.

Adaptation-Level Theory and Psychophysics

The classical approach in psychophysics has tended to study the sensory processes by manipulating certain characteristics of stimuli and measuring the correlated responses. Given a tone of 1000 cps, what is the minimal amount of acoustic energy that will elicit a response a given percentage of the time; or, given a 100 gm weight, how much weight must be added before the change in the stimulus is judged to be heavier a given percentage of the time? The traditional problems of absolute and differential thresholds were concerned with specific values of stimuli which could serve as "landmarks" to locate specific points on a psychological continuum. The judgments made in establishing these "landmarks" were ordinarily not related to any conditions other than those characterizing the standard stimulus. The same sort of dimensionalism prevails in most contemporary studies on sensory scaling. Specific stimuli are "halved," "doubled," or assigned appropriate numbers in accordance with a given set of instructions. The results of this classical approach yield quantitative measurements and psychophysical functions that are reproducible but that, from the AL point of view, are limited in generality, since no consideration is given to the functioning level of the organism other than the organism being classified as "normal" with respect to the behavior being studied. The implication is that psychophysical data are uniquely determined by the characteristics of the stimuli and that each sensory modality has a fixed scale of sensitivity that must be discovered. While it is clear that under certain circumstances the context in which psychophysical judgments are made may affect the outcome (Garner, 1954), it is maintained, for example, "that the effect of context does not account for the basic fact that loudness is a power function of intensity" (Stevens, 1956, p. 12).

While there is some justification in the position adopted by the adaptation-level theorists, it should be pointed out that the field of psychophysics encompasses more than procedures for establishing absolute and differential thresholds. This view of psychophysics is entirely too restricted. In its broader connotation, psychophysics is the science which deals with the responses of organisms to stimulus configurations. Within this definition, the assertion that classical psychophysics ignores the organism cannot be so readily defended. Consider, for example, the many studies which have been done on the relation of the confidence of a judgment to judgment time (Volkmann, 1934) or to the size of stimulus differences (Johnson, 1939).

Nevertheless, the orientation of AL theory differs from the classical approach in that stimuli are ordered (judged) as members of a class of stimuli and, in addition, the judgments are considered to reflect the adjustment (adaptation) made by the organism to the composite set (class) of stimuli. Simply stated, the pooled effects of present and past stimulation establish an internal (subjective) norm with respect to which comparative judgments are made. Thus, *all judgments are relative;* they depend upon the relation of stimulation to the level of adaptation which has been established under a given set of conditions. A 40-foot boat will appear *long* if viewed among a group of canoes, but will seem *short* when docked alongside a pier with ocean-going vessels. In a yacht club, it might be judged *medium* in length. For each class of stimuli there is a unique behavioral adjustment and the judgments of size, weight, duration, intensity, color, area, and other magnitudes will be made with respect to the particular frame of reference adopted by the respondent.

The concept of adaptation level emerged from a series of studies conducted by Helson (1938) on color constancy, color contrast, and sensory adaptation to color. The general question (p. 439) was, "Given any object as stimulus, what will be its hue, saturation, and lightness when viewed on any background under any illuminant?" To answer this question, a special booth was constructed so that samples of colored papers could be placed on a shelf (see *S*, Figure 13-1) and the background formed by the walls and a piece of cardboard could be changed from white to gray or black, as required by the experimental design. Light from a 500-watt lamp entered the booth through two small openings in the ceiling. The openings were made so that filters and screens could be inserted as needed to change the composition or intensity of the light falling on the samples and background. White light entered through opening W.L. and filtered light through opening F.L. (see Figure 13-1).

The stimuli were 16 samples from the Hering series of grays, and a white, gray, and black sample identical with the background. The reflectances (in percent) of the latter three samples were 80, 23, and 3, respectively. In judging the hues of the samples, the subjects could use any one of sixteen classifications. The primary hues were called red (R), green (G), yellow (Y), and blue (B), while samples which appeared as binary colors were given a double name, for example, Red-Blue. If one component seemed to be predominant, the adjectival form was used for the *minor* component, as in *yellowish* Green (yG). Reports on lightness and saturation conformed to the Munsell system. Each of these dimensions was judged on a 10-point scale, with 10 denoting maximal lightness (value) or saturation (chroma) and zero, a minimum. These two ratings are expressed as a ratio in which lightness is given in the numerator and saturation in the denominator. According to this system, a designation of R 2/8 refers to a red having a lightness near the black end of the scale and a saturation approaching spectral purity. White is given as A (achromatic) 10/0 and black, A 0/0. After they were given a considerable amount of prior training in judging the colored chips shown in the Munsell book of color, the subjects made their judgments inside the testing booth, after five minutes' adaptation, in the same illuminance as the displayed samples.

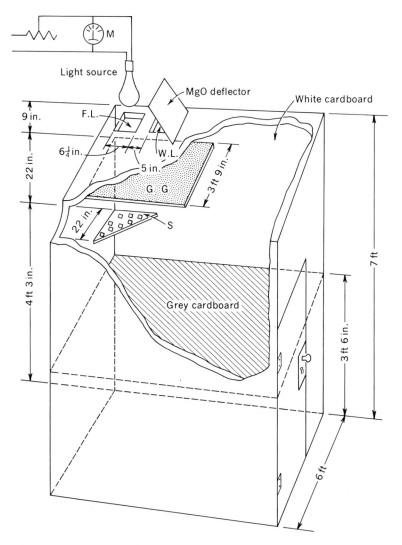

Figure 13-1. Drawing of the testing booth in which psychophysical judgments of color were obtained in a series of studies. (From Helson, *J. exp. Psychol.,* 1938, **23**, 439–476.)

The data obtained in this study for a typical subject are given in Table 13-1. The table contains the judgments of hue, lightness, and saturation for the 19 samples presented in random order under four different colored illuminants. Inspection of Table 13-1 shows a remarkable ordering of the three dimensions when nonselective achromatic stimuli are viewed under strong chromatic lights. The data reveal that "samples of high reflectance have the illuminant hue, samples of intermediate reflectance are achromatic, and samples of low reflectance have the

Table 13-1   Reflectance (R), Hue, Lightness, and Saturation for Samples on Three Backgrounds in Four Different Illuminations (Subject 1)

Backgrounds were White (W), Gray (G), and Black (B) in daylight. Numerator indicates lightness and denominator indicates saturation as in the Munsell notation.

R	Red Illuminant W Bkgd.		Red Illuminant G Bkgd.		Red Illuminant B Bkgd.		Green Illuminant W Bkgd.		Green Illuminant G Bkgd.		Green Illuminant B Bkgd.	
0.80	R	9.0/0.5	R	8.5/7.0	R	7.0/7.0	YG	9.0/1.0	YG	8.0/7.0	YG	9.0/7.0
0.52	R	7.0/1.0	R	7.5/6.0	R	7.0/7.0	YG	8.0/1.0	YG	7.0/5.0	YG	8.0/6.0
0.39	A	6.0/0.0	bR	6.0/3.0	R	6.0/7.0	A	7.0/0.0	YG	6.0/3.0	YG	6.0/5.0
0.34	A	6.0/0.0	bR	6.0/3.0	R	5.0/5.0	A	7.0/0.0	YG	6.0/3.0	YG	6.0/5.0
0.27	B	6.0/1.0	RB	6.0/3.0	bR	5.0/5.0	BR	7.0/1.0	YG	5.5/1.0	yG	5.0/5.0
0.23	B	5.0/2.0	RB	5.5/2.0	bR	5.0/5.0	BR	7.0/1.0	YG	5.5/1.0	yG	5.0/5.0
0.22	B	5.0/3.0	RB	5.5/2.0	bR	4.5/4.5	BR	7.0/1.0	A	5.0/5.0	yG	4.5/5.0
0.17	B	5.0/4.0	RB	5.0/1.0	bR	5.0/5.0	BR	6.0/2.0	A	5.0/0.0	yG	4.5/5.0
0.16	B	5.0/4.0	RB	5.0/0.5	bR	4.0/4.0	BR	6.0/3.0	A	5.0/0.0	yG	4.0/5.0
0.15	B	5.0/5.0	A	5.0/0.0	bR	4.0/4.0	BR	6.0/3.0	A	4.0/0.0	yG	4.0/5.0
0.13	B	5.0/5.0	A	5.0/0.0	bR	4.0/4.0	BR	6.0/3.0	A	4.0/0.0	yG	3.5/4.0
0.13	B	5.0/5.0	A	5.0/0.0	bR	3.0/4.0	BR	6.0/3.5	A	4.0/0.0	yG	3.5/4.0
0.11	B	5.0/5.0	A	4.0/0.0	bR	3.0/4.0	BR	6.0/3.5	A	4.0/0.0	yG	3.5/4.0
0.10	B	5.0/5.0	bG	4.0/0.5	bR	2.0/2.0	BR	5.0/4.0	RB	4.0/2.0	yG	3.0/3.0
0.07	B	4.0/6.0	bG	4.0/1.0	bR	1.0/1.0	BR	5.0/5.0	RB	3.0/3.0	yG	2.0/2.0
0.07	B	4.0/6.0	bG	3.0/3.0	bR	1.0/1.0	BR	5.0/5.0	RB	3.0/3.0	yG	2.0/2.0
0.05	B	4.0/6.0	bG	3.0/3.0	bR	1.0/1.0	BR	4.0/6.0	RB	3.0/4.0	yG	1.0/1.0
0.03	gB	4.0/6.0	bG	2.0/5.0	bR	1.0/0.5	BR	3.0/7.0	RB	2.0/5.0	yG	0.5/0.5
0.03	BG	3.0/7.0	BG	1.0/8.0	A	0.0/0.0	BR	3.0/8.0	RB	1.5/6.0	A	0.0/0.0

R	Blue Illuminant W Bkgd.		Blue Illuminant G Bkgd.		Blue Illuminant B Bkgd.		Yellow Illuminant W Bkgd.		Yellow Illuminant G Bkgd.		Yellow Illuminant B Bkgd.	
0.80	B	9.0/1.0	B	8.0/8.0	B	7.0/6.0	gY	9.0/1.0	Y	8.0/7.0	Y	9.0/7.0
0.52	B	7.0/1.0	B	7.0/7.0	B	6.0/5.0	gY	8.0/1.0	Y	7.0/5.0	Y	7.0/5.0
0.39	A	6.0/0.0	B	6.0/5.0	B	5.0/5.0	A	7.0/0.0	Y	6.5/3.0	Y	6.0/4.0
0.34	rB	6.0/1.0	B	6.0/5.0	B	4.5/5.0	A	7.0/0.0	Y	6.5/2.0	Y	6.0/3.0
0.27	rB	5.0/1.0	rB	6.0/2.0	B	4.0/5.0	RB	7.0/2.0	Y	6.0/0.5	Y	5.0/2.0
0.23	Y	5.0/1.0	rB	6.0/2.0	B	4.0/5.0	RB	6.0/2.0	Y	6.0/0.5	Y	5.0/2.0
0.22	Y	5.0/1.0	rB	5.0/1.0	rB	4.0/4.0	RB	6.0/2.0	A	6.0/0.0	Y	5.0/1.0
0.17	Y	5.0/1.0	A	4.0/0.0	rB	3.5/4.0	RB	6.0/3.0	A	5.5/0.0	Y	5.5/1.0
0.16	Y	5.0/1.0	A	4.0/0.0	rB	3.5/4.0	RB	6.0/3.0	A	5.0/0.0	Y	5.0/1.0
0.15	Y	5.0/1.0	A	4.0/0.0	rB	3.5/4.0	RB	6.0/3.5	A	5.0/0.0	Y	5.0/1.0
0.13	Y	4.0/2.0	A	3.5/0.0	rB	3.5/4.0	RB	6.0/3.5	A	5.0/0.0	Y	5.0/1.0
0.13	Y	3.0/1.0	A	3.5/0.0	rB	3.5/4.0	RB	6.0/4.0	A	5.0/0.0	Y	5.0/1.0
0.11	Y	3.0/1.0	A	3.0/0.0	rB	3.0/4.0	RB	5.0/4.0	RB	4.5/1.0	Y	4.0/1.0
0.10	Y	3.0/2.0	Y	2.5/0.5	rB	2.5/3.0	RB	5.0/5.0	RB	4.0/1.5	A	5.0/0.0
0.07	Y	4.0/4.0	Y	2.0/2.0	rB	1.0/2.0	RB	4.0/6.0	RB	3.0/2.0	A	3.0/0.0
0.07	Y	3.0/3.0	Y	2.0/2.0	RB	1.0/1.0	RB	3.0/6.0	RB	3.0/3.0	A	3.0/0.0
0.05	Y	3.0/5.0	Y	2.0/2.0	RB	1.0/1.0	RB	3.0/6.0	RB	3.0/3.0	RB	2.0/2.0
0.03	Y	2.0/6.0	RY	1.0/5.0	A	0.5/0.0	RB	3.0/7.0	RB	2.0/5.0	RB	1.0/3.0
0.03	Y	2.0/6.0	RY	1.0/5.5	A	0.0/0.0	rB	2.0/8.0	B	1.0/6.0	A	0.0/0.0

Source: H. Helson. Fundamental problems in color vision I. The principle governing changes in hue, saturation, and lightness of non-selective samples in chromatic illumination. *J. exp. Psychol.*, 1938, **23**, 439–476. By permission of the American Psychological Association.

hue of the after-image complementary to the illuminant hue" (Helson, 1938, p. 449). Examine, for example, the data in Table 13-1 for the red illuminant with the samples of gray papers viewed against the gray background. The grays with high reflectance values (0.34 to 0.80 or 34 percent to 80 percent) appear as red or bluish-red. Then there is a gradual transition, until at intermediate reflectance values (0.11 to 0.15) the samples appear achromatic. For the low reflectance values (below 0.10) the samples appear bluish-green, that is, the afterimage complement to the red illuminant.

Notice, also, that for the different illuminants, there is a systematic shift in the reflectances which appear achromatic as the background is changed from white to gray to black. *Adaptation reflectance,* therefore, is defined as the range of reflectances over which samples with similar reflectances are judged to be achromatic when viewed under a colored illuminant. In Table 13-1, Red Illuminant, the stimulus which is achromatic on a daylight white background, has a reflectance of 0.34 to 0.39, on a gray background it is a stimulus of 0.11 to 0.15, and on a black background a stimulus reflectance of 0.03. It is apparent that the neutral (adaptation; achromatic) level is determined primarily by the reflectance of the background. Helson's *principle of color conversion* may now be stated:

> In every viewing situation there is established an adaptation level such that stimuli above adaptation reflectance are tinged with the hue of the illuminant, stimuli below adaptation reflectance are tinged with the afterimage complementary to the hue of the illuminant, and stimuli at or near adaptation reflectance are either achromatic or weakly saturated colors of uncertain hue (1959, p. 579).

Given this principle, can the concept of adaptation level be stated quantitatively so that it may serve as a frame of reference for psychological judgments and for the prediction of psychophysical data? Several solutions have been proposed, but the equation which Helson (1938) found most appropriate for predicting adaptation level in the series of color studies was of the form:

$$A = K(\overline{X}\, Y^3)^{\frac{1}{4}}, \tag{13-3}$$

where A is adaptation level, K is a fractional constant equal to $\frac{4}{5}$, Y is the reflectance of the background, and $\overline{X}$ is the logarithmic mean of the reflectances of the test stimuli. This equation indicates that AL is a weighted geometric mean in which the background factor is weighted three times as heavily as the logarithmic mean of the primary stimuli in the experimental situation.

Equation 13-3 may be rewritten in logarithmic form as:

$$\log A = \log K + \frac{(\log \overline{X} + 3 \log Y)}{4}, \tag{13-4}$$

in which the symbols have the same meaning as in Equation 13-3.

Equations 13-3 and 13-4, however, were derived to predict adaptation levels in visual experiments involving colors. To be useful generally, the AL concept must be extended to other judgmental situations. The first extension of the concept was to the classical problem of lifted weights (Helson, 1947); the objective was to determine whether a "background" weight, that is, a comparison stimulus or *anchor*, would function like a visual background, and if the formula in Equations 13-3 or 13-4 would predict the stimulus judged "medium" in terms of lifted weights. In the experiments, the subjects lifted a given (comparison) weight before each stimulus in a set of weights and gave judgments of the test stimulus on a 9-point absolute scale from very, very heavy, through medium, to very, very light. In this way the effect of the background stimulus could be studied when it was far heavier or lighter than the stimuli in the series or when it was equal in weight to one of the stimuli. The subjects were free to judge the stimuli as they appeared psychophysically, with no instructions being given regarding the "meaning" of the various response categories.

The results of part of this study are shown in Figure 13-2. The ordinate gives the judgment categories translated into numerical form, for example, 90 for very, very heavy, 80 for very heavy, 70 for heavy, and so on; the abscissa shows the magnitude of the series stimuli in grams. The three curves with anchor weights

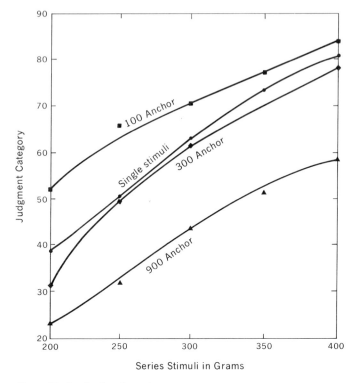

Figure 13-2. Scale values of stimuli obtained by two different methods in an experiment on the judgment of lifted weights. The absolute method is designated as single stimuli; the comparative method is shown with three different standards or anchors: 100, 300, and 900 grams. (From Helson, *Amer. J. Psychol.*, 1947.)

of 100, 300, and 900 gm were obtained according to the comparative method which has already been described; the curve for "single stimuli" was derived from judgments in which no comparison (anchor) stimulus was presented. The two middle curves ("single stimuli" and 300 anchor) confirm the prediction from the theory that AL should be the same in the absolute method ("single stimuli") and the relative (comparative) method when the standard (anchor) is physically equal to, or approximates, the logarithmic mean of the test series of weights; the two curves are essentially coincident for the stimulus series.

Since the AL in this situation ("single stimuli" and 300 gm anchor) is below the midpoint of the stimulus series, it follows that asymmetry in judgments should be present and that it should be similar for both cases. This prediction is supported by the two middle curves in Figure 13-2; the greater portions of the two curves lie above AL, which is the numerical value of 50 ("medium") in the judgment scale.

Figure 13-2 also shows the change in scale values when anchors (100 gm and 900 gm) are used which lie outside the range of values in the stimulus series (200 to 400 gm). When the 100 gm weight is used as the comparison, the judgments are shifted upward; with the 900 gm weight, they are shifted downward. In other words, the AL is shifted *toward* the anchor, with the result that compared to the 100 gm anchor the 200–400 gm stimuli seem much heavier; with the 900 gm anchor, much lighter. This phenomenon is sometimes referred to as "*the repellent effect of anchors.*"

Again the question is raised: Can a formula be derived that will predict the judgments of lifted weights and, if so, will it be consistent with the weighted logarithmic mean formula developed for the achromatic point in vision? Starting with the formula for vision (Equation 13-3), a satisfactory solution may be derived. After rewriting Equation 13-3 in logarithmic form (Equation 13-4), a more general expression may be written to conform to the requirements of the lifted weights experiment:

$$\log A = \log K + \left[\frac{(k_1 \Sigma \log X_i/n) + k_2 \log C}{k_1 + k_2} \right], \qquad (13\text{-}5)$$

where K is a constant, X_i refers to the test series of weight stimuli, C is the comparison stimulus or anchor, and k_1 and k_2 are constants. This is the formula for judgments in the comparative (relative) method.

When no standard is used (single stimuli; absolute method) or the anchor is ineffective, the C term in Equation 13-5 becomes zero. It is also possible to eliminate the constant for the C term (when it is present) by dividing both numerator and denominator (in Equation 13-5) by k_2 and defining a new constant $k = k_1/k_2$ (Helson, 1947, p. 4). The series stimuli now have a weighting coefficient of k and the coefficient for the comparison stimulus becomes 1.0; the constant in the denominator assumes a value of $k + 1.0$. Taking the changes in constants into account, Equation 13-5 becomes:

$$\log A = \log K + \left[\frac{(k \, \Sigma \log X_i/n) + \log C}{k + 1.0} \right] \qquad (13\text{-}6)$$

but since $\log C = 0$, Equation 13-6 reduces to:

$$\log A = \log K + \frac{\Sigma \log X_i}{n}. \qquad (13\text{-}7)$$

The application of Equation 13-5 to the lifted-weight data requires that the stimulus series be weighted more than the comparison stimulus in order to obtain a good fit. This differs from the weighting in the visual case where the background was weighted considerably more than the series of samples. According to Helson (1947) an explanation of this difference may lie in the fact that in vision the background is always present and surrounds the sample, whereas in lifted weights the comparison is presented momentarily and either precedes or follows the stimuli in the series. The weighting coefficient for the test series that yielded the best fit to the experimental data was found to be 3.0.

Equation 13-5 must also be revised to take into account *order* of presentation of the variables and standard, as well as the *size* of the step interval between stimuli. These two constants, denoted as c and d, respectively, replace the constant K in Equation 13-5 so that the new constant becomes cd. When the psychophysical judgments are made with the standard preceding the variable, the best value of cd is 0.75 d; for the variable preceding the standard, the best value of cd is zero (Helson, 1947). Since for lifted-weight data the best predictions are made when cd is taken as an additive constant in the logarithmic expression, the constant is placed on the left-hand side of Equations 13-5 or 13-6. This gives:

$$\log (A + 0.75d) = \frac{(3 \, \Sigma \log X_i/n) + \log C}{4}. \qquad (13\text{-}8)$$

Following Helson's argument, when no background or anchor stimulus is used (method of single stimuli; absolute method), the anchor term (C) drops out and AL becomes the logarithmic mean of the series stimuli minus the d factor. Equation 13-7 becomes:

$$\log (A + 0.75d) = \frac{\Sigma \log X_i}{n}. \qquad (13\text{-}9)$$

It may be seen why, in referring to Figure 13-2, the prediction was made that AL should be the same in the absolute method and the relative method under certain circumstances; specifically, if an appropriate value of the anchor is selected, the AL computed from Equation 13-8 will be identical with (or approximate) the value obtained from Equation 13-9.

We can illustrate this point by referring to the specific data in Figure 13-2.

Given a set of five weights: 200, 250, 300, 350, and 400 gm, what is the predicted AL by the method of single stimuli? Since no anchor is used, apply Equation 13-9.

$$\log (A + 0.75d) = \frac{\Sigma \log X_i}{n}$$
$$= (\log 200 + \log 250 + \log 300 + \log 350 + \log 400)/5$$
$$= (2.30103 + 2.39794 + 2.47712 + 2.54407 + 2.60206)/5$$
$$= 12.32222/5$$
$$\log (A + 0.75d) = 2.46444;$$

but, since the difference between stimuli (d) equals 50 gm,

$$0.75d = 37.50, \text{ and}$$
$$A = \text{antilog } 2.46444 - 0.75d$$
$$= 291.4 - 37.50$$
$$A = 253.9 \text{ gm.} \tag{13-10}$$

Thus, by solving Equation 13-9, we see that the predicted AL with the single method and this particular set of weights is equal to 253.9 gm.

To find the predicted AL for the relative method with an anchor of 300 gm, apply Equation 13-8.

$$\log (A + 0.75d) = \frac{(3.0 \, \Sigma \log X_i/n) + \log C}{4}$$

Substituting the value of $\Sigma \log X_i/n$, as computed in the method of single stimuli, we obtain:

$$\log (A + 0.75d) = \frac{(3)(12.32222/5) + 2.47712}{4}$$
$$= \frac{9.87044}{4}$$
$$\log (A + 0.75d) = 2.46761;$$
$$\text{but } 0.75d = 37.50, \text{ as computed in the method of single stimuli, so}$$
$$A = \text{antilog } 2.46761 - 0.75d$$
$$= 293.5 - 37.50$$
$$A = 256.0 \text{ gm.} \tag{13-11}$$

Comparing the solutions obtained by the formulas for the single method and relative method, 253.9 gm and 256.0 gm, respectively, we see that the difference is only approximately 2 gm. This indicates that the two methods of judgment will yield similar results if the anchor weight used in the relative method is appropriately chosen. A strict test of the theory would, in fact, use a background stimulus of 254 gm instead of 300 gm.

The extent to which the results obtained from Equations 13-8 and 13-9 agree with experimental data is shown in Table 13-2. The table contains the predicted

Table 13-2   Shifts in Point of Symmetry with Change in Comparison Stimulus and Identity of *PSE* in Absolute and Comparative Methods when the Standard is Near the AL

Condition	Theoretical AL	Observed Medium	Urban Limen $\phi\gamma$	Geometric Mean
Single stimuli (200, 250, 300, 350, 400 gm)	253.9	249.0	251.0	291.0
Comparison with 300 gm	256.0	250.0	261.0	296.0
Comparison with 100 gm	185.5	197.0	184.0	171.0
Comparison with 900 gm	348.8	349.0	345.0	512.0
Single stimuli (88, 92, 96, 100, 104 gm)	92.8	96.2	96.2	95.8
Comparison with 96 gm	92.7	95.4	95.0	95.8
Comparison with 40 gm	74.0	77.0	63.9	61.9
Comparison with 260 gm	120.0	—[a]	138.9	157.8
Comparison with 5 gm	42.7	—[a]	37.3	21.9

[a] The observed values are so far below 50 that extrapolation does not yield a reliable figure for medium in these cases.

Source: H. Helson. Adaptation level as far as a frame of reference for prediction of psychophysical data. *Amer. J. Psychol.,* 1947, **60,** 1-29.

AL values for two different series of weights (200, 250, 300, 350, and 400 gm; and 88, 92, 96, 100, and 104 gm) under two methods of judgment (single stimuli and relative method), together with the observed AL values as computed from three different techniques. These include (1) the "medium" stimulus determined by linear interpolation between the weights falling immediately above and below 50 on the judgment scale; (2) the Urban limen (threshold) computed from the 50 percent value of the psychometric (phi-gamma) function; and (3) the geometric mean of the weights in the series. The comparison of predicted and obtained values (observed "medium" and Urban limen) shows excellent agreement in the heavier weight series and fair agreement in the lighter series. This difference in the accuracy of prediction between series may reflect individual differences in the composition of the two groups of subjects (Helson, 1947). It may also be seen that the geometric means do not agree with the predicted AL values nor the observed values and, hence, do not provide a satisfactory estimate of the center point of the psychological scale of judgments.

If the effects of practice and past experience are to be considered as significant factors in establishing AL, Equations 13-8 and 13-9 need to be modified. It is now well recognized that subjects do enter into experimental situations with a prior history of exposure to sounds, lights, temperatures, language, and other forms of stimulation which affect their behavior and judgments both within and outside the laboratory setting. These "residues" are often referred to as "practice effects," "past experience," "frame of reference," "familiarity," "prior exposure," and other similar expressions. The theory of adaptation level takes these internal factors into account in the form of "remote anchors" and provides a quantitative estimate of their effects.

To illustrate how this may be done, consider part of the data reported by Pratt (1933) in which subjects were required to judge the loudness of sounds made by a falling pendulum, such that the greater the angle of fall the more intense the sound. The angles in one series were 41, 37, 32, 26, and 18 degrees and the subjects judged the sounds in terms of categories from 1 to 9, with 1 for the softest category, 5 for the middle, and 9 for the loudest. The results showed that the point of subjective equality (*PSE*) was at 32.6 degrees with a scale value of 1.61. Observe that this value is above the midpoint of the series at 32.0 degrees with a scale value of 1.6. This suggests that a "remote anchor" was operating to "pull" the *PSE* toward the loud end of the judgment scale. Can this effect be quantitatively estimated?

To answer this, we recall that in Equation 13-8 there is a term (log *C*) which refers to an anchor stimulus. Now we may also consider that prior stimulation acts as an anchor—a "remote anchor." If the remote anchor has magnitude *R*, a properly weighted geometric mean of *C* and *R* can be used in Equation 13-8 as follows (Helson, 1964*b*):

$$\log (A + 0.75d) = \frac{(3.0 \ \Sigma \log X_i/n) + (W_1 \log C + W_2 \log R)/(W_1 + W_2)}{4},$$

(13-12)

where W_1 and W_2 are weighting factors. Under most circumstances it is reasonable to assume that $W_1 = W_2$ or, if the weights are unequal, the anchor fraction may be simplified following the procedure suggested for Equation 13-6. By dividing W_1 by W_2 and letting $W_1/W_2 = W$, the value of W_2 reduces to unity and the denominator of the fraction becomes $W + 1$.

Equation 13-12 which was derived from data obtained in lifted weight experiments is a special case of the more general expression given in Equations 13-1 and 13-2. These equations define AL and make it possible to determine the relative contributions of focal, background, and residual stimuli to a particular AL. Specifically, these equations indicate the stimulus value above which positive, or one kind of responses, will be elicited, below which negative or opposite responses will be elicited, and at or near which indifferent or no responses will be elicited. Extensions of AL theory (Helson, 1948) provide equations from which quantitative predictions of responses to specific stimuli may be obtained, that is, given a particular stimulus, what will be its scale value on a specified response continuum? A review of these equations and their derivation, however, would lead into an advanced discussion of psychological scaling problems and scaling theory and will not be considered in this treatment of the theory of adaptation level. We will turn, now, to studies involving AL theory in areas outside traditional psychophysics.

Adaptation-Level Theory
and Perceptual Judgments

In Chapter 2 the traditional view of psychophysics was presented in which a stimulus was defined as a form of energy or change in energy which was capable of arousing a particular response. Some investigators (for example, Helson, 1964a) believe, however, due to the great diversity in the kinds of stimuli that can initiate or inhibit behavior and the numerous possibilities that exist for the interaction of external and internal stimuli, that the energy concept of stimulus is too narrow and should be broadened. This view holds that if behavior is to be predicted, consideration should be given to variables other than stimulus energy and, in terms of adaptation level theory, these variables should include background factors and organismic dispositions. Additional support for this view is found in experimental studies in which perceptual judgments have been found to be affected by personal needs, values, and attitudes. In its general form, however, this position does not differ from the relation among variables as given in Equation 5-1, but within the context of adaptation-level theory this general expression has been replaced by a specific functional relationship from which predictions may be made. Now we will consider a few of the studies dealing with perceptual judgments in which adaptation-level theory has been applied.

Contextual and Perceptual Judgments

The theory of adaptation level holds that judgments of magnitude are the product of focal stimuli and contextual (background) stimuli, with residual (organismic) variables held constant. Focal stimuli are those which are in the "immediate focus of attention" and, since they stand out as distinctive figures, comprise the stimuli to which a response is made. The contextual stimuli include all other stimuli which are immediately present and form the background or context within which the focal stimuli are judged or responded to. Depending upon the purpose of a given experiment, the characteristics of either the focal stimuli or the background may be independently varied to determine the effects of these changes upon perceptual judgments. Adaptation-level theory predicts that perceptual judgments will be altered if the context of the focal stimuli is modified.

In an experiment dealing with the estimation of the number of beans in a jar (Bevan, Maier, and Helson, 1963), two properties of the context were experimentally manipulated: size and figure-ground relation. The variable of size was manipulated by placing the beans to be estimated in a large, cylindrical glass container (3.5 in. dia × 7.25 in. high) or a small container (2 in. dia × 4.5 in. high). The figure-ground relation was manipulated by verbal instructions to the subjects. For part of the subjects, "the integral relationship between beans and jars" was emphasized with the beans and jars going together as "a single organic unit;" for the remainder of the subjects, the beans were identified as figure and the jars as ground, that is, the jar was a container and a separate object in the background. Four groups of subjects were tested, one for each condition obtained by combining each size of jar with each figure-ground relation (that is, a 2 × 2 factorial design). It was predicted that jar size would produce a significant effect on the estimate of number and that this effect would be most marked under the instructions which designated the jar and beans as figure.

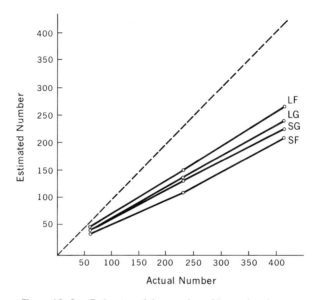

Figure 13-3. Estimates of the number of beans in a jar as a joint function of jar size and figure-ground relation. Large and small jars are identified as L and S respectively; the identification of the jar as figure and ground is labeled F and G, respectively. If the estimates of the subjects were perfectly accurate, the experimental points would fall along the dotted line. (From Bevan *et al., Amer. J. Psychol.,* 1963.)

The results of this study are shown in Figure 13-3 in which the estimated number is plotted as a function of the actual number of beans in a given jar under a given figure-ground relation. Notice that all four groups grossly underestimated the number of beans under the four conditions of the study. The underestimates range from 37 percent to 45 percent. By extrapolating the curves at the lower end, it is suggested that correct estimates would be obtained at about 20 beans. The data also reveal that, ignoring the figure-ground variable, larger estimates are made when the beans are in the larger container than the smaller. The size of container, however, has little effect when the jar is taken as ground (see curves LG and SG), but under the figure instructions, the larger jar increases the estimates while the smaller decreases them. Thus, the data support the experimental prediction of adaptation-level theory that *perceptual judgments will be altered if the context of the focal (test) stimuli is varied.*

As part of a larger study, Behar and Bevan (1961) studied the anchor effect in judgments of temporal duration. The stimulus series to be judged consisted of five visual durations: 1, 2, 3, 4, and 5 sec, as provided by a neon glow-lamp mounted in a black wooden screen. The lamp was turned on in a predetermined random order under three conditions: (1) with no anchor, (2) with a short anchor of 0.2 sec, and (3) with a long anchor of 9 sec. When presented, the anchor dura-tion was interspersed with the test stimuli so that it appeared as every fourth stimulus. The task of the subject was to judge each visual duration in terms of an 11-category scale extending from very, very, very short (vvvs) through medium (M) to very, very, very long (vvvl).

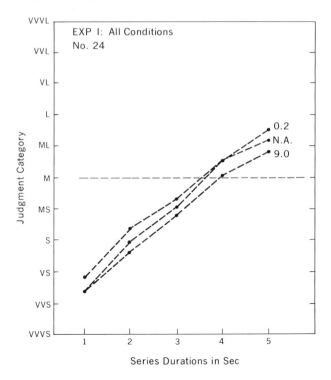

Figure 13-4.   The anchor effect for visual duration with anchors above and below the series stimuli. (From Behar and Bevan, *Amer. J. Psychol.,* 1961.)

Figure 13-4 shows the results of this part of the study. The ordinate indicates the judgment category as a function of stimulus duration. There are three curves presented in Figure 13-4, one for each of the two anchors (0.2 sec and 9.0 sec) and one for the no-anchor condition (N.A.). It may be seen that when the longer anchor was used in the test series, the series stimuli tended to be perceived as of shorter duration than when the series stimuli were presented alone (no anchor, N.A.). When presented in conjunction with the light anchor (0.2 sec), the series stimuli were judged to be longer than when they were presented without an anchor. Furthermore, the long anchor (9 sec) produced relatively greater effects than the short anchor (0.2 sec), as may be seen from the spacing of the two curves above and below the "no anchor" function. These data support the position that the *characteristics of the background (anchor) affect judgments of temporal duration.*

As part of this same study, a comparison was made of anchor effects with visual and auditory (noise filled) durations. Given no anchor, 10-sec and 20-sec anchors, the extent of the anchor's influence was found to be proportional to its magnitude. Also, the auditory durations were judged to be significantly longer than the visual durations by approximately 20 percent, thereby demonstrating that *the modality of stimulation is an important variable in establishing anchor effects in the estimation of temporal duration.* This was found to be especially relevant under hetero-modal conditions of judgment, that is, light stimuli with a noise anchor or noise stimuli with a light anchor. In this situation, however, the influence of the visual anchors was still directly proportional to their magnitude, but opposite effects were obtained for the auditory anchors. The 20-sec light anchor had a greater shortening effect on the series (noise) stimuli than the 10-sec anchor, but the 20-sec noise anchor produced less shortening on the series (light) stimuli than the 10-sec anchor. These findings are presented in Figure 13-5.

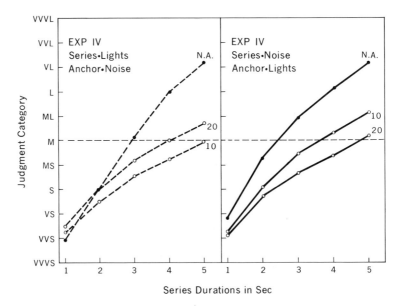

Figure 13–5. Heteromodal effects of a visual test series with an auditory (noise) anchor (left panel) and an auditory test series with a visual (light) anchor (right panel). (From Behar and Bevan, *Amer. J. Psychol.,* 1961.)

Hirsh, Bilger, and Deatherage (1956) have also shown that the duration of visual and auditory stimuli depends upon background stimulation. In this study the subjects were presented with a series of tones or lights for a certain length of time and at the end of this time, were required to hold down a response button

(which turned on the same stimulus) for the same duration. For the control conditions, the ambient conditions under which the tones or lights were judged were
the same during the periods of both stimulation and response; these were light
and quiet (LQ), light and noise (LN), dark and quiet (DQ), and dark and noise
(DN). The response estimates obtained under these conditions for the five stimulus
durations (1, 2, 4, 8, and 16 sec) are presented in the middle curve of Figure 13-6.

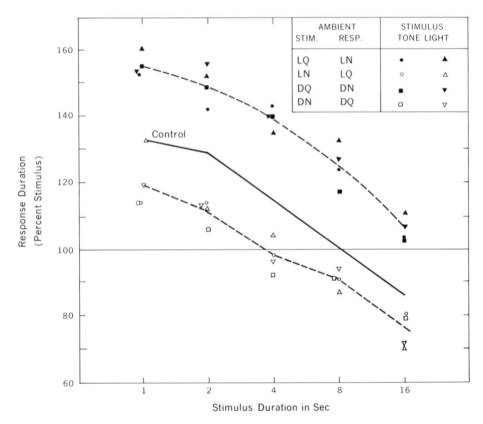

Figure 13–6. Response duration as a function of stimulus duration when stimuli (tones or
lights) were presented during quiet and responses were made during noise (filled symbols) and
when stimuli were presented during noise and responses were made during quiet (open symbols).
(From Hirsh *et al.*, *Amer. J. Psychol.*, 1956.)

If the judged durations were perfectly correct, the data points would all fall along
the horizontal line at 100 percent since the response durations would be identical
with stimulus durations. The data indicate, however, that the durations of 1, 2,
and 4 sec are on the average overestimated; the duration of 16 sec is underestimated, while the 8-sec interval is accurately judged. In classical terms, this
interval which is neither over- nor underestimated is called the "*indifference
interval.*"

Now, according to adaptation-level theory, this indifference interval is not an absolute value, but is dependent upon the conditions under which the perceptual judgments are made. In Figure 13-6, the indifference interval is at 16 sec, approximately, for temporal estimates of stimuli that were presented during quiet but were judged during noise; the indifference interval is at 4 sec for temporal estimates of stimuli that were presented during noise but were judged during quiet. These curves show that "a response made in the presence of noise to a tone or light presented in the quiet is longer than a response made in the quiet to stimuli presented in noise" (p. 566). Thus, supporting adaptation-level theory, a change in the acoustic background against which a stimulus is presented does change its apparent duration. This holds, however, only for ambient auditory conditions; changes in ambient light conditions do not affect the reproduced temporal intervals. Nevertheless, it is clear that *an absolute indifferent interval does not exist apart from the series stimuli and background stimuli that are present in the judgmental situation.*

Although changes in ambient light conditions were not shown to influence judgments of temporal duration in the study by Hirsh, Bilger, and Deatherage (1956), data are available which indicate that the perceived length of lines is a function of the background or context within which the judgments are made. Künnapas (1955) performed a study in which the subjects were required to report whether a variable line was shorter, equal to, or longer than a constant line (50 mm long × 0.4 mm wide) when the constant line was presented in a square 7 × 7 cm and the variable was presented in a series of squares of larger size (9 × 9 cm, 12 × 12 cm, 16 × 16 cm). The results showed that as the size of the square (frame) became larger, the enclosed line appeared to be shorter, that is, the lengths of the variable line judged to be perceptually equal to the standard were in fact physically longer. For the four larger squares (from 9 × 9 cm to 21 × 21 cm), the point of subjective equality was found to be 51.33, 52.68, 54.16, and 55.63 mm, respectively. The larger the square, the longer (physically) must be the variable line in order for it to be judged perceptually equal to a constant line of 50 mm presented in the middle of a constant square. In terms of adaptation-level theory, *the direction of change in perceived length was,* as expected, *away from the frame and demonstrates the repellent effect of the anchoring stimulus.*

Judgmental Effects
Within and Between Stimulus Series

In this section we will consider two phenomena usually associated with visual perception: *contrast* and the so-called *paradoxical distance effect* (*PDE*); however, the presentation will be based not on visual data, but on a study dealing with lifted weights (Helson and Nash, 1960). In this study the subjects judged seven successive sets of weights. Each set contained five weights, with the difference between weights (stimuli) equal to 50 gm; the weights in Set I ranged from 100 to 300 gm; for Set II, 150 to 350 gm; for Set III, from 200 to 400 gm; for Set IV, 250 to 450 gm; for Set V, from 300 to 500 gm; for Set VI, 350 to 550 gm; for Set VII, from 400 to 600 gm. In the control condition, judgments for the various sets of weights were made in an ascending and descending order by the method of single stimuli (no anchor) according to a predetermined plan; nine categories of judgments were used ranging from very, very heavy, through medium, to very, very light. A week or two later, the procedure was repeated with a 90-gm or a 900-gm stimulus as the anchor (background). The anchor was lifted, but not judged, before each of the stimuli in each set, and the subjects were instructed "to judge the second weight by itself, not as a comparison with the first weight." In the treatment of data, the judgments given by the subjects were translated into numbers in steps of ten ranging from 10 for very, very light, through 50 for medium, to 90 for very, very heavy.

According to Helson and Nash, the results of this study reveal two major effects on the judgments of the series stimuli as a consequence of introducing the anchor (background) stimuli. The first effect is the contrast effect: *stimuli which are nearer the background in physical magnitude are displaced more in perceptual judgments than are stimuli farther from the background.* In Table 13-3, this may be seen in the data for

Table 13-3 Judgments of Seven Sets of Weights in Ascending and Descending Orders by Method of Single Stimuli (S.S.) and Following a 900-Gm Background Stimulus (B.S.) Showing Differential Effects of the Background on Stimuli within Sets (Contrast) and Between Sets (Paradoxical Distance Effect)

	Ascending Series Order											
Stimuli:	100	150	200	250	300	350	400	450	500	550	600	Total
S.S.:	20	41	61	75	86							
900 B.S.:	7	16	27	39	49							
Diff.:	−13	−25	−34	−36	−37							−145
S.S.:		34	48	62	72	80						
900 B.S.:		12	24	31	41	50						
Diff.:		−22	−24	−31	−31	−30						−138
S.S.:			39	58	70	83	89					
900 B.S.:			17	27	35	44	49					
Diff.:			−22	−31	−35	−39	−40					−167
S.S.:				48	64	72	81	90				
900 B.S.:				29	38	44	52	60				
Diff.:				−19	−26	−28	−29	−30				−132
S.S.:					50	62	76	82	89			
900 B.S.:					35	43	51	56	62			
Diff.:					−15	−19	−25	−26	−27			−112
S.S.:						55	65	77	86	88		
900 B.S.:						41	45	55	62	68		
Diff.:						−14	−20	−22	−24	−20		−100
S.S.:							58	68	80	83	88	
900 B.S.:							47	57	64	69	73	
Diff.:							−11	−11	−16	−14	−15	−67

Source: H. Helson and Myrtle C. Nash. Anchor, contrast and paradoxical distance effect. *J. exp. Psychol.,* 1960, **59,** 113–121.

the ascending series with the 900-gm anchor. Each row in Table 13-3 contains the data for one series of stimuli as judged without the anchor, that is, in the single stimulus condition (S.S.), and with the anchor, that is, with the 900-gm background stimulus (B.S.). Except for a few isolated inversions, the data in each row show that the larger stimuli are affected more by the anchor than the smaller stimuli. For example, in the lighter series (Set I: Weights 100 to 300 grams) the 100-gm stimulus was judged as 20 in the S.S. condition (without anchor) and as 7 in the 900-gm anchor condition; this is a decrease of 13 scale points from the S.S. to the anchor condition. The 300-gm stimulus, however, was judged as 86 in the S.S. condition and as 49 in the anchor condition, yielding a difference of 37. These data, and those for the other sets of weights, indicate that *there is a greater displacement of stimuli nearer the anchor than farther from the anchor.* This holds whether the anchor is heavier than the series (900 gm) or lighter than the series (90 gm). With the 90-gm anchor the lighter stimuli in each set are affected more than the heavier. This effect is a *within-series* effect, attributable to the repulsion produced by anchor stimuli, and is identified as a *contrast phenomenon.*

The second effect that may be seen by referring to Table 13-3 is *PDE.* This involves a comparison *between* series of stimuli. For example, in Table 13-3, the 100 to 300-gm series is displaced downward by 145 scale points (-145) with the 900-gm anchor, but the 350 to 550-gm series is displaced by only -100 scale points by the same anchor. This indicates that *the farther a given set of stimuli is from the anchor, the greater will be the total shift in judgments of the series due to the introduction of the anchor.* The 900-gm stimulus produces a greater effect on the total judgments of the lighter sets of stimuli than on the heavier sets; in the opposite direction, the 90-gm anchor produces a greater effect on the total judgments of the heavier sets than on the lighter sets.

The greater displacing effects of a remote anchor, when compared with a near anchor, are consistent with expectations from adaptation-level theory. Although we will not present all the findings of Helson and Nash (1960) with respect to changes in adaptation level produced by different backgrounds with various series stimuli, Table 13-4 shows the results for the 900-gm anchor. Recall that adaptation level is defined as the weighted geometric mean of series, background, and residual stimuli. It follows from this, for example, that averaging the 900-gm anchor with the 100 to 300-gm series raises the level more than averaging the 900-gm anchor with the 300 to 500 gm series. In Table 13-4, the calculated values of adaptation level are shown for the seven sets of weights under the two conditions: without anchor (single stimuli) and with anchor (900 gm). Notice that the anchor produces a shift in adaptation level of 152 scale points for the 100 to 300-gm series, but only a 48-point shift for the 400 to 600-gm series. Since a remote anchor affects the adaptation level more than a near anchor, the judgments dependent upon adaptation level will be correspondingly affected. The greater the shift in adaptation level, the greater the change in judgments from series to series. It appears, therefore, that adaptation-level theory can account for both classical *contrast* effects (intraseries effects) and *paradoxical distance effects* (interseries effects) on the basis of the interaction of series stimuli and background stimuli.

Table 13-4 Shifts in Adaptation Level in Direction of Background Stimuli with Greater Movement in Sets Farther from Value of Background as Analogue of *PDE* (Ascending Order)

	Adaptation Level		
Stimulus Sets	Single Stimuli	900-Gm Background	Diff.
100–300	165	317	+152[a]
150–350	202	357	+155[a]
200–400	227	404	+177[a]
250–450	257	380	+123[a]
300–500	301	398	+97[a]
350–550	332	415	+83[a]
400–600	361	409	+48[b]

[a] $p < 0.01$.
[b] $p < 0.05$.

Source: H. Helson and Myrtle C. Nash, Anchor, contrast and paradoxical distance effect. *J. exp. Psychol.,* 1960, 59, 113–121.

Residual Influences
on Perceptual Judgments

Adaptation-level theory asserts that judgments of physical, aesthetic, and symbolic objects are dependent upon the pooled effect of three classes of variables: contextual, focal, and organismic. The pooled effect of these three classes of variables establishes the adaptation level or the level of adjustment which underlies all forms of behavior. We have already considered in the preceding sections of this chapter some experiments in which the outer determinants of behavior (contextual and focal stimuli) effected changes in adaptation level and, accordingly, changes in perceptual judgments. Now we will describe some representative experiments involving the inner determinants of behavior, that is, organismic variables, and show how changes in the variables of this class affect perception.

One of the most important influences on behavior is the effect of past experience; in an appropriately designed experiment the effect of past experience as an organismic variable may be demonstrated. In an experiment with lifted weights (DiLollo, 1964), one group of subjects judged the heaviness of a heavy (H) series of weights (400 to 600 gm) and a second group judged a light (L) series of weights (100 to 300 gm). The stimuli of each series were separated by steps of 50 gm. Nine categories of judgment were used ranging from very, very heavy, through medium, to very, very light. Following the initial (training) trials, the two groups of subjects were shifted to the opposite series for the testing trials. Two nonshifted groups served as controls.

The results of this study are shown in Figure 13-7. Four curves are shown, two for the experimental (reversed) group (designated as HL and LH) and two for the control group (designated HH and LL). In the training trials, the only significant variable on the level of judgment was the specific series of weights being judged, that is, the heavy series gave higher scale values than the light; but, in the testing

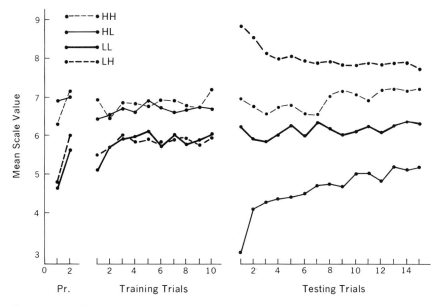

Figure 13-7. Scale values of lifted-weight judgments for four groups of subjects in training trials and testing trials. The two control groups (HH and LL) judged the same series of weights (H, Heavy Series, or L, Light Series) in both training and test trials. The two experimental groups (HL or LH) judged a heavy series or a light series in the training trials and then shifted to the opposite series in the testing trials. (From DiLollo, *J. exp. Psychol.*, 1964.)

series, the control (nonreversed groups, HH and LL) gave judgments similar to the training trials while the experimental (reversed groups, LH and HL) showed a marked shift in judgments. For the LH group, the obtained scale values showed a marked rise, while the HL group showed a marked downward shift. This indicates that before the shift, the H series was judged heavier than the L series; after the shift, the H series was perceived as heavier by the upward-shifted group (LH) than by the control group (HH), and the L series was perceived as lighter by the downward-shifted group (HL) than by the control group (LL). *These results clearly demonstrate the effects of prior experience on succeeding judgments of lifted weights.* Also, these findings suggest the possibility of using adaptation-level theory to account for the effects obtained in a learning situation following shifts in the amount of incentive (Crespi, 1942).

The influence of contextual factors has also been shown by Helson and Bevan (1964) who demonstrated that *judgments of relative size for visual stimuli are affected when stimulus variables are manipulated within groups,* rather than across (between) groups. In a series of experiments designed to study the variables involved in the overestimation of areal size as a visual illusion, one experiment was performed in which each of three randomized groups judged a series of seven stimuli. The overall dimensions of the series stimuli varied from 1.5 in. × 2.0 in. to 10.5 in. ×

14 in., with each card being 1.5 in. wider and 2.0 in. longer than the preceding card in the series. The central black area was the area to be judged in size and was held physically constant; since the background (white) size was increased, this resulted in a series of stimuli in which the central black area covered a different amount of the total area of the card. For the first group, this was 21 percent; for the second, 53 percent, and for the third, 81 percent.

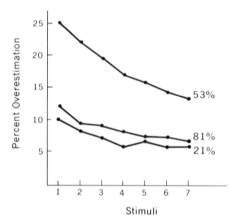

Figure 13-8. Error of overestimation in the judged area of a central black area, held physically constant, as the size of the white background is varied from Stimulus Card 1 to 7. The parameters indicate the relative size, in per cent, of the area judged to the background. (From Helson and Bevan, *J. exp. Psychol.*, 1964.)

The results are presented in Figure 13-8 and indicate that a constant error of overestimation was obtained in each group. It was largest for the intermediate-sized black area (53 percent) and approximately equal for the other two series of stimuli (21 percent and 81 percent). However, unlike the findings of another experiment in this series in which the subjects experienced no variation in the overall size of the stimulus and showed no change in overestimation as a function of the size of the test card, the present data show that the error of estimation was inversely related to the size of the stimulus field. In each of the three groups, the largest error was obtained with the smallest overall size of the test field. This demonstrates the importance of *contextual* factors. Each subject was allowed to experience the central black area on different sizes of field, and the overestimation was found to vary with changes in this variable for each of the three groups. Since comparisons between groups exposed to different field size did not show such differences, it may be concluded that it was *the manipulation of the variable within groups* which produced the effect, thereby supporting adaptation-level theory and *stressing the role of prior experience as a contributing factor in visual perception.*

Another experiment in which a residual factor was involved is that of Künnapas (1957). In an attempt to explain the vertical-horizontal illusion, Künnapas proposed that the elliptical form of the visual field might exert some influence in this situation in which a vertical line is overestimated as compared with a horizontal line of equal physical length. Since it was established that the size of the visual frame influences judgments of length (Künnapas, 1955), it was hypothesized that the vertical line would be overemphasized as the visual field has the form of a horizontal ellipse, that is, the major axis extends in the horizontal direction and the minor axis, in the vertical direction. Thus, if two lines of equal length are drawn at right angles starting at the center of the ellipse, the frame will be closer to the end of the vertical line than to the horizontal line and the vertical line should appear longer. However, given two luminous lines, the illusion should be reduced or disappear in the dark since there would be no visible boundary (frame) under this condition to distort the judgments.

Künnapas tested his hypothesis by using an L shaped stimulus consisting of two luminous lines; the horizontal line provided a standard stimulus of 50 mm and the vertical line was the variable stimulus that could be adjusted from 35 to 60 mm by turning a knob. A comparison of the judgments made in light and in darkness showed that in the dark condition there was a significant reduction of 33 percent in the illusion. These results are consistent with the prediction and show that *the shape of the visual field does influence perceived length by contributing,* according to adaptation-level theory, *to the residual component* in the behavioral equation.

Adaptation-Level Theory and Learning

While there is considerable controversy in psychology regarding the conditions and principles involved in learning, there is no question that, as a minimal requirement, learning depends upon experience. If learning is considered as a kind of adaptation to the environmental situation, then it may be interpreted within the context of adaptation-level theory and the principles of frequency, contiguity, reinforcement, discontinuous learning, and so on, may be taken as factors or phenomena that affect adaptation level, or that are manifestations of adaptation level. Learning viewed in this way can be considered essentially as the result of the interaction between present stimulation and residual effects from prior stimulation, given a particular state of the organism at the time learning occurs. By varying the relative contribution of present and residual factors, it is possible to subsume some of the unique problems in the area of learning under adaptation-level theory. For example, "insightful" learning might be considered as a learning situation in which present stimulation is considerably more important than residual effects from prior stimulation. It would appear, therefore, that adaptation-level theory could be used to account for certain types of learning if the problems were restated in terms of the relative significance of focal and background stimuli as opposed to residual stimuli resulting from experience or prior practice.

Reinforcement and Reinforcing Stimuli

The classic work of Crespi (1942) on the effects of differential reinforcement has led to a large number of experiments designed to identify the significant characteristics of reinforcement in the learning situation. Some psychologists have argued that the asymptotic running speed of rats in a straight alley (runway) is determined by the effects of contrasting amounts of reward in two concurrent learning situations. Bower (1961) found that if rats were given eight pellets of food in one alley and were alternated over a series of trials with one pellet in another alley, their asymptotic running speed was not significantly different from that of a control group that always received eight pellets, but that it did differ from that of a one-pellet control group. This is identified as a *downward "contrast" effect* in which the effectiveness of a small reward is reduced when it is presented in a learning situation where the organism sometimes receives a reward of larger magnitude. Others contend that it is not the contrast or interactive effect of differential rewards that produces differences in response, but the *absolute magnitudes* of the rewards that produce the differences. Goldstein and Spence (1963) have reported that for four groups of rats that were differentially reinforced (that is, received a reward of ten and zero, ten and one, ten and five, or five and one pellets in each of two alleys for seventy-five trials) there were no differences in the asymptotic performance of the three groups that received ten pellets of reward in one alley, despite the fact that they received zero, one, or five pellets in the other alley. Also, comparing the running speeds to reward magnitudes of zero, one, and five pellets, it was found that there was a consistent rise in the function for the same three groups. These results suggest that *the asymptotic performance level in a differential conditioning situation is a function of the absolute magnitude of the reward, rather than a contrast effect.* It should be noted, however, that Helson (1964a) has reinterpreted the data of Goldstein and Spence and has concluded that "higher reward ratios are paralleled by higher running ratios, thus showing the existence of contrast or relative effects of reward as well as of the absolute effects" (pp. 443–444).

As examples of the research literature in this area, the studies by Bower and by Goldstein and Spence typify one of the controversial issues concerning reinforcement. Bevan and Adamson (1960) have attempted to approach a resolution to the magnitude problem by applying adaptation-level theory. In this, they have distinguished between reinforcement as an *internal process* and reinforcers as *stimulus agents;* in addition, they have taken the position that if reinforcement could be shown to possess certain demonstrable properties, then the theory of adaptation level could be appropriately applied to a wide variety of problems in the area of learning.

In the first of three experiments in this series, Bevan and Adamson (1960) attempted to determine whether electric shock, which has been used in many experiments as a reinforcer, would yield different indifference points for different magnitudes of shock presented with different relative frequencies of occurrence. Five intensities of shock (1300 to 3300 μ amp AC with a pulse rate of 100 cps) were used with a control series (rectangular distribution) in which each shock was presented equally often (20 times) in random order, and in two other types of distribution: positively skewed (30, 25, 20, 15, 10 times for the weakest to strongest stimuli) and more positively skewed (35, 30, 20, 10, and 5 times for each stimulus from weakest to strongest). For each series the subject was required to judge the magnitude of the shock on a rating scale with nine categories from very, very weak, through medium, to very, very strong. It was found that for the rectangular distribution, the indifference point was 2287 μ amp; for the positively skewed distribution it was 2087 μ amp; and for the more positively skewed distribution it was 1900 μ amp. This indicates that as the smaller shock magnitudes were presented more often, the intensity judged medium decreased systematically, and consequently the judgments of intensity for the series as a whole tended to increase. Thus, the first experiment demonstrated that *the effective values of shock magnitudes are a function of internal norms* (adaptation level) *and can be scaled by psychophysical methods* to yield data consistent with the expectations from adaptation-level theory.

The second experiment was designed to show that, if the adaptation-level concepts were applicable to the reinforcement problem, the efficiency of performance would be dependent upon the *effective* value of the reinforcing agent (stimulus) rather than on its physical magnitude. This contrast effect has already been described in relation to the work cited for Crespi (1942) and Bower (1961). In a pretest situation, three groups of subjects (A, B, and C) were used with each subject receiving 30 shocks of a given magnitude at 10-sec intervals; the shock magnitudes for the three groups were, respectively, 1300, 2300, and 3300 μ amp. Following the pretest, all subjects were required to make five trips through a 2-choice bolt-head maze problem with 28 units; each time the subject made contact with the incorrect bolthead of each unit, he received a single shock on his wrist of 2300 μ amp for 200-msec. It was predicted that if performance is a function of the apparent (effective) value of the shock, the three groups would show differential performance on the maze problem, that is, the constant shock stimulus in the learning situation would have a different effective value for each group and this value would be dependent upon the prior exposure in the pretest situation (the prevailing adaptation level).

The results of this study are shown in Figure 13-9. Since the three curves are significantly different, the experimental hypothesis is supported by the data. For Group A, the reinforcing shock was greater in physical magnitude than in the pretest situation; for Group B, it was the same; for Group C, it was less. Performance in the learning situation differed for the three groups even though all groups received the same physical magnitude of shock for each incorrect choice in the maze. The apparent intensity of shock was greatest for Group A and acquisition was most rapid; performance was poorest for Group C in which the reinforcement was relatively weak relative to the pretest; and Group B (control) showed a performance level intermediate to these two. The results indicate that *the effects of a reinforcing stimulus depend upon the prevailing adaptation level* of the subjects in the experimental situation *which*, in turn, *is a function of prior experience.*

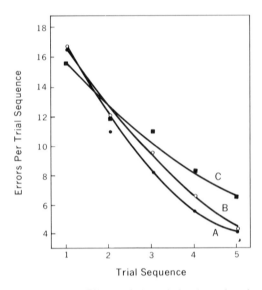

Figure 13-9. Effects of the relative intensity of reinforcing shock to pretest adaptational shock as measured in a learning task using a bolthead maze. For all groups, the reinforcing shock was equivalent in magnitude, but for Groups A, B, and C it was respectively, greater than, equal to, and less than the pretest shock. (From Bevan and Adamson, *J. exp. Psychol.*, 1960.)

In the third experiment, data were collected to determine whether maze performance would vary as a function of the average intensity of the reinforcing agent. The basic design compared the performance of a control group (Group C′, a shock of 2300 μ amp for each error) with (1) a group (Group C) receiving a symmetrical distribution of shocks with the same mean intensity as the control group, (that is, 7, 22, 42, 22, and 7 percent of 70 shocks distributed among five shock intensities ranging from weak to strong), and (2) two groups receiving positively and negatively skewed distributions of shocks. One of these latter groups (Group A) received on incorrect trials 70 shocks distributed as follows: 31, 26, 22, 14, and 7 percent, weakest to strongest, with a mean of 200 μ amp; the other group (Group B) received a negatively skewed distribution (7, 14, 22, 26, and 31 percent, weakest to strongest) with a mean intensity of 2600 μ amp. It was anticipated that the performance of Group C and Group C′ would not differ since the mean intensity of shock was the same for the two groups; Groups A and B, however, were expected to show differential performance, since one group (Group A) had a lower mean shock intensity than the control group, while the other group (Group B) had a higher mean shock intensity.

The results of this experiment are shown in Figure 13-10. As expected, the performance for Group C and C′ do not differ significantly, and the data for these two groups were combined for the subsequent analyses. The poorest performance

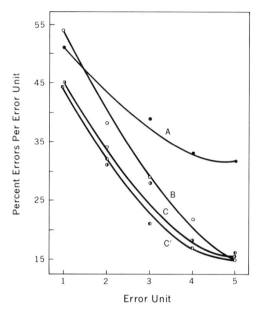

Figure 13-10. Maze performance as a function of the mean intensity of reinforcing shock. For Group A the mean intensity was 2000 μamp; for Group B, 2600 μamp; for Groups C and C', 2300 μamp. Five different shock intensities were used with different frequencies of occurrence for Groups A, B, and C, but only one intensity was used for Group C. (From Bevan and Adamson, *J. exp. Psychol.,* 1960.)

was given by Group A (lowest mean intensity of shock) and the next poorest, by Group B (highest mean intensity of shock). The best performance was given by the two groups (Group C and C') which received the same mean shock of intermediate intensity. The results indicate, therefore, that *the level of performance is a function of mean intensity level,* with the best performance obtaining for *intermediate* values of negative (shock) reinforcement. When these findings are considered in conjunction with other data, it may be concluded that *the pooling* (adaptation level) *model may be used for the investigation of reinforcement problems.*

The assumptions of the Bevan-Adamson (1963) model of reinforcement have been summarized by Helson (1964*b*, p. 448) as follows:

1. Primary stimuli (S_p) and background stimuli (S_b) can be differentiated by organisms in a learning situation.

2. Stimuli are averaged over time to produce organismic norms ($\bar{S}$). These norms are weighted averages where

$$\bar{S} = \frac{(S_{p1} + S_{p2} + \ldots + S_{pn})^x}{N_p} \cdot \frac{(S_{b1} + S_{b2} + \ldots S_{bn})^y}{N_b}, \qquad (13\text{-}13)$$

and N_p and N_b refer, respectively, to the number of primary and secondary stimuli and x and y are weighting coefficients which indicate the relative contribution of these stimuli to the internal norm.

3. The magnitude of the reinforcing stimulus (S_p) produces a reinforcing effect which is a direct function of the difference (ΔS) between S_p and the prevailing norm, $\bar{S}$.

4. The magnitude of the reinforcing stimulus (S_p) also produces a reinforcing effect which is related to the tension or drive level (D) of the organism which, in turn, has temporal continuity and reflects the amount of deprivation, physiological condition, etc., of the organism. There is a curvilinear relation between D-level and performance, with maximal performance at medium levels of D and poorer performance for low and high levels.

5. The effectiveness of reinforcing stimuli is, therefore, a function of both ΔS and D acting concurrently.

A number of implications follow from the Bevan-Adamson model (Helson, 1964*b*, pp. 448–451). Within the general context of this textbook, three of these should be mentioned. First, there is the experimental indication that *reinforcing stimuli*, like psychophysical stimuli, *can be scaled on continua possessing a neutral region or a region of indifference;* also, these stimuli exhibit *series* and *anchor* effects. Second, *reinforcing stimuli,* such as psychophysical stimuli, *exhibit an effectiveness which depends upon the existing levels of stimulation.* These stimuli do not, therefore, possess fixed values, but if the reinforcing stimulus is above its background level, it will seem intense; if below, it will seem weak. Consequently performance may be expected to vary as some function of the effectiveness of the reinforcing stimuli. Third, from the concept of sensory adaptation, it would appear that *with repetition the effectiveness of reinforcing stimuli should be reduced,* that is, since reinforcing stimuli tend to shift the prevailing level in their own direction, the difference between S_p and $\bar{S}$ would be reduced, and the reinforcing effectiveness of the stimuli would also be reduced. It may be seen, therefore, that the Bevan-Adamson model may be applied to a wide variety of reinforcement situations. The important point for our purposes is that the model brings learning theory and motivation into juxtaposition with psychophysical theory. Both approaches utilize the pooling concepts of adaptation-level theory in which given stimuli are evaluated in terms of internal norms. Thus, a rapprochement between learning theory and psychophysics may eventually be achieved via adaptation-level theory.

Background and Contextual Stimuli as Factors Affecting Learning

In discussing adaptation-level theory and perceptual judgments, it was shown that background and contextual stimuli were important factors in determining the responses made under a wide variety of experimental situations. Likewise, background and contextual stimuli are significant factors in learning.

Peterson and Peterson (1957) demonstrated this in a study dealing with the influence of contextual stimuli in verbal learning. Four nonsense syllables (VIH, VES, XEH, XIJ) were used as stimuli which had to be associated with four verbal responses (foot, salt, lamp, moon). The contextual stimuli consisted of nonsense syllables which appeared on two colors of paper (red and green). This produced two responses for each color since each color was paired with two nonsense sylla-bles. The arrangement made it impossible for the acquisition task to be learned by associating the contextual stimuli with the responses. During the acquisition trials, one of the two responses following a particular color occurred twice as frequently as the other; the subjects were instructed to avoid the distraction of the colored backgrounds. In the test trials, the subjects were instructed to respond with the first of the English words that had been learned and that occurred to them as they were presented with a dot on colored paper.

The results of this study showed that a colored background acquired discrim-inative properties for the high-frequency response, for example, when the red-colored background was presented alone, it was responded to with the high-frequency word salt rather than the low-frequency word "foot." Transfer was also tested and it was found to be greater in new paired-associates learning when the same background color was used with the response word in the acquisition and transfer trials. These findings support the contention that *contextual stimuli are important in human learning.*

Postman and Phillips (1964) have also demonstrated the effects of context by studying contexts with high and low meaningfulness in the acquisition and reten-tion of paired associates. The learning task consisted of a list of ten paired associ-ates containing words selected according to a criterion of medium frequency of usage. The stimulus members of each pair were always presented in the context of two irrelevant items so that a given list had items of high frequency of usage (HC) or low frequency (LC). This provided two arrangements of the lists of paired associates to be learned, with each arrangement having contextual items of differ-ent word frequency (high and low). In the acquisition trials, the subject read aloud the three words presented simultaneously (the stimulus and the two con-textual items) and was required to call out the response member of the pair dur-ing the period of anticipation (4 sec). Learning was continued until the subject was able to respond on a single trial with eight correct anticipations for the list of ten paired associates.

The results of the acquisition phase of the study are shown in Figure 13-11. In the early stages of acquisition there is no difference between the two conditions (high and low frequency of word usage). For the higher criteria of performance (five or more correct responses), the rates of learning do diverge. Learning was faster when the meaningfulness (word frequency) of the contextual items was low rather than high. This suggests that the disadvantage of the high-frequency group may be attributable to the *cumulative effects of intraserial interference.*

However, while the meaningfulness of the contextual items hindered learning, it favored retention. When retention was measured both 30 sec and 7 days after the end of original learning, the mean number of responses recalled was greater for the stimuli presented in the context of the more meaningful (high frequency)

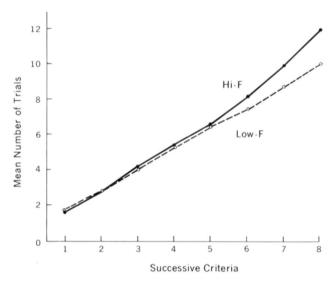

Figure 13–11. Performance curves in a verbal learning task with two levels of meaningfulness of contextual items. (From Postman and Phillips, *Amer. J. Psychol.*, 1964.)

words. This study indicates that context does produce a significant effect in a verbal learning situation; *the more meaningful the context, the better the retention of paired associates, but the poorer the acquisition of responses.* Thus, whether contextual stimuli will facilitate or interfere with verbal performance depends upon the specific psychological process involved in the particular experimental situation, for example, acquisition or retention.

These findings serve to supplement the classic work of Pan (1926) who studied contextual verbal cues "logically related" to the responses in paired associate learning. In this situation the subjects had to give the response member of a pair, after seeing the stimulus member, but the context conditions under which the pairs were presented varied in the learning and recall sessions. There were six context conditions used in the study: (1) no context (control), (2) unrelated context (no relation of the two added words to stimulus or response members of a pair) (3) context related to response word, (4) context related to stimulus word, (5) context related to both stimulus and response words, and (6) context was a number, not a word.

The results of this study showed that learning was facilitated by three kinds of contexts: (1) a context in which the extraneous word was related logically to the *response* member of the paired associates, (2) a context in which the extraneous words were related to both the stimulus and response members of the paired associates, and (3) a variable context in which the background (extraneous) word was changed during the acquisition trials, but was always related to the response word. The remaining three context conditions were detrimental to learning, including the conditions in which the extraneous words were related to the *stimulus* members or were unrelated to both members of the pair. In the recall situation, it was found that if the context present in original learning was removed, recall was impaired, provided the context was logically related to the response; if the context was related to the stimulus and it was not present in recall, recall was not impaired. While, in general, recall was aided by a context which was related to the response word of the paired associates, a variable context was decidedly detrimental to recall. These findings show that contexts do influence learning and recall, but *the influence of the context is dependent upon the degree of relationship between the context and the stimulus or response members of the paired associates.*

The Effects of Practice on Adaptation Level

Although in the preceding paragraphs we have indicated how some of the material in the area of learning may be treated within the framework of adaptation-level theory, we have not considered the manner in which learning per se may affect adaptation level. If judgments are affected by practice or prior experience, then we should expect that estimates of adaptation level should vary in some manner over trials until a point of judgmental stabilization has been reached. Helson (1959) has indicated that learning is involved in the formation of a stable adaptation level, but the theory of adaptation level does not directly specify the course of adaptation level as a function of practice.

This problem has been studied by Rambo and Johnson (1964). They performed and replicated an experiment in which estimates of adaptation level were obtained from judgments of numerousness over a series of 45 trials. The stimuli consisted of nine cards with unsystematic patterns containing 5, 7, 10, 14, 19, 26, 36, 49, or 68 dots. Each of these 9-dot patterns was reproduced in five different patterns, thereby providing a set of 45 cards. The cards were exposed randomly for 0.1 sec, each tachistoscopically, and the subjects were required to judge the numerousness of the dots on a 9-category scale ranging from very large, through average, to very small.

The data of this study were manipulated statistically to provide the regression of the average judgments across groups on the logarithm of the stimulus magnitudes. From this straight line, values of adaptation level were obtained by computing the predicted stimulus magnitudes for the category of "average" judgments. These results are shown in Figure 13-12 in which AL is plotted as a function of trials. There is a marked nonlinear increase in AL with succeeding trials. The best-fitting curve for the experimental values of AL is a hyperbolic function: $AL = T/(0.0755 + 0.0451T)$, where T represents trials. The ordinate asymptote was estimated to be 22.17 and defines the terminal value of AL, or the final value of AL, after it has completely stabilized in a judgmental situation. During the very early trials, there is a very rapid shift in AL but, within five trials, AL has reached a value corresponding to approximately 77 percent of its final value. In ten trials, AL has reached approximately 86 percent of its final value. The next thirty-five trials produce a shift in AL of only about 14 percent. It may be concluded that the *estimates of AL move toward a stable value in accordance with a*

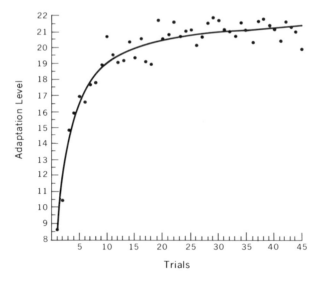

Figure 13-12. Adaptation level as a hyperbolic function of the number of trials. (From Rambo and Johnson, *Amer. J. Psychol.*, 1964.)

negatively accelerated hyperbolic function. These findings are consistent with those of Johnson (1949) who reported that judgments of pitch were affected by learning after a shift in the stimulus series.

Additional Implications
of Adaptation-Level Theory

In the earlier portions of this chapter we have seen how adaptation-level theory relates to certain areas of psychology, such as psychophysics, perception, and learning. This treatment of adaptation-level theory was not intended to be exhaustive, but exemplary. The implications of adaptation-level theory, however, have been found to extend into other areas of psychology; these will not be considered in detail, but a few studies will be mentioned to reveal the wide range of problems encompassed by the theory.

Affective Behavior

Feelings and emotions, as motivational states, may serve to initiate, sustain, and direct the behavior of individuals under a given set of circumstances. Since affective states, like sensory processes, exhibit bipolarity ranging from pleasantness to unpleasantness, it follows that there is a transitional zone (neutral or indifferent region) between these two extremes and that changes in this affective level should be evidenced by behavioral changes in a given situation. Culbert and Posner (1960) showed that the effective level of annoyance produced by jet-aircraft noises could be altered by repeated presentation of these noises until habituation occurred. When subjects were required to equate the annoyance level of jet-airplane and propeller-airplane noises, the difference in SPL (sound pressure level) between the two was successively decreased from the first test session, through the second, to the third. That is, with repeated exposure the jet noise became less annoying to the subjects.

In terms of adaptation-level theory, *the indifferent zone moved in the direction of stimulation,* thereby serving to neutralize stimulation that would otherwise continue to be as annoying as it was on the first presentation. The important point regarding the effects of habituation to affective stimuli is that, classically, habituation was considered simply to neutralize or reduce the effects of stimulation. The repeated presentation of pleasant or unpleasant stimuli leads to an affective state of neutrality. Adaptation-level theory, however, not only accounts for shifts from pleasantness or unpleasantness to neutrality (indifference) but also *predicts a reversal of affect* (passing through the neutral zone) with continued repetition of stimulation (Helson, 1964b, p. 373). Consider, for example, the affective changes in the child who, given a box of chocolates, proceeds to eat his first, second, third, tenth, and twentieth piece of candy. Adaptation-level theory, then, may be utilized as a point of departure for developing experiments related to affective responses and motivational problems and, alternately, may serve to account for reported findings through such concepts as habituation, affective equilibrium (as in approach-avoidance conflict situations), pooling of aesthetic experiences, and discrepancies between "expected" stimulus magnitudes and adaptation level.

Cognitive Processes

Another area of interest in contemporary psychology involves cognitive processes. For many psychologists, such processes as cognition, thinking, and memory are forms of behavior that may be observed and studied in the same way as many other types of behavior, although not so readily or easily as behaviors with motor components. For the adaptation-level theorist, cognitive processes are considered to be biologically important since they assist the organism in adapting to its environment; as behavioral processes, these processes are held to be lawful and regular. The laws pertaining to cognition and thinking have the same formal structural properties as those pertaining to sensory, perceptual, or other psychological phenomena. This does not mean, however, that thinking and perception, as examples of typical behavior, are systematically identical; in fact, many writers have attempted to identify significant dimensions by means of which these two processes may be differentiated.

To determine, in part, whether the concept of adaptation level is appropriate in dealing with cognitive processes, we will consider IQ as an acceptable index of cognitive ability or level (Helson, 1964b, p. 486). In this setting, level may be measured in terms of the individual's best intellectual performance, given a test in which the items are graded for increasing difficulty from easy to hard (a power test). According to this view, cognitive (adaptive) level may be considered as the point of transition from easy to hard items. If the adaptation level in this situation follows the same trend as in psychophysics, we would expect an intellectual adjustment depending upon the specific tasks presented in a given testing situation.

Heim (1955) showed that in the measurement of intelligence there is adaptation to the level of difficulty of the items and to the rate of work. When a short time limit is imposed on a first test, there is an increased rate of work on a second test, but when the first test has a longer time limit, there is a slower rate of work on the second test. This indicates that the subjects adapt successively from test to test, that is, that *rate of work functions as a residual effect.* The level of difficulty also produces adaptation effects. When difficult items are included in a set of easy items, performance is poorer on the difficult items than when they are included in a set of difficult items. Apparently the subjects adapt immediately to a given level of difficulty as they perform on a test. If the items of a test are generally easy, performance tends to be poorer on harder (out of context) items. Also, successive adaptation occurs in test performance. Given a test with difficult items first and an easy test second, subjects will adapt to a high level of difficulty and will perform better on difficult items on the second (easy) test than will subjects who took the easy test first and the hard test (with the criterion items) second. The results of this study indicate that the measured cognitive level of an individual will depend upon (1) the conditions that serve to establish the individual's adaptation level to the testing instrument and (2) the residual testing factors within the individual. It may be, therefore, that the often-reported lack of stability or constancy of the IQ is attributable in some degree to the operation of these two sets of factors, rather than reflecting primarily the effects of changes in the individual's home or school environment. *The conditions that control the adaptation of the individual to the measuring instrument must be considered as significant variables in the assessment of cognitive ability.*

Personality

The final area of psychology to which adaptation-level theory will be applied in this book is personality. While dozens of different definitions of "personality" may be found in the psychological literature, a common element in many of these definitions is that the behavior patterns of an individual tend to be consistent in a wide variety of situations and to persist for long periods of time. These characteristics of behavioral consistency and persistence are part of the individual's unique mode of responding and this uniqueness, in turn, is held by many to reflect some inner (organismic) factors which determine the behavior. According to this view, personality depends upon the composite of inner determinants—the precise nature of these determinants being described by the particular theory of personality espoused by a particular psychologist.

In contrast to this approach to personality which emphasizes the inner (organismic) factors determining behavior, adaptation-level theory stresses *stimulus variables as sources of variance in personality characteristics and in interpersonal situations* (Helson, 1964*b*, p. 522). In a general way, an interpersonal or social situation may be considered to consist of focal, background, and residual stimuli. At a given moment, a particular person provides focal stimuli, other individuals provide the background stimuli against which the primary social interaction is occurring, and still others, as residual stimuli from prior situations, serve to influence the individual's behavioral patterns. It is surprising that many psychologists dealing with social behavior do not recognize the intrinsic nature of this situation in terms of stimulus variables. The interpersonal reactions that take place are responses to stimulus elements, some auditory, some visual, some tactile, some olfactory, and so on. Social behavior in this view is mediated, at least in part, by the activation of sensory processes; these processes require stimulus inputs from the attendant conditions in the environment, whether they are in the form of facial expressions, gestures, verbalized attitudes or expectations, or other kinds of "social" stimuli.

We will consider only one study in this area. It is the study of Podell (1961) in which he determined the relative influence of background stimuli on the ratings of personality traits. From a list of seventy-eight traits scaled by the method of equal-appearing intervals, thirty-one words were selected designating favorable, neutral, and unfavorable personality characteristics. On the equal-interval scale, these items varied in 0.2 step intervals, with a value of 1.2 for most favorable to 6.6 for most unfavorable. From the list of thirty-one words, three favorable traits (capable, informed, and considerate) and three unfavorable traits (mediocre, smug, and harsh) were designated as background stimuli (the initial list). The subjects were given one of the two sets of background words and were required to pick out four words from the remaining twenty-five words (the check list) that were "most likely to describe the kind of person denoted by the background terms." It was predicted that the favorableness of the terms chosen would lie "somewhere between that of the initial list and that of the check list." The three favorable words in the initial list had an arithmetic mean value of 1.80 and the check list had a mean scale value of 3.6.

The results showed that the four favorable words selected had a mean scale value of 1.89 which fell, as predicted, between the value of the favorable terms on the initial list and the value of the check list. However, the obtained value of 1.89 was not significantly greater than that of the background words (1.80). For the unfavorable words, the obtained mean of the four chosen words (5.12) was, as predicted, significantly below that of the background words (5.33). The results are in both instances consistent with adaptation-level theory. Furthermore, an analysis of the data was performed to determine the relative contribution of the initial and final (check) lists on the selection of the four personality terms. It was found that the influence of the initial lists was from 5 to 19 times greater than that of the check list. *The meaning of words, then, depends not only on the context in which they appear, but is influenced to a much greater extent by preceding words that provide the background against which specific words are interpreted.*

Comment

Many other studies could have been cited in this chapter to illustrate the general applicability of adaptation-level theory; nevertheless, the studies that were described should suffice to support the view that the theory provides a quantitative approach to problems in widely diverse areas of psychology. It identifies three sources of variance (focal, background, and residual stimuli) which pool their effects to establish a neutral zone (adaptation level) that serves as a reference for an individual's responses in a given situation. While the theory brings together a number of significant factors in an operationally meaningful way, it should not be assumed that the theory has reached its final stage of development (Corso, 1967). Parducci *et al.* (1960) have argued that adaptation level should not be taken as the weighted logarithmic mean of the stimulus series, but as the weighted mean of the *median* and the *midpoint* (defined as the mean of the end members) of the presented stimuli, or the logarithmic *mean of the two end values* of the series. More recently, Engel and Parducci (1961) have proposed a modification of the theory in which the value of each stimulus used in calculating adaptation level is specified in terms of the "weighted mean of the stimulus and its simultaneously presented background." Whether these or other modifications of the theory are subsequently justified, the general concept of adaptation level (stated in operational and quantitative form) appears to be well-established and provides a basis for the understanding of behavior in the substantive areas of psychology.

Chapter 14

SENSORY DEPRIVATION

Orientation

The reader who has proceeded systematically from the beginning of this book to the present chapter has been exposed repeatedly to the view that human behavior is dependent in part upon the stimulus conditions that exist in the environment. When the individual is exposed to these conditions, certain psychological processes are initiated, modified or sustained, and certain behavioral consequences may be observed. Some of the fundamental laws and general theories that relate to these functional dependencies between stimuli and responses have been described in detail in the preceding chapters. Now we will consider an alternative situation.

Suppose than an individual is placed in an environment which does not contain the kinds of stimulation that are normally encountered in our daily lives. Consider that the individual is isolated and restricted in a small chamber in which there is no light or sound; in addition, he is instructed to lie on a bed as still and as quiet as possible. One day passes, then two, or three or more. What happens to man's psychological processes under these conditions in which all stimuli transmitted to the brain are reduced to a minimum? This is a state of *sensory deprivation* (SD); the usual daily exposure to stimulation is absent. How does man function in this new and strange environment? What effect does the lack of stimulation have on perceptual judgments? On learning? On problem-solving behavior? These are the kinds of questions with which we are now concerned.

From our earlier consideration in Chapters 8 and 9 of the kinesthetic, auditory, cutaneous, olfactory, and other sensory systems, it should be apparent that it is impossible to produce a state of complete sensory deprivation in an experimental situation in which a human subject is expected to respond to various forms of stimulation, or lack of stimulation. Even in a soundproof room in which all sounds from external sources have been excluded, the subject will hear his "heart pound-ing" as the blood moves through blood vessels near the ear; his stomach will "growl" or "rumble," and he will also hear the sounds he generates while breath-ing. Sensory stimulation will be provided through muscular movement of various parts of the body; changes in body temperature or room temperature may be de-tected; dryness of the throat and mouth will be noted; body odors may arise; touch sensations will be present whenever the cutaneous receptors are stimulated by clothing or come into contact with hard surfaces or materials. The term *sensory deprivation* is in this sense a misnomer; it implies that the level of stimulation is be-low the absolute threshold for the various sensory modalities.

In the present context, the term *sensory deprivation* will be used merely to indicate that the level of stimulation has been *reduced* or *altered* in such a manner that it no longer conforms to an individual's normal range of exposure, nor to the usual variety. More specifically, sensory deprivation will be used to include at least two kinds of experimental situations: (1) the *absolute reduction* situation in which efforts are directed toward the elimination of stimulus inputs to the organism from the external environment; and (2) the *reduced patterning* situation in which the stimu-lus-input levels are maintained near normal, but the patterns inherent in the input are modified or destroyed. Whenever the emphasis in a given situation is on the social dimension, that is, on the absence of interpersonal relations in a par-ticular setting, the term *isolation* or *sensory isolation* is commonly used. Such isolation may involve the actual loss of personal contact, the absence of speech and its asso-ciated acoustic patterns, the visual separation of the experimenter and the subject, and other interpersonal restrictions. Thus, problems, theories, and research in this area are designated as falling within the general domain of experimental depriva-tion and, whenever methodological distinctions are to be emphasized or identi-fied, the subcategories of sensory deprivation, perceptual deprivation, and sensory isolation are often employed as descriptive terms.

The problem of SD is not new. It has existed since prehistoric times in the form of solitude and social isolation; prisoners, writers, explorers, and others have described their experiences under unusual conditions of isolation. Most of us have heard or read about "cabin fever," solitary confinement, "Kayak disease," and other circumstances in which enforced solitude and the restriction of bodily move-ment are reported to have led to marked changes in thinking, extreme feelings of loneliness, and hallucinatory-like behavior. For many years these unusual be-haviors have aroused the curiosity of the public, but, only in the last decade has the scientist become interested in such problems.

The experimental approach to problems of SD appear to be the result of three converging lines of influence (Shurley, 1961). The first major influence was the advancement of neurophysiological techniques and electrophysiological methods which have provided the basis for a revised physiological model of the central nervous system. This model no longer considers the brain as a simple switchboard for connecting a stimulus to a response; we now must consider reverberating cir-cuits, feedback systems, probability concepts, alerting centers, and other recent innovations. The second major line can be traced to developments in psychology as an academic discipline. In this area numerous experiments have been performed with animals to determine the effects of early SD in the life span of the organism on its subsequent development and learning. The third major source of interest in SD phenomena has been developed within the context of national security. It has become a military necessity that we investigate and attempt to understand the factors involved in "thought-reform" movements, indoctrination programs, and "brainwashing" techniques. The possible relation of SD to space flight is still another problem of primary significance.

This chapter is concerned with the experimental study of the effects of restricted environmental conditions upon various aspects of human behavior, including basic sensitivity functions, cognitive and learning processes, motor reactions, hallucinations and other related clinical phenomena. The approach will be to provide a brief review of the experimental literature in each of several behavioral categories in order to ascertain the present status of knowledge in this area; special attention will be directed toward research methodology and the theoretical implications of SD as it relates to the understanding of basic psychological processes.

General Experimental Methods and Techniques

While the specific conditions in SD vary from experiment to experiment, there are some general procedures and techniques that are more or less common and that provide the broad background within which specific studies are conducted. Basically, three different approaches have been used to reduce the sensory input from the environment to the subject in an SD experiment. One of these approaches attempts to achieve the absolute reduction of sensory stimulation, as in the work of Lilly (1956) and Shurley (1960); these investigators and others have used a water tank in which subjects have been immersed nude except for a blacked-out face mask attached to a breathing tube. A schematic elevation of a laboratory designed for this type of SD investigation is shown in Figure 14-1. The laboratory consists of two rooms: the experimenter's control room and the immersion room. The general construction of the immersion room was such that there was a marked reduction of light, sound, vibration, odor, and taste stimuli. The large tank of water provided a simulated state of weightlessness and a uniform tactile field; the water in the tank flowed continuously and was maintained at a temperature of approximately 93.5°F (34.5°C). One advantage of the tank was that it provided for the elimination of body wastes. When the subject was immersed in the water, he was instructed to inhibit body movements as much as possible, consistent with comfort. By carefully placing appropriate weights or material with low stimulating properties around the mask or body, neutral buoyancy of the body was achieved.

A typical subject wearing the headmask is shown in Figure 14-2 as he is descending into the tank of water. The mask and air-control system permitted effortless breathing; there was no reduction in oxygen and no accumulation of carbon

HYDROHYPODYNAMIC ENVIRONMENT (ELEVATION)

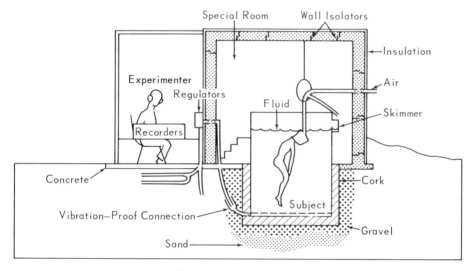

Figure 14–1. Schematic elevation of a laboratory designed for research in sensory deprivation. (From Shurley, 1960.)

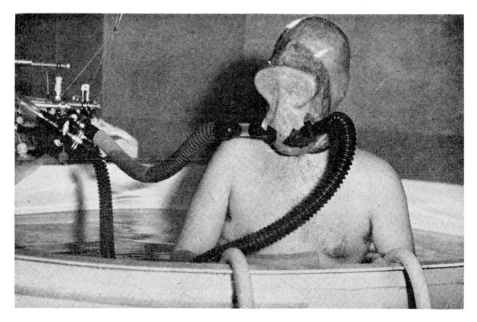

Figure 14–2. Typical subject wearing a blacked-out headmask provided with breathing tubes. (From Shurley, 1960.)

dioxide. The inspired air was free from odors and was maintained at 70°F and 45 percent relative humidity under a constant low pressure. The air-control system and the remainder of the equipment were essentially under automatic operation. The overall system provided a constant environment with a maximal degree of reduction in the ambient physical stimuli.

The subject was free from all sources of pain and discomfort and was positioned so as to remain comfortable, but motionless, for several hours. In some experiments he was instructed to communicate his experience, with minimal distortion and omission, during the test run; in other experiments, he reported after the test run. Microphones were suspended above the tank and the sounds and reports of the subject were monitored in the control room where tape recordings were made. The subjects were granted permission to limit their participation in the experiments or to terminate their participation at any point in the experiments if for any reason they so desired.

A second major approach in SD studies has been to reduce or alter the patterns and relationships in the sensory input from the environment, as exemplified in the work of Bexton, Heron, and Scott (1954). In this setting, the subjects reclined twenty-four hours a day on a comfortable bed in a lighted, semi-soundproof cubicle. The subjects wore translucent goggles which prevented normal patterned vision but passed diffuse light. To limit tactual stimulation, each subject also wore gloves and had his arms and hands encased in cardboard tubes; these were removed only when the subject was eating or at the toilet. Auditory stimulation was held constant by placing the subject's head in a U-shaped pillow of foam rubber and turning on the exhaust fan of a thermostatically regulated air-conditioner. The fan was located in the ceiling above the subject's head and provided a continuous masking noise. A two-way speaker system was imbedded in the foam rubber pillow to permit communication between the subject and the experimenter. For some experiments, the leads from an electroencephalograph were attached to the subject's head. The experimental arrangement is shown in Figure 14-3. Unlike the water tank, this arrangement is designed to minimize the patterning in the sensory environment, while retaining the general level of the stimulus input at a normal value.

The subjects were requested to participate as long as they could in the SD experiments, usually two or three days. While serving in the experiments they were not told the time of day. An experimenter was always present and the subjects were informed that if they needed anything they merely had to request it. Upon request they were given a food tray, which was placed beside the bed; also, they were permitted to go to the toilet in an adjacent room. These breaks occupied approximately two to three hours per day for the average subject.

A more severe restriction of conditions was adopted by Vernon (1963) in a series of studies which may be considered as falling within this second approach. The subjects were placed in a basement room that was both lightproof and soundproof. Soundproofing was obtained by constructing a room "floating" within a room. The outer room was essentially a shell of sixteen-inch reinforced concrete; the inner room had walls eight inches thick which were separated from the outer room by a five-inch air gap. The floor of the inner room was specially constructed to prevent sound vibrations from entering the room through contact with the ground. Noises generated within the inner room were partially absorbed by the soft fiberboard which lined the walls and ceiling. There was no illumination within the inner room or light leaks around the door.

The inner room, which measured four feet in width, nine feet in length, and eight feet in height, contained a king-size bed. The subject was instructed to remain on the bed except when obtaining food or at the toilet. The food consisted of sandwiches, fresh fruit, and soup; this was placed in a picnic ice chest located at the foot of the bed. The toilet facilities consisted of relief bottles placed inside the room and a chemical receptacle placed within the soundproof room but outside the confinement area.

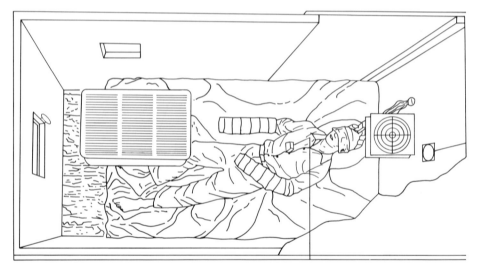

Figure 14–3. Schematic drawing of an experimental cubicle for research in sensory deprivation. The ceiling has been removed and the subject is viewed from above. (From Heron, in Solomon et al., *Sensory deprivation.* Cambridge: Harvard University Press, 1961.)

The subjects were instructed to be as quiet as possible, consistent with comfort, and not to generate any sounds such as talking, singing, and so on. A microphone was concealed in the inner room and provided the means for monitoring the subject's activities. Each subject was also instructed that he could terminate his participation in the SD experiment simply by pushing a "panic button" located within easy reach in the inner room. No subject was ever left unmonitored, that is, without the presence of the experimenter in an adjacent chamber. The various studies that were performed involved confinement in the inner room from 24 to 96 hours.

A third type of approach to problems in SD has imposed highly structured or monotonous conditions in the sensory environment, rather than a reduction in the levels of stimulation. This is the approach used by Wexler, Mendelson, Leiderman, and Solomon (1958). The subject was placed in a polio tank-type respirator with a specially built mattress, as shown in Figure 14-4. His arms and legs were encased in rigid but comfortable cylinders which inhibited movement and minimized tactile impressions. Since the subject was lying on his back, it was impossible for him to see any part of his body. The subject breathed for himself; the vents of the respirator remained open. To provide a constant masking noise that was monotonous and dull, the motor of the respirator was kept running. The only light in the room was from an electrical source and was maintained at a constant and minimal level. The subjects did not wear goggles but were prevented, by means of a large hood placed about the respirator, from seeing anything except the front of the tank and the blank white walls and ceiling. The experimenter could not be seen by the subject and the sounds of his movements were masked by the noise from the motor.

Figure 14–4. An experimental subject shown in position in a tank-type respirator. During a sensory deprivation study the vents of the respirator are left open and the subject breathes for himself. (From Wexler et al., AMA Arch. Neurol. Psychiat., 1958, **79**, 225–233.)

The subject was able at any time to drink an eggnog mixture from a feeding tube placed near his mouth. Bedpans or urinals were provided at his request. The subject was informed that the experiment would last up to 36 hours, but that it could be terminated at any prior point if the subject so desired. He was also informed that an observer would always be present, although not visible or available for communication. The subject's verbal responses during the test period were tape-recorded and his general motor activity and sleeping patterns were noted. Polygraphic recordings were made of cardiac rate and the sleep-wakefulness patterns were recorded by an electroencephalograph. Urine specimens were also collected for each 12-hour interval.

The brief description of these three major approaches to research in SD makes it clear that there is considerable complexity in the experimental setting. The parameters of stimulation that are significant for deprivation have not yet been isolated; consequently, there is no clear indication of the stimuli that need to be removed or altered to achieve a state of SD. Each experimenter proceeds according to his own operational view of the relevant variables. In general, the strategy has been to deprive the subjects of sensory input over several modalities simultaneously, or to alter the usual patterns of stimulation. With this general methodological introduction, we will now review some of the findings that have been reported in SD research.

Sensitivity and Perceptual Functions in Sensory Deprivation

From the early studies in SD (Bexton, Heron, and Scott, 1954), it was observed that nearly all subjects displayed gross disturbances in visual perception when the methodology involved the wearing of translucent goggles. When the goggles were removed following a period of SD, unusual effects were reported; these effects lasted for several minutes or, as in some cases, for several hours. There were several kinds of effects: objects in the visual field seemed to be moving, for example, they changed their size and shape, or the walls of the room moved in and out; plane surfaces seemed to be swayed or curved; parallel lines seemed to have a barrel shape; and movements of the subject were accompanied by a corresponding apparent movement in perceived objects. Other visual disturbances were also subjectively reported, but when a battery of tests was administered to establish the quantitative characteristics of certain visual functions after SD, the results indicated that *only certain functions, such as size constancy, were affected.*

Further studies were later performed to investigate some of these perceptual disturbances in greater detail. In one study, two kinds of apparent movement were observed (Heron, Doane, and Scott, 1956). In one type the subjects who had experienced six days of SD reported apparent movement that was independent of their own movements, for example, "the wall bulged toward me and then went back," "the whole room is undulating, swirling. . . ." After the initial gross effects were stabilized somewhat, the fixated region remained relatively still, but the immediate surrounding area tended to drift and become distorted, for example, "when I fixate here, the box behind you moves." These independent movements persisted for as long as twenty-four hours. The other type of apparent movement was associated with the head and eye movements of the subject. As the subject approached or withdrew from objects, the objects themselves seemed to move toward or away from him, for example, "things just don't stay put . . . there's no position constancy." The investigators suggest on the basis of this and related work that *"exposing the subject to a monotonous sensory environment can cause disorganization of brain-function similar to, and in some respects as great as, that produced by drugs or lesions"* (p. 18).

A large number of visual functions were subsequently investigated in a study in which 13 subjects were exposed to four days of isolation (Doane, Mahatoo, Heron, and Scott, 1959). The subjects wore a translucent mask, gloves, and arm gauntlets; the performance of the thirteen experimental subjects was evaluated against the performance of a control group which consisted of 13 to 20 subjects, depending upon the particular test. Only part of the findings will be considered for our purposes. There was statistical evidence that size constancy was decreased in the experimental (SD) group. This was determined by presenting six different-sized discs at a distance of 3 ft, and for each disc having the subject judge which one of a graduated series of seventeen discs at 12 ft appeared equal in size. The subjects were instructed to "pick the far disc that looks the same as the near one." The experimental group chose significantly larger comparison discs than the control group, indicating that *there was a decrease in size constancy*.

In testing for the effects of SD on autokinetic movement, the subjects were dark adapted for 3 min and were then seated at a distance of 10 ft from a point source of light in a dark room. Two minutes after the subjects reported the onset of movement, the illuminance of the surroundings was increased until the autokinetic movement was eliminated. A comparison of the experimental and control groups indicated that there was no difference in the time required for the onset of the movement, but the movement in the experimental group persisted with higher levels of illuminance of the surroundings, that is, *the autokinetic movement was more difficult to abolish in the SD group*.

It has been proposed that the autokinetic effects obtained in these studies might be due to social deprivation rather than sensory deprivation. Accordingly, a study was performed to determine whether perceptual distortions of movement found in subjects under sensory and social deprivation could also be found in subjects who had been exposed only to social isolation without the accompanying sensory deprivation (Walters and Quinn, 1961). Forty subjects were divided into four groups of ten: sensory and social deprivation; social deprivation; sensory deprivation; no deprivation. Sensory deprivation was accomplished by having the subjects wear ear plugs and padded headphones over their ears, as well as underwater goggles in which the plastic lenses were replaced by aluminum discs. The subjects in all groups were presented individually with a standard task for 30 min in which tactual judgments of size were made. The social deprivation condition was effected by removing the experimenter from the room during this period. Following this, the subjects were tested on the autokinetic task.

It was found that the initial latency of response, that is, the time elapsing from the appearance of the light until the perception of movement, was shortest for the group under both social and sensory deprivation; the latency was intermediate for those who had experienced either social or sensory deprivation alone; and the latency was longest for the group without either kind of deprivation. The results of this study indicate that *social deprivation may operate in a manner analogous to sensory deprivation; both conditions facilitate the onset of apparent movement. Furthermore, the two conditions combine in some manner to reduce the latency beyond that brought about by one condition by itself.*

The earlier reports on improved visual sensitivity as a result of SD, however, have not been completely substantiated (Doane, Mahatoo, Heron, and Scott, 1959). These investigators required their subjects to locate a gap in a series of fourteen black vertical lines. The lines were 1 in. apart; each line was ¹⁄₆₄ in. wide and 3 in. in vertical length. A test gap across the series of lines varied from ³⁄₃₂ in. at the left to ¹⁄₆₄ in. at the right. The lines were on a white card and were presented at a distance of 10 ft. The subject's task was to indicate whether the gap was at the bottom, top, or middle of the line. Comparison of the results for the control group and experimental group after four days of SD was interpreted as an indication that visual acuity was "probably improved."

Some of the early work in SD also suggested that an improvement in visual efficiency might be expected from relatively complete visual deprivation, whereas decrements in visual efficiency might result from partial visual deprivation, that is, a condition involving the continuous reception of unpatterned light. Rosenbaum, Dobie, and Cohen (1959) tested this hypothesis by determining the recognitive thresholds for 5-digit numbers presented tachistoscopically after periods of 0, 5, 15, and 30 min of visual deprivation under the two conditions: total and partial deprivation. The experimental design permitted each subject to serve as his own control; also, each subject was tested for visual efficiency on four successive days following each period of visual deprivation. The subjects were 32 adults with normal vision. The results of this study show that *there is an improvement in visual efficiency as a function of successive days' practice regardless of the exposure condition,* particularly for the 5-min period. Also, there were no significant differences in visual efficiency between total and partial deprivation for any of the four experimental periods. When the data for the two groups (total and partial) were then combined, the *5-min period resulted in a significant improvement in visual efficiency.* It appears, therefore, that *total and partial deprivation do not produce differential effects in visual perception* as measured by tachistoscopic thresholds.

These negative findings were confirmed and extended by the work of Batten (1961). Fifty-two male college students were divided into three groups: two experimental and one control. One experimental group experienced pattern deprivation for both the auditory and visual modalities; the other experienced normal visual conditions but was deprived of patterned auditory stimulation; the control group experienced no sensory deprivation in either modality. The nonpatterned auditory stimulation in the deprivation period consisted of white noise presented over a loudspeaker; nonpatterned visual stimulation was obtained by placing halved ping-pong balls over the subject's eyes. For each group, difference thresholds were obtained by a modified method of constant stimuli, with a warble tone for audition and a variable intensity light for vision. A comparison of the difference thresholds before and after one hour of sensory deprivation showed no significant differences for the three groups. It was concluded that *deprivation of patterned visual and auditory stimulation for one hour does not produce an increase in differential sensitivity for pitch or brightness.*

The problem of "perceptual lag" as a function of SD has also received increasing attention. In an early study (Heron, Doane, and Scott, 1956) it was reported that, after prolonged SD, when a thin black line was rotated slowly against a dimly illuminated milk glass screen in a dark room, the line appeared S shaped; the ends of the line seemed to lag behind the center part. Held and White (1959) set out to obtain quantitative data on this phenomenon, but failed to find any evidence for the reported distortion of shape. However, there seemed to be a change in the apparent speed of rotation of the line. This "perceptual lag" was studied with 13 subjects after 8 hours of SD (Freedman and Greenblatt, 1959). The subjects wore translucent goggles and were exposed to continuous white noise. The test consisted of a black line (8 in. in height and ⅛ in. in width viewed at a distance of 2 ft) which rotated counterclockwise from one end at approximately 11 rpm. The movement of the line started in the horizontal position and, when the line reached the vertical position (90 degrees), it disappeared. Ten degrees beyond this (at an angle of 100 degrees from the starting position) there was a fixed marker with the same dimensions as the moving line. The subject's task was to release a switch when he judged that the moving line was directly underneath the fixed marker. The subject did not see the line moving through the last 10 degrees of arc but was required to estimate its position, or the time elapsed, in terms of the perceived speed of movement of the line during the initial 90 degrees of rotation. After the 8-hr period of SD, the reports of the subjects indicated that *the line seemed to be rotating more slowly than before SD;* there was a 16 percent mean reduction in speed. Control subjects with an 8-hr period of isolation without SD showed no effects of perceptual lag.

A more extended study of this phenomenon was performed by administering the perceptual lag test at the beginning of an 8-hr period of SD and, thereafter, at 30-min intervals for a total of three hours (Freedman and Held, 1960). Three conditions of visual SD were used: (1) diffuse light through translucent goggles; (2) random flashes of three incandescent lamps located 24 in. above the subject's eyes, and (3) blackout (blackout goggles worn in a blacked-out room). All subjects wore gloves and cuffs to limit tactile stimulation; they rested supine on a bed and were exposed to white noise. The results of this study are presented in Figure 14-5. The greatest effect for each time period of exposure was produced by the random flashes; *after two hours of SD, there was over a 40 percent reduction in estimated speed of rotation.* For all conditions the maximal change in apparent speed occurs during the first hour of SD. The random flash condition produced significantly greater lag effects for each period of exposure except at 150 min; there were no significant differences between the blackout and diffuse light conditions. Five of seven subjects retested one-half hour after the experiment was over showed a marked decrease in the lag effect, but not complete recovery; two subjects remained at ap-

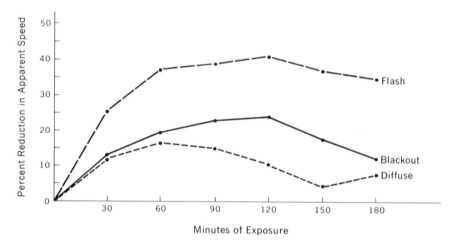

Figure 14-5. Perceptual lag induced under three experimental conditions of sensory deprivation. (From Freedman and Held, *Percept. mot. Skills*, 1960.)

proximately the same level as in the test situation. The results of this study have practical implications in that personnel assigned continuous monitoring tasks under restricted stimulus conditions, that is, monotonous or uniform visual and auditory conditions, may develop visual perceptual distortions even within the first half-hour of duty.

This conclusion has been substantiated in an experiment in which a significant impairment of vision on a vigilance task was produced by SD (Zubek, Pushkar, Sansom, and Gowing, 1961). Sixteen subjects were placed in a darkened, sound-proofed chamber for a period of 7 to 10 days; they were instructed to lie quietly on a mattress and to avoid any physical or vocal activity. It was unnecessary for the subjects to leave the chamber during the isolation period since toilet facilities, a food pantry, a panic button, an air-conditioning unit, and a two-way intercommunication system were installed in the floor. A battery of perceptual motor tests, including a vigilance test, was administered before isolation and immediately after the subjects completed their period of confinement. The vigilance task consisted of a modified Mackworth clock test. It consisted of an 8-in. electric laboratory clock with a single hand which stopped rotating briefly for 0.10 sec and then started again; during a 30-min test, the "breaks" were presented at intervals of 2, 2, 3, 1, 6, 7, 3, and 5 min. This cycle was repeated four times for each subject; the task of the subject was to press a button upon detection of the signal, that is, the "break."

The results of this test are shown in Figure 14-6 for two groups of subjects (experimental and control). Four successive 30-min periods were run before and after isolation of the experimental subjects; the control subjects were tested at corresponding time periods but did not undergo isolation. The scores of both groups are given in terms of the percentage of detected signal changes in each of the four successive 30-min tests. Before the isolation period, the performance of both

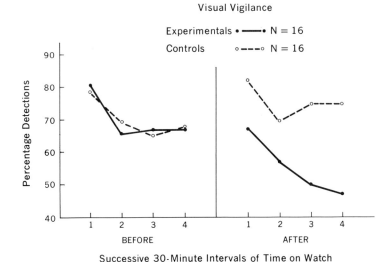

Figure 14-6.   Performance on a visual vigilance task for control subjects
and experimental subjects before and after a prolonged period of sensory
isolation. (From Zubek *et al.*, *Canad. J. Psychol.*, 1961.)

groups was the same, but *after one week of isolation, the overall vigilance performance of
the experimental group was significantly poorer than that of the control group.* The experimental group was poorer at each test period and become progressively worse with
each additional period, whereas the vigilance performance of the control group
was essentially constant for the last 60 minutes.

The results of these and other studies indicate that when human subjects are
exposed for several days to an environment in which there is minimal stimulus
change and diffuse light stimulation, a variety of visual disturbances will be reported. *There will be a general disruption of visual perception, but these disturbances will be
manifested quantitatively only in selected tasks,* such as perceptual lag, size and shape
constancies, color perception, figural aftereffects, apparent movement, and loss
of spatial, temporal, and tactual orientation. Some functions, for example, critical
flicker frequency, visual and auditory thresholds, phi-phenomenon, and brightness contrast, do not appear to be affected within the deprivation periods imposed
in current studies. Most SD experiments dealing with problems of sensitivity and
perceptual functions have been concerned with the visual modality; it would seem
that additional studies in the other modalities would be warranted.

The results of the studies that have been performed with respect to SD and
sensitivity or perceptual functions, however, are not all in complete agreement.
Several investigators have failed to obtain significant visual impairment in depth
perception, size constancy, reversible figures, and auditory discrimination (Batten, 1961; Vernon, McGill, Gulick, and Candland, 1959; Zubek, Pushkar, Sansom, and Gowing, 1961). Others have reported that no gross perceptual changes
were experienced by their subjects involving the distortion of the size and shape
of objects following sensory isolation (Ruff and Levy, 1959; Vernon and Hoffman,

1956; Zubek, Pushkar, Sansom, and Gowing, 1961). The observed discrepancies between those studies in which positive effects of SD on visual processes were obtained and those in which they were not may, perhaps, be accounted for in terms of differences in general methodology. Some studies have employed prolonged darkness and silence (Zubek, Pushkar, Sansom, and Gowing, 1961), while others have used prolonged diffuse light and masking noise as part of the experimental conditions (Heron, Doane, and Scott, 1956). Such differences in testing conditions and in periods of experimental deprivation may actually produce different behavioral effects; whether this is an acceptable explanation remains to be determined.

The Effects of Sensory Deprivation on Cognitive and Learning Processes

The early studies in SD, in addition to revealing that there were gross perceptual distortions as a result of isolation, suggested that the cognitive processes might also be affected. Nearly every experimental subject who experienced SD for a relatively long period of time reported having difficulty in thinking coherently and in concentrating. Some were unable to count consecutively for more than twenty or thirty numbers (Freedman, Grunebaum, and Greenblatt, 1961); others found it extremely difficult to talk. These effects occurred regardless of the general nature of the SD conditions. Many subjects approached the SD experiments with the expectation that this would be an excellent time for concentration and for attempting to resolve various types of personal and academic problems. While, in general, the subjects claimed to be able to concentrate better, to think more clearly, and so on, during those parts of the first day in which they were not asleep, they later reported extreme difficulty in thinking. Many ideas or problems would be initiated but no orderly thought processes could be sustained for any long period of time. When the thought processes became disordered, the subjects engaged in extensive daydreaming. These are some of the typical subjective impressions which have been reported in various SD studies.

One of the major questions to be asked, then, is whether under controlled conditions of SD, the cognitive processes are affected quantitatively as evidenced in problem-solving behavior; a second major question is whether learning is facilitated or impeded. If the learning process is affected in a measurable way, are these differences which may be attributed to the kinds of learning tasks that are imposed? We will consider each of these issues separately.

Sensory Deprivation and Cognitive Processes

In one series of SD experiments (Scott, Bexton, Heron, and Doane, 1959), two batteries of tests (A and B) were administered to an experimental group at three stages in time. One battery (Battery A) was administered immediately before isolation, during isolation (after 2, 24, and 48 hr) and following isolation (on the third and fourth days); the other battery (Battery B) was administered in the post-isolation period. A control group was also given the same tests in the same order and with the same time intervals, but did not experience isolation. The battery of tests used during the isolation period consisted of five parts: (1) multiplication of two- and three-digit numbers, (2) "catch" questions in arithmetic, for example, "how many times greater is 2½ than half of 2½?"; (3) completion of a number series; (4) word-making using letters from a longer word; and (5) construction of a word from a group of jumbled letters (anagrams). The subjects were scored on the basis of the time spent on each problem, the number of incorrect answers, and the number of times that the problem was repeated at the subject's request. All tests were given orally and were solved "in the subject's head."

The results of these tests for the experimental and control groups are shown in Figure 14-7. There is a significant impairment in the performance of the experimental group on the word-making test and on the 12-hr test in the number series during the isolation period. Although the performance of the experimental group appears inferior to that of the control group on the other tests given during the isolation period, the differences are not statistically significant. No significant differences were obtained between groups in any test in the pre-isolation or post-isolation periods. *For the error scores, there was a significant difference between groups on the anagrams test at the 24-hour test period during isolation, and on the word-making test at the 12-hour and 48-hour test periods.* The requests for repetitions were significantly greater for the experimental group only on the word-making test in the first test period of isolation. Other tests given on digit span, analogies, and associative learning did not produce any differences between groups.

The results on the seven post-isolation tests (Battery B) are shown in Table 14-1. The p values were computed from t ratios using the difference between the

Table 14-1 Comparison of Mean Scores of Experimental and Control Groups on Seven Post-Isolation Tests

Test	Score Basis	Experiment Group			Control Group			p
		N	Before	After	N	1st Test	2d Test	
Kohs' Blocks	Total time (sec)[a]	20	1088	931	25	1095	762	0.01
Digit symbol	Number correct	19	52.9	68.2	24	52.0	74.5	0.01
Thurstone-Gottschaldt	Number correct	12	5.5	5.4	18	5.2	8.1	0.01
Copy passage	Time (sec)	18	594	640	25	634	639	0.05
Delta Blocks	Number correct	12	9.4	13.2	19	11.4	19.9	0.01
Picture anomaly	Number errors	15	3.0	5.9	23	4.0	4.9	0.01
Mirror drawing	Time	12	219	108	19	223	103	0.10

[a] The number of Kohs' items on which the time score increased, in the second test, was also significantly greater for the experimental group ($p < 0.001$). (From Scott *et al.*, Canad. J. Psychol., 1959.)

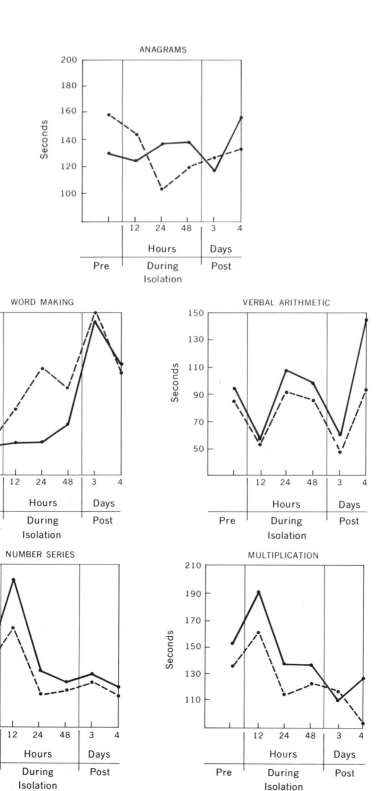

Figure 14–7. Comparison of the performance of experimental and control groups on five cognitive tests administered during the three stages of an experiment on sensory deprivation. (From Heron, in Solomon *et al.*, *Sensory deprivation*, Cambridge: Harvard University Press, 1961.)

mean scores of the two groups (experimental and control) immediately after isolation relative to their scores in the pre-isolation period. The experimental subjects are significantly poorer than the control subjects on all tests except mirror drawing. The results of this study suggest that *performance on certain types of intellectual tasks is impaired by SD;* however, *there is no general loss of cognitive functioning.*

One further and puzzling aspect of SD, as it appears to affect intellectual functioning in this study, is that *differences between experimental and control groups do not increase with increased perceptual isolation.* Evidently, SD produces an effect, but this effect is constant and is not a progressive decrement. Several possibilities exist which may account for this (Scott, Bexton, Heron, and Doane, 1959). It may be that graduated differences between groups would be obtained if longer periods of SD were employed. For example, while there was no decline in intellectual functioning between 12 and 48 hours of isolation, there might have been between 48 and 72 hours if the SD conditions had been extended for that period of time. Motivational factors may also be entering in to contaminate the results. For the SD subjects, the tests occupied about two hours of time which would otherwise have been "empty" for the control subjects. The tests may have been perceived as preempting valuable time. This would tend to increase the motivational level of the experimental subjects, while decreasing that of the control subjects, thereby counterbalancing the SD effects to yield essentially equal performance in the two groups.

Similar results were obtained with respect to intellectual functioning in a pilot study with four subjects who remained individually isolated in a darkened soundproof chamber for five hours (Cohen, Silverman, Bressler, Shmavonian, 1961). Prior to isolation a battery of tests was administered to evaluate, among other factors, each subject's level of intellectual performance. The tests included certain portions of the Wechsler Adult Intelligence Scale, the Kahn symbol test, the Rorschach Psychodiagnostic Ink Blot Test, the Blacky Test, and the Goodenough Draw-a-Person Test. In terms of the intellectual functions, the results indicated that isolation and SD tended to produce variations in individual performance. *Short-term retentive ability* (as measured by the digit span subtest) *was increased for all subjects, but there was a decrease in arithmetical reasoning, in the ability to abstract and to generalize, and in reasoning ability.* The major difficulties seemed to be related to tasks that depended upon problem-solving ability or required logical thinking. These findings, however, need to be viewed cautiously, since the sample size was small and no control group was used in the experimental design.

In a study dealing with individual differences under conditions of SD, 12 subjects were tested on a set of intellectual tasks administered several weeks before, and again immediately after, the period of confinement (Goldberger and Holt, 1961). The subjects experienced perceptual deprivation in vision (visual occlusion with halved table-tennis balls) and in audition (masking by white noise via earphones mounted in a lightweight helmet). They were required to recline on a bed in a cubicle for a period of eight hours, but were encouraged to verbalize even though there was no communication from the experimenter. The tests that were administered to evaluate the degree of cognitive impairment included a logical deductions test, an arithmetic reasoning test, a digit span test, and a story recall test. The results, based on a difference score for pre- and postconfinement, showed that *only performance on the story recall test was significantly impaired.* These findings support the contention that *SD does not affect cognitive functioning in general, but instead produces a deterioration of performance on certain tasks.*

Other studies provide further support to this position. In a tank-respirator situation, five pairs of visually separated subjects showed no difference on a block design task before and after ten hours of isolation (Davis, McCourt, and Solomon, 1959). Following one hour in an isolation chamber, four subjects showed no gross deterioration in cognition as measured by the number of word associations elicited in a 2-min period (Cohen, Rosenbaum, Dobie, and Gottlieb, 1959). In a more extended study (Zubek, Sansom, and Prysiazniuk, 1960), 16 subjects were confined in a darkened, soundproof chamber for a period of 7 to 10 days. They were instructed to lie on a mattress as quietly as possible and not to engage in any vocal activity. Before, during, and one day after isolation, a battery of eleven different tests of intellectual functioning was administered to each subject. A control group of 16 matched subjects was also given the same battery at corresponding time intervals and under the same testing conditions. The results of this study indicate that there were no statistically significant differences in performance between the experimental and control groups before, during, or after isolation on the tests of verbal reasoning (for example, "lend is to borrow as rich is to _____."), abstract reasoning (that is, given four designs or figures in a series, the subject must indicate what the fifth in the series would be), verbal fluency (write down all the words that can be recalled beginning with a certain letter), number facility (simple arithmetical operations), and numerical reasoning (the solution of various numerical sequences).

Robertson and Wolter (1963) found that neither the separate IQ scores nor the individual subtest scores on the Wechsler Adult Intelligence Scale were changed significantly by three hours of social isolation and partial sensory deprivation.

Since the number of studies performed in this area is limited, and some of these studies are characterized by the lack of a rigorous experimental design, it is difficult to formulate a general statement indicating the effects of SD and isolation upon cognitive processes. *There is a tentative indication that reasoning and problem-solving may be impaired, whether the experimental task involves verbal material or numbers, but this finding is not generally supported.* The evidence on block design, which involves the analysis and synthesis of visual material, is also equivocal: sometimes there is deterioration as a result of deprivation and sometimes there is no change. As in the case of SD and sensitivity or perceptual functions, the inconclusive findings may be attributable to differences in experimental procedures or in the duration of the periods of confinement. Also, in several studies a battery of cognitive tests was administered following isolation. It is conceivable that the sequence of these tests may have produced interactive effects tending to inflate or deflate the influence of SD on certain tasks. Goldberger and Holt (1961) have postulated that *tasks involving logical reasoning* (that is, the manipulation of ideas) *are most likely to be affected by SD,* whereas *tasks involving overlearned operations* (for example, simple arithmetic problems) *or simple learning processes* (digit span) *are likely to be little affected, if at all.* Considerable additional research needs to be performed in this area before a firm generalization can be made indicating in quantitative terms that SD tends to decrease the ability of a subject to reason precisely and to solve complex arithmetical or verbal problems. *At present it appears that SD does not have a marked general effect upon cognitive functioning.*

Sensory Deprivation and Learning Processes

Shortly after the work on SD was initiated, a study was performed on five subjects to determine whether isolation would affect the rate of learning (Vernon and Hoffman, 1956). The general method of isolation was described in an earlier section of this chapter. The subjects were confined for a period of 48 hours. The learning tasks were presented aurally and consisted of 12-item lists of adjectives which had been tape-recorded; the anticipation method was used with a 2-sec interstimulus (between word) interval. In this method, the subject listened to the entire list of words on the first play-though, then he tried to anticipate the first word on the list before it was presented by the tape recorder. After his response, the tape recorder presented the first word and the subject anticipated the second word, and so on through the list. The subject's ability to learn was measured by the number of trials required to reproduce an entire list without error. The learning tests were administered before confinement, after 24 and 48 hours of confinement, and at 24 and 48 hours after release from confinement.

The results of this study are presented in Figure 14-8. The mean values for the four subjects in the experimental group suggest that *"the ability to learn adjective lists improves with continued sensory deprivation"* (p. 1075); since the performance of the control group did not show a similar trend, it was concluded that the improvement was not dependent upon the particular lists of adjectives nor upon practice effects. When tested 24 hours and 48 hours after confinement, the differences between experimental and control groups were no longer present.

These findings, however, pertain only to a simple rote learning task with short word lists. In a subsequent study (Vernon and McGill, 1957), nine experimental and nine control subjects were required to learn a longer list of adjectives, again presented aurally. The same set of experimental conditions was used, except that the list to be learned contained fifteen words rather than twelve. Learning was measured after 24, 48, and 72 hours of SD. Unlike the earlier study, this study failed to produce a significant difference between groups when their performance in the predeprivation, deprivation, and postdeprivation periods was compared in terms of trials to criterion or errors to criterion, but, the experimental group was significantly less variable than the control group on the deprivation tests. It appears that *SD does not facilitate the rote learning of long word lists but with continued confinement individual differences in learning ability tend to be reduced.*

As part of the study dealing with intellectual changes in prolonged perceptual isolation (Zubek, Sansom, and Prysiazniuk, 1960), several learning tests were

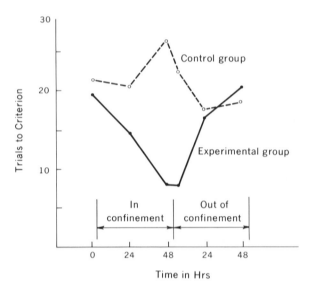

Figure 14-8. The effect of sensory deprivation on the rate of learning lists of adjectives by the anticipation method. (From Vernon and Hoffman, *Science*, 1956, **123**, 1074–1075.)

administered to 16 subjects who remained in confinement for at least seven days. One task involved the rote learning of a list of nine three-letter words (for example, red, ask, tub) presented aurally. The criterion was two successive errorless trials. A comparison of the performance of the experimental subjects and control subjects before, during, and one day after isolation showed no differences in the rate of rote learning. *Tests of recall and recognition, however, did show significant impairment in the SD group from the third day on.* The recall task consisted of the subject's attempt to reproduce as many nonsense syllables as possible from a 20-syllable list which he had studied visually for 3 min; the recognition task followed the recall task and required the subject to select from an enlarged list of 30 syllables the 20 syllables which he had previously studied visually. The results for the recall and recognition tests are given in Figure 14-9. The difference between the experimental and control groups is significant one day after confinement.

The findings from this series of studies suggest that *prolonged sensory deprivation does affect intellectual functioning as measured by simple rote learning and immediate retention* (recall and recognition). There is some evidence that *the rote learning of easy and short word lists may be improved* during the first few days of isolation; on the other hand, *the retention of recently learned material seems to be impaired.* It should be recalled that the studies reviewed in this section did not all employ the same sensory modality for presenting the material to be learned. One group of investigators used audition and found that in certain instances learning was improved; the others used vision and found that retention was impaired. *This suggests that prolonged periods of sensory deprivation may differentially affect cognitive and learning processes depending upon the particular modality used in the testing situation.* This may in part explain some of the con-

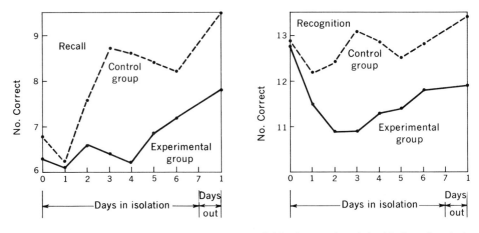

Figure 14-9. Mean retention scores for nonsense syllables for experimental subjects and control subjects on a recall test and a recognition test administered before, during, and one day after sensory discrimination. (From Zubek et al., J. Psychol., 1960.)

flicting results that have been obtained in the past. Other factors, however, may be even more important, such as the duration of the testing period and the specific conditions imposed during the time of confinement. Nevertheless, since SD has been shown to affect significantly the processes of learning and remembering, further work in this area should be encouraged in order to provide a broader understanding of the variables involved in these processes and to determine those factors which can be manipulated to facilitate learning and retard forgetting.

Perceptual Motor Reactions in Sensory Deprivation

The research described in the preceding section involved the learning and retention of verbal material in both meaningful and meaningless categories. This situation, except for the use of nonsense syllables, corresponds to a high degree to tasks with which the subjects are thoroughly familiar. Now, the question is whether different results might be expected to obtain if the experimental situation involves a less familiar or novel task, such as mirror drawing, and a different mode of response.

In a major study (Vernon, McGill, Gulick, and Candland, 1959), several perceptual motor tasks were used to compare the performance of experimental subjects (confined for one, two, or three days) with that of control subjects tested at similar intervals. The SD conditions for the experimental subjects consisted of light and sound deprivation in a room which contained a bed, an icebox with food, and chemical toilet facilities. The subjects wore gauntlets to reduce tactile stimulation and inhibit movement; the gauntlets extended from above the elbow to below the fingertips. The effects of SD were evaluated by a comparison of the difference scores between the preconfinement and postconfinement periods for the experimental and control groups. Since the difference scores for the experimental group included both the effects of the SD conditions and of practice, it was necessary to estimate the magnitude of the practice effect alone from the data of the matched control group. Any remaining difference between the scores of the two groups across the preconfinement and postconfinement periods was then attributed to SD.

Several tests were run to determine the effects of SD on motor performance. One of these tests required the subject to maintain contact on a rotating disc with a hand-held flexible stylus. The disc (1 cm in diameter) rotated in a circle (13 cm in diameter) at a speed of 44 rpm; the criterion of performance was the total time on target in a 60-sec trial.

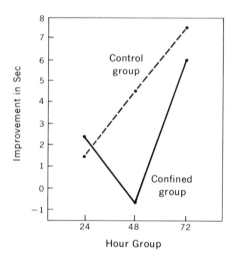

Figure 14–10. Rotary pursuit data for an experimental (confined) group and a control group plotted in terms of the improvement (in sec.) from the initial test, that is, the preconfinement test, to a second test administered after a specified number of hours. (From Vernon et al., Percept. mot. Skills, 1959.)

The results of this test are shown in Figure 14-10; the ordinate indicates the improvement in performance, computed with reference to the preconfinement base line, for the experimental (confined) and control groups after 24, 48, and 72 hours. As the time interval between the preconfinement period and the test period increases, there is a linear increase in improvement for the control group. Since a separation of 24 hours yielded a mean improvement of 1.53 sec and a separation of 72 hours yielded a mean improvement of 7.35 sec, it appears that *rotary pursuit performance can be improved by increasing the time interval between the initial and final test.*

The experimental group in this study shows a similar tendency to improve, except for the 48-hour test; *the performance of the group at this point is significantly poorer than the control group.* However, when the control and experimental groups were tested (24 hours following the confinement period for the experimental group only), there was no significant difference in performance on the pursuit task. The decline for the 48-hour experimental group was temporary; by 24 hours after release, all groups had improved in rotary pursuit performance and were at the same level of ability.

Another test of motor coordination that was administered in this study was the rail-walking test. In this test the subject's performance consisted of walking in his stocking feet along a wooden rail which extended for 18 feet; the rails were 1.75 inches wide and were raised 3.75 inches. The criterion was the total number of seconds required to walk the full length of the rails without stepping off or falling. Each time the subject made an error (stepping off or falling) he was required to return to the starting point for another trial. Only the actual time spent on the rail was accumulated to obtain the criterion score. As in the rotary pursuit task, the effect of SD was determined by the amount of improvement (in sec) from the initial or preconfinement test to a second test administered after a given number of hours (24, 48, or 72). During this interval of time the experimental group was confined under conditions of SD.

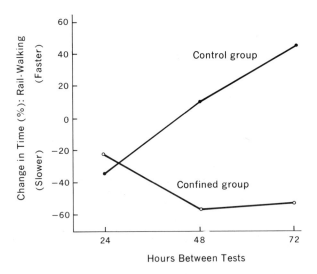

Figure 14–11. Change in the time required to complete the rail-walking task from the initial test to a second test administered after a given number of hours. (From Vernon *et al.,* *Percept. mot. Skills,* 1959.)

The results are shown in Figure 14-11. With an interval of 24 hours between the two tests, both the experimental and control groups show a loss of approximately 5.5 sec in the time required to traverse the 18 ft rails. The experimental (confined group) remained at this level for the 48- and 72-hour tests, but for these same intervals, the control group showed a linear improvement which was statistically significant at the 72-hour interval. It appears, therefore, that *confinement does affect rail-walking performance,* due perhaps to the lack of opportunity for exercise or to the impairment of visual ability. A test given 24 hours after release from confinement showed that the experimental and control groups were more similar in performance; the confined group showed improvement, while the control group improved at a slower rate than it had up to that point.

A third task in this study involved mirror drawing. In this task, the subject was required to learn how to trace a pathway in the form of a six-pointed star while looking into a mirror. The pathway consisted of two parallel lines and the subject's performance was based on (a) the time (in sec) required to complete one tracing, and (b) the number of errors, that is, the number of times the pencil touched one of the guidelines during one tracing.

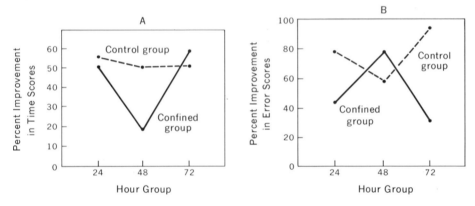

Figure 14–12. Time scores (Part A) and error scores (Part B) in a mirror-tracing task for control subjects and experimental (confined) subjects plotted in terms of the improvement (in percent) from the initial test or preconfinement test to a second test administered after a specified number of hours. (From Vernon *et al., Percept. mot. Skills,* 1959.)

The data in terms of time and errors are presented in Figure 14-12 for the control and confined groups. Part A of Figure 14-12 contains the time data and Part B, the error data. In Part A, it may be seen that, except for the 48-hr confined group, all groups improved at least 50 percent from the first to the second test separated by 24, 48, or 72 hours. In Part B, *the 48-hour confined group did significantly better than the 24- or 72-hour confined groups but not significantly* better than the 48-hour control group. Apparently, the 24- and 72-hour confined groups were emphasizing speed rather than accuracy, whereas the 48-hour group was performing just the opposite. Again, 24 hours after the confinement period was ended, both groups performed more nearly alike.

A fourth test of motor ability in this study was strength of grip as measured with a hand dynamometer. All groups, whether confined or control, showed a gain in strength of grip by approximately 8 percent, except for the 72-hour confined group which had a mean loss of about 4 percent. This is somewhat surprising since all but one subject in the three confined groups (24, 48, and 72 hours) lost, on the average, approximately 2 to 3 pounds in body weight.

In summary, it may be stated that *the effects of SD on perceptual motor performance will depend upon both the duration of confinement and the nature of the specific task imposed.* For most subjects, *the maximal change in performance occurs at the end of a 48-hour confinement period;* for this period, rotary pursuit performance is significantly impaired, as is mirror drawing measured in terms of tracing time. Rail-walking also shows impairment, but strength of grip is not affected adversely until after 72 hours of confinement. Hand tremor and reaction time are not affected even after 96 hours (Vernon, 1963). The results indicate that *difficulty is experienced in performing new perceptual motor tasks in a sensory-deprived environment,* but the question of disruption of old motor responses (excluding handwriting) has not been posed and should be investigated. The evidence also indicates that the disruptive effects of SD on perceptual motor behavior are of relatively short duration; additional studies are needed to determine the specific forms of the recovery functions.

Hallucinations and Imagery in Sensory Deprivation

The subject screamed in panic: "There is an animal—having a long slender body with many legs. It's on the screen, crawling in back of me!" The screen was examined by the observer and no animal was seen. The subject continued to be disturbed for 5 minutes. He insisted the animal was there and was an inch long (Solomon and Mendelson, 1962, p. 137).

This is an example of hallucinatory experience which was reported by a subject under a particular set of SD conditions. Such phenomena have been described by a number of different terms, including hallucinations, imagery, delusions, illusions, daydreams, dreams, fantasies, and hypnagogic states. In discussing these phenomena, some investigators have argued against the use of the term "hallucination," since the term implies not only an illusory image but the failure to recognize that the image is unrelated to "reality" (Goldberger and Holt, 1958). While sensory or perceptual deprivation may increase the vividness, amount, or structure of imagery, this may occur without a loss in reality contact and, hence, the experience should not, according to this view, be called hallucinatory. Inasmuch as there is no general agreement on this point and a more precise definition of terms is lacking, the various terms that have been used in the past to describe such imaginal effects will be employed interchangeably in the present section, this does not of course obviate the need for a more adequate scientific vocabulary to avoid the confusions and inconsistencies which are prevalent in this area. As used in this section, the term "hallucination" is similar in meaning to that employed in contemporary clinical and experimental psychiatry. It refers to a sense perception which has no external basis and in which the person may or may not realize that there is a lack of an external basis in the generation of the perception (Solomon and Mendelson, 1962). This broader conceptualization of hallucination encompasses the notion that illusory, hypnagogic, and hallucinatory processes may all be part of a continuous system. One classification scheme has already been proposed which makes it possible to specify each of these types of perceptual reactions in terms of a particular set of values in a tridimensional system (Cohen, Rosenbaum, Dobie, and Gottlieb, 1959).

Hallucinatory activities represent one of the most dramatic aspects of research in SD and have been observed in numerous studies; for those investigators with a clinical orientation, the ability to produce these hallucinatory phenomena in an experimental setting has opened a vast new area of research. Since the phenomena can be elicited within the context of a laboratory setting, the situation provides the possibility of improved observation, which might lead to a more adequate understanding of the phenomena and perhaps to their subsequent control. We will turn now to the literature on this problem and note the reports given by normal persons regarding their feelings of depersonalization, the breakdown in bodily image, and the arousal of vivid imagery.

In an early study on color adaptation (Hochberg, Triebel, and Seaman, 1951), two groups of subjects were exposed for 20 min to a homogeneous field of light while wearing eyecaps made from halved table-tennis balls carved to fit snugly over the eyes and eyelids. One group was exposed to red light; the other, to green. The major finding was that *after adaptation (within 3 to 6 min) the color reported by the subjects was dark gray or black.* As a subsidiary finding, *five of eleven subjects reported the appearance of hallucinatory shapes or objects* in the course of the experiment. At least one subject exhibited anxiety toward the "perceived" form, and two subjects found it difficult to believe that the shapes had not been introduced by the experimenter as a part of the testing procedure. The authors suggest that, on the basis of the individual differences observed in the hallucinatory objects and patterns during adaptation, the experimental method might be used for the investigation of personality structure.

In another study in which translucent goggles were worn under conditions of SD (Bexton, Heron, and Scott, 1954), the last 14 of 22 male subjects were asked to report any "visual imagery" they observed during the confinement period of two or three days. All 14 subjects reported *some form of imagery, usually visual in quality,* which ranged from shifts from light to dark, dots of light, and simple geometric patterns to complex visual experiences (for example, "wallpaper patterns") and integrated three-dimensional scenes (for example, "a procession of squirrels with sacks over their shoulders marching 'purposefully' across a snow field"). Sometimes the figures appeared "like cartoons" and some of the scenes were inverted or tilted at an angle. The content of the imagery could not be readily controlled by the subjects and the vividness of the imagery often interfered with sleep. The imagery tended to disappear when the subject was involved in performing a complex task, such as multiplying three-place numbers "in his head." The images frequently involved elements from the auditory, kinesthetic, and somesthetic senses. One subject reported "seeing" a small rocket ship which fired pellets that repeatedly struck him on the arm. Two subjects reported that there were two bodies lying next to each other within the confinement cubicle, as if "there were two of me." Another said that his head felt as though it were detached from his body.

A follow-up study (Heron, 1961) revealed that in general *the subjects did not believe that these images were "real" or produced by stimulation from external sources;* compared to normal imagery, the hallucinations (that is, perceptions "without object") were more vivid and were localized in front of the subject. The visual patterns often involved considerable movement, to the extent that some subjects became nauseated. The time of onset of the hallucinatory images varied from 20 min to approximately 70 hours.

These same investigators set out to determine whether the hallucinatory activity was due to the diffuse light that passed through the translucent goggles. After several days of confinement opaque goggles were placed on three subjects who had been hallucinating persistently. At first the imagery became much more vivid, but within two hours it had disappeared for two subjects and was considerably reduced in the third. The translucent goggles were again put on and the hallucinatory activity reappeared. Two other subjects initially wore opaque goggles during confinement and were then shifted to translucent goggles; both subjects reported vivid hallucinations under the latter condition while only one reported imagery in the former condition.

The implication that *the presence of a diffuse light field is responsible for the hallucinatory activity* is also found in the work of Vernon, McGill, and Schiffman (1958). In this study, nine subjects were permitted periodically to leave the confinement cubicle while blindfolded; this condition exposed the subjects to light leaks and other varieties of visual stimulation. A second group of eleven subjects was confined entirely within the lightproof cubicle for the entire period of sensory deprivation. When the two conditions of deprivation were compared, it was found that more hallucinatory activity was present in the less extreme situation. Also, the greater the period of confinement, the greater the number of images. It was concluded that *there is some hallucinatory activity and a greater variety when confinement is carried out in conjunction with nonpatterned visual stimulation, rather than complete darkness.* It should be noted, however, that subsequent studies in which the experimental conditions were duplicated failed to replicate the original findings. Since this was the only study by the Princeton group in which hallucinatory activity was obtained, it appears that "the original data . . . are in series doubt" (Vernon, 1966, p. 58).

Nevertheless, a similar conclusion regarding the effect of nonpatterned stimulation was reached in another study performed in a military laboratory (Ruff, Levy, and Thaler, 1961). Eight different experiments were performed with a total of more than 60 subjects. All studies involved a confinement procedure in which the subjects were placed in a soundproof room furnished with a bed, refrigerator, and toilet facilities. A wide variety of experimental conditions was imposed in the series of studies; one category of variables involved the quantity, modality, and pattern of sensory stimulation. While many subjects reported simple imagery, for example, "I saw spots before my eyes," only 2 subjects had hallucinations. One occurred in a total darkness situation; the other, after two hours in which frosted goggles and a masking white noise were used as part of the conditions of confinement. In the latter case the subject saw a vision of "a little German man walking down the road away from me" (p. 82). None of the subjects reported a somatic delusion.

The authors indicate that *perceptual changes are produced more readily when unpatterned light fields are used rather than a total reduction of sensory input.* It was suggested that the low rate of hallucinatory activity in this study may have been due in part to the type of subjects tested. Since the subjects were older men from military and civilian populations, it was hypothesized that, unlike a college population, they may have been accustomed to stressful situations and were not anxious in the SD situation. These investigators believe that *behavior in SD experiments depends not only on the experimental variables but also on a complex set of factors related to the subject's personality.* After studying two subjects confined in a tank-type respirator for 24 hours, Mendelson *et al.* (1961) also concluded that experimental stress serves to mobilize the "subject's characteristic defense mechanisms" and that the production of hallucinations seems to be definitely related to the "subject's premorbid personality."

In a more extended study (Wexler, Mendelson, Leiderman, and Solomon, 1958) 17 subjects were placed in a tank-type respirator for as long as 36 hours. The perceptual isolation in this restricted environment was sufficient to produce a wide range of hallucinatory experiences in the subjects. These experiences were described as including "daydreams," "fantasies," "illusions," "hallucinations," "analogies," and "pseudosomatic delusions." Contrary to what might be expected, *there was no relationship between the occurrence of these phenomena and the duration of confinement in the respirator.*

It has been suggested that the auditory and visual hallucinations may be the result of an attempt by the subject to order the stimuli that are available during confinement into a meaningful pattern, that is, there may be a need to find meaning in the environment (Freedman, Grunebaum, and Greenblatt, 1961). In this study one group of eight subjects was required to lie on a bed in a small room for eight hours; the subjects wore translucent goggles and were provided with earphones carrying a masking white noise. These conditions occluded normal vision and audition and permitted only continuous nonpatterned stimulation; in addition, cotton gloves and elbow-length cardboard cuffs minimized tactile stimulation. A second (control) group of six subjects was treated in the same way as the first, except that no goggles, earphones, gloves, or cuffs were used.

Among other findings, it was determined that none of the control group experienced hallucinatory activity, whereas four of the experimental group experienced changes in body image, for example, the arms appeared to be dissociated from the body, the body appeared to become smaller, or the body seemed to be floating in the air. Four of the eight subjects experienced auditory imagery, for example, music, buzz saws, the chirping of birds, or the voices of unidentified persons. Three subjects experienced visual illusions similar to those described for mescal intoxication and hypnogogic states. One subject had the following hallucination:

> The herd of elephants. Oh, that was pretty. That came very spontaneously. It was just sort of elephants in back, with pink and blue and purple . . . They were moving. The elephants themselves weren't moving, the picture was moving as if it were a closeup, a sort of backdrop . . . the elephants were gray . . . the background was pink . . . they weren't real elephants, because they were more like cutouts (p. 68).

It was postulated by the investigators that *it is the "process of seeking order where there is no order and attempting to incorporate nonorder into previously existing schemata which accounts for the perceptual changes, instabilities, and inconsistencies described . . . in the present study"* (p. 70).

This same general notion formed the basis for one study that was performed to test the hypothesis that it is not the absence of sensory stimulation which produces the hallucinatory effects, but the absence of *meaningful* stimulation (Davis, Mc-Court, and Solomon, 1960). The prediction was made that adding visual stimulation to the standardized procedure of sensory deprivation in a tank-type respirator would not prevent the occurrence of psychological aberrations. Ten adult subjects were placed in the tank for a planned period of isolation of 10.5 hours; five subjects remained for the entire required time, while the others asked to be released after confinement intervals of 38 min to 6.75 hours. The tank was in a semidarkened room and the vents of the tank remained open; the subject wore cardboard cuffs over his arms and legs and was able to hear the steady sounds from the motors of the respirator and air-conditioner. The visual stimulation was provided by a white 150-watt light that flashed on according to a random schedule; also, colored Rorschach cards were flashed on the wall tachistoscopically for a random duration of 0.1 to 1.0 sec at the rate of one every 50 to 99 min.

The results of this study are presented in Table 14-2. *Nine of the 10 subjects experienced imagery* which included analogies, daydreams, fantasies, pseudosomatic delusions, illusions, and hallucinations. In Table 14-2, the hallucinations are classified according to certain criteria (Vernon, McGill, Schiffman, 1958). Type I includes "flashes of light, flickering lights, dim glowing lights, and so on, that appear in the visual periphery. Type II includes hallucinations "of definite shape that are geometric in nature (squares, circles, and so on). Type III includes "structural integrated scenes which sometimes are even animated." The letter "A" in Table 14-2 indicates that the subject was aware that his "hallucination" was not real; the letter "B" denotes the absence of this realization. Of the various kinds of imagery produced by the experimental conditions, analogies (for example, "It feels like . . .") and daydreams were most frequent. The hallucinations included "playing baseball, skin diving, being on a troop ship, feeling chips of paint or specks of dirt falling from the ceiling, water dripping, delusions of eggnog being poisoned, feeling shocks from the electrocardiograph leads, and smelling the electrode jelly melting.

When the number of subjects in this experiment who experienced imagery or

Table 14–2 Kinds of Imagery Reported by 10 Subjects Exposed to Modified Sensory Deprivation in a Tank-Type Respirator

Subjects	Analogies	Daydreams	Fantasies	Pseudo-somatic Delusions	Illusions	Halluci-nations
A	X	X		X		
B	X				X	
E	X	X	X	X		X A, B III
J		X				
K	X	X				X A, I
L						
M	X				X	
P		X			X	
T			X			
W	X	X	X			X A, B III
	6	6	3	2	3	3

Source: J. M. Davis, W. F. McCourt, and P. Solomon. The effect of visual stimulation on hallucinations and other mental experience during sensory deprivation. *Amer. J. Psychiat.*, 1960, **116**, 889–892.

hallucinations was compared to that in a previous experiment without visual stimulation, there was no significant difference. It was concluded, therefore, that *the psychological aberrations occurred not as a result of sensory deprivation, but as a consequence of isolation from meaningful contact with the environment.* Random visual stimulation is apparently not sufficient to prevent the occurrence of imagery or hallucinations.

When subjects were kept in the tank-type respirator in another experiment in which no additional visual stimulation was provided, only seven of 28 subjects developed hallucinations (Solomon and Mendelson, 1962). This tends to confirm the hypothesis that it is not the reduction in the quantity of stimulation per se that produces hallucinations, since, if this were so, a larger percentage of subjects in this study would have been expected to report hallucinatory activities. Of the seven subjects who had hallucinations, all experienced visual hallucinations, three also had somesthetic hallucinations, and none experienced auditory hallucinations

The quality of hallucinations, together with their temporal onset, duration, and termination, are summarized in Table 14-3. It may be seen that "the visual hal-

Table 14-3 The Quality of Hallucinations and Their Temporal Onset, Duration, and Termination as a Function of 36 Hours of Confinement in the Tank-Type Respirator

Subject	2	13		16	C		E	F	K	
Type	Visual	Visual	Somesthetic	Visual	Visual	Somesthetic	Visual	Visual	Visual	Somesthetic
Imagery V—vivid C—color 3D—three-dimensional	VC 3D, rapidly changing organized people, animals, and so on	VC 3D, figures not organized	Crushed in football pile-up	VC 3D, horrendous moving animal	VC 3D, bathysphere scenes	Body displaced 90° in space; feeling of leaning on table	VC 3D, flat geometric forms	V, black and white flat newspaper over face; "Frank"	VC 3D, people and geometric forms	Sudden explosive pressure over face
Onset (hrs)	1.25	?	1.5	16	?	?	3.0	?	?	?
Durations (mins)	45	?	10	2	?	?	30	?	?	?
Spontaneous Remission	x	x		x	x	x		x	x	x
Terminated Experiment			x				x			

Source: P. Solomon and J. Mendelson. Hallucinations in sensory deprivation. In *Hallucinations*, New York: Grune & Stratton, 1962. By permission of the publisher.

lucinations were vivid, largely three-dimensional, upright with respect to gravity, and usually in brilliant color" (p. 137). One subject reported the following visual illusion: "I was in a bathysphere. Everything was in beautiful color. I realized things weren't real, so I didn't try to touch them" (p. 137). One subject reported the following somesthetic hallucination: "I feel as though I were at the bottom of a big football pile-up, crushed down by weight and unable to move" (p. 137).

The time of onset of the hallucinations varied from approximately an hour to 16 hours after the isolation period was started; the duration of the hallucinations ranged from 2 to 45 minutes. *No differences were found between those subjects who did and did not experience hallucinations* with respect to the following factors, among others: motivation for participating, personality characteristics as measured by the Minnesota Multiphasic Personality Inventory and the Edwards Personal Preference Schedule, length of stay in confinement, amount of verbalization, duration of sleep, the number of references to somatic complaints per hour, and the reasons for terminating the period of confinement.

Other investigators have also attempted to establish the relationship between specific personality variables and individual differences in the response patterns observed during the period of deprivation (Cohen, Silverman, Bressler, Shmavonian, 1961). In one experiment both male and female subjects were isolated for two hours in a dark acoustical chamber with the only sound arising from a ventilator motor. The subjects were not informed of the nature of the study nor of its duration; they were seated and asked not to move, speak, or to make any noise. At the end of two hours, the investigator interviewed the subjects and recorded the interviews on tape.

Among other observations, it was noted that seven of the ten subjects, including both men and women, experienced some sort of visual phenomena during confinement. These phenomena were of the visual variety such as spots, flashing lights, and "banners of different colors which were moving back and forth." One subject experienced auditory imagery and reported that he heard "a captain's chair scooting about the room." Several subjects maintained that there were changes in the texture and consistency of the walls and floor of the chamber. The metal walls were characterized as feeling like "velvet" and the rug seemed "soft and spongy."

In summarizing the many variables which may affect the outcome of a sensory deprivation experiment, the authors pointed out that *the experimenter may contribute to differences in the subjects' degree of uncertainty, anxiety level, and emotional arousal during the confinement period by imposing his expectations upon the subject by verbal or nonverbal means.* In this study there were no specific orienting instructions, thereby perhaps introducing an element of anxiety. Although the importance of personality factors as possible determinants of behavioral responses in the confinement situation was indicated, the study did not provide any indication of what this relationship might be. There was, however, a suggestion that the *sex of the person in relation to the sex of the subject being placed in the testing chamber might lead to the arousal of certain feelings, attitudes, or fantasies on the part of the subject.* When married couples are used in isolation experiments, the amount of imagery or hallucinatory experience is greatly reduced, and there is no difference between the number of males and females who experience the various types of mental aberrations (Davis, McCourt, Courtney, and Solomon, 1961).

Up to this point we have seen that several factors may account to some extent for the hallucinatory experiences that are observed in sensory deprivation experiments. These include *homogeneous or nonpatterned visual light fields, experimental stress or anxiety, personality characteristics, and to a lesser degree, the duration of confinement.* In some of the studies cited, there have been statements which suggest that the inhibition of body movement may also be a contributing factor in the production of imagery and hallucinatory phenomena. Empirically it is seen that those investigators who restricted the movement of their subjects during the period of confinement obtained a high incidence of imagery (Davis, McCourt, and Solomon, 1960; Goldberger and Holt, 1958; Wexler, Mendelson, Leiderman, and Solomon, 1958), whereas those who permitted free, or relatively free, movement obtained little or no imagery (Levy, Ruff, and Thaler, 1959; Vernon, McGill, and Schiffman, 1958).

To test the specific hypothesis that movement tends to reduce the amount of imagery obtained under conditions of sensory deprivation, two groups of nine subjects each were isolated for four hours with special instructions (Courtney, Davis, and Solomon, 1961). The subjects in one group, the "large body movement group," were required, upon receiving a small puff of air on the leg, to sit up in bed and touch a metal bar placed at the end of the bed; the subjects in the other group, the "finger movement group," were required simply to touch a key with the index finger each time the air puff was presented. The air puffs were presented randomly every 1 to 5 min. The subjects in both groups wore cardboard cuffs around their arms and legs and were provided with translucent goggles; they also listened to a masking noise presented via earphones.

The results of this study revealed that the subjects in both groups experienced the common effects of sensory deprivation, including imagery, visual distortion, cognitive impairment on the Wechsler-Bellevue Digit Symbol Test, and characteristic emotional reactions. However, of these, only the difference in visual distortion was statistically significant, with the finger-movement group showing more frequent and more persistent distortions. Thus, *body movement does not appear to be an important variable in relation to the production of imagery or hallucinatory experiences in SD experiments,* at least in those experiments in which the confinement period does not exceed 4 hours. In another context, it has been found that the ability to discriminate minute time differences between paired clicks is significantly impaired if the subjects walk about while listening to one hour of dichotic white noise; with restricted body movement the performance is not affected (Freedman and Zachs, 1964).

It appears, therefore, that body movement is not a significant factor in the production of hallucinatory experiences in sensory deprivation. Part of the difficulty in making direct comparisons among the various studies in this area of research is that there is no systematic classification of the descriptive parameters which characterize the hallucinatory experiences. The general concept of imagery encompasses a diverse range of phenomena which does not permit easy quantification. Some attempts have been made to work out numerical schemes of classification, but more needs to be done. The establishment of quantitative dimensions would permit a more adequate assessment of both the experimental conditions and their attendant consequences. If such measures were available, it would also be possible to compare the results of these studies with those obtained in related areas of investigation, such as mescal intoxication and visual flicker.

Another difficulty relates to the manner in which the reports of imagery or hallucinatory experiences have been obtained in SD experiments. Ordinarily this is done by a retrospective report following confinement, although in some studies verbalization during the period of confinement was noted or tape-recorded (Solomon and Mendelson, 1962). Either procedure raises questions on the reliability of the observations and makes it difficult to assess the frequency, vividness, and quality of the experiences in sensory deprivation. By simultaneously recording other kinds of responses, such as those in electroencephalography or in sensory physiology, it might be possible to arrive at independent estimates of the quantitative characteristics of these phenomena. It has been found, for example, that EEG tracings from the parieto-occipital area showed greatly reduced amplitudes while a subject was hallucinating than when he was not (Heron, 1961). In another study, a group of subjects exposed to minimal levels of stimulation for about 40 min showed decreased respiratory activity, but increased muscular and circulatory activity, when compared to a group of subjects who received normal levels of stimulation that were unpatterned (Davis, 1959). Another possibility would be to study the characteristics of eye movements during the occurrence of imagery and compare these with the characteristics present during dreams or during confinement when no imagery is being experienced. Comparisons such as these might provide information of value in understanding the wide spectrum of behavior which has been observed in SD experiments. It appears that such understanding cannot be based solely upon the verbal reports of imaginal phenomena, nor upon some singular model of psychopathology, but must be derived from a variety of techniques, approaches and theories which may be applicable to the SD situation.

Some Clinical Aspects
of Sensory Deprivation

In the preceding section of this chapter, a number of studies were reviewed in which normal subjects reported the presence of imagery or hallucinatory experiences when they were exposed to conditions of sensory deprivation. These studies showed that by limiting or modifying the environmental stimuli a marked change in behavior could be produced, without the use of drugs or other medical agents. While the psychological or physiological mechanisms underlying such behavior are not yet understood, some of the relevant physical variables have been tentatively delineated. These include the quantitative reduction in stimulation, the elimination of perceptual meaning in the stimulating conditions, and the monotonous or repetitive character of the stimuli. In addition to the physical aspects of the stimuli and their modification, some investigators have attempted, as indicated, to identify personality variables which may be related to the behaviors observed in SD experiments. The resemblance between the effects of sensory deprivation and certain behavioral syndromes has aroused considerable interest among psychiatrists and clinical psychologists, and attempts are being made both experimentally and theoretically to account for these observed similarities. The possibility is intriguing that certain clinical disturbances, such as schizophrenia, may involve elements or processes which are similar or related to those found under conditions of a restricted sensory environment. As we have seen, these conditions may involve the development of a seemingly transient psychotic state in individuals who are otherwise normal.

Both situations, the clinical and the experimental, may give rise to apparently comparable behaviors. A typical case is presented to demonstrate this point.

> (This) case is illustrated by a 38-year-old woman with retinal detachment being prepared for surgery, on whom psychiatric consultation was requested because of the development of the delusion that her medication was poisoned. She was a married lady, described as "high-strung," but otherwise without prior psychiatric difficulty. Family history was also completely negative for mental illness.
>
> When seen she was one of five patients remaining on a ward that had been largely evacuated for redecorating. The patient's bed was some distance from the other remaining patients, and was surrounded by screens. Both of her eyes were covered with bandages. She was noted to be quite restless, her hands and face in constant movement. Her thought processes were confused and rambling. Her voice was whiney and childish. She complained that her medication was poisoned, and that she was being smothered. She told of seeing a "funny little man" like a cartoon, and said she was unable to tell whether she had been dreaming or awake at the time.
>
> The patient was operated on the following day, after which only one eye was bandaged and she was brought into closer contact with other patients and staff. The psychotic aspects cleared almost at once and the patient was discharged a week after surgery, free from mental abnormality (Rosenzweig, 1959, p. 2).

This example is not unique; many psychologists and psychiatrists have seen such cases or are familiar with them through published works. The transient psychotic behaviors which characterize some normal subjects under conditions of sensory deprivation appear similar in many respects to those observed in clinical patients. Both subjects and patients have difficulty in maintaining organized thought processes, in controlling their own activities, and in separating imaginary and real experiences in relation to the environment. They both also attempt to cope with their situation by adopting procedures which tend to structure and order their activities, such as adhering to a rigid schedule, solving verbal or mathematical problems, and following a particular routine. To minimize or avoid anxiety, both types of individuals try to recall past experiences of a pleasant nature; despite this, depression may set in with thoughts of suicide or even attempts at suicide being present. It appears logical and meaningful, therefore, to consider these aspects of sensory deprivation in clinical terms and, if possible, to interpret the effects of isolation and confinement within a theoretical framework that is broad enough to encompass both the effects of deprivation and the manifestations of certain clinical syndromes (Rosenzweig, 1959).

One current view is that schizophrenia is a state involving excessive psychological activity which interferes with the usual interaction between the individual and his environment and prevents normal behavioral responses to stimuli from the external environment. This concept is implied in such clinical terms as "withdrawal," "retreat from reality," "autism," and "lack of reality testing." Since autistic phenomena, for example, visual hallucinations, have been observed in normal subjects under SD conditions, it has been hypothesized that schizophrenic subjects would be more susceptible than normal subjects to SD and should show a more marked deterioration of behavior under these conditions.

One experiment in which this hypothesis was tested involved 12 schizophrenic patients who were exposed to conditions in which perception was no longer possible (Harris, 1959). The patients reclined on a couch in a soundproof cubicle while wearing opaque goggles and the usual arm cuffs. Their period of confinement was half an hour in the first session, then up to two hours on another day. One patient was tested for two further periods of three hours each.

The results of this study showed that the schizophrenics tolerated the SD experience quite well. All 12 patients completed the first half hour without protest; only five failed to complete the second 2-hour period and, of these, only two felt marked distress. (One was a girl who had a pronounced erotic hallucination of being raped, the other was a young man who believed that he would be seized by his throat and throttled by an extra pair of gloves which he saw lying in a corner of the cubicle.) The hebophrenic type of patients found the cubicle restful and peaceful and liked it so much they were reluctant to come out at the end of the period. All of the patients underestimated the duration of their confinement, but they also underestimated time when in the ward. The only effect produced by the confinement was a reduction in vividness of the hallucinations and in their disturbing characteristics. While in confinement, one patient no longer experienced visual hallucinations and another no longer heard voices "in her head." Other diminutions in hallucinatory experiences were also noted. No substantial change was observed in the patients' condition during the week in which the SD study was being conducted. It was suggested that there is a difference in the conditions which elicit or suppress hallucinations in normal subjects and schizophrenic patients. *In normal subjects, visual deprivation tends to produce hallucinations in contrast to schizophrenia in which ordinary sensory stimuli tend to reinforce the hallucinatory experiences.*

In another study four normal, one neurotic, two sociopathic, and three schizophrenic subjects were confined individually for one hour in an isolation room (Cohen, Rosenbaum, Dobie, and Gottlieb, 1959). The auditory input was minimized by providing the subjects with ear plugs and earphones with a constant masking noise; tactual stimulation was reduced by wrapping the subject's fingers in cotton and enclosing the lower arm in elbow-length mittens; and visual stimulation was restricted by the use of goggles. Four subjects wore blackened-out goggles (no visual stimulation) and six wore either white or red, frosted goggles (diffuse light stimulation). The experiences of the subjects were scored on the basis of an original rating scale for classifying sensory and hallucinatory reports. The anxiety neurotic reported no hallucinations. The two sociopathic patients experienced more typical clinical hallucinations, as did the three schizophrenic patients, with the content and frequency of the hallucinations corresponding to the clinical condition of the patient. However, the frequency of these experiences was no greater than is ordinarily anticipated for schizophrenic patients in nonisolation conditions. *In general, the content of the experiences seemed to reflect the dominant needs and habit systems of individual subjects.* For example, an adolescent patient with known religious preoccupations indicated she heard the ringing of church bells. Neither the frosted nor black goggles produced visual hallucinations, although there was a greater number of visual sensory reactions with the white goggles. This is consistent with the other studies which have shown that *diffuse visual stimulation produces a more frequent occurrence of abnormal visual phenomena.* The conclusions of this study indicate that *one hour of sensory isolation does not produce any cognitive dysfunction or vivid pictorial hallucinations,* even though it was suggested to the subjects that unusual perceptions were appropriate and acceptable in that type of experimental situation. It has also been shown that *normal subjects exposed to three hours of sensory deprivation do not manifest an increase in the "primary process,"* as measured by responses to Rapaport's Word Association Test in terms of reaction time, popular responses, errors of recall, or traumatic words (Robertson and Browning, 1963).

Sensory Deprivation and Some Theoretical Implications

There is little question that hallucinatory experiences, in the form of imaginary events, may be produced in sensory deprivation if appropriate environmental conditions are present. These hallucinations may differ from those which occur in other circumstances, particularly in terms of the sensory modality involved, the vividness or intensity of the experience, and the emotional affect that is aroused. Nevertheless, in some instances, the hallucinations are similar to those of certain psychotic states, or to those produced by pharmacological agents such as mescaline and lysergic acid diethylamide (LSD-25).

Why do these hallucinations occur? The answer is speculative. One view holds that the symptoms of schizophrenia are the result of certain disruptions in the internal processes of an individual that prevent the reliable determination of the significance of perceptions (Rosenzweig, 1959). The orderly association of sensory and perceptual material is destroyed, and the schizophrenic is unable to establish the relevance of his immediate experience for ongoing cognitive or other processes. An analogous situation is postulated for the condition of sensory deprivation, except that the source of the interference is said to be external rather than internal with respect to the individual. When the environmental conditions are so manipulated that the stimuli are restricted, depatterned, or redundant, the stimuli lose their meaningfulness for the subject. When this occurs, the relevance of the stimulation cannot be established in terms of the subject's immediate psychological needs. It is asserted that it is this restriction of meaning and not the specific physical limitation of the stimuli per se that produces the effects of sensory deprivation. This means that the significance of sensory deprivation lies in the restriction or limitation of useful external information and, even with considerable input, the elimination of stimulus relevance should lead to schizophrenic-type behaviors. The common factor in schizophrenia and sensory deprivation, therefore, is considered to be *relevance* deprivation, which may be produced by a variety of environmental manipulations.

In a related but somewhat different view, it has been proposed that an individual's response to SD can be considered as a manifestation of preoccupation and suggestibility and that, within the context of these two terms, abnormal behavior may be described as a deprivation phenomenon (Robertson, 1961*a*). It is assumed that an individual's response is a function of the external and internal stimuli which interact in a reciprocal manner at any given moment. The internal "stimuli" (feelings, memories, thoughts, images) predispose the individual through attention to perceive certain stimuli in the environment and to ignore others; likewise, particular responses lead to external stimulation which serves as a selective factor in arousing or emphasizing certain thoughts or feelings. Under conditions of SD, the interaction is presumably reduced and the behavior is determined almost in its entirety by various internal stimuli. This leads to *preoccupation* in which the individual's perceptual and ideational reactions are considerably restricted and are directed toward internal psychological states or processes; excessive attention is placed upon whatever stimulation remains available and the condition of *suggestibility* is said to develop. Since external stimulation is greatly diminished and the thoughts and feelings of the individual are separated from the customary background of contextual stimuli, suggestibility becomes intensified and abnormal behavior is manifested.

This theoretical view has been extended to consider the therapeutic possibilities of sensory deprivation (Robertson, 1961*b*). The basic notion is that SD can be used to reinstate the normal level and range of stimulation, external and internal. For some individuals this would be accomplished by increasing the total amount of stimulation; for others, by emphasizing certain classes or types of conditions to which they would be exposed. In a given instance, the therapeutic program would be based on the total amount of stimulation and the corresponding pattern of deprivation. SD has already been used as a therapeutic method for selected types of hospitalized psychotic patients and moderate success has been reported (Adams, Carrera, and Gibby, 1960; Azima and Cramer, 1956).

A physiologically based theory has been proposed as another possible explanation for the subjective and behavioral phenomena that have been observed in deprivation experiments (Lindsley, 1961*b*). The theoretical formulation posits the ascending reticular activating system (ARAS) of the lower brain stem as the primary structure involved in the mediation of these phenomena. In its normal functioning, the ARAS serves as a relay station at which neural impulses arrive from the various sensory receptors; impulses from the ARAS are in turn conducted centrally to different parts of the brain, including the cortex. These neural impulses from ARAS exert an alerting or arousal effect at the cortex which is essential for the occurrence of normal perceptions. If the ARAS is not functioning, as when the subject is under barbiturate anesthesia, neural impulses will arrive at the primary projection areas but discrimination or perception does not occur. Another segment of the reticular system (centrifugal afferent control) functions in such a way that the level of neural activity in the cortex and in the reticular formation serves to regulate the amount of sensory input in the ARAS by blocking incoming impulses from the receptor systems. Thus, the ARAS is functionally capable of monitoring the input-output levels of neural excitation.

This regulatory or adjustive action of the ARAS leads to the concept of an adaptation level in which the ARAS mediates a correspondingly high, low, or neutral level of attention ("anticipatory set"). Under conditions of sensory deprivation, the level would be expected to decrease markedly with attendant boredom, inactivity, and, finally, sleep being present. Repeated disruption of the normal level of activity in the ARAS would in a similar manner be expected to produce distorted perceptions. For increments and decrements in the level of activity in the ARAS, compensatory adjustments may be made within limits in the corresponding activity of the afferent and efferent portions of the central nervous system; it is hypothesized that when the extent of the compensatory adjustment is exceeded as in SD, behavior deteriorates and becomes disorganized. In short, the reticular system monitors all input and output activities of the sensory systems and, as a consequence, becomes adapted to certain levels of excitation; this response level of the reticular system is projected to the cortex which, in turn, influences subjective and behavioral activities. When the level of activation exceeds the normal limits of operation, the "unusual" effects of sensory deprivation are obtained.

A related theoretical position asserts that the occurrence of all visual imagery and "mental symptoms" in acute sensory deprivation is not the result of reduced sensory input per se, but is a function of the reduced level of arousal which is concomitantly present (Ziskind, 1965). Thus, "reduced awareness" (as assessed by clinical observation) is claimed to be the necessary, but not sufficient, condition for producing abnormal symptoms. This position was evolved after five years of research on binocularly-patched patients in a hospital eye ward and on control subjects which showed that: (1) subjects frequently failed to comply with instructions in periods of half-sleep and that the acts of noncompliance were often associated with pseudo-hallucinations; (2) an increase in stimulation did not significantly alter the occurrence of mental symptoms, whereas changes were related to states of wakefulness; and (3) specific instructions could be given which greatly enhanced the occurrence of visual imagery.

The interpretation of this position suggests that the symptom complex in SD research occurs in periods of "reduced awareness" (the necessary condition) in conjunction with "precipitating internal and external stimuli and goal-directed action" (the sufficient condition). The sufficient condition is implied to be related in part to the instructions and psychological set of the experiment. Within this framework, the imaginal, perceptual, and cognitive distortions of SD are held to occur. These are not viewed as clinically abnormal behaviors, but are seen as normal manifestations that may be expected to occur outside the experimental situations of SD whenever the conditions impose a period of minimal arousal or half-sleep.

Several additional theories have been offered to account for the experimental findings on sensory deprivation. These theories range from psychoanalytic accounts (Goldfried, 1960; Goldberger and Holt, 1961), derived in part from the analogy between the treatment situation in psychoanalysis and the experimental situation in sensory deprivation, to behavioral views which stress the motivational effects produced by exteroceptive stimulation. Some theories postulate the existence of specific developmental stages that are critical for the emergence of certain skills and behaviors; others emphasize the possible relevance of hypothalamic functions in modifying the activities of the optic and auditory sytems. The theories of SD vary considerably in their levels of abstraction, their scope, and their ability to account for the observed phenomena; there is no lack of theory or speculation. The problem remains of accumulating critical evidence in relation to these theories under more stringent experimental conditions. The significant parameters of stimulation need to be established, specific hypotheses need to be tested with quantitative data, the etiological basis for imagery must be determined, the extraneous psychological effects of unique instrumentation must be minimized or eliminated, the selection of subjects must involve a serious consideration of personality variables, more rigorous experimental designs should be used with adequate numbers of subjects and appropriate control groups, and, in general, studies should be carried out that will extend our knowledge of the effects of SD beyond that of the initial experiments. This challenge is already being met by a number of investigators and we should expect to see marked advances in SD research in the near future.

BIBLIOGRAPHY

Aborn, M., and H. Rubenstein. Information theory and immediate recall. *J. exp. Psychol.,* 1952, **44,** 260–266.

Abrahams, H., D. Krakauer, and K. M. Dallenbach. Gustatory adaptation to salt. *Amer. J. Psychol.,* 1937, **49,** 462–469.

Adams, H., G. Carrera, and R. Gibby. Personality and intellectual changes following brief sensory deprivation. *Arch. gen. Psychiat.,* 1960, **3,** 33–42.

Adelson, M., F. A. Muckler and A. C. Williams, Jr. Verbal learning and message variables related to amount of information. In H. Quastler (Ed.), *Information theory in psychology.* New York: Free Press, 1955. Pp. 291–299.

Adrian, E. D. *The physical background of perception.* New York: Oxford Univer. Press, 1946.

Adrian, E. D., and Y. Zotterman. The impulses produced by sensory nerve endings, Part 3. Impulses set up by touch and pressure. *J. Physiol.,* 1926, **61,** 465–483.

Albrite, J. P., M. D. Burkhard, R. K. Cook, E. L. Corliss, R. E. Shutts, and M. B. Whilock, Jr. Research in normal threshold of hearing. *Arch. Otolaryngol.,* 1958, **68,** 194–198.

Alluisi, E. A. Conditions affecting the amount of information in absolute judgments. *Psychol. Rev.,* 1957, **64,** 97–103.

Alluisi, E. A. On the use of information measures in studies of form perception. *Percept. mot. Skills,* 1960, **11,** 195–203.

Alluisi, E. A., and H. B. Martin. An information analysis of verbal and motor responses to symbolic and conventional arabic numerals. *J. appl. Psychol.,* 1958, **42,** 79–84.

Alluisi, E. A., and P. F. Muller, Jr. Verbal and motor responses to seven symbolic codes: a study in S-R compatibility. *J. exp. Psychol.,* 1958, **55,** 247–254.

Alonso de Florida, F., and J. M. R. Delgado. Lasting effects on behavior evoked by cerebral stimulation of the cat. *Amer. J. Physiol.,* 1955, **183,** 592.

American Academy of Ophthalmology and Otolaryngology, Committee on Conservation of Hearing. *Guide for the conservation of hearing in noise.* Los Angeles: Research Center, Subcommittee on Noise in Industry, 1957.

American Medical Association, Council on Industrial Health. Estimation of loss of visual efficiency. *AMA Arch. industr. Hlth,* 1955, **12,** 439–449.

American Standards Association, Subcommittee on Noise Measurement. American standard for noise measurements, Z24.2-1942. *J. acoust. Soc. Amer.,* 1942, **14,** 102–112.

American Standards Association. *American standard specification for audiometers for general diagnostic purposes,* Z24.5-1951. New York: American Standards Ass., 1951.

American Standards Association, Exploratory Subcommittee, Z24-X2. *The relations of hearing loss to noise exposure.* New York: American Standards Ass., 1954.

Archer, E. I. Identification of visual patterns as a function of information load. *J. exp. Psychol.,* 1954, **48,** 313–317.

Arey, L. B., M. J. Tremaine, and F. L. Monzingo. The numerical and topographical relations of taste buds to human circumvallate papillae throughout the life span. *Anat. Rec.,* 1935, **64,** 9–25.

Armstrong, H. G. *Principles and practice of aviation medicine.* (2d ed.) Baltimore: Williams and Wilkins, 1943.

Attneave, F. Some informational aspects of visual perception. *Psychol. Rev.*, 1954, **61**, 183–193.

Attneave, F. *Application of information theory to psychology: a summary of basic concepts, methods, and results.* New York: Holt, Rinehart and Winston, 1959.

Attneave, F., and M. D. Arnoult. The quantitative study of shape and pattern perception. *Psychol. Bull.*, 1956, **53**, 452–471.

Azima, H., and F. Cramer. Effects of partial perceptual isolation in mentally disturbed individuals. *Dis. nerv. Syst.*, 1956, **17**, 117.

Baker, C. A., and W. F. Grether. Visual presentation of information. *WADC Technical Report* 54–160, Aero-Medical Lab., Wright Air Development Center, Wright-Patterson Air Force Base, Ohio, 1954.

Barber, T. X. The concept of "hypnosis." *J. Psychol.*, 1958, **45**, 115–131.

Barber, T. X. Toward a theory of pain: Relief of chronic pain by prefrontal leucotomy, opiates, placebos, and hypnosis. *Psychol. Bull.*, 1959, **56**, 430–460.

Barlow, H. B. Comment on neutral quanta. In W. A. Rosenblith (Ed.), *Sensory communication.* New York: Wiley, 1961. Pp. 786–790.

Barrows, W. E. *Light, photometry and illuminating engineering.* (2d ed.) New York: McGraw-Hill, 1938.

Bartley, S. H. The psychophysiology of vision. In S. S. Stevens (Ed.), *Handbook of experimental psychology.* New York: Wiley, 1951. Pp. 921–984.

Batten, D. E. The effects of sensory deprivation on auditory and visual sensitivity. Unpublished doctoral dissertation, Washington State Univer., 1961.

Battig, W. F. Parsimony in psychology. *Psychol. Rep.*, 1962, **11**, 555–572.

Baumgardt, E. Les théories photochimiques classiques et quantitiques de la vision et l'inhibition nerveuse en vision liminaire. *Rev. d'optique*, 1949, **28**, 453–478, 661–690.

Bazett, H. C., B. McGlone, R. G. Williams, and H. M. Lufkin. Sensation 1. depth, distribution and probable identification in the prepuce of sensory end-organs concerned in sensations of temperature and touch; thermometric conductivity. *AMA Arch. Neurol. Psychiat*, 1932, **27**, 489–517.

Beales, P. H. *Noise, hearing and deafness.* London: Michael Joseph, 1965.

Beebe-Center, J. G., M. S. Rogers, and D. W. O'Connell. Transmission of information about sucrose and saline solutions through the sense of taste. *J. Psychol.*, 1955, **39**, 157–160.

Behar, I., and W. Bevan. The perceived duration of auditory and visual intervals: crossmodel comparison and interaction. *Amer. J. Psychol.*, 1961, **74**, 17–26.

Békésy, G. von. Über das Fechner'sche gesetz und seine bedeutung für die theorie der akustischen beobachtungsfehler und die theorie des Hörens. *Ann. Physik*, 1930, **7**, 329–359.

Békésy, G. von. Über die hörschwelle und fühlgrenze langsamer sinusförmiger luftdruckschwankungen. *Ann. Physik*, 1936, **26**, 554–566.

Békésy, G. von. Über die resonanzkurve und die abklingzeit der verschiedenen stellen der schneckentrenvuand. *Akust. Z.*, 1943, **8**, 66–76. (Translation: On the resonance curve and the decay period at various points on the cochlear partition.) *J. acoust. Soc. Amer.*, 1949, **21**, 245–254.)

Békésy, G. von. Lateral inhibition of heat sensations of the skin. *J. appl. Physiol.*, 1962, **17**, 1003–1008.

Bendig, A. W. An application of information theory to a problem in multiple prediction. *Psychol. Newsltr*, 1959, **10**, 148–150.

Berger, R. L., and E. Ackerman. The Penn State Anechoic Chamber. *Noise Control*, 1956, **2**, No. 5, 16–21.

Bergmann, G. Outline of an empiricist philosophy of physics. *Amer. J. Phys.*, 1943, **11**, 248–258, 335–342.

Bergmann, G. The logic of quanta. *Amer. J. Phys.*, 1947, **15**, 397–408, 497–508.

Bergmann, G. Duration and the specious present. *Phil. Sci.*, 1960, **27**, 39–47.

Berkson, J. Application of the logistic function to bioassay. *J. Amer. Statist. Ass.*, 1944, **39**, 357–365.

Berry, R. N. Quantitative relations among vernier, real depth, and stereoscopic depth acuities. *J. exp. Psychol.*, 1948, **38**, 708–721.

Berry, W., and H. Imus. Quantitative aspects of flight of colors. *Amer. J. Psychol.*, 1935, **47**, 449–457.

Bevan, W., and R. Adamson. Reinforcers and reinforcement: their relation to maze performance. *J. exp. Psychol.*, 1960, **59**, 226–232.

Bevan, W., and R. Adamson. Internal referents and the concept of reinforcement. In N. F. Washburne (Ed.), *Decisions, values, and groups.* Vol. 2. New York: Pergamon Press, 1963.

Bevan, W., R. A. Maier, and H. Helson. The influence of context upon the estimation of number. *Amer. J. Psychol.*, 1963, **76**, 464–469.

Bexton, W. H., W. Heron, and T. H. Scott. Effects of decreased variation in the sensory environment. *Canad. J. Psychol.*, 1954, **8**, 70–76.

Bishop, G. H. Natural history of the nerve impulse. *Physiol. Rev.*, 1956, **36**, 376–399.

Black, M. *Problem of analysis.* Ithaca, New York: Cornell Univer. Press, 1954.

Blackwell, H. R. Evaluation of the neural quantum theory in vision. *Amer. J. Psychol.*, 1953, **66**, 397–408.

Blakemore, C. B., and W. A. H. Rushton. Bleached rhodopsin and the regeneration of "dark light." *J. Physiol.*, 1962, **165**, 30–31P.

Blondel, A., and J. Rey. Sur la perception des lumières brève à la limite de leur portée. *J. de Physique*, 1911, **1**, 530–550.

Bloom, G., and H. Engström. The structure of the epithelial surface in the olfactory region. *Exp. Cell. Res.*, 1952, **3**, 699–701.

Boring, E. G. A chart of the psychometric function. *Amer. J. Psychol.*, 1917, **28**, 465–470.

Boring, E. G. *Sensation and perception in the history of experimental psychology.* New York: Appleton-Century-Crofts, 1942.

Boring, E. G., H. S. Langfeld, and H. P. Weld. *Foundations of psychology.* New York: Wiley, 1948.

Bouman, M. A. Absolute threshold conditions' for visual perception. *J. opt. Soc. Amer.*, 1955, **45**, 36–43.

Bouman, M. A., and P. L. Walraven. Some color naming experiments for red and green monochromatic lights. *J. opt. Soc. Amer.*, 1957, **47**, 834–839.

Bower, G. H. A contrast effect in differential conditioning. *J. exp. Psychol.*, 1961, **62**, 196–199.

Boynton, R. M. Some temporal factors in vision. In W. A. Rosenblith (Ed.), *Sensory communication.* New York: Wiley, 1961. Pp. 739–756.

Boynton, R. M. Quantum- and energy-based visual sensitivity on a single plot. *J. opt. Soc. Amer.*, 1963, **53**, 641–642.

Bradley, J. V. Studies in research methodology. II. Consequences of violating parametric assumptions: fact and fallacy. *WADC Technical Report* 58–574 (II), Wright Air Development Center, Wright-Patterson Air Force Base, Ohio, September, 1959.

Brainard, R. W., T. S. Irby, P. M. Fitts, and E. A. Alluisi. Some variables influencing the rate of gain of information. *J. exp. Psychol.*, 1962, **63**, 105–110.

Bridgman, P. W. *The logic of modern physics.* New York: Macmillan, 1928.

Broadbent, D. E. *Perception and communication.* New York: Pergamon Press, 1958.

Broadbent, D. E. The approach to information processing through behavior. In *Information processing in the nervous system.* Vol. III. Proc. int. union physiol. Sci., Twenty-second International Congress, Leiden, 1962.

Brown, P. K., and G. Wald. Visual pigments in single rods and cones of the human retina. *Science,* 1964, **144,** 45–52.

Brown, W. The judgment of difference. *Univer. Calif. Pub. Psychol.,* 1910, **1,** 1–71.

Bunge, M. (Ed.). *The critical approach to science and philosophy.* New York: Free Press, 1964.

Bürck, W., P. Kotowski, and H. Lichte. Der aufbau des tonhöhenbewusstseins. *Elek. Nachr.-Techn.,* 1935, **12,** 326–333.

Burke, C. J. Measurement scales and statistical models. In M. H. Marx (Ed.), *Theories in contemporary psychology.* New York: Macmillan, 1963. Pp. 147–159.

Burns, M., and K. M. Dallenbach. The adaptation of cutaneous pain. *Amer. J. Psychol.,* 1933, **45,** 111–117.

Burt, C. Definition and scientific method in psychology. *Brit. J. Statist. Psychol.,* 1958, **11,** 31–70.

Burt, C. The structure of mind. *Brit. J. Statist. Psychol.,* 1961, **14,** 145–170.

Burt, C., and W. L. Gregory. Scientific method in psychology. II. *Brit. J. Statist. Psychol.,* 1958, **11,** 105–128.

Campbell, N. R. Symposium: measurement and its importance for philosophy. *Proc. Arist. Soc. Suppl.,* 1938, **17,** 121–142.

Carnap, R. Formal and factual science. In H. Feigl, and M. Brodbeck (Eds.), *Readings in the philosophy of science.* New York: Appleton-Century-Crofts, 1953. Pp. 123–128. (Translated from R. Carnap, Formalwissenschaft und realwissenschaft. *Erkenntnis,* 1935, **5,** 30–37.)

Carterette, E. C., and M. Cole. Comparison of the receiver-generating characteristics received by the ear and by eye. *J. acoust. Soc. Amer.,* 1962, **34,** 172–178.

Cattell, J. M. On errors of observation. *Amer. J. Psychol.,* 1893, **5,** 285–293.

Cattell, M., and H. Hoagland. Response of tactile receptors to intermittent stimulation. *J. Physiol.,* 1931, **248,** 392–404.

Cawthorne, T. Adventures with the stapes. *Ann. Otol., Rhinol., Laryngol.,* 1957, **66,** 514–520.

Chapanis, A. Spectral saturation and its relation to color vision defects. *J. exp. Psychol.,* 1944, **34,** 24–44.

Chapanis, A. How we see: a summary of basic principles. In *Human factors in undersea warfare.* Washington, D. C.: National Research Council, 1949. Pp. 3–60.

Chapanis, A. Theory and methods for analyzing errors in man-machine systems. *Am. N. Y. Acad. Sci.,* 1951, **51,** 1179–1203.

Chapanis, A., and R. M. Halsey. Absolute judgments of spectrum colors. *J. Psychol.,* 1956, **42,** 99–103.

Cheesman, G. H., and S. Mayne. The influence of adaptation on absolute threshold measurements for olfactory stimuli. *Quart. J. exp. Psychol.,* 1953, **5,** 22–30.

Clark, B., and A. Graybiel. Linear acceleration and deceleration as factors influencing nonvisual orientation during flight. *J. aviat. Med.,* 1949, **20,** 92–101.

Clark, W. C. Relations between the thresholds for single and multiple light pulses. Unpublished doctoral dissertation, Univer. of Michigan, 1958. Cited in W. N. Dember, *The psychology of perception.* New York: Holt, Rinehart and Winston, 1960.

Clarke, F. R. Confidence ratings, second-choice responses and confusion matrices in intelligibility tests. *J. acoust. Soc. Amer.,* 1960, **32,** 35–46.

Cleghorn, T. E., and H. D. Darcus. The sensibility to passive movement of the human elbow joint. *Quart. J. exp. Psychol.,* 1952, **4,** 66–77.

Cohen, A. U. S. Public Health Service field work on the industrial noise hearing loss problem. *Occup. Hlth Rev.,* 1965, **17,** 3–10, 27.

Cohen, B. D., G. Rosenbaum, S. I. Dobie, and S. J. Gottlieb. Sensory isolation: hallucinogenic effects of a brief exposure. *J. nerv. ment. Disord.*, 1959, **129**, 486–491.

Cohen, S. I., A. J. Silverman, B. Bressler, and B. Shmavonian. Problems in isolation studies. In P. Solomon, *et al.* (Eds.), *Sensory deprivation.* Cambridge: Harvard Univer. Press, 1961. Pp. 114–129.

Cole, L. E. *Human behavior.* Yonkers-on-Hudson, New York: World Book, 1953.

Conant, J. B. The scientist in our unique society. *Atlantic mon.*, 1948, **181**, 47–54.

Conover, D. W. The amount of information in the absolute judgment of Munsell hues. *WADC Technical Report* 58–262, Wright Air Development Center, Wright-Patterson Air Force Base, Ohio, 1959.

Corso, J. F. An experimental re-examination of the theory of the neural quantum in the sensory discrimination of pitch and loudness. Ph.D. dissertation. State Univer. of Iowa, Iowa City, Iowa, 1950.

Corso, J. F. The neural quantum in discrimination of pitch and loudness. *Amer. J. Psychol.*, 1951, **64**, 350–368.

Corso, J. F. An electronic device for the production and measurement of warble-tones. *Amer. J. Psychol.*, 1955, **68**, 306–311.

Corso, J. F. The neural quantum theory of sensory dicrimination. *Psychol. Bull.*, 1956, **53**, 371–393.

Corso, J. F. Absolute judgments of musical tonality. *J. acoust. Soc. Amer.*, 1957, **29**, 138–144.

Corso, J. F. Absolute thresholds for tones of low frequency. *Amer. J. Psychol.*, 1958a, **71**, 367–374.

Corso, J. F. Proposed laboratory standard of normal hearing. *J. acoust. Soc. Amer.*, 1958b, **30**, 14–23.

Corso, J. F. The quantal hypothesis and the threshold of audibility. *Amer. J. Psychol.*, 1961, **74**, 191–204.

Corso, J. F. A theoretico-historical review of the threshold concept. *Psychol. Bull.*, 1963a, **60**, 356–370.

Corso, J. F. Bone-conduction thresholds for sonic and ultrasonic frequencies. *J. acoust. Soc. Amer.*, 1963b, **35**, 1738–1743.

Corso, J. F. Age and sex differences in pure tone thresholds. *Arch. Otolaryngol.*, 1963c, **77**, 385–405.

Corso, J. F. Aging and auditory thresholds in men and women. *Arch. environ. Hlth*, 1963d, **6**, 350–356.

Corso, J. F. Air-conduction thresholds for high frequency tones. Paper presented at the Eastern Psychol. Ass., Atlantic City, N. J., April 22-24, 1965.

Corso, J. F. Sensory processes: systematic developments and related data. In H. Helson, and W. Bevan (Eds.), *Contemporary approaches to psychology.* Princeton, N. J.: D. Van Nostrand, 1967. Pp. 273–309.

Corso, J. F., and A. Cohen. Methodological aspects of auditory threshold measurements. *J. exp. Psychol.*, 1958, **55**, 8–12.

Corso, J. F., and M. Levine. The pitch of ultrasonic frequencies heard by bone conduction. *Proc. Penna. Acad. Sci.*, 1963, **37**, 22–26.

Council on Industrial Health, American Medical Ass. Estimation of loss of visual efficiency. *AMA Arch. indust. Hlth.*, 1955, **12**, 439–449, 527.

Courtney, J., J. M. Davis, and P. Solomon. Sensory deprivation: the role of movement. *Percept. mot. skills*, 1961, **13**, 191–199.

Crawford, B. H. Sketch of the present position of the Young-Helmholtz theory of color vision. In A. V. S. DeReuck, and J. Knight (Eds.), *Colour vision: physiology and experimental psychology.* Boston: Little, Brown, 1965. Pp. 152–173.

Creelman, C. D. Human discrimination of auditory duration. *J. acoust. Soc. Amer.*, 1962, **34,** 582–593.

Crespi, L. P. Quantitative variations of incentive and performance in the white rat. *Amer. J. Psychol.*, 1942, **55,** 467–517.

Crossman, E. R. F. W. Entropy and choice time: the effect of frequency unbalance on choice response. *Quart. J. exp. Psychol.*, 1953, **5,** 41–51.

Crowe, S. J., S. R. Guild, and L. M. Polvogt. Obeservations on the pathology of high-tone deafness. *Bull. Johns Hopkins Hosp.*, 1934, **54,** 315–379.

Culbert, S. S., and M. I. Posner. Human habituation to an acoustical energy distribution spectrum. *J. appl. Psychol.*, 1960, **44,** 263–266.

Dallos, P. J. Dynamics of the acoustic reflex: phenomenological aspects. *J. acoust. Soc. Amer.*, 1964, **36,** 2175–2183.

Dartnall, H. J. A., and K. Tansley. Physiology and vision: retinal structure and visual pigments. *Ann. Rev. Physiol.*, 1963, **25,** 433–458.

Datta, L. E. G. Learning in the earthworm: *Lumbricus terrestris. Amer. J. Psychol.*, 1962, **75,** 531–553.

Davis, H., and F. Kranz. International audiometric zero. *J. acoust. Soc. Amer.*, 1964, **36,** 1450–1454.

Davis, J. M., W. F. McCourt, J. Courtney, and P. Solomon. Sensory deprivation. *Arch. gen. Psychiat.*, 1961, **5,** 84–90.

Davis, J. M., W. F. McCourt, and P. Solomon. *Sensory deprivation: (1) effects on social contact, (2) effects on random visual stimulation.* Paper presented at Amer. Psychiat. Ass. meeting, Philadelphia, April 1959.

Davis, J. M., W. F. McCourt, and P. Solomon. The effect of visual stimulation on hallucinations and other mental experiences during sensory deprivation. *Amer. J. Psychiat.*, 1960, **116,** 889–892.

Davis, T., N. Moray, and A. Treisman. Imitative responses and the rate of gain of information. *Quart. J. exp. Psychol.*, 1961, **13,** 78–89.

Davis, R., N. S. Sutherland, and B. R. Judd. Information content in recognition and recall. *J. exp. Psychol.*, 1961, **61,** 422–429.

Davis, R. C. Somatic activity under reduced stimulation. *J. comp. physiol. Psychol.*, 1959, **52,** 309–314.

Day, E. Science is we. *Trans. N.Y. Acad. Sci.*, 1966, **28,** 371–374.

DeCillis, O. E. Absolute thresholds for the perception of tactual movement. *Arch. Psychol.*, 1944, **294,** 1–52.

Deininger, R. L., and P. M. Fitts. Stimulus-response compatibility, information theory, and perceptual motor performance. In H. Quastler (Ed.), *Information theory in psychology.* New York: Free Press, 1955. Pp. 316–341.

Delgado, J. M. R. A transistor-timed stimulator. *Electroenceph. clin. Neurophysiol.*, 1959, **11,** 591–593.

Delgado, J. M. R. Chronic implantation of intracerebral electrodes in animals. In D. E. Sheer (Ed.), *Electrical stimulation of the brain.* Austin, Tex.: Univer. of Texas Press, 1961. Pp. 25–36.

Delgado, J. M. R., W. W. Roberts, and N. E. Miller. Learning motivated by electrical stimulation of the brain. *Amer. J. Physiol.*, 1954, **179,** 587–593.

Dember, W. N. *Psychology of perception.* New York: Holt, Rinehart and Winston, 1960.

Dempsey, E. W. Homeostasis. In S. S. Stevens (Ed.), *Handbook of experimental psychology.* New York: Wiley, 1951. Pp. 209–235.

Denny-Brown, D. *The basal ganglia.* New York: Oxford Univer. Press, 1962.

DeVries, H., and Stuiver, M. The absolute sensitivity of the human sense of smell. In W. A.

Rosenblith (Ed.), *Sensory communication*. New York: Wiley, 1961. Pp. 159–167.

DiLollo, V. Contrast effects in judgment of lifted weights. *J. exp. Psychol.*, 1964, **68**, 383–387.

Doane, B. K., W. Mahatoo, W. Heron, and T. H. Scott. Changes in perceptual function after isolation. *Canad. J. Psychol.*, 1959, **13**, 210–219.

Doughty, J. M., and W. R. Garner. Pitch characteristics of short tones. I. Two kinds of pitch threshold. *J. exp. Psychol.*, 1947, **37**, 351–365.

Duncan, D. B. Multiple range and multiple F tests. *Biometrics*, 1955, **11**, 1–42.

DuCroz, J. J. and W. A. H. Rushton. Cone dark-adaptation curves. *J. Physiol.*, 1963, **168**, 52–54P.

Edes, B., and K. M. Dallenbach. The adaptation of pain aroused by cold. *Amer. J. Psychol.*, 1936, **48**, 307–315.

Edwards, W. Behavioral decision theory. In P. R. Farnsworth (Ed.), *Annual review of psychology*. Palo Alto: Annual Reviews, 1961, **12**, 473–498.

Egan, J. P., G. Z. Greenberg, and A. I. Schulman. Operating characteristics, signal detectability and the method of free response. *J. acoust. Soc. Amer.*, 1961, **33**, 993–1007.

Eijkman, C., and A. J. H. Vendrik. Detection theory applied to the absolute sensitivity of sensory systems. *Biophys. J.*, 1963, **3**, 65–78.

Einstein, A. Considerations concerning the fundaments of theoretical physics. *Science*, 1940, **91**, 487–492.

Eisler, H. A choice model for paired comparison data based on imperfectly nested sets. *Psychometrika*, 1964, **29**, 363–370.

Ekdahl, A. G., and S. S. Stevens. The relation of pitch to the duration of a tone. Unpublished study, 1937. Cited in S. S. Stevens, and H. Davis, *Hearing: its psychology and physiology*. New York: Wiley, 1938.

Ekman, G. Two generalized ratio scaling methods. *J. gen. Psychol.*, 1958, **45**, 287–295.

Ekman, G. A simple method for fitting psychophysical power functions. *J. Psychol.*, 1961, **51**, 343–350.

Elsberg, C. A., and I. Levy. The sense of smell. I. A new and simple method of quantitative olfactometry. *Bull. neurol. Inst. N. Y.*, 1935, **4**, 5–19.

Ely, J. H., H. M. Bowen, and J. Orlansky. Man-machine dynamics. In C. T. Morgan, J. S. Cook, III, A. Chapanis, and M. W. Lund (Eds.), *Human engineering guide to equipment design*. New York: McGraw-Hill, 1963. Pp. 217–245.

Engel, G., and A. Parducci. Value of background in the specification of the stimulus for judgment. *Amer. J. Psychol.*, 1961, **74**, 569–575.

Engen, T., and C. Pfaffmann. Absolute judgments of odor intensity. *J. exp. Psychol.*, 1959, **58**, 23–26.

Engen, T., and C. Pfaffmann. Absolute judgments of odor quality. *J. exp. Psychol.*, 1960, **59**, 214–219.

Epstein, A., and E. D. Schubert. Reversible auditory fatigue resulting from exposure to a pure tone. *Arch. Otolaryngol.*, 1957, **65**, 174–182.

Eriksen, C. W., and H. W. Hake. Multidimensional stimulus differences and accuracy of discrimination. *J. exp. Psychol.*, 1955, **50**, 153–160.

Estes, W. K. Toward a statistical theory of learning. *Psychol. Rev.*, 1950, **57**, 94–107.

Farnsworth, D., and H. Kalmus. Impairment and recovery of taste following irradiation of the oropharynx. *J. Laryngol. Otol.*, 1959, **73**, 180–182.

Fechner, G. T. *Elemente der psychophysik*. Leipzig, Germany: Breitkopf and Härtel, 1860.

Fehrer, E., and I. Biederman. A comparison of reaction time and verbal report in the detection of masked stimuli. *J. exp. Psychol.*, 1962, **64**, 126–130.

Feigl, H. Naturalism and humanism. *Amer. quart.*, 1949, **1**, 135–148.

Feigl, H. The mind-body problem in the development of logical empiricism. *Rev. int. Phil.*, 1950, **4**, 64–83.

Fitts, P. M., and R. L. Deininger. S-R compatibility: correspondence among paired elements within stimulus and response codes. *J. exp. Psychol.*, 1954, **48**, 483–492.

Fitts, P. M., J. R. Peterson, and G. Wolpe. Cognitive aspects of information processing. II. Adjustments to stimulus redundancy. *J. exp. Psychol.*, 1963, **65**, 507–514.

Fitts, P. M., and C. M. Seeger. S-R compatibility: spatial characteristics of stimulus and response codes. *J. exp. Psychol.*, 1953, **46**, 199–210.

Fitts, P. M., and G. Switzer. Cognitive aspects of information processing. I. The familiarity of S-R sets and subsets. *J. exp. Psychol.*, 1962, **63**, 321–329.

Flexner, J. B., L. B. Flexner, and E. Stellar. Memory in mice as affected by intracerebral puromycin. *Science*, 1963, **14**, 57–59.

Flynn, B. Pitch discrimination. *Arch. Psychol.*, 1943, **280**, 3–41.

Foster, D., E. H. Scofield, and K. M. Dallenbach. An olfactorium. *Amer. J. Psychol.*, 1950, **63**, 431–440.

Fowler, R. G., and D. I. Meyer. *Physics for engineers and scientists.* Boston: Allyn and Bacon, 1958.

Frank, P. *Modern science and its philosophy.* New York: Collier, 1961.

Frank, P. G. (Ed.) *The validation of scientific theories.* New York: Collier, 1961.

Freedman, S. J., and M. Greenblatt. Studies in human isolation. *WADC Techical Report* 59–266, Aero-Medical Lab., Wright Air Development Center, Wright-Patterson Air Force Base, Ohio, 1959.

Freedman, S. J., H. U. Grunebaum, and M. Greenblatt. Perceptual and cognitive changes in sensory deprivation. In P. Solomon, *et al.* (Eds.), *Sensory deprivation.* Cambridge: Harvard Univer. Press, 1961. Pp. 58–71.

Freedman, S. J., and R. Held. Sensory deprivation and perceptual lag. *Percept. mot. Skills*, 1960, **11**, 277–280.

Freedman, S. J., and J. L. Zachs. Effects of active and passive movement upon auditory function during prolonged atypical stimulation. *Percept. mot. Skills*, 1964, **18**, 361–366.

Freeman, M. F., and J. W. Tukey. Transformations related to the angular and square foot. *Ann. Math. Statist.*, 1950, **21**, 607–611.

Freides, D., and P. Phillips. Power law fits to magnitude estimates of groups and individuals. *Psychonom. Sci.*, 1966, **5**, 367–368.

Frick, F. C., and G. A. Miller. A statistical description of operant conditioning. *Amer. J. Psychol.*, 1951, **64**, 20–36.

Friedman, A. P. Evaluation of nonnarcotic chemical agents in headaches. *Ann. N. Y. Acad. Sci.*, 1960, **86**, 216–225.

Fry, W. J. Intense ultrasound in investigations of the central nervous system. In *Advances in biological and medical physics*, Vol. VI. New York: Academic Press, 1958.

Fry, W. J., and F. J. Fry. Fundamental neurological research and human neurosurgery using intense ultrasound. *IRE Trans. Med. Electronics*, 1960, **ME-7**, 166–181.

Fry, W. J., W. H. Mosberg, J. W. Barnard, and F. J. Fry. Production of focal destructive lesions in the central nervous system with ultrasound. *J. Neurosurg.*, 1954, **11**, 471–478.

Fullerton, G. S., and J. M. Cattell. On the perception of small differences. *Univer. Penna. Phil. Ser.*, No. 2, 1892.

Gaito, J. Nonparametric methods in psychological research. *Psychol. Rep.*, 1959, **5**, 115–125.

Gaito, J. Scale classification and statistics. *Psychol. Rev.*, 1960, **67**, 277–278.

Games, P. A., and G. R. Klare. *Elementary Statistics: data analysis for the behavioral sciences.* New

York: McGraw-Hill, 1967.

Gardner, E. *Fundamentals of neurology.* Philadelphia: W. B. Saunders, (2d ed.) 1952; (4th ed.) 1963.

Gardner, W. J., and J. C. R. Licklider. Audio analgesia. *J. Amer. dental Soc.,* 1959, **59,** 1144–1149.

Garner, W. R. An informational analysis of absolute judgments of loudness. *J. exp. Psychol.,* 1953, **46,** 373–380.

Garner, W. R. Context effects and the validity of loudness scales. *J. exp. Psychol.,* 1954, **48,** 218–224.

Garner, W. R. *Uncertainty and structure as psychological concepts.* New York: Wiley, 1962.

Garner, W. R., and H. W. Hake. The amount of information in absolute judgments. *Psychol. Rev.,* 1951, **58,** 446–459.

Garrett, H. E. *General psychology.* New York: American Book, 1955.

Gatti, A., and R. Dodge. Über die unterschiedsempfindlichkeit bei reizung eines einzelnen, isolierten tastorgans. *Arch. ges. Psychol.,* 1929, **69,** 405–425.

Geldard, F. A. *The human senses.* New York: Wiley, 1953.

Geldard, F. A. Some neglected possibilities of communication. *Science,* 1960, **131,** 1583–1588.

Geldard, F. A. Cutaneous channels of communication. In W. A. Rosenblith (Ed.), *Sensory communication.* New York: Wiley, 1961. Pp. 73–87.

Gerard, R. W. The physiology of pain. *Ann. N. Y. Acad. Sci.,* 1960, **86,** 6–12.

Gerstein, G. L., and N. Y. S. Kiang. An approach to the quantitative analysis of electrophysiological data from single neurons. *Biophys. J.,* 1960, **1,** 15–28.

Gibson, J. J. The concept of the stimulus in psychology. *Amer. Psychol.,* 1960, **15,** 694–703.

Gibson, K. S., and E. P. T. Tyndall. Visibility of radiant energy. *Sci. Pap. Bur. Stand.,* 1923, **19,** No. 475.

Gilmer, B. von Haller. Toward cutaneous electropulse communication. *J. Psychol.,* 1961, **52,** 211–222.

Glaser, E. M., M. S. Hall, and G. C. Whittow. Adaptation to localized warming and cooling. *J. Physiol.,* 1958, **140,** 42P.

Glass, B. The ethical basis of science. *Science,* 1965, **150,** 1254–1261.

Glorig, A., R. Quiggle, D. E. Wheeler, and W. Grings. Determination of audiometric zero. *J. acoust. Soc. Amer.,* 1956, **28,** 1110–1113.

Glorig, A., W. D. Ward, and C. W. Nixon. Damage risk criteria and noise-induced hearing loss. *Arch. Otolaryngol.,* 1961, **74,** 413–423.

Goldberger, L., and R. R. Holt. Experimental interference with reality contact (perceptual isolation): method and group results. *J. nerv. ment. Dis.,* 1958, **127,** 99–102.

Goldberger, L., and R. R. Holt. Experimental interference with reality contact: individual differences. In P. Solomon, *et al.* (Eds.), *Sensory deprivation.* Cambridge: Harvard Univer. Press, 1961. Pp. 130–142.

Goldfried, M. R. A psychoanalytic interpretation of sensory deprivation. *Psychol. Rec.,* 1960, **10,** 211–214.

Goldman, H. B. Hypoadrenocorticism and endocrinologic treatment of Ménière's disease. *N. Y. S. J. Med.,* 1962, **62-1,** 377–383.

Goldscheider, A. Untersuchungen über den muskelsinn. *Arch. Anat. Physiol.,* 1889, 369–502.

Goldstein, H., and K. W. Spence. Performance in differential conditioning as a function of variation in magnitude of reward. *J. exp. Psychol.,* 1963, **65,** 86–93.

Götlind, E. Two views about the function of models in empirical theories. *Theoria, Swed. J. Phil. Psychol.,* 1961, **27,** 58–69.

Götlind, E. Stimulus meaning. *Theoria, Swed. J. Phil. Psychol.,* 1963, **29,** 93–114.

Graham, C. H. Behavior, perception and the psychophysical methods. *Psychol. Rev.,* 1950, **57,** 108–118.

Graham, C. H. Visual perception. In S. S. Stevens (Ed.), *Handbook of experimental psychology.* New York: Wiley, 1951. Pp. 868–920.

Graham, C. H., and N. R. Bartlett. The relation of size of stimulus and intensity in the human eye. III. The influence of the area on foveal intensity discrimination. *J. exp. Psychol.,* 1940, **27,** 149–159.

Graham, C. H., and R. Margaria. Area and the intensity-time relation in the peripheral retina. *Amer. J. Phys.,* 1935, **113,** 299–305.

Graybiel, A., W. A. Kerr, and S. H. Bartley. Stimulus thresholds of the semicircular canals as a function of angular acceleration. *Amer. J. Psychol.,* 1948, **61,** 21–36.

Green, D. M. Psychoacoustics and detection theory. *J. acoust. Soc. Amer.,* 1960, **32,** 1189–1203.

Gregg, L. W. The effect of stimulus complexity on discrimination responses. *J. exp. Psychol.,* 1954, **48,** 289–297.

Gregory, R. L. On physical model explanations in psychology. *Brit. J. Phil. Sci.,* 1953, **4,** 192–197.

Grünbaum, A. Causality and the science of human behavior. *Amer. Sci.,* 1952, **40,** 665–676, 689.

Guilford, J. P. *Psychometric methods.* New York: McGraw-Hill, (1st ed.) 1936; (2d ed.) 1954.

Guilford, J. P., and E. M. Lovewell. The touch spots and the intensity of the stimulus. *J. gen. Psychol.,* 1936, **15,** 149–159.

Haig, C. The course of rod adaptation as influenced by the intensity and duration of pre-adaptation to light. *J. gen. Physiol.,* 1941, **24,** 735–751.

Hake, H. W., and W. R. Garner. The effect of presenting various numbers of discrete stages on scale reading accuracy. *J. exp. Psychol.,* 1951, **42,** 358–366.

Hall, C. *Psychology.* Cleveland: Howard Allen, 1960.

Hall, N. B., and K. M. Dallenbach. The duration of the aftersensation of cold aroused by punctiform stimulation. *Amer. J. Psychol.,* 1947, **60,** 260–271.

Halsey, R. M., and A. Chapanis. On the number of absolutely identifiable spectral hues. *J. opt. Soc. Amer.,* 1951, **41,** 1057–1058.

Hardy, H. C. Tentative estimates of a hearing damage risk criterion for steady-state noise. *J. acoust. Soc. Amer.,* 1952, **24,** 756–761.

Hardy, J. D., and T. W. Oppel. Studies in temperature sensation. III. The sensitivity of the body to heat and the spatial summations of the end organ responses. *J. clin. Invest.,* 1937a, **16,** 533–540.

Hardy, J. D., and T. W. Oppel. Studies in temperature sensation. IV. The stimulation of cold sensation by radiation. *J. clin. Invest.,* 1937b, **17,** 775–778.

Hardy, J. D., H. G. Wolff, and H. Goodell. Studies on pain; a new method for measuring pain threshold: observations on spatial summation of pain. *J. clin. Invest.,* 1940, **19,** 649–657.

Hardy, J. D., H. G. Wolff, and H. Goodell. Studies on pain: discrimination of differences in intensity of a pain stimulus as a basis of a scale of pain intensity. *J. clin. Invest.,* 1947, **26,** 1152–1158.

Hardy, J. D., H. G. Wolff, and H. Goodell. *Pain sensations and reactions.* Baltimore: Williams and Wilkins, 1952.

Hardy, M. Observations on the innervation of the macula sacculi in man. *Anat. Rec.,* 1935, **59,** 403–418.

Harris, A. Sensory deprivation and schizophrenia. *J. ment. Sci.,* 1959, **105,** 235–237.

Harris, H., and H. Kalmus. The measurement of taste sensitivity to phenylthiourea (P.T.C.) *Ann. Eugenics*, 1949, **15**, No. 1, 24–31.

Harris, J. D. Pitch discrimination. *J. acoust. Soc. Amer.*, 1952, **24**, 750–755.

Harris, J. D. Normal hearing and its relation to audiometry. *Laryngoscope*, 1954, **64**, 928–957.

Harris, J. D. Steps toward an international audiometric zero. *J. Sp. H. Disord.*, 1961, Monogr. Suppl. No. 9, 63–68.

Harris, J. D. Loudness discrimination. *J. Sp. H. Disord.*, 1963, Monogr. Suppl. No. 11, 1–63.

Harris, J. D., and A. I. Rawnsley. The locus of short duration auditory fatigue or "adaptation." *J. exp. Psychol.*, 1953, **46**, 457–461.

Hartman, E. B. The influence of practice and pitch-distance between tones on the absolute identification of pitch. *Amer. J. Psychol.*, 1954, **67**, 1–14.

Hawkes, G. R. Cutaneous discrimination of electrical intensity. *Amer. J. Psychol.*, 1961, **74**, 45–53.

Hawkes, G. R. Predictability of multidimensional absolute identifications from information transmitted with unidimensional stimuli. *J. Psychol.*, 1962, **54**, 309–316.

Hebb, D. O. *A textbook of psychology*. Philadelphia: W. B. Saunders, 1958.

Hecht, S., C. Haig, and G. Wald. The dark adaptation of retinal fields of different size and location. *J. gen. Physiol.*, 1935, **19**, 321–339.

Hecht, S., S. Shlaer, and M. H. Pirenne. Energy, quanta, and vision. *J. gen. Physiol.*, 1942, **25**, 819–840.

Hecht, S., and R. E. Williams. The visibility of monochromatic radiation and the absorption spectrum of visual purple. *J. gen. Physiol.*, 1922, **5**, 1–33.

Heim, A. W. Adaptation to level of difficulty in intelligence testing. *Brit. J. Psychol.*, 1955, **46**, 211–224.

Held, R., and B. L. White. Sensory deprivation and visual speed: an analysis. *Science*, 1959, **130**, 860–861.

Helmholtz, H. von. *Sensations of tone*. 1st German ed., 1862; 6th English ed. New York: Peter Smith, 1948.

Helson, H. Fundamental problems in color vision. I. The principle governing changes in hue, saturation, and lightness of non-selective samples in chromatic illumination. *J. exp. Psychol.*, 1938, **23**, 439–476.

Helson, H. Adaptation-level as frame of reference for prediction of psychophysical data. *Amer. J. Psychol.*, 1947, **60**, 1–29.

Helson, H. Adaptation-level as a basis for a quantitative theory of frames of reference. *Psychol. Rev.*, 1948, **55**, 297–313.

Helson, H. Adaptation level theory. In S. Koch (Ed.), *Psychology: a study of a science*. Vol. 1. *Sensory, perceptual and physiological foundations*. New York: McGraw-Hill, 1959. Pp. 565–621.

Helson, H. *Adaptation-Level Theory*. New York: Harper & Row, 1964a.

Helson, H. Current trends and issues in adaptation-level theory. *Amer. Psychol.*, 1964b, **19**, 26–38.

Helson, H., and W. Bevan. An investigation of variables in judgments of relative area. *J. exp. Psychol.*, 1964, **67**, 335–341.

Helson, H., and M. C. Nash. Anchor, contrast, and paradoxical distance effects. *J. exp. Psychol.*, 1960, **59**, 113–121.

Hempel, C. G. Fundamentals of concept formation in empirical science. In O. Neurath, *et al.* (Eds.), *International encyclopedia of unified science*, Vol. 3, No. 7. Chicago: Univer. of Chicago Press, 1952.

Hensel, H., and K. K. A. Boman. Afferent impulses in cutaneous sensory nerves in human subjects. *J. Neurophysiol.*, 1960, **23**, 564–578.

Hensel, H., and Y. Zotterman. Action potentials of cold fibres and intracutaneous temperature gradient. *J. Neurophysiol.*, 1951, **14**, 377–385.

Herbart, J. F. *Psychologie als wissenschaft, neu gegrundet auf erfahrung, metaphysik, und mathematik.* Könisburg, Germany: Unzer, 1824.

Herget, C. M., L. P. Granath, and J. D. Hardy. Thermal sensation and discrimination in relation to intensity of stimulus. *Amer. J. Physiol.*, 1941, **134**, 645–655.

Heron, W. Cognitive and physiological effects of perceptual isolation. In P. Solomon, *et al.* (Eds.), *Sensory deprivation.* Cambridge: Harvard Univer. Press, 1961. Pp. 6–33.

Heron, W., B. K. Doane, and T. H. Scott. Visual disturbances after prolonged perceptual isolation. *Canad. J. Psychol.*, 1956, **10**, 13–18.

Hess, C. J. *The brain of the tiger salamander, Ambystome tigrinum.* Chicago: Univer. of Chicago Press, 1948.

Hesse, M. B. Models in physics. *Brit. J. Phil. Sci.*, 1953, **4**, 198–214.

Hick, W. E. On the rate of gain of information. *Quart. J. exp. Psychol.*, 1952, **4**, 11–26.

Hirsch, J. Individual differences in behavior and their genetic basis. In E. L. Bliss (Ed.), *Roots of behavior.* New York: Harper & Row, 1962. Pp. 3–23.

Hirsh, I. J., and R. C. Bilger. Auditory-threshold recovery after exposure to pure tones. *J. acoust. Soc. Amer.*, 1955, **27**, 1186–1193.

Hirsh, I. J., R. C. Bilger, and B. H. Deatherage. The effect of auditory and visual background on apparent duration. *Amer. J. Psychol.*, 1956, **69**, 561–574.

Hochberg, J. E., W. Triebel, and G. Seaman. Color adaptation under conditions of homogeneous visual stimulation (*Ganzfeld*). *J. exp. Psychol.*, 1951, **41**, 153–159.

Holway, A. H., and L. M. Hurvich. Differential gustatory sensitivity to salt. *Amer. J. Psychol.*, 1937, **49**, 37–48.

Hood, J. D. Studies in auditory fatigue and adaptation. *Acta Oto-Laryngol.*, 1950, Suppl. 92, 1–57.

House, W. F. Subarachnoid shunt for drainage of endolymphatic hydrops, a preliminary report. *Laryngoscope*, 1962, **72**, 713–729.

Huggins, W. H., and J. C. R. Licklider. Place mechanisms of auditory frequency analysis. *J. acoust. Soc. Amer.*, 1951, **23**, 290–299.

Hull, C. L. *Principles of behavior: an introduction to behavior theory.* New York: Appleton-Century-Crofts, 1943.

Hull, C. L. The hypothetico-deductive method. In M. H. Marx (Ed.), *Psychological theory: contemporary readings.* New York: Macmillan, 1951. Pp. 218–232.

Hutten, E. H. The role of models in physics. *Brit. J. Phil. Sci.*, 1954, **4**, 284–301.

Hyman, R. Stimulus information as a determinant of reaction time. *J. exp. Psychol.*, 1953, **45**, 188–196.

International Commission on Illumination. *Proc. Eighth Session*, 1931. Cambridge: Harvard Univer. Press, 1932. P. 19.

International Organization for Standardization (ISO), Technical Committee 43, Acoustics. *A standard reference zero for the calibration of pure-tone audiometers*, 1964, No. 554.

Irwin, F. W., and W. A. S. Smith. Value, cost, and information as determiners of decisions. *J. exp. Psychol.*, 1957, **54**, 229–232.

Jacobson, H. Information and the human ear. *J. acoust. Soc. Amer.*, 1951, **23**, 463–471.

James, J. A., M. A. Dalton, H. F. Bullen, H. F. Freundlich, and J. C. Hopkins. The ultrasonic treatment of Ménière's disease. *J. Laryngol. Otol.*, 1960, **74**, 730–757.

Jarrard, L. E. The role of visual cues in the performance of ergographic work. *J. exp. Psychol.*, 1960, **60**, 57–63.

Jastrow, J. A critique of psycho-physic methods. *Amer. J. Psychol.*, 1888, **1**, 271–309.

Jenkins, W. L. Adaptation in isolated cold spots. *Amer. J. Psychol.*, 1937a, **49**, 1–22.

Jenkins, W. L. Studies in thermal sensitivity. I. Adaptations with a series of small circular stimulators. *J. exp. Psychol.*, 1937b, **21**, 670–677.

Jerome, E. A. Olfactory thresholds measured in terms of stimulus pressure and volume. *Arch. Psychol.*, 1942, **274**, 1–44.

Johnson, D. M. Confidence and speed in the two-category judgment. *Arch. Psychol.*, 1939, **34**, No. 241.

Johnson, D. M. Learning function for a change in the scale of judgment. *J. exp. Psychol.*, 1949, **39**, 851–860.

Jones, A. R., and F. W. Church. A criterion for the evaluation of noise exposure. *Amer. Ind. Hyg. Ass. J.*, 1960, **21**, 481–485.

Jones, F. N. An olfactometer permitting stimulus specification in molar terms. *Amer. J. Psychol.*, 1954, **67**, 147–151.

Judd, D. B. Chromaticity sensibility to stimulus differences. *J. opt. Soc. Amer.*, 1932, **22**, 72–108.

Judd, D. B. *Color in business, science, and industry.* New York: Wiley, 1952.

Jung, R. Neuronal integration in the visual cortex and its significance for visual information. In W. A. Rosenblith (Ed.), *Sensory communication.* New York: Wiley, 1961. Pp. 627–674.

Kalmus, H., and S. J. Hubbard. *The chemical senses in health and disease.* Springfield, Ill.: Charles C Thomas, 1960.

Kantor, J. R. Behaviorism: whose image? *Psychol. Rev.*, 1963, **13**, 499–512.

Kantor, J. R. Perspectives in psychology. XXI. Psychology: scientific status-seeker. *Psychol. Rec.*, 1962, **12**, 351–357.

Katsuki, Y., J. Sumi, H. Uchiyama, and T. Watanabe. Electric response of auditory neurons in cat to sound stimulation. *J. Neurophysiol.*, 1958, **21**, 569–588.

Kempthorne, O. The randomization theory of experimental inference. *J. Amer. Statist. Ass.*, 1955, **50**, 946–967.

Kenshalo, D. R. Improved method for the psychophysical study of the temperature sense. *Rev. scient. Instrum.*, 1963, **34**, 883–886.

Kety, S. S. A biologist examines the mind and behavior. *Science*, 1960, **132**, 1861–1870.

King, H. E. Psychological effects of excitation in the limbic system. In D. E. Sheer (Ed.), *Electrical stimulation of the brain.* Austin, Tex.: Univer. of Texas Press, 1961. Pp. 477–486.

Klemmer, E. T., and F. C. Frick. Assimilation of information from dot and matrix patterns. *J. exp. Psychol.*, 1953, **45**, 15–19.

Klemmer, E. T., and P. F. Muller, Jr. The rate of handling information. Key-pressing responses to light patterns. *Human Factors Oper. Res. Lab. Memo Report 34.* Bolling Air Force Base, Washington, D.C. March, 1953.

Kline, N. S. On the relationship between neurophysiology, psychophysiology, psychopharmacology, and other disciplines. *Ann. N. Y. Acad. Sci.*, 1961, **92**, 1004–1016.

Koester, T., and W. N. Schoenfeld. Some comparative data on differential pitch sensitivity under quantal and non-quantal conditions. *J. gen. Psychol.*, 1947, **36**, 107–112.

Krakauer, D., and K. M. Dallenbach. Gustatory adaptation to sweet, sour, and bitter. *Amer. J. Psychol.*, 1937, **49**, 469–475.

Kroger, W. S. Introduction and supplemental reports. In J. Esdaile, *Hypnosis in medicine and surgery*. New York: Julian Press, 1957.

Krulee, G. Information theory and man-machine systems. *J. Oper. Res. Soc. Amer.*, 1954, **2**, 320–328.

Kryter, K. D. Exposure to steady-state noise and hearing impairment. *J. acoust. Soc. Amer.*, 1963, **35**, 1515–1525.

Kryter, K. D., W. D. Ward, J. D. Miller, and D. H. Eldredge. Hazardous exposure to intermittent and steady-state noise. *J. acoust. Soc. Amer.*, 1966, **39**, 451–464.

Künnapas, T. M. Influence of frame size on apparent length of a line. *J. exp. Psychol.*, 1955, **50**, 168–170.

Künnapas, T. M. The vertical-horizontal illusion and the visual field. *J. exp. Psychol.*, 1957, **53**, 405–407.

Lachman, R. The model in theory construction. *Psychol. Rev.*, 1960, **67**, 113–129.

Laidlaw, R. W., and M. A. Hamilton. The quantitative measurement of passive movement. *Bull. Neurol. Inst.*, 1937, **6**, 145–153.

Lele, P. P., G. Weddell, and C. M. Williams. The relationship between heat transfer, skin temperature and cutaneous sensibility. *J. Physiol.*, 1954, **126**, 206–234.

Le Magnen, J. L'odeur des hormones sexuelles. *C. R. Acad. Sci.*, 1950, **230**, 1367–1369.

Leonard, J. A. The effects of "machine" lag on a serial choice task with balanced and biased input frequencies. *Ergonomics*, 1958, **2**, 44–51.

Levy, E. Z., G. E. Ruff, and V. H. Thaler. Studies in human isolation. *J. Amer. Med. Ass.*, 1959, **169**, 236–239.

Lewis, A., and V. T. Kanareff. Use of autocorrelation and uncertainty measures for the analysis of decision behavior. *WADC Technical Report* 59–434, Aero-Medical Lab., Wright Air Development Center, Wright-Patterson Air Force Base, Ohio, 1959.

Lewis, D. *Quantitative methods in psychology*. New York: McGraw-Hill, 1960.

Lewis, D., and C. J. Burke. The use and misuse of the chi-square test. *Psychol. Bull.*, 1949, **46**, 433–489.

Lewis, T. *Pain*. New York: Macmillan, 1942.

Licklider, J. C. R. Basic correlates of the auditory stimulus. In S. S. Stevens (Ed.), *Handbook of experimental psychology*. New York: Wiley, 1951. Pp. 985–1039.

Licklider, J. C. R. Quasi-linear operator models in the study of manual tracking. In R. D. Luce (Ed.), *Developments in mathematical psychology*. New York: Free Press, 1960. Pp. 169–279.

Licklider, J. C. R. On psychophysiological models. In W. A. Rosenblith (Ed.), *Sensory communication*. New York: Wiley, 1961. Pp. 49–72.

Lilly, J. C. Mental effects of reduction of ordinary levels of physical stimuli in intact, healthy persons. *Psychiat. Res. Rep.*, 1956, **5**, 1–28.

Lim, R. K. S. Visceral receptors and visceral pain. *Ann. N. Y. Acad. Sci.*, 1960, **86**, 73–89.

Lindquist, E. F. *Design and analysis of experiments in psychology and education*. Boston: Houghton Mifflin, 1953.

Lindsley, D. B. The reticular activating system and perceptual integration. In D. E. Sheer (Ed.), *Electrical stimulation of the brain*. Austin, Tex.: Univer. of Texas Press, 1961a. Pp. 331–349.

Lindsley, D. B. Common factors in sensory deprivation, sensory distortion, and sensory overload. In P. Solomon, *et al.* (Eds.), *Sensory deprivation*. Cambridge: Harvard Univer. Press, 1961b. Pp. 174–194.

Linker, E., M. E. Moore, and E. Galanter. Taste thresholds, detection models, and disparate results. *J. exp. Psychol.*, 1964, **67**, 59–66.

Little, N. C. *Physics*. Boston: D. C. Heath, 1953.

Livingston, W. K. *Pain mechanisms*. New York: Macmillan, 1943.

Loewenstein, W. R., and M. Mendelson. Components of receptor adaptation in a Pacinian corpuscle. *J. Physiol.*, 1965, **177**, 377–397.

Lordahl, D. S. Concept identification using simultaneous auditory and visual signals. *J. exp. Psychol.*, 1961, **62**, 283–290.

Lotze, R. H. Medicinische psychologie; oder, physiologie der seele. Leipzig, Germany: Weidmann, 1852.

Lüscher, E., and J. Zwislocki. Adaptation of the ear to sound stimuli. *J. acoust. Soc. Amer.*, 1949, **21**, 135–139.

Lyon, D. O. The relation of length of material to time taken for learning and the optimum distribution of time. *J. educ. Psychol.*, 1914, 1–9, 85–91, 155–163.

MacCarty, C. S., and R. L. Drake. Neurosurgical procedures for the control of pain. *Proc. Staff Meetings Mayo Clinic*, 1956, **31**, 208–214.

MacCorquodale, K. Effects of angular acceleration and centrifugal force on nonvisual space orientation during flight. *J. aviat. Med.*, 1948, **19**, 146–157.

Mackworth, N. H. Effects of heat on wireless telegraphy operators hearing and recording Morse messages. *Brit. J. Indus. Med.*, 1946, **3**, 143–158.

Magee, K. R., S. F. Schneider, and N. Rosenzweig. Congenital indifference to pain. *J. nerv. ment. Disord.*, 1961, **132**, 249–259.

Margarida, R., J. D. Hardy, and H. T. Hammel. Measurements of the thermal pain threshold of the hard palate. *J. appl. Physiol.*, 1962, **17**, 338–342.

Marks, M. R. How to build better theories, tests, and therapies: the off-quadrant approach. *Amer. Psychol.*, 1964, **19**, 793–798.

Marriott, F. H. C. Colour vision: theories. In H. Davson (Ed.), *The eye*. Vol. 2. New York: Academic Press, 1962. Pp. 299–320.

Martin, I. Adaptation. *Psychol. Bull.*, 1964, **61**, 35–44.

Mashhour, M. A comparison of the method of ratio estimation and the method of magnitude estimation. *Rep. Psychol. Lab.*, Univer. Stockholm, 1962, No. 110.

Mathews, B. H. C. The response of a single end organ. *J. Psychol.*, 1931, **71**, 64–110.

Mauro, A., W. L. M. Davey, and A. M. Scher. Central nervous system stimulation by an implanted high frequency receiver. *Fed. Proc.*, 1950, **9**, 86–89.

Megel, H. Effect of altitude upon tolerance of rats to vibration stress. Paper read at Aerospace Medical Ass., Atlantic City, April, 1962.

Melzack, R., and P. D. Wall. Pain mechanisms: a new theory. *Science*, 1965, **150**, 971–979.

Mendelson, J. H., P. E. Kubansky, P. H. Leiderman, D. Wexler, and P. Solomon. Physiological aspects of sensory deprivation: a case analysis. In Solomon, *et al.* (Eds.), *Sensory deprivation*. Cambridge: Harvard Univer. Press, 1961. Pp. 91–113.

Meyers, R., F. J. Fry, W. J. Fry, R. C. Eggleton, and D. F. Schultz. Determination of topologic human brain representations and modifications of signs and symptoms of some neurologic disorders by the use of high level ultrasound. *Neurol.*, 1960, **10**, 271–277.

Michon, J. A. Temporal structure of letter groups and span of attention. *Quart. J. exp. Psychol.*, 1964, **16**, 232–240.

Miller, G. A. What is information measurement? *Amer. Psychol.*, 1953, **8**, 3–11.

Miller, G. A. The magical number seven, plus or minus two: some limits on our capacity for processing information. *Psychol. Rev.*, 1956, **63**, 81–97.

Miller, G. A., and F. C. Frick. Statistical behavioristics and sequences of responses. *Psychol. Rev.*, 1949, **56**, 311–324.

Miller, G. A., and W. R. Garner. Effect of random presentation in the psychometric function: implications for a quantal theory of discrimination. *Amer. J. Psychol.,* 1944, **57,** 451–467.

Miller, G. A., G. A. Heise, and W. Lichten. The intelligibility of speech as a function of the context of the test materials. *J. exp. Psychol.,* 1951, **41,** 329–335.

Miller, G. A., and P. E. Nicely. An analysis of perceptual confusions among some English consonants. *J. acoust. Soc. Amer.,* 1955, **27,** 338–352.

Miller, I. Perception of nonsense passages in relation to amount of information and speech-to-noise ratio. *J. exp. Psychol.,* 1957, **53,** 388–393.

Miller, J. G. Toward a general theory for the behavioral sciences. *Amer. Psychol.,* 1955, **10,** 513–531.

Miller, J. G. Information input overload and psychopathology. *Amer. J. Psychiat.,* 1960, **116,** 695–704.

Miskolczy-Fodor, F. Relation between loudness and duration of tonal pulses. I. Response of normal ears to pure tones longer than click-pitch threshold. *J. acoust. Soc. Amer.,* 1959, **31,** 1128–1134.

Moncrieff, R. W. *The chemical senses.* New York: Wiley, 1946.

Moncrieff, R. W. Olfactory adaptation and odor-intensity. *Amer. J. Psychol.,* 1957, **70,** 1–20.

Morgan, C. T., A. Chapanis, J. S. Cook, and M. W. Lund (Eds.), *Human engineering guide to equipment design.* New York: McGraw-Hill, 1963.

Morgan, C. T., and E. Stellar. *Physiological psychology.* (2d ed.) New York: McGraw-Hill, 1950.

Morris, H. *Human anatomy.* (12th ed.) Edited by B. J. Anson. New York: McGraw-Hill-Blakiston, 1966.

Mountcastle, V. B. Modality and topographic properties of single neurons of cat's somatic sensory cortex. *J. Neurophysiol.,* 1957, **20,** 408–434.

Mueller, C. G. Numerical transformation in the analysis of experimental data. *Psychol. Bull.,* 1949, **46,** 198–223.

McBurney, D. H., and C. Pfaffmann. Gustatory adaptation to saliva and sodium chloride. *J. exp. Psychol.,* 1963, **65,** 523–529.

McCormick, E. J. *Human engineering.* New York: McGraw-Hill, 1957.

McFarland, R. A. *Human factors in air transport design.* New York: McGraw-Hill, 1946.

McGrath, R. N. An objective method for classifying industrial noise environments. *AMA Arch. Ind. Hyg. and Occup. Med.,* 1952, **5,** 436–444.

McGuigan, F. J. *Experimental psychology: a methodological approach.* Englewood Cliffs, N. J.: Prentice-Hall, 1960.

Nafe, J. P., and K. S. Wagoner. The nature of pressure adaptation. *J. gen. Psychol.,* 1941, **25,** 323–351.

National Health Survey (1935–36): Preliminary Reports, Hearing Study Series, Bulletins 1–7. Washington, D. C.: U. S. Public Health Service, 1938.

Neisser, U. Response-sequences and the hypothesis of the neural quantum. *Amer. J. Psychol.,* 1957, **70,** 512–527.

Nelson, T. M., and S. H. Bartley. Numerosity, number, arithmetization, measurement and psychology. *Phil. Sci.,* 1961, **28,** 178–203.

Neurath, O. *International encyclopedia of unified science.* Vol. 2, No. 1. Chicago: Univer. of Chicago Press, 1938–39.

Newbury, E. Philosophic assumptions in operational psychology. *J. Psychol.,* 1953, **35,** 371–378.

Newbury, E. The significance of assumptive and philosophic operations in psychological methodology. *J. gen. Psychol.*, 1958, **59**, 185–199.

Newman, E. B. Computational methods useful in analyzing series of binary data. *Amer. J. Psychol.*, 1951, **64**, 252–262.

Noble, C. E. The role of stimulus meaning (m) in social verbal learning. *J. exp. Psychol.*, 1952, **43**, 437–446.

Oberlin, K. W. Variations in intensive sensitivity to lifted weights. *J. exp. Psychol.*, 1936, **19**, 438–455.

O'Brien, B. Vision and resolution in the central retina. *J. opt. Soc. Amer.*, 1951, **41**, 882–894.

Olds, J., and P. M. Milner. Positive reinforcement produced by electrical stimulation of the septal area and other regions of the rat brain. *J. comp. physiol. Psychol.*, 1954, **47**, 419–427.

Oppenheimer, R. Analogy in science. *Amer. Psychol.*, 1956, **11**, 127–135.

Osgood, C. E. *Method and theory in experimental psychology.* New York: Oxford Univer. Press, 1953.

Ough, C. S., and H. Stone. An olfactometer for rapid and critical odor measurement. *J. Food Sci.*, 1961, **26**, 452–456.

Pan, S. Influence of context upon learning and recall. *J. exp. Psychol.*, 1926, **9**, 468–491.

Parducci, A., R. C. Calfee, L. M. Marshall, and L. P. Davidson. Context effects in judgment: adaptation level as a function of the mean, midpoint, and median of the stimuli. *J. exp. Psychol.*, 1960, **60**, 65–77.

Parsons, H. L. Dewey's religious thought: the challenge of evolution. *J. Philos.*, 1961, **58**, 113–121.

Pattle, R. E., and G. Weddell. Observations on electrical stimulation of pain fibres in an exposed human sensory nerve. *J. Neurophysiol.*, 1948, **11**, 93–98.

Patton, H. D. Physiology of smell and taste. In V. E. Hall (Ed.), *Ann. Rev. Physiol.*, 1950, **12**, 469–484.

Peterson, A. P. G., and E. E. Gross, Jr. *Handbook of noise measurement.* West Concord, Mass.: General Radio Co., 1963.

Peterson, L. R., and M. J. Peterson. The role of context stimuli in verbal learning. *J. exp. Psychol.*, 1957, **53**, 102–105.

Peterson, W. W., T. G. Birdsall, and W. C. Fox. The theory of signal detectability. *Trans. Prof. Group on Information Theory*, PGIT-4, 1954, 171–212.

Pfaffmann, C. Gustatory afferent impulses. *J. cell. comp. Physiol.*, 1941, **17**, 243–258.

Pfaffmann, C. Taste and smell. In S. S. Stevens (Ed.), *Handbook of experimental psychology.* New York: Wiley, 1945. Pp. 1143–1171.

Pfaffmann, C. The sense of taste. In J. Field (Ed.), *Handbook of physiology.* Vol. I., Sect. 1: Neurophysiology. Washington, D. C.: American Physiology Society, 1959, Pp. 507–533.

Pfaffmann, C. De gustibus. *Amer. Psychol.*, 1965, **20**, 21–33.

Pierce, J. R. Some work on hearing. *Amer. Sci.*, 1960, **48**, 40–45.

Pierce, J. R., and J. E. Karlin. Reading rates and the information rate of a human channel. *Bell System Tech. J.*, 1957, **36**, 497–516.

Piéron, H. Recherches sur les lois de variation des temps de latence sensorielle en fonction des intensités excitatrices. *Ann. Psychol.*, 1914, **20**, 17–96.

Piéron, H. De la variation de l'énergie liminaire en fonction de la durée d'excitation. I: Vision foveale. II: Vision périphérique. *C. R. Acad. Sci.*, 1920. Pp. 170, 525, 1203.

Piéron, H. *The sensations: their functions, processes, and mechanisms.* Paris: Editions Gallimard, 1945. Translated by M. H. Pirenne and B. C. Abbott. New Haven: Yale Univer. Press, 1952.

Pilkington, G. W. Scientific method in psychology. III. *Brit. J. Statist. Psychol.*, 1958, **11**, 129–132.

Pilkington, G. W. Taylor on "law" and "theory" in psychology. *Brit. J. Statist. Psychol.*, 1960, **13**, 47–54.

Pillsbury, W. B. Does the sensation of movement originate in the joints? *Amer. J. Psychol.*, 1901, **12**, 346–353.

Pirenne, M. H., and E. J. Denton. Accuracy and sensitivity of the human eye. *Nature*, 1952, **170**, 1039–1042.

Platt, J. R. *The step to man.* New York: Wiley, 1966.

Podell, J. E. A comparison of generalization and adaptation level as theories of connotation. *J. abnorm. soc. Psychol.*, 1961, **62**, 593–597.

Pollack, I. The atonal interval. *J. acoust. Soc. Amer.*, 1948, **20**, 146–149.

Pollack, I. Specification of sound pressure levels. *Amer. J. Psychol.*, 1949, **62**, 412–417.

Pollack, I. The information of elementary auditory displays. *J. acoust. Soc. Amer.*, 1952, **24**, 745–749.

Pollack, I. The information of elementary auditory displays. II. *J. acoust. Soc. Amer.*, 1953, **25**, 765–769.

Pollack, I. Message uncertainty and message reception. *J. acoust. Soc. Amer.*, 1959, **31**, 1500–1508.

Pollack, I., and L. Ficks. Information of multidimensional auditory displays. *J. acoust. Soc. Amer.*, 1954, **26**, 155–158.

Polyak, S. L. *The retina.* Chicago: Univer. Chicago Press, 1941.

Polyak, S. L. *The vertebrate visual system.* Edited by H. Klüvier. Chicago: Univer. of Chicago Press, 1957.

Popper, K. R. *The logic of scientific discovery.* London: Hutchinson, 1959. New York: Basic Books, 1959.

Postman, L., and L. W. Phillips. The effects of variable contexts in the acquisition and retention of paired associates. *Amer. J. Psychol.*, 1964, **77**, 64–74.

Pradham, P. L., and P. J. Hoffman. Effect of spacing and range of stimuli on magnitude examination judgments. *J. exp. Psychol.*, 1963, **66**, 533–541.

Pratt, C. C. The time-order error in psychological judgments. *Amer. J. Psychol.*, 1933, **45**, 292–297.

Pratt, C. C. Operationism in psychology. *Psychol. Rev.*, 1945, **52**, 262–269.

Priestly, H. *Introductory physics.* Boston: Allyn and Bacon, 1958.

Quastler, H. *Three survey papers.* Rept. No. R-71, Urbana, Ill.: Control Systems Lab., Univer. of Illinois, 1956.

Rambo, W. W., and E. L. Johnson. Practice-effects and the estimation of adaptation level. *Amer. J. Psychol.*, 1964, **77**, 106–110.

Rasmussen, A. T. *Outlines of neuroanatomy.* (3d ed.) Dubuque, Ia.: William C. Brown, 1943.

Rawnsley, A. I., and J. D. Harris. Studies in short-duration auditory fatigue. II. Recovery time. *J. exp. Psychol.*, 1952, **43**, 138–142.

Reading, P. *Common diseases of the ear, nose and throat.* (4th ed.) London: J. and A. Churchill, 1966.

Riesz, R. R. Differential intensity sensitivity of the ear for pure tones. *Phys. Rev.*, 1928, **31**, 867–875.

Riggs, L. A. Visual acuity. In C. H. Graham (Ed.), *Vision and visual perception.* New York: Wiley, 1965. Pp. 321–349.

Robertson, M. H. Theoretical implications of sensory deprivation. *Psychol. Rec.,* 1961*a*, **11,** 33–42.

Robertson, M. H. Sensory deprivation and some therapeutic considerations. *Psychol. Rec.,* 1961*b*, **11,** 343–347.

Robertson, M., and R. Browning. The effect of brief sensory deprivation upon responses to a word association test. *Pschol. Rec.,* 1963, **13,** 259–264.

Robertson, M. H., and D. J. Wolter. The effect of sensory deprivation upon scores on the Wechsler Adult Intelligence Scale. *J. Psychol.,* 1963, **56,** 213–218.

Rosenbaum, G., S. I. Dobie, and B. D. Cohen. Visual recognitive thresholds following sensory deprivation. *Amer. J. Psychol.,* 1959, **72,** 429–433.

Rosenblith, W. A., K. N. Stevens, and the Staff of Bolt, Beranek, and Newman. Handbook of acoustic noise control. Vol. II. Noise and man. *WADC Technical Report* 42–204, Wright Air Development Center, Wright-Patterson Air Force Base, Ohio, 1953.

Rozeboom, W. W. Do stimuli elicit behavior? A study in the logical foundations of behavioristics. *Phil. Sci.,* 1960, **27,** 159–170.

Rosenzweig, N. Sensory deprivation and schizophrenia: clinical and theoretical similarities. *Amer. J. Psychiat.,* 1959, **116,** 326–329.

Royce, J. R. Psychology in mid-twentieth century. *Amer. Sci.,* 1957, **45,** 57–73.

Rubenstein, H., and M. Aborn. Immediate recall as a function of degree of organization and length of study period. *J. exp. Psychol.,* 1954, **48,** 146–152.

Ruch, T. C., H. D. Patton, J. W. Woodbury, and A. L. Towe. *Neurophysiology.* Philadelphia: W. B. Saunders, 1961.

Rudner, R. Remarks on value judgments in scientific validation. *Sci. Mon.,* 1954, **79,** 151–153.

Ruff, G. E., and E. Z. Levy. Psychiatric research in space medicine. *Amer. J. Psychiat.,* 1959, **115,** 793–797.

Ruff, G. E., E. Z. Levy, and V. H. Thaler. Factors influencing reactions to reduced sensory input. In P. Solomon, *et al.* (Eds.), *Sensory deprivation.* Cambridge: Harvard Univer. Press, 1961. Pp. 72–90.

Rushton, W. A. H. Kinetics of cone pigments measured objectively on the living human fovea. *Ann. N. Y. Acad. Sci.,* 1958, **74,** 291–304.

Rushton, W. A. H. Visual pigments in man and animals and their relation to seeing. *Prog. Biophys.,* 1959, **9,** 239–283.

Rushton, W. A. H. Dark-adaptation and the regeneration of rhodopsin. *J. physiol.,* 1961*a*, **156,** 166–178.

Rushton, W. A. H. Rhodopsin measurement and dark adaptation in a subject deficient in cone vision. *J. Physiol.,* 1961*b*, **156,** 193–205.

Rushton, W. A. H. The Sherrington lectures. VI. *Visual pigments in man.* London: Liverpool Univer. Press, 1962.

Rushton, W. A. H. A cone pigment in the protanope. *J. physiol.,* 1963, **168,** 345–359.

Rushton, W. A. H. Bleached rhodopsin and visual adaptation. *J. Physiol.,* 1965, **181,** 645–655.

Rushton, W. A. H., F. W. Campbell, W. A. Hagins, and G. S. Brindley. The bleaching and regeneration of rhodopsin in the living eye of the albino rat and of man. *Optica acta,* 1955, **1,** 183–190.

Rushton, W. A. H. and R. D. Cohen. Visual purple level and the course of dark adaptation. *Nature,* 1954, **173,** 301–302.

Russell, B. *Our knowledge of the external world.* New York: Norton, 1929.

Ryan, T. A. Multiple comparisons in psychological research. *Psychol. Bull.,* 1959, **56,** 26–47.

Saetveit, J. G., D. Lewis, and C. E. Seashore. *Revision of the Seashore measures of musical talent.* University of Iowa Studies, New Series No. 388, No. 65, 1–62. Iowa City, Univer. of Iowa Press, 1940.

Saldanha, E., and J. F. Corso. Timbre cues and the identification of musical instruments. *J. acoust. Soc. Amer.,* 1964, **36,** 2021–2026.

Sand, A. The function of the ampullae of Lorenzini, with some observations on the effect of temperature of sensory rhythms. *Proc. Roy. Soc.,* London, Ser. B., 1938, **125,** 524–553.

Sataloff, J. *Industrial deafness.* New York: McGraw-Hill, 1957.

Schodder, G.·R., and E. E. David, Jr. Pitch discrimination of two-frequency complexes. *J. acoust. Soc. Amer.,* 1960, **32,** 1426–1435.

Schuknecht, H. F. Presbycusis. *Laryngoscope.* 1955, **65,** 402–419.

Scott, T. H., W. H. Bexton, W. Heron, and B. K. Doane. Cognitive effects of perceptual isolation. *Canad. J. Psychol.,* 1959, **13,** 200-209.

Senders, V. L. *Measurement and statistics.* New York: Oxford Univer. Press, 1958.

Shands, H. S. Adaptation and information in psychiatry. *J. nerv. ment. Disord.,* 1959, **128,** 204–213.

Shaw, M. E. Some factors influencing the use of information in small groups. *Psychol. Repts.,* 1961, **8,** 187–198.·

Shaw, M. E., G. H. Rothschild, and J. F. Strickland. Decision processes in communication nets. *J. abnorm. soc. Psychol.,* 1957, **54,** 323–330.

Sheer, D. E. Emotional facilitation in learning situations with subcortical stimulation. In D. E. Sheer (Ed.), *Electrical stimulation of the brain.* Austin, Tex.: Univer. of Texas Press, 1961, 431–464.

Shlaer, S. The relation between visual acuity and illumination. *J. gen. Physiol.,* 1937, **21,** 165–188.

Shower, E. G., and R. Biddulph. Differential pitch sensitivity of the ear. *J. acoust. Soc. Amer.,* 1931, **3,** 275–287.

Shurley, J. T. Profound experimental sensory isolation. *Amer. J. Psychiat.,* 1960, **117,** 539–545.

Shurley, J. T. Problems and methods in experimental sensory input alteration and variance. Unpublished paper, 1961.

Siegel, S. *Nonparametric tests for the behavioral sciences.* New York: McGraw-Hill, 1956.

Simon, H. A., and K. Kotovsky. Human acquisition of concepts for sequential patterns. *Psychol. Rev.,* 1963, **70,** 534–546.

Sinclair, D. C. Cutaneous sensation and the doctrine of specific energy. *Brain,* 1955, **78,** 584–614.

Singer, J. R. Information theory and the human visual system. *J. opt. Soc. Amer.,* 1959, **49,** 639–640.

Skinner, B. F. The operational analysis of psychological terms. *Psychol. Rev.,* 1945, **52,** 270–277.

Skinner, B. F. Are theories of learning necessary? *Psychol. Rev.,* 1950, **57,** 193–216.

Skinner, B. F. *Science and human behavior.* New York: Macmillan, 1953.

Smith, P. K. The pharmacology of salicylates and related compounds. *Ann. N.Y. Acad. Sci.,* 1960, **86,** 38–63.

Smith, S. W., C. M. Cutchshaw, and W. M. Kincaid. *A test of the physical quantum theory of vision using foveally-presented rectangular targets.* Vision Research Labs., Rept. 2144-345T. Ann Arbor, Mich.: Univer. of Michigan, 1958.

Solomon, P., and J. Mendelson. Hallucinations in sensory deprivation. In L. J. West (Ed.), *Hallucinations.* New York: Grune & Stratton, 1962.

Sorkin, R. D. Extension of the theory of signal detectability to matching procedures in psychoacoustics. *J. acoust. Soc. Amer.,* 1962, **34,** 1745–1751.

Spence, K. W. The postulates and methods of "behaviorism." *Psychol. Rev.,* 1948, **55,** 67–78.

Sperry, R. W. Neurology and the mind-body problem. *Amer. Sci.,* 1952, **40,** 291–312.

Spiegel, E. A., and H. T. Wycis. Chronic implantation of intracerebral electrodes in humans. In D. E. Sheer (Ed), *Electrical stimulation of the brain.* Austin, Tex.: Univer. of Texas Press, 1961. Pp. 37–44.

Steinhardt, J. Intensity descrimination in the human eye. I. The relation of $\Delta I/I$ to intensity. *J. gen. Physiol.,* 1936, **20,** 185–209.

Stevens, S. S. The operational definition of psychological concepts. *Psychol. Rev.,* 1935, **42,** 517–527.

Stevens, S. S. A scale for the measurement of a psychological magnitude: loudness. *Psychol. Rev.,* 1936, **43,** 405–416.

Stevens, S. S. Sensation and psychological measurement. In E. G. Boring, H. S. Langfeld, and H. P. Weld (Eds.), *Foundations of psychology.* New York: Wiley, 1948. Pp. 250–268.

Stevens, S. S. Mathematics, measurement, and psychophysics. In S. S. Stevens (Ed.), *Handbook of experimental psychology.* New York: Wiley, 1951. Pp. 1–49.

Stevens, S. S. On the averaging of data. *Science,* 1955, **121,** 113–116.

Stevens, S. S. The direct estimate of sensory magnitudes: loudness. *Amer. J. Psychol.,* 1956, **69,** 1–25.

Stevens, S. S. On the psychophysical law. *Psychol. Rev.,* 1957, **64,** 153–181.

Stevens, S. S. Measurement and man. *Science,* 1958, **127,** 383–389.

Stevens, S. S. The psychophysics of sensory function. In W. A. Rosenblith (Ed.), *Sensory communication.* New York: Wiley, 1961. Pp. 1–33.

Stevens, S. S. The surprising simplicity of sensory metrics. *Amer. Psychol.,* 1962, **17,** 29–39.

Stevens, S. S. Concerning the psychophysical power law. *Quart. J. exp. Psychol.,* 1964, **16,** 383–385.

Stevens, S. S., and H. Davis. *Hearing: its psychology and physiology.* New York: Wiley, 1938.

Stevens, S. S., C. T. Morgan, and J. Volkmann. Theory of the neural quantum in the discrimination of loudness and pitch. *Amer. J. Psychol.,* 1941, **54,** 315–335.

Stevens, S. S., and J. Volkmann. The relation of pitch to frequency: a revised scale. *Amer. J. Psychol.,* 1940a, **53,** 329–353.

Stevens, S. S., and J. Volkmann. The quantum of sensory discrimination. *Science,* 1940b, **92,** 583–585.

Stone, L. J., and K. M. Dallenbach. Adaptation to the pain of radiant heat. *Amer. J. Psychol.,* 1934, **46,** 229–242.

Straus, H. H., and F. R. Uhlmann. Adaptation of superficial pain. *Amer. J. Psychol.,* 1919, **30,** 422–424.

Strughold, H. Über die dichte und schwellen der smerzpunkte der epidermis in der verschidenen körperregionen. *Z. Biol.,* 1924, **80,** 367–380.

Strumwasser, F. A circadian rhythm of activity and its endogenous origin in a neuron. *Fed. Proc.,* 1963, **22,** 220.

Stuiver, M. *Biophysics of the sense of smell.* Thesis, Groningen, 1958.

Sumby, W. H., D. Chambliss, and I. Pollack. Information transmission with elementary auditory displays. *J. acoust. Soc. Amer.,* 1958, **30,** 425–429.

Sumby, W. H., and I. Pollack. Visual contribution to speech intelligibility in noise. *J. acous. Soc. Amer.,* 1954, **26,** 212–215.

Sweet, W. H. Pain. In J. Field (Ed.), *Handbook of physiology.* Vol. I., Sec. 1: Neurophysiology. Washington, D. C.: American Physiology Society, 1959. Pp. 459–506.

Swets, J. A. Is there a sensory threshold? *Science,* 1961, **134,** 168–177.

Swets, J. A. (Ed.), *Signal detection and recognition by human observers*. New York: Wiley, 1964.

Swets, J. A., W. P. Tanner, Jr., and T. G. Birdsall. Decision processes in perception. *Psychol. Rev.*, 1961, **68**, 301–340.

Tanner, W. P., Jr. Theory of recognition. *J. acous. Soc. Amer.*, 1956, **28**, 882–888.

Tanner, W. P., Jr. What is masking? *J. acous. Soc. Amer.*, 1958, **30**, 919–921.

Tanner, W. P., Jr., and T. G. Birdsall. Definitions of d' and η as psychophysical measures. *J. acous. Soc. Amer.*, 1958, **30**, 922–928.

Tanner, W. P., Jr., and J. A. Swets. A new theory of visual detection. *Technical Report No. 18.* Ann Arbor, Mich.: Univer. of Michigan, Electronic Defense Group, 1953.

Tanner, W. P., Jr., J. A. Swets, and D. M. Green. Some general properties of the hearing mechanism. *Technical Report No. 30.* Ann Arbor, Mich.: Univer. of Michigan, Electronic Defense Group, 1956.

Tatarkiewicz, W. Nomological and typological sciences. *J. Philos.*, 1960, **57**, 234–240.

Taylor, D. W., W. R. Garner, and H. F. Hunt. Education for research in psychology. *Amer. Psychol.*, 1959, **14**, 167–179.

Taylor, J. G. Scientific method in psychology. IV. *Brit. J. Statist. Psychol.*, 1958, **11**, 133–136.

Teevan, R. C., and R. C. Birney. *Color vision.* Princeton, N.J.: D. Van Nostrand, 1961.

Thurstone, L. L. Psychophysical analysis. *Amer. J. Psychol.*, 1927, **38**, 368–389.

Thurstone, L. L. The phi-gamma hypothesis. *J. exper. Psychol.*, 1928, **11**, 293–305.

Thurstone, L. L. The relation between learning time and length of task. *Psychol. Rev.*, 1930, **37**, 44–53.

Titchener, E. B. *Experimental psychology.* Vol. II. *Instructor's manual. Part II.* New York: Macmillan, 1905.

Titchener, E. B. A textbook of psychology. New York: Macmillan, 1909.

Tobias, C. A., and J. H. Lawrence (Eds.), Advances in biological and medical physics, Vol. VI. New York: Academic Press, 1958.

Toch, H. H. The effect of "meaning" on the autokinetic illusion. *Amer. J. Psychol.*, 1962, **75**, 605–611.

Tonndorf, J., F. A. Brogan, and D. D. Washburn. *Auditory difference limen of intensity in normal-hearing subjects.* USAF School of Aviation Medicine, Rept. No. 55–31, 1955.

Torgerson, W. S. *Theory and methods of scaling.* New York: Wiley, 1958.

Troland, L. T. *Psychophysiology.* Vol. II. *Sensation.* New York: D. Van Nostrand, 1930.

Turner, J. Maxwell on the method of physical analogy. *Brit. J. Phil. Sci.*, 1955, **6**, 226–238.

Turner, R. H. New uses for the oscilloscope as an instrument of research and demonstration. *Amer. J. Psychol.*, 1959, **72**, 122–134.

Urban, F. M. On the method of just perceptible differences. *Psychol. Rev.*, 1907, **14**, 244–253.

Urban, F. M. The method of constant stimuli and its generalizations. *Psychol. Rev.*, 1910, **17**, 229–259.

Urban, F. M. The future of psychophysics. *Psychol. Rev.*, 1930, **37**, 93–106.

U. S. Air Force hazardous noise exposures, USAF Reg. 160-3. Washington, D.C.: Dept. of Air Force, 1956.

Vaneklasen, P. S. City noise: Los Angeles. *Noise control,* 1956, **2**, No. 4. 14–19.

Vernon, J. A. *Inside the black room.* New York: Clarkson N. Potter, 1963.

Vernon, J. Sensory deprivations. *Sci. J.,* 1966, **2**, No. 2, 57–61.

Vernon, J., and J. Hoffman. Effects of sensory deprivation on learning rate in human beings. *Science,* 1956, **123**, 1074–1075.

Vernon, J. A., and T. E. McGill. The effect of sensory deprivation upon rote learning. *Amer. J. Psychol.,* 1957, **70,** 637–639.

Vernon, J. A., T. E. McGill, W. L. Gulick, and D. K. Candland. Effect of sensory deprivation on some perceptual and motor skills. *Percept. mot. Skills,* 1959, **9,** 91–97.

Vernon, J. A., T. E. McGill, and H. Schiffman. Visual hallucinations during perceptual isolation. *Canad. J. Psychol.,* 1958, **12,** 31–34.

Volkmann, J. The relation of time of judgment to certainty of judgment. *Psychol. Bull.,* 1934, **31,** 672–673.

Wald, G. Retinal chemistry and the physiology of vision. In *Visual problems of colour,* 1. London: H. M. Stationery Office, 1958. Pp. 7–61.

Wald, G., P. K. Brown, and P. H. Smith. Iodopsin. *J. gen. Physiol.,* 1955, **38,** 623–681.

Walker, A. E., and C. Marshall. Stimulation and depth recording in man. In D. E. Sheer (Ed.), *Electrical stimulation of the brain.* Austin, Tex.: Univer. of Texas Press, 1961. Pp. 498–518.

Wallace, S. R. Studies in binocular interdependence. I. Binocular relations in macular adaptation. *J. gen. Psychol.,* 1937, **17,** 307–322.

Walsh, T. E. The surgical treatment of hearing loss. In H. Davis (Ed.), *Hearing and deafness: a guide for laymen.* New York: Holt, Rinehart and Winston, 1947. Pp. 101–121.

Walters, R. H., and M. J. Quinn. A comparison of the effects of social deprivation and sensory deprivation on autokinetic judgments. Unpublished manuscript, 1961.

Walzl, E. M., and V. Mountcastle. Projection of vestibular nerve to cerebral cortex of the cat. *Amer. J. Physiol.,* 1949, **159,** 595.

Ward, W. D. Subjective musical pitch. *J. acous. Soc. Amer.,* 1954, **26,** 369–380.

Ward, W. D. Recovery from high values of temporary threshold shift. *J. acoust. Soc. Amer.,* 1960, **32,** 497–500.

Ward, W. D., A. Glorig, and D. L. Sklar. Dependence of temporary threshold shift at 4kc on intensity and time. *J. acoust. Soc. Amer.,* 1958, **30,** 944–954.

Weale, R. A. *The eye and its function.* London: Hatton Press, 1960.

Weale, R. A. Limits of human vision. *Nature,* London, 1961, **191,** 471–473.

Webster, J. C., M. Lichenstein, and R. S. Gales. Individual differences in noise masked thresholds. *J. acoust. Soc. Amer.,* 1950, **22,** 483–490.

Wechsler, D. *The measurement of adult intelligence.* Baltimore: Williams and Wilkins, 1939.

Welford, A. T. The measurement of sensory-motor performance: survey and reappraisal of twelve years' progress. *Ergonomics,* 1960, **3,** 189–230.

Welford, A. T. Arousal, channel capacity, and decision. *Nature,* 1962, **194,** 365–366.

Wenger, M. A., F. N. Jones, and M. H. Jones. *Physiological psychology.* New York: Holt, Rinehart and Winston, 1956.

Wever, E. G. *Theory of hearing.* New York: Wiley, 1949.

Wever, E. G., and C. W. Bray. The perception of low tones and the resonance volley theory. *J. Psychol.,* 1937, **3,** 101–114.

Wexler, D., J. Mendelson, P. H. Leiderman, and P. Solomon. Sensory deprivation: a technique for studying psychiatric aspects of stress. *AMA Arch. Neurol. Psychiat.,* 1958, **79,** 225–233.

Whitrow, G. J. The study of the philosophy of science. *Brit. J. Phil. Sci.,* 1956, **7,** 189–205.

Williams, H. L. *Ménière's disease.* Springfield, Ill.: Charles C Thomas, 1952.

Willis, T. P. Scientific method in psychology. I. *Brit. J. Statist. Psychol.,* 1958, **11,** 97–104.

Winter, J. W. The sensation of movement. *Psychol. Rev.,* 1912, **19,** 374–385.

Wolf-Heidegger, G. *Atlas of systematic human anatomy.* New York: Hafner Publishing Company, Inc., 1962.

Wolfle, D. The spirit of science. *Science,* 1966, **152,** 1699.

Woodger, J. H. *The axiomatic method in biology.* London: Cambridge Univer. Press, 1937.

Woodrow, H., and B. Karpman. A new olfactometric technique and some results. *J. exp. Psychol.,* 1917, **2,** 431–447.

Woodworth, R. S. *Experimental psychology.* New York: Holt, Rinehart and Winston, 1938.

Woollard, H. H., G. Weddell, and J. A. Harpman. Observations on the neurohistological basis of cutaneous pain. *J. Anat.,* 1940, **74,** 413–440.

Wright, A. J. Ménière's disease; alcohol injection of the labyrinth. *J. Laryngol. oto.,* 1942, **57,** 120–122.

Wright, W. D. The response of the eye to light in relation to measurement of subjective brightness and contrast. *Trans. Illum. Eng. Soc.,* 1939, **4,** 1–8.

Wright, W. D. *Researches on normal and defective colour vision.* London: Kimpton, 1946.

Wrigley, C. Theory of fact-finding in a computer age. *Behav. Sci.,* 1960, **5,** 183–186.

Zigler, M. J. Pressure adaptation time; a function of intensity and extensity. *Amer. J. Psychol.,* 1932, **44,** 709–720.

Zigler, M. J., and A. H. Holway. Differential sensitivity as determined by amount of olfactory substance. *J. gen. Psychol.,* 1935, **12,** 372–382.

Ziskind, E. An explanation of mental symptoms found in acute deprivation: researches 1958–1963. *Amer. J. Psychiat.,* 1965, **121,** 939–946.

Zotterman, Y. Thermal sensations. In J. Field (Ed.), *Handbook of physiology.* Vol. I. Sec. 1: Neurophysiology. Washington, D. C.: Amer. Physiol. Soc., 1959. Pp. 431–458.

Zubek, J. P., D. Pushkar, W. Sansom, and J. Gowing. Perceptual changes after prolonged sensory isolation (darkness and silence). *Canad. J. Psychol.,* 1961, **15,** 83–100.

Zubek, J. P., W. Sansom, and A. Prysiazniuk. Intellectual changes during prolonged perceptual isolation (darkness and silence). *Canad. J. Psychol.,* 1960, **14,** 233–243.

AUTHOR INDEX

SUBJECT INDEX